SOME PHYSICAL CONSTANTS (see also Appendix 3)

Gravitational constant	G	6.67×1
Avogadro's number	N_0	6.02×10
Boltzmann's constant	k	1.381×10^{-23} J/K
Gas constant	R	8.31 J/mole K
Quantum unit of charge	e	1.602×10^{-19} C
Permittivity constant (combined form)	$\dfrac{1}{4\pi\epsilon_0}$	$8.99 \times 10^9 \ (\cong 9 \times 10^9)$ N m²/C²
Permeability constant (combined form)	$\dfrac{\mu_0}{4\pi}$	10^{-7} N/A²
Speed of light	c	3.00×10^8 m/sec
Planck's constant	h	6.63×10^{-34} J sec
	$\hbar$	1.055×10^{-34} J sec
Mass of electron	m_e	9.11×10^{-31} kg
Mass of proton	m_p	1.673×10^{-27} kg
Bohr radius	a_0	5.29×10^{-11} m

SOME PHYSICAL DATA (see also Appendix 3)

Acceleration of gravity at earth's surface	(g)	9.8 m/sec²
Mass of earth		5.98×10^{24} kg
Radius of earth		6.37×10^6 m
Earth-moon distance (center to center)		3.84×10^8 m
Average earth-sun distance		1.50×10^{11} m
Average orbital speed of earth		2.98×10^4 m/sec
Standard conditions		1 atm = 1.013×10^5 N/m²
		0 °C = 273.15 K
Standard dry air density		1.293 kg/m³
Speed of sound in standard dry air		331 m/sec
Density of water		1.00×10^3 kg/m³

SOME CONVERSION FACTORS (see also Appendix 4)

2.54 cm/in

0.3048 m/ft

1.609 km/mile

10^{-10} m/Å

10^{-15} m/fm

3.156×10^7 sec/yr

0.447 (m/sec)/(mile/hr)

57.3 deg/radian

0.454 kg/lb

1.661×10^{-27} kg/amu

10^3 (kg/m³)/(gm/cm³)

10^5 dyne/N

10^7 erg/J

4.184 J/cal

4,184 J/kcal

1.602×10^{-19} J/eV

1.80 F°/C°

3.00×10^9 esu/C (charge)

10^4 G/T (magnetic field)

Classical and Modern Physics

THIS BOOK IS AVAILABLE IN THREE VOLUMES
AND IN A COMBINED EDITION OF VOLUMES 1 AND 2

In Volume 1

Introduction to Physics
Mathematics
Mechanics

In Volume 2

Thermodynamics
Electromagnetism

In Volume 3

Relativity
Quantum Mechanics

Kenneth W. Ford

UNIVERSITY OF MASSACHUSETTS AT BOSTON

Volume 2

Classical and Modern Physics

A TEXTBOOK FOR STUDENTS OF SCIENCE AND ENGINEERING

XEROX COLLEGE PUBLISHING Lexington, Massachusetts | Toronto

CONSULTING EDITOR

Brenton F. Stearns, *Hobart and William Smith Colleges*

to Joanne

Preface

This is a textbook for a three-semester introductory physics course for students of science and engineering. Roughly the first two-thirds of the book (Parts 1–5) could serve as a text for a one-year course in classical physics; the last third (Parts 6 and 7) could serve as a text for a one-semester course in modern physics. With certain sections and subsections—or even whole chapters—omitted, it should also meet the needs of a one-year course that includes modern physics. Because of its substantial length and because of the several kinds of courses in which it might be used, the book is published in two volumes as well as in a combined edition of Volumes 1 and 2. The parts of the volumes are as follows:

Volume 1	1. *Introduction to Physics*
	2. *Mathematics*
	3. *Mechanics*
Volume 2	4. *Thermodynamics*
	5. *Electromagnetism*
Volume 3	6. *Relativity*
	7. *Quantum Mechanics*

The appendices and the index for the complete book appear in each volume.*

   Probably every author has in mind a particular kind of student for whom he is writing. My "model student" has had high-school physics and is taking calculus concurrently with college physics. He or she is a serious but not necessarily gifted student, is interested in ideas as well as technical skills, and

---

* This early printing contains an index for Parts 1–5 only.

learns best when mathematical derivations are supplemented by verbal explanations and physical examples. In terms of the intellectual demand placed on the student, this text is comparable to the popular text by Halliday and Resnick.* It is less demanding than the Berkeley Physics Course† or the M.I.T. Introductory Physics Series.‡

As originally conceived, this book was to be a "calculus version" of my earlier text, *Basic Physics*.§ Having passed through numerous evolutionary stages of writing and rewriting, deleting and adding, however, the book as now published is distinct from the earlier one in various ways besides its mathematical level.

Some of the principal features of this text are the following: (1) I have tried to give a unified presentation of both classical and modern physics. Although theoretical developments of relativity and quantum physics are saved for the last two parts of the book, certain ideas (mass-to-energy conversion, for instance, and nature's speed limit) are introduced early, and modern examples often serve to illustrate classical laws. (2) A series of introductory chapters give time for some maturing of the student's view of physics and his command of mathematics before the intricacies of classical mechanics are approached. (3) Ideas of calculus are introduced (in Chapter 5) somewhat more fully than in most other physics texts. (4) I have tried to steer a course through the discipline of physics that keeps the student in touch with the large view of the subject—the economy and simplicity of its concepts, the elegance of its overall structure—at the same time that he is mastering practical skills and polishing his problem-solving ability. (5) As aids to study and review, the text is divided into fairly numerous sections and subsections, marginal notes highlight key ideas and important equations, and summaries of ideas and definitions appear at the end of every chapter. (6) I have tried to bring out the excitement of physics as a living, evolving discipline, powerful yet incomplete. A limited amount of historical material is included; I have taken some care with this and hope that most of it is real history and not myth.

The "Notes on the Text" that begin on page xiii are intended as a brief guide to instructors. Students, too, can be encouraged to read these notes. As an aid to selective use of the material, some sections and subsections are marked with a star (★) to indicate that they are optional. A section or subsection may be so marked either because it is of greater than average difficulty or because it is peripheral to the main development of a chapter. Any such designation of optional material is necessarily rather arbitrary. Most instructors will have their own ideas about which material to include and which to omit; the stars provide only a first set of suggestions.

At the end of each chapter appear questions, exercises, and problems. *Questions*, with few exceptions, are to be answered in words. Many of them are intended to be thought-provoking and may have no specific right answer.

---

* David Halliday and Robert Resnick, *Physics* (New York: John Wiley and Sons, Inc., 1966).
† *The Berkeley Physics Course*, a five-volume series by various authors (New York: McGraw-Hill Book Co.).
‡ *The M.I.T. Introductory Physics Series*, three volumes by A. P. French in print in 1971, with three more volumes scheduled (New York: W. W. Norton and Co.).
§ Xerox College Publishing, 1968.

Some are difficult. *Exercises* are intended to be straightforward tests of understanding of the material in the chapter without special twists or subtleties. The exercises involve numerical work as well as algebra and some calculus. Often an exercise may ask for a brief explanation as well as a quantitative result. *Problems* are, in general, more challenging. They may be in the nature of difficult exercises; they may draw together material from more than one section; or they may build on material in the text but go somewhat beyond it. The number of questions, exercises, and problems is large—much larger than the number that would ordinarily be assigned in a course. This large number is provided in order to meet the needs and tastes of different instructors, to enable the student to practice on items that are not assigned, and to enable the instructor, if he wishes, to choose examination questions from the text. Because the chapters are rather long and the end-of-chapter items are numerous, marginal notes are used to classify the questions, exercises, and problems. Questions and exercises are keyed to specific sections. Problems are labeled by their subject.

I have used SI (mks) units throughout. Some special units—such as the calorie, the astronomical unit, and the electron volt—are introduced, and some exercises and problems require conversion of units. However, no effort is made to have the student develop any routine familiarity with more than one set of units. To aid the student in case he encounters Gaussian (cgs) units in another text or in a research paper, Appendix 5 contains an extensive list of the equations of electromagnetism in SI and Gaussian units. My only significant deviation from "purity" in handling units occurs in Chapters 13 and 14, where calories and kilocalories are used as often as joules and where Avogadro's number is defined as the number of molecules in 1 mole rather than the number in 1 kmole.

I want students to enjoy this book and to profit from it. I think it will serve its purpose best if students are not rushed too quickly through too much of it. Careful treatment of some material and judicious omission of other material will probably provide better preparation for further work in physics, engineering, and other sciences than will a fast trip through every section.

KENNETH W. FORD

Acknowledgments

I have had the great benefit of collaboration with Neal D. Newby, Jr., and Brenton F. Stearns on questions, exercises, and problems. Their hundreds of suggestions for end-of-chapter items were vitally important when my own imagination began to flag. In his role of Consulting Editor, Brenton Stearns has also been of inestimable value as careful reader and thoughtful critic throughout the writing and rewriting of this text. I am indebted to Russell K. Hobbie, Donald E. Schuele, and N. S. Wall, who read one draft of the manuscript, and to David J. Cowan, who read two, for their numerous helpful suggestions. So many colleagues have contributed facts, data, photographs, and suggestions that a complete list is impossible. Among them are Olexa-Myron Bilaniuk, Alfred M. Bork, George J. Igo, Henry H. Kolm, Alexander Landé, Arthur W. Martin, Edward M. Purcell, Frederick Reines, Gerald Schubert, and Barry N. Taylor.

Yale Altman and Warren Blaisdell encouraged the initiation of this project and helped to keep it going. They deserve the credit (or blame) for turning me into an author in the first place. At Xerox College Publishing, James Piles has been an agreeable and helpful mentor, and many others, including Bernice Borgeson, Barbara Johnson, Martha Johnson, and Marret McCorkle, have put their dedicated efforts into the book. I have been fortunate in having the services of two outstanding typists, Lisa Munsat and Elizabeth Higgins.

Notes on the text

Of the book's seven sections, the first two (*Introduction to Physics* and *Mathematics*) provide introductory and background material. There is great latitude in the way these two parts may be used. The remaining five parts (*Mechanics, Thermodynamics, Electromagnetism, Relativity*, and *Quantum Mechanics*) are devoted to specific major theories of physics. The fullest mathematical development is carried out for the theories of mechanics, electromagnetism, and special relativity. Thermodynamics and quantum mechanics are handled with somewhat more attention to phenomena and less to mathematical formalism. (Nevertheless, I have avoided more modest titles, such as *Heat* and *Atomic and Nuclear Phenomena*, because these parts do also emphasize the unity and power of physical theories, and they are by no means lacking in mathematics.) The division of the book into parts and the choice of rather long chapters in preference to more numerous shorter chapters are designed to serve the same end: to keep the overall structure of physics in view at a time when it is all too easy for the student to see the subject as a bewildering array of unrelated pieces.

PART 4: The approach to thermodynamics in this part of the text is more often microscopic than macroscopic. Wherever possible, however, microscopic and macroscopic views are juxtaposed and compared. Special emphasis is placed on the fact that thermodynamics is a theory that links and unifies the large-scale and small-scale worlds.

The principal subjects of Chapter 13 are the concepts of heat and temperature, the kinetic theory of gases, the zeroth and first laws of thermodynamics, and the properties of gases. The distinction between heat and internal energy is emphasized (Section 13.5). The kinetic-theory derivation of the ideal-gas law (Sections 13.7 and 13.8) is reasonably simple yet rigorous. The chapter ends with a discussion of the effects of quantization on degrees of freedom and specific heats.

In Chapter 14, the second law of thermodynamics is approached through the idea of probability in random events. A feature of this chapter is the fact that entropy and the second law are examined from a number of different perspectives—through ideas of heat flow, a priori probability, disorder, and perpetual motion. Most of the actual applications in the chapter are to ideal gases. The much broader range of application of the second law may require additional emphasis by the instructor.

PART 5: Each of the four chapters in this part of the text contains a balanced mixture of theoretical developments, practical applications, and qualitative discussions. The basic laws of electromagnetism are developed and applied in Chapters 15, 16, and the first half of 17. The second half of Chapter 17 ties electromagnetic theory to waves. Chapter 18 goes on to a unified treatment of waves and optics. Qualitative discussions are used for two purposes: either to introduce new ideas that are then to be developed quantitatively (as in Sections 15.1, 16.1, and 18.9) or to present material whose mathematical development is beyond the level of this text (as in Section 17.11). Different aspects of electromagnetism are brought together in three special sections: Section 16.3, which previews the laws to be developed in later sections; Section 16.11, which summarizes the laws to that point; and Section 17.5, which summarizes all the laws of electromagnetism. The interdependence of different laws is also emphasized in several places. Line and surface integrals are used (sparingly) in this part of the book in applications that have a high degree of symmetry.

The first two sections of Chapter 15 provide historical background and some general facts about electrical phenomena and electric charge. Important ideas and techniques of electrostatics are then developed in Sections 15.3–15.9. In Section 15.5, the law of superposition is introduced both as a basic law and as a tool of calculation. In Section 15.6, Gauss's law is presented as a more powerful tool for problems of high symmetry, and the surface integral is introduced. Practical applications to circuits and accelerated charges occur in Sections 15.10, 15.11, and 15.14. Note that Ohm's law is introduced first in the form $J = \sigma E$, then in the form $V = IR$. Section 15.12 on capacitance includes the RC circuit and also ties into the discussion of field energy in Section 15.15. The optional Section 15.13 approaches dielectrics from the microscopic viewpoint. The displacement vector $\mathbf{D}$ is not introduced.

Chapter 16 begins with magnets and magnetic poles. This approach helps to emphasize that magnetism and electricity are *distinct* (although related) phenomena. It also makes possible a discussion of the hypothetical magnetic monopole. The qualitative survey in Section 16.3 sets the stage for the developments to follow in both Chapters 16 and 17. The laws of force and field for charges in motion are presented in Sections 16.4 and 16.6, with the intervening Section 16.5 being devoted to applications. Section 16.7 (force on a current) is parallel to Section 16.4, and Section 16.8 (field of a current) is parallel to Section 16.6. Ampère's law is introduced and applied in Section 16.8. In the optional Section 16.10, magnetism in matter is approached from the microscopic viewpoint. The magnetic intensity vector $\mathbf{H}$ is not introduced.

In Chapter 17 the parallelism of the laws of electromagnetic induction and magnetoelectric induction (Sections 17.1 and 17.3) is emphasized, as is the consistency of these laws with laws introduced in Chapter 16. In Section 17.4, Lenz's law is introduced as an important implication of energy conservation and as a handy tool for determining directions of induced effects. The practical topic of inductance (Sections 17.6 and 17.7) provides a bridge from the laws of induction to radiation. Only simple *LR* and *LC* circuits are treated in the text; the *RLC* circuit appears in a problem. In a challenging optional subsection, the wave equation is derived in a special case. Otherwise, the material in Sections 17.8–17.11 is largely qualitative. Section 17.11 may be considered optional. The important results stated in the first paragraph of Section 17.9 should not be overlooked.

The first three sections of Chapter 18 introduce the theoretical description of waves, with special reference to polarization and coherence. Huygens's principle appears at the end of Section 18.3. Further development of the formalism of waves is then postponed to the last three sections of the chapter, where interference and diffraction phenomena are treated. Geometrical optics is found in Sections 18.4–18.8. Standard derivations of the laws of reflection and refraction appear in Sections 18.4 and 18.6. The chapter includes discussions of several optical instruments, from the hand magnifier to the grating spectroscope.

Several precursors of quantum mechanics appear in this part of the book: charge quantization in Section 15.2, emission and absorption of radiation in Section 17.11, and spectral lines in Section 18.11.

Contents

* Sections and subsections marked with stars are optional.

PART V *Electromagnetism*

15 | ELECTRICITY

16 | ELECTROMAGNETISM

APPENDICES

FOUR

Thermodynamics

13

Temperature, Heat, and the Kinetic Theory

Man's imagination has always been challenged by domains of nature far removed from his immediate human scales of reference. Concerning the limit of the very large, he has pondered the system of the world. Concerning the limit of the very small, he has puzzled over the ultimate structure of matter. Newton's mechanics bridged the gap between the macroscopic (human-sized) and cosmological domains. The theory of thermodynamics links the macroscopic and submicroscopic domains.

13.1 Introduction to thermodynamics

Thermodynamics links the macroscopic and the submicroscopic

Thermodynamics is the theory of heat and temperature superimposed on the theory of mechanics. Its great triumph is the explanation of bulk properties of matter, especially thermal properties, in terms of the submicroscopic mechanics of atoms and molecules. This is the aspect of thermodynamics that will be emphasized in this chapter and the next—its role as a bridge between two domains of nature.*

Thermodynamics is not directly a theory of the structure of matter, although its development paralleled and supported the development of the atomic theory of matter. The theory of heat and temperature was beginning to achieve a firm footing late in the eighteenth century, at about the same time that chemical experiments were providing the first solid evidence for the existence of atoms. By the middle of the nineteenth century evidence from chemistry had left little

---

* Sometimes the meaning of the term "thermodynamics" is limited to the macroscopic approach to thermal phenomena, reserving the meaning of the term "statistical mechanics" for the submicroscopic approach. We use the word "thermodynamics" alone to mean the full theory of thermal phenomena, encompassing both approaches.

doubt as to the existence of atoms, and it was at this time that the microscopic and macroscopic threads of physical theory united to form what we now call thermodynamics. By the end of the nineteenth century there was monumental evidence for the existence of atoms, but all of it was indirect. Finally in 1905, Einstein rendered the bridge of thermodynamics visible. His application of thermodynamics to Brownian motion (Section 13.13) made clear that a grain of dust dancing in a liquid is reacting visibly to molecular impact. Before long other and even more direct manifestations of atoms and molecules were being observed.

When an object is set into motion, its structure is normally unaffected. If the same object is electrically charged, it is also unlikely to change its shape or size or appearance. At the macroscopic level, mechanical and electrical phenomena may be studied without concern for the structure of matter. This is not true of heat phenomena. If an object is heated, it will, at the very least, change its size slightly. It may also melt or boil or cook or catch fire or explode. How the object reacts will depend very much on its composition. Thermodynamics, being concerned with heat, cannot separate itself from the structure of matter. It must be concerned not only with the fact that matter consists of atoms and molecules, but also with how these atoms or molecules are arranged—whether in solids, liquids, or gases—how they move, and how they interact with each other.

Thermal physics cannot ignore the structure of matter

For several reasons thermodynamics is mathematically and conceptually more complicated than mechanics. For one reason, it is concerned not with simple systems of a few particles or objects, but with intrinsically complex systems of vast numbers of particles. A drop of water, considered at the molecular level, is a system far more complicated than the solar system. For another reason, thermodynamics looks at nature through a variety of magnifying glasses simultaneously, from the atomic scale to the human scale and beyond. For yet another reason, thermodynamics is concerned with matter in all of its forms—solid, liquid, and gas—and with both its physical and chemical transformations of form.

In this part of the book, we shall attempt neither a panoramic survey of the whole theory of thermodynamics nor a logical presentation of all of its fundamentals. Rather, we shall focus our attention on several of the key ideas of thermodynamics, particularly on the following two:

1. Heat and temperature are both manifestations of molecular energy.
2. Spontaneous change in the large-scale world is governed by laws of probability in the small-scale world.

Two key ideas

These two ideas, both concerned with links between the macroscopic and microscopic domains, suffice to support the bridge of thermodynamics. They suffice also to make clear the meaning of the two great principles known as the first and second laws of thermodynamics.

13.2   The concept of temperature

In approaching a new concept such as temperature, it is of the utmost importance to remember that definition and measurement are inseparable. It is perfectly correct to say that temperature is defined by the reading of a thermometer. Then the real essence of the definition is contained in the detailed instructions on how to construct the thermometer. The *usefulness* of the definition, which is another question but a vital one, will depend on whether the concept defined by a particular thermometer can be used to describe natural phenomena in a simple and self-consistent way.

In this section we shall approach temperature from the macroscopic side. With this approach, temperature is a distinct new concept, a primitive concept not directly derivable from the mechanical concepts of mass, length, and time. Later, in Section 13.8, we shall investigate the microscopic aspect of temperature and discover that at the molecular level it does, after all, have a mechanical basis.

Various ways to measure temperature

Looking around us, we have no trouble thinking of reactions of inanimate matter to heat and cold that might serve as a basis for defining and measuring temperature. When heated, a metal bar gets longer; a liquid expands; a gas expands, or its pressure increases, or both. When very hot, most substances glow and emit radiant energy. In addition, certain marked changes take place at definite temperatures—freezing, boiling, igniting. In principle, any of these effects could be used to define and measure temperature, and most of them do find a use for temperature measurement. An oven thermometer, for example, uses a metal strip. A typical outdoor thermometer uses a column of liquid. A device called a pyrometer measures high temperature by measuring emitted energy.

THE GAS THERMOMETER AND THE KELVIN SCALE

As a standard for a laboratory definition of temperature (at temperatures neither extremely high nor extremely low), the gas thermometer has been found most suitable. One version of the gas thermometer—the so-called constant-volume gas thermometer—is very simple* (Figure 13.1). It is a device used to measure the pressure of a fixed volume of gas. When the gas is heated, its pressure rises. When it is cooled, its pressure falls. The pressure, which is a *mechanical* property of the gas (force per unit area), is evidently related to what may be called a *thermal* property of the gas—that is, how hot or cold it is. The new concept, temperature, may therefore be defined in terms of the already-established concept, pressure. Most simply, temperature may be defined to be directly proportional to pressure:

Temperature defined by a gas thermometer

$$T = aP \qquad \text{(fixed volume)}. \tag{13.1}$$

There are two aspects to this definition. First, and most important, is the proportionality of temperature to pressure, which specifies the nature of the temperature concept. Second is the choice of the constant of proportionality, a, which determines the numerical value of T (or, equivalently, the unit of T).

---

* Another version, the constant-pressure gas thermometer, is equally simple in principle but somewhat less versatile in practice. The constant-pressure gas thermometer is considered in Problem 13.2.

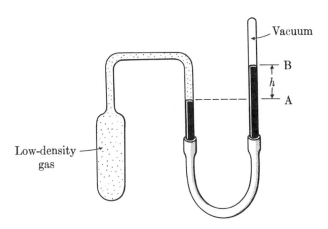

FIGURE 13.1   Constant-volume gas thermometer (idealized). The vertical column on the right can be moved to keep the liquid level A fixed and thereby keep the gas volume fixed. Then the difference in levels A and B (height h) provides a measure of the gas pressure. Higher pressure means higher temperature (see also Figure 13.3).

Equation 13.1 defines what is called *absolute temperature* if the gas in the gas thermometer behaves as an "ideal gas." At the molecular level, an ideal gas is one for which the size of the molecules is negligible compared with their average separation, and the average potential energy of interaction between two molecules is negligible compared with their average kinetic energy. At the macroscopic level, an ideal gas is defined by a process of extrapolation. Air at normal density in a gas thermometer defines a certain temperature scale. At lower density, it defines a slightly different temperature scale. Extrapolation to zero density then defines a definite temperature scale. The same process can be repeated for other gases in gas thermometers. Experimentally, it is found that all gases define the same temperature scale in the extrapolated limit of zero density. This is the absolute temperature scale. In the low-density limit, all gases are ideal gases. Even at normal densities, most gases—such as hydrogen, helium, nitrogen, and oxygen—are very nearly ideal gases. In the discussion that follows, we shall assume that the actual gas in the gas thermometer is so close to being an ideal gas that no corrections are required.

Ideal gas: submicroscopic definition

Ideal gas: macroscopic definition

The SI unit of temperature, the kelvin, is defined by setting the temperature of the triple point of water equal to 273.16 K:

$$T_t \equiv 273.16 \text{ K}. \qquad (13.2)$$

At normal pressure, water freezes at one temperature and boils at another. As pressure is lowered, the temperature difference between the boiling and freezing points decreases. At some critical pressure (which, for water, is about 0.006 atm), the difference vanishes. At this critical condition, called the triple point, solid, liquid, and gas phases coexist in equilibrium. Because of the uniqueness and reproducibility of this condition, it serves as a good calibration point. A device used to establish the triple-point temperature is shown in Figure 13.2. The number 273.16 is chosen in order to match closely the previous

The triple-point of water defines the kelvin

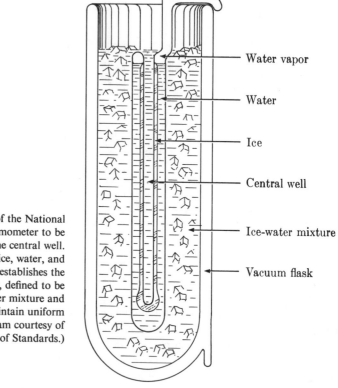

— Water vapor

— Water

— Ice

— Central well

— Ice-water mixture

— Vacuum flask

FIGURE 13.2   Triple-point cell of the National Bureau of Standards. A thermometer to be calibrated is inserted into the central well. The equilibrium mixture of ice, water, and water vapor that surrounds it establishes the standard temperature, defined to be 273.16 K. The outer ice-water mixture and vacuum flask help to maintain uniform thermal conditions. (Diagram courtesy of the National Bureau of Standards.)

standard calibration points, which were the freezing and boiling points of water at standard pressure. On the absolute kelvin scale these points occur at very nearly 273.15 K and 373.15 K, so their difference is almost exactly 100 K.

If the bulb of a gas thermometer is brought to the temperature of the triple point of water, the gas pressure takes on some value P_t. Equation 13.1 may then be written

$$T = \left(\frac{273.16}{P_t}\right) P. \qquad (13.3)$$

The constant a, equal to $273.16/P_t$, has a unique value for a particular thermometer. For another thermometer, P_t could be different, so a could be different. Both thermometers, however, would establish the same temperature scale. The characteristic straight-line graph of T vs P is shown in Figure 13.3.

THE MEASUREMENT OF TEMPERATURE

It is obvious that the gas thermometer should be able to *measure* as well as *define* temperature. When the bulb of a gas thermometer is placed in a steady thermal environment, the pressure of the gas stabilizes at some definite value.

The idea of thermal equilibrium

We say that the thermometer is then in *equilibrium* with its environment.

Through Equation 13.3, the measurement of pressure determines the temperature. This is the temperature *of the thermometer*. That it is also the temperature of the environment is a fact that requires a separate experimental foundation (Section 13.4). If a mercury thermometer or any other kind of thermometer is brought into equilibrium with a gas thermometer at various temperatures, the new thermometer may be calibrated so that it also measures absolute temperature, even though no equation as simple as Equation 13.1 governs its behavior.

Calibration of other thermometers

Temperature is, by definition, a scalar quantity. A thermometer provides a single numerical value for T. Temperature has no directional property and no dependence on coordinates. Like other definitions in physics, this one is justified by experience: It is simple, self-consistent, and useful.

Temperature is a scalar quantity

ABSOLUTE ZERO

If the bulb of a gas thermometer is placed in successively colder environments, it records successively lower pressures. The lowest pressure expected of a gas is zero. This suggests, according to Equation 13.3, that there is a lowest possible temperature, zero kelvin. It would be risky to reach this conclusion on the basis of the gas thermometer alone, since, cooled far enough, every gas liquifies, so a "gas thermometer" no longer contains gas and no longer functions as a simple thermometer. However, the existence of a real temperature floor is confirmed by many other pieces of evidence, and modern experimenters have been within one-thousandth of a degree of it. The idea that temperature is a manifestation of molecular energy (Section 13.8) makes clear that there must be an absolute

Zero kelvin is the lowest possible temperature

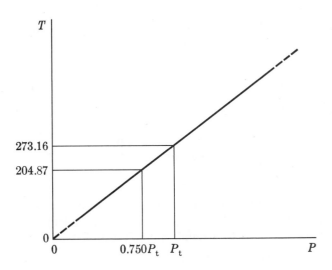

FIGURE 13.3   Kelvin temperature scale as established by a gas thermometer. At the triple point of water, the gas takes on some pressure P_t. The temperature at this point is defined to be 273.16 K. In some other environment, the gas takes on some other pressure; there the temperature is determined by the defining condition $T = aP$. For example, where $P = 0.750P_t$, the temperature is $T = 0.750 \times 273.16 = 204.87$. The dashed part of the line represents an extrapolated region where the gas thermometer may no longer be suitable for measuring temperature.

TABLE 13.1   LIQUEFACTION TEMPERATURES OF SOME COMMON GASES (AT ATMOSPHERIC PRESSURE)

Substance	Liquefaction Temperature	
	K	°C
Helium	4.2	−268.9
Hydrogen	20.4	−252.8
Neon	27.2	−245.9
Nitrogen	77.4	−195.8
Carbon monoxide	81.7	−191.5
Oxygen	90.2	−183.0
Methane	111.7	−161.5
Chlorine	238.6	−34.6
Ammonia	239.8	−33.4
Steam	373.2	+100.0

zero, for when no more energy can be extracted from a system, no further diminution of its temperature is possible.

The liquefaction temperatures of some common gases are shown in Table 13.1. Of all substance, helium condenses to liquid at the lowest temperature, only 4 degrees above absolute zero.* At temperatures close to absolute zero, entirely new methods of temperature measurement based on the connection between temperature and energy must be devised.

OTHER TEMPERATURE SCALES

The Celsius temperature scale, formerly defined by the freezing and boiling points of water at normal temperature, is now defined in terms of the kelvin scale by means of the simple equation

Celsius scale

$$T(°C) = T(K) - 273.15.† \tag{13.4}$$

The freezing point of water at normal pressure (0°C) is only 0.01 K below the triple-point temperature.

The Fahrenheit scale is defined by the calibration points, 32 °F = 0 °C and 212 °F = 100 °C. The transformation equation is

Fahrenheit scale

$$T(°F) = \tfrac{9}{5}T(°C) + 32. \tag{13.5}$$

Finally, the Rankine scale is an absolute scale (that is, its zero is at absolute zero), with its unit temperature interval being equal to that of the Fahrenheit scale. It is related to the kelvin scale by a simple multiplicative factor:

Rankine scale

$$T(°R) = \tfrac{9}{5}T(K). \tag{13.6}$$

---

* Helium is unique among all known substances in that it remains liquid at absolute zero (at atmospheric pressure).

† The degree sign is no longer used for the kelvin scale, but it is retained for the other temperature scales. A *value* of temperature on the Celsius scale is indicated by °C; *differences* of temperatures are sometimes indicated by C°.

The Fahrenheit and Rankine scales are rarely used in scientific research, although they are still encountered in some branches of engineering. The four temperature scales that we have discussed are compared in Figure 13.4.

13.3 The mole

Before proceeding with the discussion of temperature, we must mention a few facts about atoms and early chemistry. Gradually, during the nineteenth century, long before the mass of a single atom was known, chemists had deduced the *relative* masses of many atoms. These relative masses, referred to the hydrogen atom as a unit standard, were called *atomic weights*. Today the same nomenclature is used, although the standard reference atom has changed. The atom of carbon whose nucleus contains 6 protons and 6 neutrons (designated $^{12}_{6}C_6$, or simply ^{12}C) is now defined to be exactly 12 atomic mass units (amu).

An isotope of carbon defines the amu

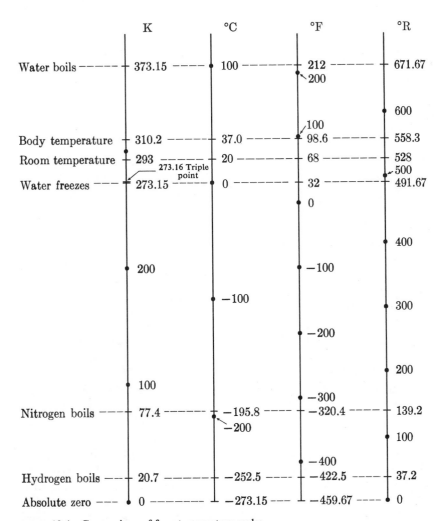

FIGURE 13.4 Comparison of four temperature scales.

On this scale, the atomic weight of the lightest isotope of hydrogen ($_1^1H$) is 1.0078. In chemistry the atomic weight usually refers to the average mass of the various isotopes of an element in the normal isotopic mixture. The physicist is more likely to be interested in the masses of specific isotopes; to avoid confusion, these are called *atomic masses* rather than atomic weights. *Molecular weights*, as the name suggests, are the masses of molecules expressed in atomic mass units.

Atomic and molecular weight; atomic mass

By the end of the nineteenth century, chemists had gained a fair idea of the connection between the atomic mass unit and the gram; that is, they knew something about absolute atomic masses as well as relative atomic masses. Accurate values of this conversion factor were not known until early in this century. A recent precise value for the atomic mass unit expressed in grams and kilograms is

$$1 \text{ amu} = 1.6605 \times 10^{-24} \text{ gm} = 1.6605 \times 10^{-27} \text{ kg}. \qquad (13.7)$$

The mole

During the nineteenth century, a unit of chemical currency called the *mole* came into use. One mole of atoms is the number of atoms required to make an amount of material whose mass in grams is numerically equal to the mass of a single atom in atomic mass units. To put it approximately, 1 mole of hydrogen atoms is the number of hydrogen atoms in 1 gm of hydrogen; 1 mole of carbon atoms is the number of carbon atoms in 12 gm of carbon. Similarly, 1 mole of water molecules is the number of water molecules in 18 gm of water. Because two hydrogen atoms unite to form a hydrogen molecule of molecular weight 2, it is also true that 2 gm of hydrogen contain 1 mole of hydrogen *molecules*. Since the mass of a mole of material is chosen to be proportional to the atomic or molecular weight, the *number* of atoms or molecules in a single mole is always the same. The mole, then, is simply a convenient way of designating a fixed number of particles. The number of particles in a mole, for which we use the symbol N_0, is called *Avogadro's number*, and it is a very large number indeed. A little thought will show you that Avogadro's number must be the number of atomic mass units in 1 gm. It is

Avogadro's number

$$N_0 = 6.0222 \times 10^{23} \text{ particles/mole} \quad \text{or} \quad \text{amu/gm}. \qquad (13.8)$$

The chemist working with macroscopic amounts of matter finds the mole a convenient unit of molecular number in much the same way that the director of a government agency might find one million dollars a convenient unit of dollar number. Actually, there is a difference. The chemist uses the mole not only for reason of present-day convenience but also for reason of historical precedent. Before the numerical value of Avogadro's number was known even roughly, a mole of matter—that is, 18 gm of water or 12 gm of carbon, or 56 gm of iron— could be defined and used. In working with SI units, it is now often convenient to use the kmole (10^3 mole), equal to 6.02×10^{26} particles. Molecular weight ($M.W.$) may be expressed in either of the equivalent units, gm/mole or kg/kmole.

One of the earliest important statements about molecular number was the remarkable prediction by Amedeo Avogadro in 1811 that at the same temperature and pressure equal volumes of all gases contain equal numbers of molecules. Several years earlier, Joseph Gay-Lussac had discovered a beautifully simple aspect of chemically reacting gases that is known now as the law of combining volumes. When two gases combine chemically, the volumes that enter into the reaction always have simple numerical ratios. If the product is a gas, its volume, too, is simply related to the combining volumes. For example, 2 liters of hydrogen and 1 liter of oxygen combine to yield 2 liters of steam. One liter of nitrogen and 3 liters of hydrogen combine to yield 2 liters of ammonia. Avogadro guessed correctly that such simple behavior must indicate that all gases have exactly the same number of molecules per unit volume (at a given pressure and temperature). It was nearly half a century before his prediction was adequately verified and generally accepted. Once the molecular weights of gases had been determined, it was found that the densities of gases were in direct proportion to their molecular weight. This means that the number of molecules per unit volume must be the same. Another way to state Avogadro's hypothesis (still called a hypothesis despite its ample verification) is this: At fixed temperature and pressure, the volume required to contain 1 mole of a gas is the same for all gases. Under standard conditions (273 K and 1 atm), 1 mole of gas occupies 22.4 liters (22.4×10^3 cm^3, or 22.4×10^{-3} m^3).

The law of combining volumes

Avogadro's hypothesis

13.4   Two laws of temperature

Temperature enters into the description of nature at many points, and it impinges on our own lives every day. Here we shall discuss two fundamental laws involving temperature.

THE LAW OF EQUILIBRIUM

When a roast beef is put into a freezer, its temperature falls gradually until it is just as cold (that is, until it has the same temperature) as its surroundings in the freezer. When a customer in a hurry pours some cold water into his hot coffee, the water is heated, the coffee is cooled, and the diluted coffee comes to a uniform intermediate temperature. The fact that two things in contact tend toward the same temperature is so familiar that it is easy to overlook its significance. Actually, this equalization tendency is the most basic experimental fact about temperature. Known as the law of equilibrium, or sometimes as the zeroth law of thermodynamics,* it can be stated in this way: Two systems in thermal contact tend toward the same temperature and reach equilibrium at the same temperature. There is both a dynamic and a static aspect to the law. If two systems in contact are *not* at the same temperature, the temperature of one or both will tend to change in the direction of equalization. The tendency may be countered by outside influences adding or subtracting heat energy from one or the other; for instance, a house furnace prevents the interior of the house from reaching the temperature outdoors. In the absence of such an influence, the direction of spontaneous change is always toward equalization. If two systems in contact *are* at the same temperature, there is no tendency for either to change

The law of equilibrium is the zeroth law of thermodynamics

---

* The first and second laws of thermodynamics were named in the nineteenth century before the law of equilibrium was accorded the fundamental status it deserves. In order to indicate that it ranks ahead of the first law of thermodynamics, it is called the zeroth law.

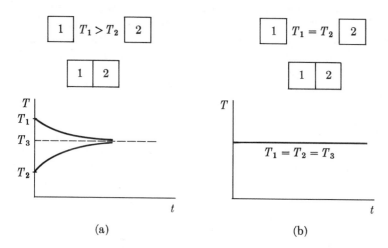

FIGURE 13.5   The law of equilibrium: (a) Dynamic form: When brought into thermal contact, two bodies not at the same temperature will tend toward the same temperature. (b) Static aspect: When brought into thermal contact, two bodies at the same temperature will be in thermal equilibrium and will maintain the same temperature.

its temperature spontaneously. They are then said to be in equilibrium (see Figure 13.5).

If one thinks of temperature not in familiar everyday terms but abstractly as a new physical concept, it will be seen that the law of equilibrium is rather special and, therefore, presumably significant. Very few quantities in physics exhibit this spontaneous tendency toward equalization. Masses do not, nor do forces, velocities, or accelerations. It is natural, therefore, to seek a deeper explanation for this fact of nature. The explanation has been found in the microscopic theory of temperature and in ideas of probability applied to molecular motion. We shall return to the law of equilibrium in Section 13.12. It is interesting that so "obvious" a fact of nature rests on some of the most fundamental ideas of thermodynamics. The scientist must approach the familiar just as carefully and cautiously as he does the unfamiliar.

It underlies the action of a thermometer

As noted in the previous section, a thermometer is itself a physical system, and what it reveals directly is its own temperature. Only because of the law of equilibrium does a thermometer also measure the temperature of its surroundings.

THE IDEAL-GAS LAW

In about 1660, Robert Boyle in England discovered the law of gases that now bears his name.* He found that if a quantity of gas is compressed or allowed to expand at constant temperature, it exerts a pressure inversely proportional to

---

* For historical background, see Marie Boas Hall, "Robert Boyle," *Scientific American,* August, 1967.

the volume it occupies. Boyle's law may be expressed by the equation

$$PV = constant \quad \text{(at constant } T\text{)}. \tag{13.9}$$

Boyle's law

The value of the constant on the right is different for different samples of gas, but for any particular sample the product of pressure and volume is a constant if the temperature is constant. Boyle's law is a statement only about the mechanical properties of a gas—its pressure and its volume. Temperature plays a subsidiary role: it must be constant, but it does not enter directly into the mathematical statement of the law.

Not until late in the eighteenth century, more than a century later, were the pressure and volume of a sample of gas related quantitatively to the temperature of the gas. Jacques Charles, and after him, Joseph Gay-Lussac, learned that at fixed pressure, the volume of a gas increases in direct proportion to the *absolute* temperature. In symbols,

$$V = constant \times T \quad \text{(at constant } P\text{)}. \tag{13.10}$$

Charles's law

This is now known as Charles's law. As in Boyle's law, the constant is fixed only for a particular sample of gas. A third gas law, basic to the operation of the gas thermometer, is the direct proportionality of pressure to absolute temperature at fixed volume. The equivalent of Equation 13.1 is

$$P = constant \times T \quad \text{(at constant } V\text{)}. \tag{13.11}$$

A third special gas law

Actually, the gas thermometer was in use long before this law had been accurately tested. The gas thermometer was invented in 1702 by Guillaume Amontons, who was the first to predict the existence of an absolute zero of temperature. He worked only with air. Charles and Gay-Lussac were the first to appreciate the universality of the gas laws, which are as applicable to oxygen or nitrogen or hydrogen as to air. It is *because* of this universality that Equation 13.11 can be both a law of nature and a definition of temperature.

The three gas laws just discussed can be assembled into a single law, now called the *ideal-gas law*. The ideal-gas law may be written

$$PV = nRT. \tag{13.12}$$

The ideal-gas law

The three variables are the pressure $P\,(\text{N/m}^2)$, the volume $V\,(\text{m}^3)$, and the temperature $T\,(\text{K})$. The quantity n is the number of moles of gas (dimensionless), and R is a universal constant called simply the gas constant. The ideal-gas law is really a more powerful statement about the behavior of gases than is provided by all three of the special laws just cited. Not until the molecular weights of gases had been measured—after the time of Charles and Gay-Lussac—could the full universality and simplicity of the ideal-gas law be appreciated. The experimental value of the gas constant R is

$$R = 8.314 \, \frac{\text{N m}}{\text{mole K}} \quad \text{or} \quad \frac{\text{J}}{\text{mole K}}. \overset{*}{} \tag{13.13}$$

---

* In Equation 13.12, if n is taken to be the number of kilomoles, R should be written $R = 8.314 \times 10^3$ J/kmole K.

(Note that the dimension of pressure × volume appearing on the left of the ideal-gas law is the same as the dimension of energy—see Equation 12.53.) Over a considerable range of pressure, density, and temperature, a large number of different gases do follow the ideal-gas law quite closely.

A good way to look at the ideal-gas law is as a connecting link between the mechanical and thermal aspects of a gas. On the left of Equation 13.12 appear only mechanical and geometric quantities: the volume occupied by the gas and the force it exerts on each unit area of the containing vessel. On the right appears the temperature. The ideal-gas law unites these aspects. Of all of the statements about nature involving the concept of temperature, this is one of the simplest and most fundamental.

The appearance on the right side of Equation 13.12 of the number of moles n is quite natural; it accompanies the appearance of the volume on the left. If the volume of a gas is doubled without changing either its pressure or its temperature, it makes sense that this can be achieved only by doubling the amount of material, that is, by doubling n. It is of some interest to re-express the ideal-gas law in terms of the number of molecules instead of the number of moles. Since there are N_0 molecules in each mole (N_0 is Avogadro's number), there are n times N_0 molecules in n moles. If N denotes the total number of molecules in a sample of gas, the relation is

$$N = nN_0. \tag{13.14}$$

This means that N/N_0 may be substituted for n in Equation 13.12, giving

$$PV = N\left(\frac{R}{N_0}\right)T.$$

Since N_0 is a fixed constant, as is R, the ratio R/N_0 is another universal constant. It is called *Boltzmann's constant*, after Ludwig Boltzmann, a leading contributor to the theory of thermodynamics in the latter part of the nineteenth century. Designated by the letter k, Boltzmann's constant has the value

$$k = \frac{R}{N_0} = 1.3806 \times 10^{-23} \text{ J/K.} \tag{13.15}$$

We might call R the macroscopic gas constant and k the microscopic gas constant. In terms of k, the ideal-gas law has the form

Another form of the ideal-gas law

$$PV = NkT. \tag{13.16}$$

This is, of course, only a re-expression of the same law, and for many purposes it is inconvenient because N is such a large number and k is such a small number. However, it puts the ideal-gas law into closer touch with fundamentals, expressing it in terms of the total number of molecules N in a given sample of gas.

The ideal-gas law has something interesting to say about absolute zero. When the temperature reaches zero on the kelvin scale, the right side of Equation 13.12 vanishes, so either the pressure or the volume (of an ideal gas) must also vanish. Negative temperature is unreachable on the absolute scale because an ideal gas cannot display negative pressure, and negative volume has no physical meaning. Both the left and right sides of Equation 13.12 must be positive.*

■ EXAMPLE 1: What volume is occupied by 1 mole of an ideal gas at standard conditions of temperature and pressure ($T = 273$ K, $P = 1.013 \times 10^5$ N/m^2)? Equation 13.12 provides an immediate answer:

$$V = \frac{nRT}{P}$$

$$= \frac{1 \times 8.31 \times 273}{1.013 \times 10^5}$$

$$= 0.0224 \text{ m}^3 = 22.4 \text{ liters.} \quad ■$$

■ EXAMPLE 2: Helium gas follows the ideal-gas law quite closely. Consider 1 liter of helium initially at a pressure of 10^5 N/m^2 (about 1 atm) and a temperature of 300 K (near room temperature). Suppose that it is cooled to 10 K at constant atmospheric pressure. By how much will its volume shrink? Now imagine that it expands back to its original volume at this low temperature. What happens to its pressure? These questions are best answered by using ratios. For constant pressure, volume is proportional to temperature (Equation 13.10 or 13.12), so

$$\frac{V_1}{V_2} = \frac{T_1}{T_2}.$$

For $V_1 = 1$ liter, $T_1 = 300$ K, and $T_2 = 10$ K, it follows that $V_2 = 0.033$ liter. Similar reasoning shows that expansion back to a volume of 1 liter at 10 K must result in a thirtyfold decrease of pressure to one-thirtieth of an atmosphere. The sequence is

$$P_1 = 1 \text{ atm}, \qquad V_1 = 1 \text{ liter}, \qquad T_1 = 300 \text{ K};$$
$$P_2 = 1 \text{ atm}, \qquad V_2 = 0.033 \text{ liter}, \qquad T_2 = 10 \text{ K};$$
$$P_3 = 0.033 \text{ atm}, \qquad V_3 = 1 \text{ liter}, \qquad T_3 = 10 \text{ K}.$$

Finally, we can ask how many moles of helium and how many atoms are contained in the original liter of helium. To give the number of moles, Equation 13.12 may be written

$$n = \frac{PV}{RT}.$$

Recalling that 1 liter $= 10^{-3}$ m^3, we can substitute numbers in this equation to get

$$n = \frac{10^5 \text{ N/m}^2 \times 10^{-3} \text{ m}^3}{8.31 \text{ N m/mole K} \times 300 \text{ K}} = 0.040 \text{ mole.}$$

---

* The idea of "negative temperature" does enter into more advanced treatments of thermodynamics. It is a way of characterizing certain systems that are *not* in thermal equilibrium. Any such system, if allowed to come to thermal equilibrium (by redistribution of its internal energy), would have positive absolute temperature.

The number of molecules is

$$N = nN_0 = 4.0 \times 10^{-2} \times 6.0 \times 10^{23} = 2.4 \times 10^{22} \text{ molecules.}$$

It is always worth remembering the enormity of molecular number in any macroscopic amount of matter. In this particular example, the number of "molecules" is the same as the number of atoms since helium atoms do not join together to form molecules.   ■

13.5   Internal energy and heat

Bulk energy = macroscopic energy = ordered energy

The total energy of a sample of matter is the sum of a macroscopic part, called *bulk energy*, and a submicroscopic part, called *internal energy*. Bulk energy is mechanical energy associated with the motion and position of the sample as a whole. Internal energy is randomly distributed energy associated with the motion and interaction of atoms and molecules within the sample. If a bubble of warm air rises in the atmosphere, its bulk energy consists of the kinetic energy of its upward motion and its gravitational potential energy (Figure 13.6).

Internal energy = submicroscopic energy = disordered energy

Its internal energy consists of all of the additional energy residing in its careening molecules. These two kinds of energy are also referred to as ordered and disordered energy. In Section 13.11 we shall consider transformations from one form of energy to another. Here we are concerned with the definitions of these kinds of energy and with the closely related concept of heat.

Heat is often considered yet another form of energy. To be more exact, it is a manifestation of energy *transfer* by molecular collisions. If warm alcohol is added to cold water, the alcohol molecules lose energy and the water molecules gain energy. Energy has been transferred from alcohol to water, and the transfer has been effected by a multitude of molecular collisions. Heat, like

Heat is a mode of energy exchange

work, is more a name for an energy currency than a name for a "real" energy. It is a mode of energy exchange.

Internal energy and heat distinguished

It is easy to confuse heat and internal energy. Such confusion has historical precedent. In the earliest days of thermodynamics, heat designated both energy content and energy exchange. This was quite a natural point of view when heat was regarded as a substance, stored in objects and capable of flowing from one object to another. Now, however, it is important to separate the two ideas. Internal energy can change not only in response to heat flow but also in response to work. Consider a certain quantity of air contained in a glass cylinder with a piston at one end (Figure 13.7). How can we increase its internal energy? One way is to heat the cylinder. The warm inner side of the cylinder transfers some energy to the air as molecules in the air collide repeatedly with molecules in the glass surface. This is heat transfer. Another way is to move the piston inward. The force required to move it multiplied by the distance it moves is work, and this work is transferred to the internal energy of the air. The temperature of the air rises, just as if it had been heated. Speaking casually, we do say that the air has been heated and that it is hotter. Technically, though, we should say that its internal energy and its temperature have increased. When

Work and heat contrasted

work is done on the air, it gains energy from the macroscopic bulk motion of the piston. When *heat* is transferred to the air, it gains energy from the microscopic motion of the molecules in the container. There are other ways to add energy,

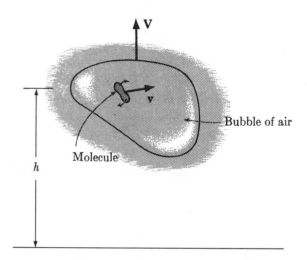

FIGURE 13.6   Bulk energy and internal energy. The bulk energy of a rising bubble of warm air is $\frac{1}{2}MV^2 + Mgh$, where M is the mass of the bubble. Its internal energy (represented by the moving molecule) is the total random kinetic energy of its molecules plus the total potential energy of interaction among its molecules plus excitation energy within its molecules.

FIGURE 13.7   Air in a cylinder. Its internal energy may be increased by heat (Bunsen flame or radiation) or by work (force moving piston). Its bulk energy is unchanged.

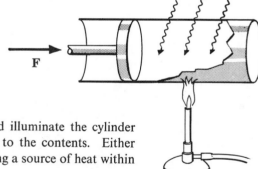

most of which may also be called heat. Light could illuminate the cylinder (Figure 13.7), or reacting chemicals could be added to the contents. Either such method of adding energy is equivalent to spreading a source of heat within the cylinder.

Since heat is a mode of energy exchange, it would be logical for the unit of measurement of heat to be the same as the unit of measurement of energy. In this case, unfortunately, history was not so logical. Heat was defined and used as a quantitative concept long before its connection with energy was known. The old practice hangs on, and heat is still often expressed in a unit different from the standard energy unit. A common unit of heat in scientific work is the calorie (cal), defined by Equation 13.17.* It is almost exactly equal to the heat required to raise the temperature of 1 gm of water from 16.5 °C to 17.5 °C. (The heat required to raise the temperature of 1 gm of water by 1 degree at any other temperature between 0 °C and 100 °C is also very nearly equal to 1 cal.) With SI units, the kilocalorie is convenient. It is approximately the heat required to raise the temperature of 1 kg of water by 1 K.

The calorie, a unit of heat

* The full name of this unit is the thermochemical calorie.

THE MECHANICAL EQUIVALENT OF HEAT

The standard unit of heat is related to the standard unit of energy by the conversion factor

Definition of the calorie

$$J = 4,184 \text{ J/kcal.} \tag{13.17}$$

(Alternative expressions are 4.184 J/cal and 4.184 × 10⁷ erg/cal.) In a contemporary setting, Equation 13.17 reports a mundane fact about units conversion, much like the equation 1 ft = 0.3048 m. At the same time, in a historical setting, this equation reports one of the great discoveries of nineteenth-century physics, the equivalence of heat and energy. That heat is a manifestation of energy was first suggested in the 1840s by Julius Mayer and by James Joule. The earliest accurate verification of the equivalence was achieved by Joule. In one of his experiments, he stirred liquids with paddle wheels activated by known external forces. He measured the work done on a liquid by a paddle wheel and the resulting rise in temperature of the liquid. He found that under all circumstances a work input of approximately 4.2 J produced the same temperature rise as a heat input of 1 cal.* To within the accuracy of the experiment, there was a constant numerical ratio between equivalent inputs of work and heat. This ratio J is called the mechanical equivalent of heat.

Some decades before the work of Mayer and Joule, there was ample evidence pointing to a *connection* between heat and mechanical energy. Based on studies of the production of heat by friction, Count Rumford in 1798 had stated very forcefully that heat is a manifestation of microscopic motions. At the same time, steam engines were demonstrating the production of mechanical energy by heat. But prior to the work of Mayer and Joule, two vital elements in the relationship were missing. These men, first of all, postulated a specific, constant ratio for equivalent amounts of heat and work. This alone transformed a qualitative idea into quantitative law. Second, and even more important, they proposed the law of conservation of energy as a single fundamental law, governing all parts of nature. The conservation of mechanical energy and the conservation of internal energy had been separately recognized in the eighteenth century as laws valid in certain limiting situations (recall that internal energy and heat were not distinguished at that time). For the motion of the earth around the sun, mechanical energy is conserved to a high degree of accuracy. For a swinging pendulum that comes gradually to rest, on the other hand, mechanical energy disappears. And in the work produced by a steam engine or by human muscle power, new mechanical energy comes into existence. Internal energy itself is conserved if its transfer is accomplished by heat flow without mechanical motion, but it may increase or diminish if its transfer is accompanied by forces and macroscopic motion. Most commonly, mechanical energy is transformed into internal energy by friction.

Two vital ideas of the 1840s

1. A constant conversion factor relates heat and work

2. Energy conservation is a general principle of nature

The two new elements of Mayer and Joule are, of course, related. If heat and work were not quantitatively connected by a conversion factor, there could be no basis upon which to build a more general law of energy conservation. Mayer and Joule independently achieved the great vision of energy as a single

---

* The name "joule" for the mks unit of energy came later, of course. At that time, the units of heat and energy were independently defined.

universal concept capable of changing its appearance drastically without ever changing its total magnitude.* Once they had unified the ideas of heat and mechanical energy, the greatest hurdle was surmounted. It was then easy to add electromagnetic energy and chemical energy and eventually nuclear energy. The important thing was their proposal of a general law of energy conservation. If stirring a container of water with a paddle seems a childish pursuit for a grown man, consider its implications. The law of conservation of energy, still a foundation stone of modern physics, has found wider applicability in science and in practical affairs than any other law of nature.

■ EXAMPLE 1:   A student reading in the bathtub has allowed the bathwater to become uncomfortably chilly. Deciding to follow Joule's example, he stirs vigorously for a few minutes in an effort to heat the water. If the tub contains 100 kg of water and he moves his hand a total distance of 140 m, exerting an average force of 30 N,† by how much should the water temperature rise? The work he has done is

$$W = Fd = 30 \text{ N} \times 140 \text{ m} = 4{,}200 \text{ J}.$$

The equivalent heat is

$$Q = \frac{W}{J} = \frac{4{,}200 \text{ J}}{4{,}184 \text{ J/kcal}} \cong 1 \text{ kcal}.$$

This is sufficient to raise the temperature of 1 kg of water by 1 K. It therefore increases the temperature of the 100 kg of bath water by only 0.01 K, an imperceptible amount.   ■

■ EXAMPLE 2:   How many flights of stairs must a 60-kg woman climb in order to "work off" an ice cream sundae rated at 500 food calories? The work required is

$$W = JQ = 4{,}184 \text{ J/kcal} \times 500 \text{ kcal}$$

$$= 2.1 \times 10^6 \text{ J}.$$

The force she must exert against gravity is $F = mg = 60 \text{ kg} \times 9.8 \text{ m/sec}^2 = 588$ N. The needed vertical distance is

$$d = \frac{W}{F} = \frac{2.1 \times 10^6 \text{ J}}{5.9 \times 10^2 \text{ N}} = 3{,}600 \text{ m}.$$

At 3 m per flight, this is about 1,200 flights, a dozen times the height of the Empire State Building. In actuality, of course, food energy makes its appearance more as heat than as work. Nevertheless, the calculation shows why decreasing the intake of calories is more effective than increasing exercise for losing weight.   ■

---

* Hermann von Helmholtz was another early contributor to the idea of a universal law of energy conservation. Two accounts of the subject that he prepared for general audiences in 1854 and 1862 can be found in his *Popular Scientific Lectures* (New York: Dover publications, 1962).

† Are these magnitudes reasonable? About how many gallons of water are contained in 100 kg? Roughly how many pounds weigh 30 N? About how long should it take to move a stirring hand 140 m?

J, the mechanical equivalent of heat, is a "large" quantity

To put the lesson of these examples in colloquial terms, a little heat is worth a great deal of work. Suppose it were otherwise. What if 4,184 kcal were equivalent to 1 J rather than 4,184 J being equivalent to 1 kcal? It is always interesting to contemplate hypothetical worlds in which physical constants have values different from those in our own world. In this *other* world, where much heat is equivalent to little work, we can be sure that the general law of energy conservation would have been discovered early. The quantitative link between work and heat would be hard to miss. Life in such a world would, at the very least, be hazardous. If a man in a bath tub developed a slight tremor, he might set the water to boiling and scald himself to death. Indeed it is very questionable whether he would exist at all. His ancestral amphibian, trying to climb out of the sea, would probably have been burned to a crisp from friction with the sand.

13.6   The kinetic theory of gases

Three early views of heat

During the late eighteenth and early nineteenth centuries, there were three rival views on the nature of heat and what we now call internal energy. The first and most widely held view stated that heat is a substance. The substance was given a name, *caloric*, and was generally assumed to be atomic in nature, like matter. To think of heat as a substance is natural, and this point of view does account easily for two main facts: that heat seems to flow from one place to another and that heat is conserved, at least under certain circumstances. On the other hand, some powerful arguments were marshalled against the caloric theory. As far as could be determined, an object weighed no more after being heated than before. From a single object, friction could apparently produce an endless supply of heat. And heat could make its way readily through the densest solid matter.

1. Heat as a substance (caloric)

2. Heat associated with random molecular motion

Both of the other two popular views attributed heat to molecular motion. They differed in the kind of molecular motion that was postulated. According to one view, which has survived to become the basis of our modern understanding, molecules of a gas move about randomly, striking each other and the walls of the container but otherwise not inhibited in their travels. The quantitative elaboration of this picture of gas behavior is called the *kinetic theory*. According to the simplest version of the kinetic theory, heat added to a gas goes into the kinetic energy of molecular motion.

3. Heat associated with rotation of molecules in fixed positions

The second popular view of heat as molecular motion attributed rotational but not translational motion to gas molecules. The minds of some scientists must have recoiled at the randomness and chaos implied by the idea of gas molecules in constant motion and frequent collision. According to their more orderly view, gas molecules remained in fixed relative positions but could rotate more or less rapidly as heat was added or taken away. This picture of gases was in fact the more popular in the early nineteenth century.

By showing heat to be a manifestation of energy, Mayer, Joule, and Helmholtz demolished the idea of caloric. Yet the decision about the nature of molecular motion remained to be made. By itself the new general law of energy conservation shed no light on this question. As of 1850, the rival views of a gas as randomly moving molecules and as molecules rotating in fixed positions appeared to have an equally good chance of surviving. Within the next decade,

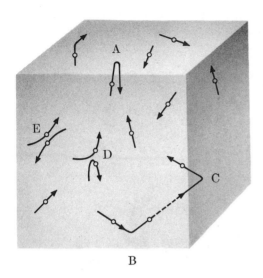

FIGURE 13.8   Random motion of molecules in a gas. Collisions of molecules with the container walls are indicated at points A, B, and C, and collisions of molecules with each other at points D and E.

the successes and the simplicity of the kinetic theory had strongly tipped the balance in favor of the picture of randomly moving molecules. We now know that molecules execute *both* rotational and translational motion.

According to the kinetic theory, molecules in a gas fly about in all directions, frequently colliding with each other and with their containing walls (Figure 13.8). In the simplest version of the kinetic theory, the following specific assumptions are made:

1. Each molecule spends most of its time in free motion between collisions and only a small fraction of its time in interaction with other molecules. This assumption—which is a good one for most actual gases at ordinary temperatures and pressures—requires for its validity (a) that the diameter of a molecule be substantially less than the mean distance between molecules and (b) that the forces acting between molecules be of short range, extending little beyond the physical dimensions of the molecules.

Basic assumptions of the kinetic theory

2. Each collision between two molecules or between a molecule and a container wall is an elastic collision, one in which kinetic energy is conserved. (Actually, this assumption is more restrictive than necessary. The results of the kinetic theory require only that the *total* molecular kinetic energy of a gas in equilibrium be constant. Changes of kinetic energy are possible in individual collisions. However, for calculational purposes, it is simpler to assume that all collisions are elastic.)

3. Newton's laws govern the motion and collision of molecules.

Conceptually simple though it may be, the kinetic theory is not something suggested directly by any of our experience with matter in bulk—except, perhaps, for the observation that a free gas tends to expand without limit. In a brilliant piece of work a century before the scientific community was ready to appreciate its significance, Daniel Bernoulli, a Swiss mathematician, in 1738 worked out the consequences of the kinetic theory. His work apparently had no impact whatever on the course of science, being noticed only after Joule in England and two German physicists, August Krönig and Rudolph Clausius,

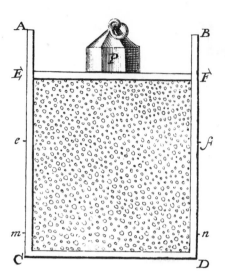

From Bernoulli's
Hydrodynamica, 1738; a
theory ahead of its time

Dover Publications, Inc., New York. Reprinted
through permission of the publisher.

had developed the same theory independently in the 1840s and 1850s. In the
intervening century, Charles and Gay-Lussac had clarified the macroscopic laws
of gas behavior, the gas thermometer had been perfected, chemical evidence for
the existence of atoms and molecules had become overwhelmingly convincing,
the steam engine was utilizing heat energy for mechanical work, thermodynamics
was well launched as a quantitative theory, caloric had been abandoned, and
the general law of energy conservation had been formulated. By the time these
strides in the science of temperature and heat had caught up with the forward
leap of Bernoulli, he had been long dead and this part of his work forgotten.
Yet, when the time was ripe, the same ideas were regenerated by several scientists
in different places at nearly the same time in a more typical pattern of scientific
development. Only rarely can a leap into the unknown come down on solid
ground, for the infinitude of possible error is vast compared to the infinitesimal
islands of truth.

13.7   The pressure of a confined gas

It might seem surprising that any mathematical derivation based on
the kinetic theory could be simple. At the submicroscopic level a gas appears to
be an incalculable chaos of flying molecules, no two moving in exactly the
same way and none moving very far before vigorously colliding with one of its
neighbors. Yet only elementary mechanics and simple ideas of probability are
required to derive the ideal-gas law. The derivation illuminates the content of
the kinetic theory and, even more important, establishes the connection between
temperature and molecular energy.

What this derivation sets out to do is to relate the pressure exerted by a
gas on the walls of its container with the mechanical properties of the molecular
motion—that is, with the mass and speed of the molecules. This is a relation
between the macroscopic and the submicroscopic, therefore a focus of our
concern with thermodynamics. When a gas molecule strikes a wall and is
turned back, it delivers a tiny hammer blow of force to the wall. The multitude

of these incessant hammer blows produces an average outward force on the container, the manifestation of the gas pressure.

To be definite, let us consider a container that is a rectangular parallelepiped, its edges parallel to a set of Cartesian axes (Figure 13.9). The dimension of the container in the x direction is L, its area parallel to the yz plane is A, and its volume, accordingly, is $V = LA$. Focus attention on any molecule within the container whose x component of velocity at a particular instant is v_x. What is the chance that this molecule will rebound from the right wall in an ensuing small time interval Δt? We may choose Δt to be so small that the molecule moves freely throughout this time with little chance to strike another molecule (Assumption 1 in the preceding section). Whether it hits the wall in this time, then, depends simply on whether it can cover the distance from its starting position to the wall in the time Δt. If its distance from the wall is initially greater than Δl, given by

$$\Delta l = |v_x|\, \Delta t, \qquad (13.18)$$

it will not make it to the wall. If it is initially within a distance Δl of the wall (see Figure 13.9) *and* if v_x is positive (so that it is moving toward the wall), it *will* hit the wall within the time interval Δt. Now we introduce the concept of probability. The molecule chosen for consideration is equally likely to be located anywhere within the volume of the container. The probability that it is within a distance Δl of the right wall at a particular moment is therefore simply $\Delta l / L$. If it is within this region near the wall, it has an equal chance to be moving toward or away from the wall. The net probability that it is within a distance Δl of the wall *and* is moving toward the wall is

$$f = \frac{1}{2}\frac{\Delta l}{L} = \frac{|v_x|\, \Delta t}{2L}. \qquad (13.19)$$

Probability for a molecule to strike the wall in time Δt

This quantity f is the probability that a randomly chosen molecule in the container whose x component of velocity has magnitude $|v_x|$ will rebound from the right wall within a time interval Δt.

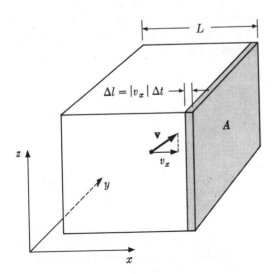

FIGURE 13.9   A container of gas. A molecule with x component of velocity v_x will strike the right wall within a time interval Δt if it starts within the shaded region of thickness $|v_x|\Delta t$ and if $v_x > 0$.

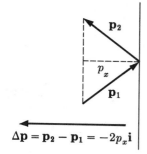

$$\Delta\mathbf{p} = \mathbf{p}_2 - \mathbf{p}_1 = -2p_x\mathbf{i}$$

FIGURE 13.10   Elastic collision of a molecule with a smooth wall.

Impulse delivered by a rebounding molecule

Consider next the details of a molecular collision with the wall. Figure 13.10 illustrates such a collision. A molecule of initial momentum $\mathbf{p}_1$ rebounds with momentum $\mathbf{p}_2$. We suppose the wall to be smooth so that it can exert only an x component of force on the molecule and change only the x component of momentum. Since the collision is elastic (Assumption 2 in the preceding section), the magnitude of the momentum does not change: $p_1 = p_2$. It is then a simple matter to show that the change of momentum of the molecule is

$$\Delta\mathbf{p} = -2p_x\mathbf{i} = -2mv_x\mathbf{i}. \tag{13.20}$$

(The proof of this statement is left as an exercise.) According to Equation 8.8, change of momentum is equal to impulse, so the impulse delivered to the molecule is $-2mv_x\mathbf{i}$ (for the molecule being considered, $v_x > 0$). From Newton's third law (Assumption 3 is being used), the molecule delivers to the wall an equal and opposite impulse, whose x component is

$$I_x = +2mv_x. \tag{13.21}$$

The probability that a molecule strikes the wall multiplied by the impulse that it delivers if it does strike is called the *expectation value* of the impulse, which we may designate by I_1:*

$$I_1 = fI_x. \tag{13.22}$$

From Equations 13.19 and 13.21, this is

$$I_1 = \frac{\Delta t}{L}mv_x{}^2. \tag{13.23}$$

The quantity I_1 is the *average* impulse delivered in the time interval Δt by a *single* molecule whose x component of velocity squared is equal to (or nearly equal to) $v_x{}^2$. If the average is then extended over all molecules, we have

Average impulse per molecule

$$\overline{I_1} = \frac{\Delta t}{L}\overline{mv_x{}^2}. \tag{13.24}$$

The bars designate averages over all molecules in the container. The quantity $\overline{I_1}$ is the average impulse per molecule delivered to the right wall in time Δt. Multiplication by N, the total number of molecules in the container, gives the total impulse I delivered to this wall during this time:

$$I = N\overline{I_1}$$

$$= \frac{N}{L}\overline{mv_x{}^2}\,\Delta t.$$

According to Equation 8.12,

$$I = \overline{F}\,\Delta t,$$

so the magnitude of the average force exerted by the rebounding molecules on the wall is

---

* More fully, the expectation value is written $I_1 = fI_x + (1 - f)0$. It is equal to (probability that molecule strikes the wall) × (impulse delivered if it strikes) + (probability that molecule does not strike the wall) × (impulse delivered if it does not strike).

$$\bar{F} = \frac{N}{L} \, m\overline{v_x^2}. \qquad (13.25) \qquad \textit{Average force on one wall}$$

The pressure on the wall is $P = \bar{F}/A$, force per unit area:

$$P = \frac{N}{LA} \, m\overline{v_x^2}.$$

Since the volume of the container is $V = LA$, this may be written

$$P = \frac{N}{V} \, m\overline{v_x^2}. \qquad (13.26)$$

To cast this important equation into a still more useful form, we note that the mean-square velocity of the molecules may be written

$$\overline{v^2} = \overline{v_x^2} + \overline{v_y^2} + \overline{v_z^2}. \qquad (13.27)$$

Since the gas is in equilibrium and since it has no bulk motion, all directions of motion are equally likely for the molecules, and the three terms on the right side of Equation 13.27 must all be equal. Therefore the mean value of v_x^2 is

$$\overline{v_x^2} = \tfrac{1}{3}\overline{v^2}. \qquad (13.28)$$

This means that the gas pressure can be written

$$P = \frac{1}{3} \frac{N}{V} \, m\overline{v^2}. \qquad (13.29)$$

Result of the kinetic-theory derivation: the pressure of a confined gas

Since neither the area A nor the direction x appears in this formula, it gives the gas pressure at every bounding surface of the container, and indeed at every point throughout the container.

Scrutiny of Equation 13.29 shows it to bear a certain resemblance to the ideal-gas law (Equation 13.16), a resemblance made more evident by writing it in the form

Macroscopic variables assembled on the left, submicroscopic variables on the right

$$PV = \tfrac{1}{3}Nm\overline{v^2}. \qquad (13.30)$$

This key result of the kinetic theory is worth examining closely. It provides a link between the large- and small-scale worlds. On the left appear macroscopic quantities, the pressure and volume; on the right appear molecular quantities, the mass and mean-square speed of a molecule* and the number of molecules in the container. Across the equal sign are joined two worlds of vastly different scales. The kinetic theory relates the bulk properties of a gas—its pressure and volume—to the motion of its invisible multitude of careening constituents.

Equation 13.30 describes an ideal gas but still falls short of perfection in describing real gases. Two aspects of molecules have been overlooked: their finite size and the forces they reach out to exert on each other at a distance. In a problem at the end of the chapter, you will be afforded the opportunity to discuss how and why molecular size and molecular force somewhat alter the ideal-gas law. In the next section, we shall assume the validity of Equation 13.30.

Two effects cause real gases to be nonideal

---

* For a gas in equilibrium, $\overline{v^2}$ is equal to both the average of v^2 for *all* molecules at a *single* time and the average of v^2 for a *single* molecule over a long time.

13.8   The submicroscopic definition of temperature

Equation 13.30 has something important to say about temperature. To make this clear, we write Equations 13.12 and 13.30 together.

An empirical law   (13.12) $$PV = nRT.$$

A theoretical law   (13.30) $$PV = \tfrac{1}{3}Nm\overline{v^2}.$$

The first is an experimental fact about the thermal behavior of gases. The second is a theoretical result derived from the assumptions of the kinetic theory. If this theory is correct, the right sides of these two equations must be equal. Note that the right side of Equation 13.12, the ideal-gas law, contains three macroscopic quantities: the number of moles n, the gas constant R, and the absolute temperature T. The right side of Equation 13.30, by contrast, is expressed in terms of molecular quantities. The equality of these expressions provides a vital new link between the macroscopic and submicroscopic worlds and a fundamental definition of temperature.

Since the total number of molecules N in a sample of gas is equal to the number of moles n multiplied by the number of molecules N_0 in a single mole, the equality of interest can be written

$$nRT = \tfrac{1}{3}nN_0m\overline{v^2}.$$

Division of both sides of this equation by nR yields the new definition of temperature:

$$T = \frac{1}{3}\frac{N_0}{R}\,m\overline{v^2}. \tag{13.31}$$

Two small changes of notation enable us to express this result more simply. First, we recall that R/N_0 is defined as Boltzmann's constant k. Second, we note that $m v^2$ is twice the kinetic energy of a molecule. Therefore, the molecular definition of temperature may be written more compactly as

A submicroscopic definition of
temperature

$$T = \frac{2}{3k}\,\overline{K}. \tag{13.32}$$

This equation makes the important statement that the temperature of a gas is proportional to the average kinetic energy of its molecular constituents. The quantity $(2/3k)$ is a constant of proportionality, not in itself fundamentally significant. Its role is to tie together the unit of temperature and the unit of energy. Turning Equation 13.32 around, we can express molecular kinetic energy in terms of temperature:

Molecular kinetic energy is
proportional to temperature

$$\overline{K} = \tfrac{1}{2}m\overline{v^2} = \tfrac{3}{2}kT. \tag{13.33}$$

In this equation, note that K denotes *translational* kinetic energy only. Other forms of molecular energy, such as rotational and vibrational energy, contribute to the internal energy of a gas but not to the definition of temperature.

If the kinetic theory and its definition of temperature are correct, there are numerous implications for the behavior of matter. We mention here only a few of the myriad of tests that have by now established beyond question the correctness of the kinetic theory. The ideal-gas law is implied, as is Avogadro's hypothesis. More direct tests of the connection between temperature and molecular energy are provided by diffusion and by sound propagation. Diffusion is the intermingling of two different kinds of gas. Sound propagation (in a gas) is the transmission of a pulse of pressure through the gas. Both of these effects occur only because the molecules are in motion, and both proceed at a rate dependent on the molecular speed. From Equation 13.33 it follows that the mean-square molecular speed is proportional to temperature and inversely proportional to molecular mass:

$$\overline{v^2} \sim \frac{T}{m}. \tag{13.34}$$

One way to test the correctness of the kinetic definition of temperature is to find out whether molecular speed indeed follows this proportionality. Numerous tests verify that it does. Helium gas, for instance, diffuses through air four times as rapidly as sulfur dioxide does. This suggests that at a given temperature a helium atom moves at four times the speed of a sulfur dioxide molecule. Since a molecule of sulfur dioxide, with a molecular weight of 64, is sixteen times as massive as a helium atom, the proportionality of the square of the speed to the inverse of the mass is verified (at fixed temperature). The important thing is that the kinetic energy of the two molecules is the same. Therefore, the more massive one must move more slowly. A perfume manufacturer who wishes his product to act more swiftly at a distance should seek out a scent with low molecular weight.

Speed of diffusion is proportional to $\sqrt{T/m}$

    As temperature changes, molecular kinetic energy changes, an effect that can be inferred, for example, from studies of the speed of sound in air. Sound propagates through air at a speed proportional to the square root of the absolute temperature. This suggests, according to Equation 13.34, that the speed of sound is proportional to the speed of the gas molecules. Indeed the kinetic theory predicts that this is the case. It is obvious that a sound wave should not make its way through a gas at a speed greater than the molecular speed because the sound must be propagated by a series of molecular collisions. Somewhat surprisingly, however, the pressure pulse travels at not a great deal less than the molecular speed. Kinetic theory predicts for the speed of sound in a gas,

$$v_{\text{sound}} = \sqrt{\gamma \frac{kT}{m}} = \sqrt{\frac{\gamma}{3}} \, v_{\text{rms}}, \tag{13.35}$$

Speed of sound is proportional to $\sqrt{T/m}$

where v_{rms} is the root-mean-square speed,

$$v_{\text{rms}} = \sqrt{\overline{v^2}}. \tag{13.36}$$

The quantity γ, equal to the ratio of the specific heat of the gas at constant pressure to its specific heat at constant volume, is equal to $\frac{7}{5}$ for a gas of diatomic molecules such as air (Section 13.14). For such a gas, this works out numerically to

$$v_{\text{sound}} = 0.68 v_{\text{rms}}. \tag{13.37}$$

■ EXAMPLE: (a) What is the root-mean-square speed of a nitrogen molecule at room temperature? (b) What is the speed of a hydrogen molecule at the surface of the sun, where the temperature is 6,000 K? From Equations 13.33 and 13.36,

Root-mean-square molecular speed

$$v_{rms} = \sqrt{\frac{3kT}{m}}. \tag{13.38}$$

A nitrogen molecule, with molecular weight 28, has a mass

$$m = 28 \text{ amu} \times 1.66 \times 10^{-27} \text{ kg/amu} = 4.65 \times 10^{-26} \text{ kg}.$$

Substituting this number, along with $k = 1.38 \times 10^{-23}$ J/K and $T = 293$ K, in Equation 13.38 gives

$$v_{rms} \cong 510 \text{ m/sec}.$$

This is a speed of about Mach 1.5, 50 percent greater than the speed of sound in air at the same temperature. A similar calculation for hydrogen (molecular weight 2) at 6,000 K gives

$$v_{rms} = 8,650 \text{ m/sec}.$$

Alternatively, one could use ratios:

$$\frac{v_{rms}(H_2)}{v_{rms}(N_2)} = \sqrt{\frac{T(H_2)}{T(N_2)} \cdot \frac{m(N_2)}{m(H_2)}} = \sqrt{20.5 \times 14};$$

$$v_{rms}(H_2) \cong 17 v_{rms}(N_2). \qquad ■$$

13.9   Specific heat

When heat energy is added to a substance, it may be divided in various ways (Figure 13.11). Some may go into bulk energy of the material, as in the acceleration of rocket exhaust gas; some may go into work on the surroundings, if the material expands; and some may go into internal energy. Of the part that goes into internal energy, some goes into translational kinetic energy, which contributes to a rise of temperature, and some into excitation of atoms and molecules. This excitation includes such things as molecular rotation and vibration and, at extreme temperatures, dissociation of molecules and ionization. The fraction of internal energy in the form of translational kinetic energy varies from one material to another and from one temperature to another. It depends on details of molecular structure that need not concern us here. Moreover, the fraction of all added energy going into internal energy depends on external conditions, such as the freedom of the material to move or expand. For these reasons, there is no simple general law relating the change of temperature of a substance to the heat energy added to it. For any particular substance heated in a particular way, the relationship between change of temperature and change of energy is summarized by an experimentally measured quantity called the *Definition of specific heat* *specific heat*. The specific heat of a material is the amount of heat that must be added to a unit mass of the material to raise its temperature by 1 degree. For specific heat we use the symbol C. Its mks unit is J/kg K. More commonly, however, it is expressed in cal/gm K or, equivalently, kcal/kg K.

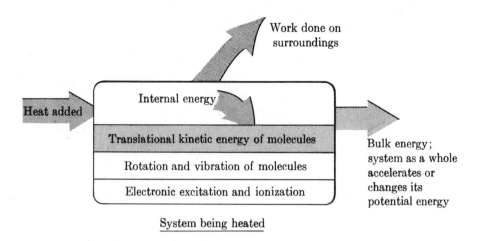

Work done on surroundings

Heat added

Internal energy

Translational kinetic energy of molecules

Rotation and vibration of molecules

Electronic excitation and ionization

Bulk energy; system as a whole accelerates or changes its potential energy

System being heated

FIGURE 13.11   The kinds of energy that can result from adding heat to a system. Only part of the heat need go into internal energy, and only part of the internal energy need be translational kinetic energy of molecules (shaded rectangle), which contributes to a rise in temperature.

Since specific heat depends not only on the material in question but also on the external conditions of its heating, it is necessary to specify these conditions.   Two standard conditions are employed for defining specific heat: heating at constant volume and heating at constant pressure. The corresponding specific heats are written C_v and C_p. Specific heats of solids and liquids are usually specified at constant pressure. For gases, both C_v and C_p are of interest.

As noted in Section 13.5, approximately 1 cal of heat is required to raise the temperature of 1 gm of water by 1 K.* The specific heat of water is, therefore,

$$C_p \text{ (water)} \cong 1 \; \frac{\text{cal}}{\text{gm K}} = 1 \; \frac{\text{kcal}}{\text{kg K}} \cdot ^\dagger \qquad (13.39)$$

Specific heat of water, originally a standard

Compared with most materials at ordinary temperature, water has a high specific heat. Note in Table 13.2 that the specific heats of other common materials are all less than 1 kcal/kg K. (The table also includes molar specific heats.) For water, only a small fraction of the internal energy is in the form of translational kinetic energy of the molecules.

From the definition of specific heat follows the formula

$$\Delta Q = CM \, \Delta T, \qquad (13.40)$$

Heat and temperature change related

which states that the amount of heat ΔQ required to raise the temperature of a

---

* This was the original definition of the calorie; later, the calorie was defined more precisely to be the heat required to raise the temperature of 1 gm of water from 14.5 °C to 15.5 °C. The thermochemical calorie used in modern scientific work, defined to be exactly 4.184 J, differs slightly from the earlier calorie.

† Over the whole range from 0 °C to 100 °C, the specific heat of water differs from 1 kcal/kg K by less than 1 percent.

TABLE 13.2   SPECIFIC HEATS OF SOME COMMON MATERIALS AT ROOM TEMPERATURE

Substance	Specific Heat (kcal/kg K)	Molar Specific Heat (cal/mole K)
Air	$C_v = 0.172$	$C'_v = 4.98$
Carbon dioxide	$C_v = 0.153$	$C'_v = 6.71$
Water*	$C_p = 1.00$	$C'_p = 18.0$
Aluminum*	$C_p = 0.22$	$C'_p = 5.8$
Iron*	$C_p = 0.11$	$C'_p = 6.0$
Copper*	$C_p = 0.092$	$C'_p = 5.9$

* For liquids and solids, C_p and C_v differ very little.

mass M through a temperature interval ΔT is equal to the product of the specific heat of the material, its mass, and the temperature interval. The formula is valid over any temperature interval within which C does not change significantly. Whether C_p or C_v or some other kind of specific heat is used in this formula depends on the particular conditions under which the heating takes place.

Also useful is the *molar specific heat*, defined as the heat required to raise the temperature of 1 mole of a substance by 1 K. For molar specific heat we use the notation C'. It is equal to the ordinary specific heat multiplied by the number of grams in one mole, which is the same as the molecular weight ($M.W.$):

$$C' \left(\frac{\text{cal}}{\text{mole K}} \right) = C \left(\frac{\text{cal}}{\text{gm K}} \right) \times M.W. \left(\frac{\text{gm}}{\text{mole}} \right). \qquad (13.41)$$

Definition of molar specific heat

An alternative expression is

$$C' \left(\frac{\text{kcal}}{\text{kmole K}} \right) = C \left(\frac{\text{kcal}}{\text{kg K}} \right) \times M.W. \left(\frac{\text{kg}}{\text{kmole}} \right). \qquad (13.42)$$

Notice that the numerical values of these quantities are the same for both sets of units. The formula $C' = C \times M.W.$ applies at constant pressure or at constant volume (or for any other special conditions):

$$C'_p = C_p \times M.W.,$$
$$C'_v = C_v \times M.W.$$

An equation equivalent to Equation 13.40, relating heat and temperature change, is

$$\Delta Q = C'n \, \Delta T, \qquad (13.43)$$

where n is the number of moles of the substance.

■ EXAMPLE 1:   A 40-gm piece of aluminum at 60 °C is dropped into an insulated container of 100 gm of water at 15 °C. If energy loss from the system of water plus aluminum is ignored, to what final temperature does the system come? The law of equilibrium tells us that the aluminum and the water will approach the same temperature, T_f. The law of energy conservation tells us that the heat gained by the water is equal to the heat lost by the aluminum (since no transformation of energy to other forms takes place), or

$$\Delta Q(H_2O) + \Delta Q(Al) = 0.$$

Simple calorimetry: Total heat is conserved

Making use of Equation 13.40, we can write

$$[C_p M \cdot (T_f - T_0)]_{H_2O} + [C_p M \cdot (T_f - T_0)]_{Al} = 0.$$

Numerically, this equation takes the form

$$1.00 \times 100 \times (T_f - 15) + 0.22 \times 40 \times (T_f - 60) = 0,$$

where C_p is expressed in cal/gm K, M is expressed in gm, and T is expressed in °C. The solution for T_f is

$$T_f = 18.6 \,°C. \qquad \blacksquare$$

■ EXAMPLE 2: A 100-watt heater is switched on in an insulated room of dimensions 4 m × 3 m × 2.5 m. How much time is required for the heater to raise the temperature of the air in the room from 0 °C to 5 °C? Equation 13.43 can be re-expressed in terms of time derivatives:

$$\frac{dQ}{dt} = C'n \frac{dT}{dt}. \qquad (13.44)$$

On the left is the input power, which is

$$\frac{dQ}{dt} = 10^2 \, W = \frac{10^2 \, J/sec}{4.184 \, J/cal}$$

$$= 24 \, cal/sec.$$

On the right side, we need to know n, the number of moles of air in 30 m³, which is the volume of the room. Since 1 mole occupies 22.4 liters = 0.0224 m³ (at the initial standard conditions),

$$n = \frac{30 \, m^3}{0.0224 \, m^3/mole} = 1,340 \, moles.$$

The rate of change of temperature is, therefore,

$$\frac{dT}{dt} = \frac{dQ/dt}{C_v' n} = \frac{24 \, cal/sec}{5.0 \, cal/mole \, K \times 1,340 \, moles}$$

$$= 0.0036 \, K/sec.$$

The required time is $\Delta t = \Delta T/(dT/dt)$, which, for $\Delta T = 5$ K, is

$$\Delta t = 1,390 \, sec \cong 23 \, min. \qquad \blacksquare$$

HEATS OF FUSION AND VAPORIZATION

A *phase change* is a structural change in a substance that occurs at a specific temperature and pressure. Phase changes include vaporization (change from liquid to gas), fusion (liquid to solid), sublimation (solid to gas), and changes

Definition of a phase change

Heats of fusion and vaporization accompany melting and boiling

from one crystalline form to another. If a change of internal energy (and, with it, a change of density) accompanies the change of phase, it is called a first-order phase transition. Melting and boiling are first-order transitions. The energy change per unit mass associated with fusion—or its opposite, melting—is called the *heat of fusion*. The energy change per unit mass associated with vaporization is called the *heat of vaporization*. For water at normal pressure, for example, these quantities are

$$l_{fusion}(H_2O) = 80 \text{ cal/gm (or kcal/kg)}, \tag{13.45}$$

$$l_{vaporization}(H_2O) = 539 \text{ cal/gm (or kcal/kg)}. \tag{13.46}$$

(These quantities are also known as latent heats: hence the notation *l*.) A few other heats of fusion and vaporization are listed in Table 13.3. As a general rule, latent heats are numerically larger than specific heats, and heats of vaporization exceed heats of fusion.

In analogy with Equations 13.41 and 13.42, molar latent heats may be defined by

Molar latent heat

$$l' = l \times M.W. \tag{13.47}$$

The usual unit of *l'* is cal/mole (or kcal/kmole).

■ EXAMPLE 3:   To 1 kg of ice at 0 °C and a pressure of 1 atm is added 240 kcal of heat. What is the fate of the ice? Melting it requires 80 kcal; then raising its temperature to 100 °C requires another 100 kcal. This leaves 60 kcal, enough to vaporize only one-ninth of the kilogram. The ice is therefore converted to a mixture of 0.89 kg of water and 0.11 kg of steam, both at 100 °C.   ■

13.10   The ideal monatomic gas

The simplest substance to treat theoretically is one in which *all* the internal energy is in the form of translational kinetic energy. This is the so-called ideal monatomic gas, which is approximated by the actual monatomic gases—helium, neon, argon, krypton, xenon, and radon. For a sample of such a gas containing N atoms, the internal energy U is the same as the total kinetic energy K (this

TABLE 13.3   HEATS OF FUSION AND VAPORIZATION OF SOME COMMON MATERIALS AT ATMOSPHERIC PRESSURE

Substance	Melting Temperature (K)	Heat of Fusion (kcal/kg)	Boiling Temperature (K)	Heat of Vaporization (kcal/kg)
Helium*			4.2	5.0
Alcohol (ethanol)	158	26	352	200
Water	273	80	373	539
Lead	601	5.5	2,020	210
Aluminum	933	96	2,600	2,520
Copper	1,356	49	2,860	1,150

* Helium does not solidify at atmospheric pressure.

use of the symbol U should not be confused with its use to designate potential energy):

$$U = K = \tfrac{3}{2}NkT. \tag{13.48}$$

Internal energy of an ideal monatomic gas

When the sample is heated at constant volume, all the heat energy goes into internal energy: $\Delta Q = \Delta U$. We may therefore write

$$\Delta Q = \tfrac{3}{2}Nk\,\Delta T \qquad \text{(constant volume)}. \tag{13.49}$$

For convenience, let us rewrite Equation 13.40, for constant volume, in the form

$$\Delta Q = C_v Nm\,\Delta T, \tag{13.50}$$

where m is the mass of a single atom. Comparison of Equations 13.49 and 13.50 shows that the specific heat at constant volume of the ideal monatomic gas is

$$C_v = \frac{3}{2}\frac{k}{m}. \tag{13.51}$$

Specific heat at constant volume

An alternative expression for C_v is obtained by multiplying the numerator and denominator on the right side of Equation 13.51 by Avogadro's number, N_0. In the numerator, $N_0 k = R$. In the denominator, $N_0 m$ is the mass of 1 mole, which in the cgs system is the same as the molecular weight, $M.W.$ We may therefore write

$$C_v = \frac{3}{2}\frac{R}{M.W.}. \tag{13.52}$$

If R is expressed in cal/mole K, C_v is given in cal/gm K, which is, of course, numerically the same as kcal/kg K. Multiplication of Equation 13.52 by the molecular weight (see Equation 13.42) yields a particularly simple formula for the molar specific heat at constant volume of an ideal monatomic gas:

$$C_v' = \tfrac{3}{2}R. \tag{13.53}$$

Molar specific heat is particularly simple

■ EXAMPLE 1 :   Experimentally, the molar specific heat of helium at constant volume is found to be 2.98 cal/mole K over a wide range of temperatures. How does this compare with the value predicted by Equation 13.53? According to this equation, with the mechanical equivalent of heat included as a conversion factor,

$$C_v' = \frac{3}{2}\cdot\frac{8.314\ \text{J/mole K}}{4.184\ \text{J/cal}}$$

$$= 2.98\ \text{cal/mole } K.$$

Helium is very nearly an ideal monatomic gas

The agreement is excellent.   ■

■ EXAMPLE 2 :   In one container of fixed volume is air; in an identical container is argon. Both gases are at the same temperature and pressure. It is found by measurement that 0.33 cal is required to raise the temperature of the air by 1 K. By how much will 0.33 cal raise the temperature of the argon? Argon is a monatomic gas; its molar specific heat C_v' is 2.98 cal/mole K, the same as that of helium. (The molar specific heat of air appears in Table 13.2.) Since the increments of heat added to the two gases are the same, it follows from Equation 13.43 that

$$(C_v' n \, \Delta T)_{Ar} = (C_v' n \, \Delta T)_{air}.$$

The given conditions imply that the number of moles of the two gases is the same: $n_{Ar} = n_{air}$. The temperature change of the argon is therefore given by

$$\Delta T_{Ar} = \frac{(C_v' \, \Delta T)_{air}}{(C_v')_{Ar}}.$$

Numerical evaluation yields

$$\Delta T_{Ar} = \frac{(4.98 \text{ cal/mole K})(1 \text{ K})}{(2.98 \text{ cal/mole K})}$$

$$= 1.67 \text{ K}.$$

Since all of the heat added to argon goes into the translational kinetic energy of its atoms, its temperature rises more than does the temperature of a gas such as air, for which only part of the added heat goes into translational kinetic energy.   ■

13.11   The first law of thermodynamics

From classical mechanics emerged a fundamental conservation law, the conservation of energy, valid in the absence of heat flow and temperature change. The extension of this law of energy conservation to include heat and internal energy is called the first law of thermodynamics—a powerful principle of nature and an important bridge between the large-scale and small-scale worlds. One way to express the principle is this:

An expression of the first law of thermodynamics

$$\Delta E = \Delta Q + \Delta W, \tag{13.54}$$

a statement that the energy change of a system (ΔE) is equal to the heat added (ΔQ) plus the work done on the system (ΔW). As a matter of convention, ΔQ and ΔW are defined to be positive when the heat or work adds energy to the system, negative when the system loses energy via heat or work. For an isolated system, $\Delta Q = \Delta W = 0$, and $E = constant$.

As discussed in Section 13.5, the total energy of a system may be divided into a macroscopic part (its bulk energy E_B) and a submicroscopic part (its internal energy U). In terms of these energies, the first law of thermodynamics is written

Another general expression of the first law

$$\Delta(U + E_B) = \Delta Q + \Delta W \tag{13.55}$$

(see Figure 13.12). Bulk energy is the mechanical energy of the system—its potential energy plus kinetic energy—calculated at the macroscopic level. In many examples of importance in thermodynamics, changes of bulk energy are negligible. For such examples, the first law takes the form

$$\Delta U = \Delta Q + \Delta W \qquad (\Delta E_B = 0). \tag{13.56}$$

Special cases of the first law

Conversely, when thermal effects are negligible, ΔU and ΔQ may be set equal to

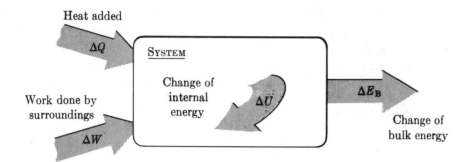

FIGURE 13.12   The first law of thermodynamics is a law of energy conservation: $\Delta U + \Delta E_B = \Delta Q + \Delta W$.

zero, and the law of energy conservation takes the form developed in Chapter 10,

$$\Delta E_B = \Delta W \qquad \text{(thermal effects negligible).} \qquad (13.57)$$

In the remainder of this section, we shall discuss various energy transformations in order to illustrate the meaning and scope of the first law of thermodynamics. Some such transformations can be classified with the help of the diagram in Figure 13.13. On the right are two forms of energy: internal energy (disordered energy) and bulk kinetic energy (ordered energy). On the left are two modes of energy exchange: heat and work. The arrows indicate four kinds of energy transformation. In every transformation, of course, total energy is conserved.

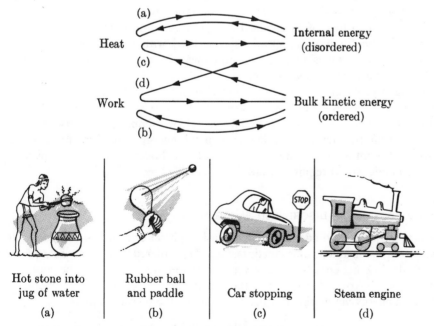

FIGURE 13.13   Some modes of energy transfer. Examples discussed in the text are illustrated by arrows in the diagram and by the corresponding numbered drawings.

HEAT FLOW WITHOUT BULK MOTION

When a primitive tribesman drops a hot stone into a jug of water, the internal energy of the stone decreases and the internal energy of the water increases. Heat is the mechanism of energy exchange. Via the transformation indicated by arrow (a), he achieves his desired result, to raise the temperature of the water. No work is done and there is no change of bulk energy. For the system as a whole, internal energy is conserved: $\Delta U = 0$. The equation of energy exchange is therefore

$$\Delta Q_{\text{stone}} + \Delta Q_{\text{water}} = 0.$$

(Example 1 in Section 13.9 describes an equivalent physical process.)

BULK MOTION WITHOUT HEAT FLOW

A rubber ball attached to a paddle by an elastic string loses energy (bulk kinetic energy) as it flies away from the paddle. In doing so, it does work on the elastic string. The string, in turn, does work on the ball as it draws it back to the paddle. As indicated by arrow (b) in Figure 13.13, kinetic energy is lost and then gained, with work as the intermediary. If the temperature of the ball does not change significantly, its energy is described by Equation 13.57.

FRICTIONAL DISSIPATION

A driver steps on the brake pedal. His automobile loses kinetic energy. The brake drums and surrounding parts are heated and gain internal energy. Probably no other form of energy transformation is more familiar in everyday experience than loss of mechanical energy accompanied by gain of internal energy. Since in most applications concerned with the smooth running of machinery, the aim is to preserve mechanical energy, this transformation is usually considered a "loss" of energy. Friction dissipates energy in the same way that a profligate dissipates a fortune, by converting it from an ordered to a disordered form. Such energy transformation is also known as energy degradation. In Figure 13.13, the arrow labeled (c) oversimplifies, because work as well as heat transfer may be involved in the energy-transformation process. (At what point is work done as an automobile is braked?) A full treatment of this example would require Equation 13.55.

THE ORDERING OF DISORDERED ENERGY

When steam in a cylinder expands to push a piston outward, work is done to move the piston and it gains kinetic energy. This ordered bulk energy is extracted from the internal energy of the steam; the steam must, therefore, be cooled as it expands. Arrow (d) indicates the transformation of disordered energy to ordered energy via work. For the steam alone, the relevant equation is

$$\Delta U_{\text{S}} = \Delta W_{\text{S}} \qquad \text{(negative).}$$

For the piston alone,

$$\Delta E_{\text{B}} = \Delta W_{\text{P}} \qquad \text{(positive).}$$

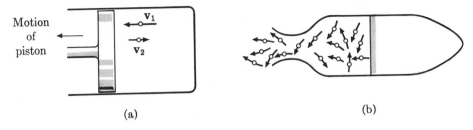

FIGURE 13.14   The molecular mechanism of energy transfer from disordered to ordered form. (a) A molecule rebounding from a retreating piston loses energy in the collision. (b) The molecules of a hot gas streaming through the nozzle of a rocket convert part of their random motion into ordered bulk motion. The exhaust is at lower temperature.

Since $\Delta W_S = -\Delta W_P$, these equations combine to give

$$\Delta E_B = -\Delta U_S.$$

That the steam expanding in the cylinder *must* lose internal energy is a necessary consequence of energy conservation. It is nevertheless interesting to inquire into the exact mechanism of this energy loss. When a molecule of the water vapor rebounds from the retreating cylinder, the molecule loses speed and kinetic energy, thereby tending to lower the temperature of the steam [Figure 13.14(a)]. Conversely, a molecule striking an advancing piston recoils with increased speed, like a tennis ball struck by a moving racket. So a gas is cooled by expansion and heated by compression.

A rocket provides a particularly interesting example of the conversion of internal energy to bulk kinetic energy because in the propulsion of a rocket, a gas pushes on itself and changes the form of its own energy. An idealized rocket motor is shown in Figure 13.14(b). On the right is a chamber containing hot gas. On the left is the nozzle through which the escaping gas streams. In the chamber the gas has large internal energy and (relative to the rocket) no bulk kinetic energy. As the gas streams out to the left, it acquires ordered energy and must therefore lose some of its disordered energy. Note that in this important transformation process, the gas molecules need undergo no change of speed at all. The change occurs in the relationship of different molecular velocities to each other. Within the hot gas chamber, molecules are moving randomly in all directions and the average velocity (the *vector* average) is zero. In the exhaust, the average molecular velocity is directed to the left since the gas as a whole is moving to the left. There remains superimposed on this bulk motion some random motion, but it is less in magnitude than it was before the gas started to expand. (Suppose the molecules in the exhaust gas moved exactly parallel to one another with equal velocity. What would be the temperature of the exhaust gas?)

Disorder to order in rocket exhaust

13.12   The equipartition theorem and the zeroth law of thermodynamics

Like the first law of thermodynamics, the zeroth law finds an explanation in the application of Newtonian mechanics to molecular motion. Although the law of thermal equilibrium—the tendency of systems in contact to come to the same temperature—was accepted as self-evident long before it was dignified by the title of the zeroth law of thermodynamics, its molecular basis is subtler than the molecular basis of energy conservation. It is by no means self-evident that the result of a myriad of collisions among molecules of different mass should be the equalization of their average kinetic energy and thereby the equalization of their temperature; yet this is precisely what happens. The understanding of this equalization is rooted in a fundamental statement about energy sharing called the equipartition theorem. The equipartition theorem, in turn, is a theoretical result derived from the ideas of mechanics and the ideas of probability and statistics applied to molecular collisions.

Degrees of freedom   Before stating the equipartition theorem, we must explore the idea of a degree of freedom. A single bead on a straight wire, free to slide but not to turn (Figure 13.15), is said to have one degree of freedom. Only one coordinate, its location along the wire, is necessary to specify its position completely. Correspondingly, it has but one mode of motion, translation along the wire. A bead free to rotate as well as to slide along a wire (Figure 13.16) has two degrees of freedom. Two coordinates are needed to specify its position, and it has two modes of motion: translation and rotation. For a system comprising two or more objects, degrees of freedom are additive. Figure 13.17 shows a system of beads with nine degrees of freedom.

A particle free to move in three dimensions has three degrees of freedom (Figure 13.18), and N such particles have $3N$ degrees of freedom. If the "particle" is in fact an extended object, it has more than three degrees of freedom because a complete specification of its position requires a knowledge of its orientation as well as its location in space. The degrees of freedom of a diatomic molecule are discussed in Section 13.14.

How to count degrees of freedom   In summary, the number of degrees of freedom of a system is the number of coordinates required to specify completely the spatial arrangement of the system. It is also the number of independent modes of motion of the system. With the concept of degree of freedom in hand, we can return to the equipartition theorem.

The equipartition theorem   It is literally an equal-division or equal-sharing theorem. It states that after a system comes to equilibrium its disordered kinetic energy is, on the average, equally divided among all the degrees of freedom. The parcel of kinetic energy assigned to each degree of freedom is

$$\text{(kinetic energy/degree of freedom)} = \tfrac{1}{2}kT. \qquad (13.58)$$

When the energy is not equally divided, the direction of spontaneous change is toward equal division.

Two limitations of Formula 13.58 ought to be noted. First, it is a classical result. In the quantum world, some degrees of freedom are prohibited from sharing equally in the disordered kinetic energy. The effects of quantization are discussed in Section 13.15. Second, the formula refers only to kinetic energy. Also associated with some degrees of freedom is potential energy. The vibrational mode of a diatomic molecule, for instance, when excited at high temperature, gains a total energy of kT, of which $\tfrac{1}{2}kT$ is kinetic energy and $\tfrac{1}{2}kT$ is potential energy. Translational and rotational degrees of freedom, however, gain only kinetic energy.

FIGURE 13.15   A bead on a wire, a system with one degree of freedom.

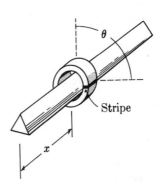

FIGURE 13.16   A bead free to rotate and slide on a wire. This system has two degrees of freedom. Two coordinates, x and θ, can specify its position exactly.

Stripe

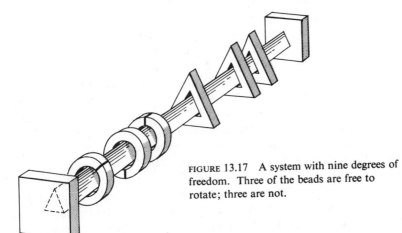

FIGURE 13.17   A system with nine degrees of freedom. Three of the beads are free to rotate; three are not.

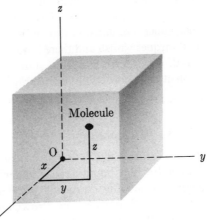

FIGURE 13.18   Three coordinates are required to specify the position of the center of mass of a molecule in space. These correspond to the three translational degrees of freedom of the molecule.

Among the implications of the equipartition theorem, none is simpler or more important than the zeroth law of thermodynamics. The spontaneous tendency of matter toward uniform temperature is merely a consequence of the spontaneous tendency of molecules in interaction toward equal division of kinetic energy among their degrees of freedom. Not all molecules have the same number of degrees of freedom. However, all have the same number of *translational* degrees of freedom, namely three. Consequently, in thermal equilibrium, the translational kinetic energy of each molecule is equal to $\frac{3}{2}kT$; from Formula 13.58 follows Equation 13.33.

To understand the role of probability in the equipartition theorem, consider the dynamics of the system pictured in Figure 13.17. The beads bear no resemblance to molecules, but they form a system, one to which the equipartition theorem can be applied if we imagine that in the beads' collisions with each other and with the end plates no energy is degraded or dissipated. Initially, five of the beads are at rest and the sixth (one of those free to turn) is sent sliding and turning down the wire with an energy of 90 ergs. At every collision energy is exchanged. According to the equipartition theorem, the result of numerous interactions (collisions) among the parts of the system is to divide the energy equally—on the average—among the degrees of freedom. Each gets 10 ergs. After enough time has elapsed for the originally concentrated energy to be spread among the beads—that is, after equilibrium is established—we can imagine a series of energy measurements. No two would give exactly the same distribution of energy. The first bead at one moment might have a total energy of 16 ergs, at a later time 21 ergs, and so on. Its average energy after many measurements would be 20 (or very nearly 20) ergs because of its two degrees of freedom. Similarly, beads 2 and 3 would each have average energies of 20 ergs, while the last three beads, each restricted to a single mode of motion, would equally share the last 30 ergs. If a bead "temperature" proportional to translational kinetic energy were defined, the system would come to uniform temperature despite its asymmetric distribution of total energy. In just the same way, a pan and the water it contains tend toward the same temperature despite the fact that the internal energy of a kilogram of water is much greater than the internal energy of a kilogram of pan.

In this discussion we have used the word "equilibrium." In macroscopic mechanics, equilibrium usually refers to a static situation, one in which forces and torques vanish and there is no motion. In thermal equilibrium, on the other hand, a system is far from static. Its molecular constituents are in constant violent agitation. Only the average properties remain constant.

13.13   Brownian motion

In 1827, the English botanist Robert Brown noticed that grains of pollen suspended in a liquid appear under a microscope to be in a constant state of agitation, moving erratically from place to place. This phenomenon, which came to be known as the Brownian motion, went unexplained for 50 years. At first Brown attributed the motion to a mobility possessed by the pollen grains by virtue of their animate nature. Later he found the motion to be shared by all microscopic bits of matter, animate or inanimate. Until 1905, when Einstein showed how to extract vital information about molecules from the Brownian motion, the phenomenon was not studied quantitatively.

Einstein assumed that the microscopically visible speck of matter is a participant in the continual dance of collision and energy exchange on exactly the same footing as an invisible molecule. This means that the speck acquires an average translational kinetic energy equal to that of each molecule:

$$\tfrac{1}{2}M\overline{V^2} = \tfrac{1}{2}m\overline{v^2}. \qquad (13.59)$$

A grain of dust and a single molecule have equal average kinetic energy

Here M and V denote the mass and speed of the speck, and m and v denote the mass and speed of the molecule. If the energy of the speck could be measured, the energy of the molecule could be inferred. It should be remarked that in 1905 molecular masses were not well known. Therefore, molecular energies were not well known. The kinetic theory was well established, but one vital constant, Avogadro's number, was known only in rough approximation.

Even with the help of microscopic observation, it is not possible to measure the average kinetic energy of a speck of dust in a liquid or a gas. Its changes of speed and direction are too frequent. Nevertheless, let us pretend for a moment that such a measurement is possible, for then we can understand the nature of Einstein's reasoning in simplified form. A measurement of the average kinetic energy of the speck would at once reveal the kinetic energy of the molecule, according to Equation 13.59. This energy in turn would yield the value of Boltzmann's constant k from Equation 13.33. Then, since the macroscopic gas constant is well known from measurements of gas properties, Avogadro's number could be calculated from the relation

$$R = N_0 k. \qquad (13.60)$$

With the constant N_0 in hand, the mass of any molecule can be determined from the molecular weight of a substance. Through these steps a single molecule could be "weighed" by measuring the average energy of a visible bit of matter.

The procedure suggested by Einstein to do the job of weighing molecules is somewhat more indirect than the procedure just described, but its basic idea is the same—to use the speck of dust as a visible link to the submicroscopic world. Since the speck is rapidly bombarded from all sides by molecules, its migration through the liquid depends on slight irregularities, or statistical fluctuations (Figure 13.19). During a given interval of time, more molecules happen to strike it from one side than another. If molecules were much smaller than they actually are and if the total number of them striking the speck were correspondingly greater, the fluctuations would be reduced. In 1 sec, the impacts of the molecules against the speck would be nearly equal in all directions, and the speck would show little tendency to move. If, on the other hand, molecules were much more massive, and therefore less numerous, the speck would be jarred into more erratic motion. The idea that fluctuations become smaller as numbers become larger is a familiar one in studies of populations. The ratio of males to females is very nearly the same in England as in the United States; but the ratio of males to females fluctuates greatly from one family to another. The fluctuations in Brownian motion provided Einstein with the key to the discovery of molecular numbers and, therefore, molecular mass.

The role of statistical fluctuations

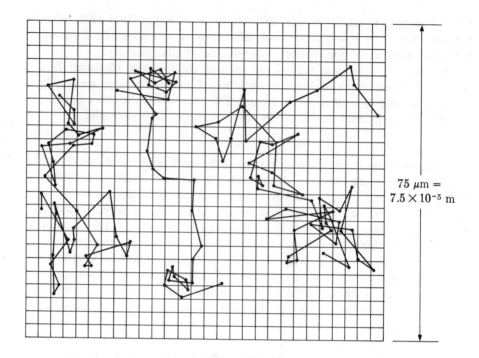

$75 \ \mu m =$
$7.5 \times 10^{-5} \ m$

FIGURE 13.19   The Brownian motion of solid particles in water. The particles are of about 1 micrometer (10^{-6} m) diameter. The dots mark their positions at 30-second intervals. The path between dots is also irregular but is represented here by straight line segments. [From J. Perrin, *Atoms* (Princeton, N.J.: D. Van Nostrand, 1923), p. 115.]

13.14   Specific heat of simple gases

If we know the number of degrees of freedom of a molecule, we can, with the help of the equipartition theorem, determine the specific heat of a gas composed of such molecules. How many degrees of freedom has a diatomic molecule, such as H_2, N_2, or O_2? Three coordinates are required to locate its center of mass (Figure 13.18). Like all molecules, therefore, it has three translational degrees of freedom. As shown in Figure 13.20, three more coordinates serve to specify its orientation in space. The first of these (called θ) is the angle that the molecular axis makes with the z axis. The second (called φ) is the angle that the projected molecular axis* makes with the x axis. The third (called ψ) is the angle of rotation of the molecule about its own axis, analogous to the rotation of a bead on a wire. It would appear that there are three more degrees of freedom associated with molecular orientation, making a total of six. We now come face to face with the first of two peculiarities added to the degree-of-freedom concept by the theory of quantum mechanics. This is that rotation about

---

* Imagine a light shining vertically downward on the molecule. Its shadow on the xy plane is its projection on the xy plane. The angle φ is the angle between the x axis and the axis of this imaginary shadow.

the molecular symmetry axis, indicated by the angle ψ, does not in fact correspond either to a mode of motion or to a degree of freedom. The molecule actually has only two orientational degrees of freedom.

A real dumbbell, held in the hand can, of course, be rotated about its symmetry axis, and this is undoubtedly an independent mode of motion of the dumbbell. To keep track of this rotation, a thin stripe can be painted along the dumbbell. The hydrogen molecule differs from the dumbbell in one all-important respect. There is no such thing as painting a stripe on it or keeping track of this kind of rotation in any other way. After rotation through any angle ψ, the hydrogen molecule is identically and indistinguishably the same as before the rotation. The irrelevance of the angle ψ is a very practical consequence (practical since it changes the number of degrees of freedom) of an almost philosophical question: If there is no experimental way to observe a rotation through an angle ψ, how can this rotation have any meaning? The answer provided by quantum mechanics is that no energy can go into this mode of motion. If a mode of motion has no energy and is unable to acquire any, then for practical purposes it does not exist.

A quantum effect: only two degrees of freedom for molecular rotation

The second peculiarity brought to the degree-of-freedom concept by quantum mechanics is the "frozen" degree of freedom. We shall return to that idea in the next section.

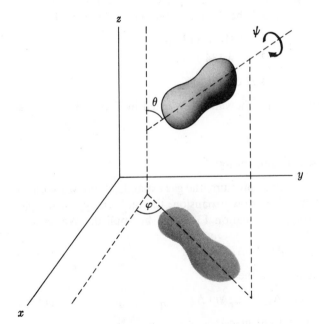

FIGURE 13.20 Three coordinates are required to specify the angular orientation in space of an object. A diatomic molecule, depicted here as a fattened dumbbell, in fact has only two rotational degrees of freedom, associated with angles θ and φ, because no energy can go into rotation about its symmetry axis (angle ψ).

DIATOMIC GAS AT CONSTANT VOLUME

Since there is no potential energy associated with molecular rotation and translation, each of the five degrees of freedom of a diatomic molecule acquires energy $\frac{1}{2}kT$. The internal energy of a collection of N such molecules is, therefore,

Internal energy of an ideal diatomic gas

$$U = \tfrac{5}{2}NkT.^*\qquad\qquad(13.61)$$

Specific heat at constant volume of diatomic gas

At constant volume a gas being heated does no work, and Equation 13.56 simplifies to

$$\Delta U = \Delta Q.\qquad\qquad(13.62)$$

To find the specific heat of a diatomic gas at constant volume, the argument of Section 13.10 may be applied, with the factor $\frac{3}{2}$ replaced by the factor $\frac{5}{2}$ (compare Equations 13.48 and 13.61). The result, analogous to Equation 13.51, is

$$C_v = \frac{5}{2}\frac{k}{m},\qquad\qquad(13.63)$$

where m is the mass of a molecule. The molar specific heat of the diatomic gas is

$$C'_v = \tfrac{5}{2}R.\qquad\qquad(13.64)$$

■ EXAMPLE 1: Compare the theoretical and experimental values of the molar specific heat of air at constant volume. Since air consists almost entirely of diatomic molecules, Equation 13.64 should apply. Numerically, it predicts

$$C'_v = \frac{5}{2}\cdot\frac{8.314 \text{ J/mole K}}{4.184 \text{ J/cal}}$$

$$= 4.97 \text{ cal/mole K.}$$

This is in excellent agreement with the value 4.98 listed in Table 13.2.   ■

DIATOMIC GAS AT CONSTANT PRESSURE

If heat is added to a gas at constant pressure, the gas expands, doing work on its surroundings (Figure 13.21). For slow expansion, the bulk energy of the gas does not change appreciably, so Equation 13.56 can be applied. We write it in the form

$$\Delta Q = \Delta U - \Delta W.\qquad\qquad(13.65)$$

From Equation 13.40, the term on the left is

$$\Delta Q = C_p Nm\,\Delta T.\qquad\qquad(13.66)$$

For a diatomic gas, Equation 13.61 gives

$$\Delta U = \tfrac{5}{2}Nk\,\Delta T.\qquad\qquad(13.67)$$

---

* Equation 13.61 is valid at normal temperatures. At very low temperature, molecular rotation is not excited, and the internal energy U is closer to $\frac{3}{2}kT$. At very high temperature, vibration and other excitation within the molecule cause U to be greater than $\frac{5}{2}kT$.

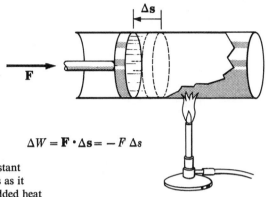

$$\Delta W = \mathbf{F} \cdot \Delta \mathbf{s} = -F\,\Delta s$$

FIGURE 13.21   Heating a gas at constant pressure. The work done *on* the gas as it expands is negative. Some of the added heat goes into internal energy, some into work.

As indicated in Figure 13.21, the work done *on* the gas as the piston is displaced through Δs is $\Delta W = -F\,\Delta s$. For slow expansion, the magnitude of the external force $\mathbf{F}$ is nearly the same as the magnitude of the force exerted on the piston by the gas, which is the product of the gas pressure and the piston area: $F = PA$. The work is therefore $W = -PA\,\Delta s$, which can be expressed in terms of the volume change ΔV by

$$\Delta W = -P\,\Delta V. \tag{13.68}$$

Work done on an expanding gas

This equation is in fact valid for any shape of container and any kind of material since it rests simply on the definition of work (see Equations 12.51 and 12.53, for instance). For the special case of an ideal gas, the right side of Equation 13.68 is easily re-expressed in terms of the change of temperature. Differentiation of Equation 13.16 at constant pressure gives $P\,dV = Nk\,dT$, or, for finite changes,

$$P\,\Delta V = Nk\,\Delta T.$$

This means that the work done on the gas as its temperature changes by ΔT is

$$\Delta W = -Nk\,\Delta T. \tag{13.69}$$

Work done on an ideal gas at constant pressure

The right sides of Equations 13.66, 13.67, and 13.69 may now be substituted in Equation 13.65, giving

$$C_{\mathrm{p}}Nm\,\Delta T = \tfrac{5}{2}Nk\,\Delta T + Nk\,\Delta T. \tag{13.70}$$

The solution for C_{p} is

$$C_{\mathrm{p}} = \frac{7}{2}\frac{k}{m}. \tag{13.71}$$

Specific heat at constant pressure of diatomic gas

This is the specific heat at constant pressure of a diatomic gas that behaves as an ideal gas. The corresponding molar specific heat is

$$C_{\mathrm{p}}' = \tfrac{7}{2}R. \tag{13.72}$$

Five-sevenths of the input heat goes into internal energy; two-sevenths is transferred to the environment via work. At constant volume, the latter expenditure of energy is not required.

MONATOMIC GAS

Only three degrees of freedom per atom

For a single spherical atom, such as a helium atom, all orientations in space are equivalent. The argument applied to angle ψ for a diatomic molecule (Figure 13.20) can therefore be applied to all angles for a single atom. As a result, no rotational mode of an atom acquires any energy, and the atom has, effectively, only three degrees of freedom. Since energy $\frac{1}{2}kT$ is associated with each translational degree of freedom, the internal energy of the ideal monatomic gas is that given by Equation 13.48. We previously found the specific heat at constant volume of such a gas (Equations 13.51 and 13.53). The derivation of its specific heat at constant pressure follows exactly the preceding derivation for a diatomic gas. In Equation 13.70, the factor $\frac{5}{2}$ is replaced by $\frac{3}{2}$. Then, for the monatomic gas,

Specific heat at constant pressure of monatomic gas

$$C_p = \frac{5}{2}\frac{k}{m}, \tag{13.73}$$

$$C_p' = \frac{5}{2}R. \tag{13.74}$$

OTHER IDEAL GASES

At low density, a gas such as carbon dioxide (CO_2) or methane (CH_4) behaves as an ideal gas (which means that it obeys Equation 13.12), although its internal energy follows no law as simple as Equation 13.48 for a monatomic gas or Equation 13.61 for a diatomic gas. Accordingly, for gases whose molecules are composed of three or more atoms, there are no simple general formulas for C_p or C_v. Even for these more complicated gases, however, the *difference* between C_p and C_v is simple. It is left as a problem to prove that the difference of the molar specific heats for any ideal gas is

Difference of specific heats is simple for all ideal gases

$$C_p' - C_v' = R. \tag{13.75}$$

■ EXAMPLE 2: At atmospheric pressure and room temperature, the specific heat at constant volume of carbon dioxide is $C_v = 0.153$ kcal/kg K (Table 13.2). What should its specific heat be at constant pressure? From Equations 13.41, 13.42, and 13.75,

$$C_p = C_v + \frac{R}{M.W.}. \tag{13.76}$$

The molecular weight of CO_2 is 44.0. The second term in Equation 13.76 is, therefore,

$$\frac{R}{M.W.} = \frac{8.314 \text{ J/mole K}}{4.184 \text{ J/cal} \times 44.0 \text{ gm/mole}}$$

$$= 0.045 \text{ cal/gm K (or kcal/kg K)}.$$

This increment added to C_v gives

$$C_p = 0.198 \text{ kcal/kg K,}$$

which compares well with the experimental value, 0.199 kcal/kg K. ■

13.15   Frozen degrees of freedom

If two marbles collide, they rebound with a total kinetic energy that is less than what they had before the collision. Each is warmed slightly by the collision since the lost energy has spread as internal energy within the marbles. Some of the original macroscopic ordered energy has been converted to microscopic disordered energy. This is a simple example of the equipartition theorem at work. Energy concentrated initially in one mode of motion tends to distribute itself evenly over all of the available modes of motion.

The situation is usually very different for atomic collisions. A helium atom, like a marble, is a system composed of smaller constituents. Yet when two helium atoms collide at low energy, there is no energy dissipation. The total kinetic energy of the atoms after the collision is exactly the same as it was before the collision, and the internal structure of the atoms is completely unaffected by the collision. This behavior is a consequence of *quantization* in the atom and is something that could not have been foreseen or explained in the framework of classical physics. If such collisions without dissipation could be arranged in the macroscopic world, it would make possible perpetual-motion machines. Indeed, on the atomic scale, perpetual motion is a reality.

The internal energy of a single atom is quantized; that is, it can take on only a certain specific set of values. For each atom there is a lowest energy state, called the ground state. At higher energies lie the "excited states" of the atom. Between the ground state and the first excited state is an energy gap that represents the smallest amount of energy the atom can absorb. This minimum energy required to excite the atom is called an energy quantum. If offered less than the required energy quantum, the atom cannot accept it; rather, it remains unchanged in its ground state.

Another quantum effect: An energy gap inhibits energy sharing

Imagine, for instance, a collision between two helium atoms, one initially at rest and the other having an initial energy of 0.2 eV. The collision results in energy sharing; one atom gains energy, the other loses energy. Because the minimum energy quantum to excite a helium atom is 20 eV, neither atom can be internally disturbed by the collision. The kinetic energy of a whole atom, on the other hand, is not restricted by such a quantum condition. The energies of motion of the atoms after the collision might be 0.12 eV and 0.08 eV, or 0.195 eV and 0.005 eV, or any other pair of values adding up to 0.2 eV. Energy sharing takes place only among the translational degrees of freedom of the whole atoms. The internal degrees of freedom associated with the motion of the electrons within the atom (and the protons and neutrons within the nucleus), because of their all-or-nothing requirement for energy gain, get none of the energy. These degrees of freedom may be called "frozen." Since they do not ordinarily participate in energy sharing, they can be ignored; indeed they must be ignored. To assign more than three degrees of freedom to a helium atom would lead to incorrect predictions (for example, of the specific heat).

No such inhibition for translational kinetic energy

The full story is more complicated than indicated so far. Degrees of freedom, like butter, freeze only gradually. A particular mode of motion is never totally excluded from energy sharing, although its exclusion may be very nearly complete. Consider a sample of helium in which the *average* kinetic energy of each atom is 0.2 eV. In almost all collisions, the available energy will be less than the 20 eV required to produce internal excitation of an atom. Occasionally, however, a single atom will by chance acquire a kinetic energy greater than 20 eV. When it collides with a neighboring atom, one of them may emerge from the collision in an excited state of internal motion. The internal degrees of freedom are almost, but not completely, frozen out of the energy sharing. When the average kinetic energy of the atoms approaches the quantum energy of internal excitation, such collisions producing internal excitation occur more often, and the internal degrees of freedom become gradually unfrozen.

At normal temperatures near 300 K, the average molecular kinetic energy of thermal motion is about 0.04 eV. Typical quantum energies of electronic excitation in atoms and molecules amount to several eV, about one-hundredfold greater than average thermal energies. (Helium is not typical. Its quantum excitation energy of 20 eV is greater than that of any other atom.) This means that the internal electronic degrees of freedom are quite effectively frozen out. When heat is added to a substance at normal temperature, a negligible part of it goes into atomic excitation. At much higher temperatures the situation changes. When collision energies become large enough to excite atoms internally, more degrees of freedom come into play; and much of the energy of the system is in the form of atomic excitation, a smaller fraction residing in the translational kinetic energy that defines temperature. As a consequence, the specific heat of most substances increases as temperature increases (Figure 13.22); the greater the number of "unfrozen" degrees of freedom, the more energy is required to produce a given temperature rise. Conversely, near absolute zero, where most degrees of freedom are frozen, specific heats are very small.

A vital ratio for the properties of matter: quantum energy scale ÷ thermal energy

The vitally important factors governing the properties of a substance are its characteristic quantum energies relative to the characteristic thermal energy, $\frac{3}{2}kT$. The behavior of a piece of matter at any particular temperature depends more than anything else on which of its degrees of freedom are open for energy sharing and which are frozen. As an originally solid piece of matter is heated, it experiences successive marked changes—melting, boiling, dissociation, ionization—as successively higher quantum energies topple under the impact of increasing thermal energy. Ice melts at 273 K, when its thermal energy of molecular vibration becomes comparable to the energies binding one molecule to another. At the boiling point of water, 373 K (where the kinetic energy $\frac{3}{2}kT$ is about one-twentieth of an eV), the translational degrees of freedom become completely unfrozen. Transformations of form occurring at still higher temperature are gradual, requiring thousands of degrees or more to be completed. Water molecules dissociate (break apart into their constituent atoms) in the range 1,000 to 10,000 K. Ionization (the separation of electrons from their parent atoms) begins in this temperature range and is completed only above 1,000,000 K. At such temperatures, which occur within stars, the gas of protons, electrons, and oxygen nuclei obviously bears little resemblance to ice or water or steam. This ionized gas is called a plasma. Because its particles are electrically charged, it has properties radically different from those of ordinary neutral gases.

Plasma: a gas of charged particles

In the stellar plasma at a temperature of millions of degrees, the energy of thermal motion, $\frac{3}{2}kT$, is large compared with most atomic quantum energies, but it is still small compared with the quantum excitation energy of the oxygen nucleus. Despite the intense heat, the internal degrees of freedom of the protons and neutrons in the nucleus remain frozen. Collisions leave the nucleus undisturbed

Nuclear degrees of freedom remain frozen in stars

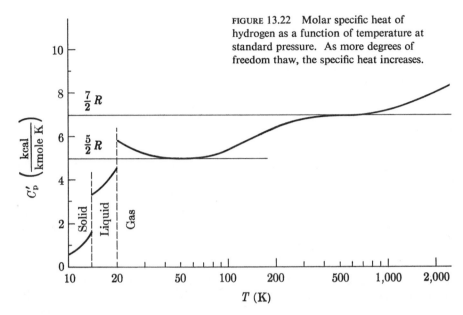

FIGURE 13.22   Molar specific heat of hydrogen as a function of temperature at standard pressure. As more degrees of freedom thaw, the specific heat increases.

in its ground state. Only if the temperature were to rise to many billions of degrees would the nuclear degrees of freedom thaw and allow the individual nuclear particles to share energy. It now appears likely that such enormous temperatures are actually reached in the late stages of the evolution of a star.

As a help for thinking panoramically over the temperature range from absolute zero to billions of degrees, Table 13.4 shows some temperature-energy comparisons. It is worth noticing that the energies in this table are all small compared with those commonly achieved in particle accelerators. In the explosion of an atomic bomb, a temperature of 40 million K might be reached, giving each particle an energy of about 5 keV. Yet a very modest accelerator produces particles a thousand times more energetic, and some accelerators concentrate 10 million times more energy on one particle than does a nuclear explosion. The difference is, of course, in numbers of particles. Vastly many more particles are heated by a nuclear explosion in a microsecond than are accelerated by all the synchrotrons on earth in a year.

TABLE 13.4   SOME TEMPERATURE-ENERGY COMPARISONS

Temperature (K)	$\frac{3}{2}kT$	Remarks
0	0	
273	0.035 eV	Water freezes
1,000	0.13 eV	Most substances gaseous
6,000	0.78 eV	Sun's surface temperature
10^6 (1 million)	130 eV	Light elements largely ionized
10^7 (10 million)	1.3 keV	Sun's central temperature
10^9 (1 billion)	130 keV	
10^{10} (10 billion)	1.3 MeV	Thermal excitation and disintegration of nuclei

Summary of ideas and definitions

Thermodynamics—the theory of thermal phenomena and molecular motion—links the macroscopic and submicroscopic domains. It must take account of the structure of matter.

Any calibrated device reacting to temperature change is a thermometer.

The constant-volume gas thermometer, with $T \sim P$, provides a macroscopic definition of temperature and also a way to measure temperature.

A result of the kinetic theory, $\bar{K} = \frac{3}{2}kT$ (Equation 13.33), provides a submicroscopic definition of temperature.

Absolute zero is the temperature at which no further energy can be removed from a system.

The kelvin temperature scale is an absolute scale (absolute zero at 0 K) with the triple point of water defined to be 273.16 K.

The Celsius, Fahrenheit, and Rankine scales are defined as simple linear functions of the kelvin scale (Equations 13.4, 13.5, and 13.6).

The number of atoms in exactly 12 gm of ^{12}C is called Avogadro's number, N_0. It is equal to 6.02×10^{23}. The mass of one atom of ^{12}C is exactly 12 amu.

One mole of a substance is the amount of the substance containing N_0 molecules. The mass in grams of 1 mole is its molecular weight, $M.W.$

The law of equilibrium, or the *zeroth law of thermodynamics*, states that systems in thermal contact tend to approach the same temperature and that they exhibit no further tendency to change once they are at the same temperature.

A thermometer measures its own temperature. Because of the law of equilibrium, it can also measure the temperature of its environment.

Bulk energy is the mechanical energy associated with the macroscopic motion of a system. It is ordered energy.

Internal energy is the submicroscopic energy associated with atoms and molecules in a system. It is disordered energy.

Heat is a mode of energy exchange via molecular collisions; it must be carefully distinguished from internal energy.

The calorie, now defined by the conversion factor, 4.184 J/cal, is approximately the heat required to raise the temperature of 1 gm of water by 1 K.

The discovery that heat is a form of energy led to the postulate of a universal law of energy conservation.

In the low-density limit, all gases are "ideal": they define the same temperature scale and obey the ideal-gas law,

$$PV = nRT. \tag{13.12}$$

The gas constant R and Boltzmann's constant k are related by $R = N_0 k$.

Submicroscopically, an ideal gas is one whose molecules (1) have a dimension that is negligible compared with their average separation, (2) move as free particles between collisions, and (3) in collisions obey Newton's laws.

The kinetic theory, using elementary mechanics and simple ideas of probability, provides a formula for the pressure of a confined gas:

$$P = \frac{1}{3}\frac{N}{V}m\overline{v^2}. \tag{13.29}$$

At temperature T, the root-mean-square speed of a molecule is given by

$$v_{\text{rms}} = \sqrt{\frac{3kT}{m}}. \tag{13.38}$$

Specific heat is the heat added to a system per unit mass per unit change of temperature. It may be defined at constant volume, at constant pressure, or for other special conditions.

Over a range where the specific heat C does not change appreciably, heat and temperature change are related by

$$\Delta Q = CM\,\Delta T. \tag{13.40}$$

A phase change is a structural change in a substance that occurs at some definite temperature and pressure.

The changes of internal energy per unit mass accompanying first-order phase changes are called latent heats; these include the heat of fusion and the heat of vaporization.

The law of energy conservation including mechanical and thermal phenomena is called the *first law of thermodynamics*. It may be written

$$\Delta(U + E_{\text{B}}) = \Delta Q + \Delta W. \tag{13.55}$$

The number of degrees of freedom of a classical system is the number of coordinates required to specify completely the spatial arrangement of the system.

The equipartition theorem states that in thermal equilibrium, the average kinetic energy associated with each degree of freedom is $\frac{1}{2}kT$.

A grain of dust in a liquid or gas acquires a mean kinetic energy of $\frac{3}{2}kT$, the same as a molecule. Its motion (Brownian motion) can reveal Avogadro's number and molecular mass.

A quantum system may exhibit fewer degrees of freedom than calculated classically for two reasons: (1) If no physical change is associated with change of a coordinate (as in rotation about a symmetry axis), the corresponding mode of motion acquires no energy. (2) If the quantum excitation energy of a mode of motion exceeds the thermal energy, the degree of freedom is "frozen" and does not fully share energy.

An ideal monatomic gas has, effectively, three degrees of freedom per atom. Its molar specific heats are $C_v' = \frac{3}{2}R$ and $C_p' = \frac{5}{2}R$.

An ideal diatomic gas near room temperature has, effectively, five degrees of freedom per molecule. Its molar specific heats are $C_v' = \frac{5}{2}R$ and $C_p' = \frac{7}{2}R$.

For any ideal gas, $C_p' - C_v' = R$.

Many important properties of matter are determined by the relative magnitudes of quantum excitation energies and thermal energy.

QUESTIONS

Q13.1   What kinds of physical behavior of a piece of ice might be adequately described by the theory of mechanics alone? For what kinds of behavior would the theory of thermodynamics also be needed?

Section 13.1

Q13.2   Applying the theory of mechanics to as few as three or four interacting particles may be exceedingly complicated. How, then, can the physicist develop a successful—even a simple—mathematical description of billions of interacting molecules?

Q13.3   When you read a household thermometer, you actually measure a length—the height of a column of liquid or the distance of a pointer from the edge of a scale. (1) What physical quantity is measured when a gas thermometer is used to determine temperature? (2) Explain how the measurement of temperature can depend on mechanical quantities, yet be a new concept distinct from mechanical quantities. (HINT: Can you think of two distinct concepts in mechanics, one of which utilizes the other in its definition?)

Section 13.2

Q13.4   Why is the triple point of water not assigned some round number, such as 300 K? If it were so assigned, what would be the approximate number of Celsius degrees between the freezing and boiling points of water at 1 atm?

Q13.5   Two gas thermometers show different pressures at the triple point of water and are therefore described by different coefficients a in Equation 13.1. Explain why they can nevertheless define the same temperature scale.

Q13.6   Suppose that you constructed a constant-volume gas thermometer using air as the working gas and that you had no other gas available. By studying air at different densities, could you learn anything about the extent to which air behaves like an ideal gas?

Q13.7   Suggest how the length of a metal bar could be used both to define and to measure temperature.

Q13.8   A thermometer outdoors in the sun may show a temperature higher than the actual temperature of the surrounding air. Why? Does this mean that the thermometer is "wrong"?

Q13.9   (1) The human body is a crude but useful thermometer. Under what conditions is your perception of temperature fairly accurate? Under what conditions is it inaccurate? (2) Name two or three physical variables other than temperature that are directly perceived by man. Which one is most accurately sensed?

Section 13.3   Q13.10   Explain carefully why Avogadro's number N_0, the number of particles in a mole, is also a conversion factor for mass units: amu/gm.

Q13.11   Why does Avogadro's hypothesis not apply to liquids and solids?

Q13.12   (1) Which has greater mass, 1 mole of ordinary hydrogen or 1 mole of "heavy hydrogen" (deuterium)? (2) Which has the greater number of molecules?

Q13.13   At the same temperature and pressure, which has greater density, oxygen (O_2) or ozone (O_3)?

Q13.14   Avogadro's hypothesis provides a simple explanation for the law of combining volumes. Suggest an alternative hypothesis that also accounts for the law (your suggestion may be fanciful and need not accord with other evidence about the structure of matter).

Section 13.4   Q13.15   Name a physical quantity other than temperature that tends toward equalization when two systems are brought into contact.

Q13.16   The law of equilibrium has nothing to say about the time required to establish equal temperature in two systems that are in thermal contact. Give one example of each of the following: (a) a system that comes into equilibrium with another system (or with its surroundings) in 1 sec or less; (b) a system that requires a few hours to establish equilibrium with its surroundings; and (c) a system that does not reach equilibrium with its surroundings even over a time span of millions of years. Do you expect the last-named system to reach equilibrium eventually?

Q13.17   A thermometer placed inside an evacuated chamber gives a specific temperature reading, which can be changed by changing the temperature outside the chamber (according to theory, this would be true even for a perfect vacuum). (1) How is the thermometer "linked" to its surrounding chamber (assume that there is no material link)? (2) The vacuum itself can be assigned a temperature. Why? (HINT: A vacuum is a region free of *material* particles.)

Q13.18   On a cloudless night, frost may form on horizontal surfaces even when the temperature of the air is above freezing. Explain this fact in terms of the law of equilibrium. (NOTE: The temperature of interstellar space is about 3 K.)

Q13.19   Explain carefully how Equation 13.1—or its equivalent, Equation 13.11—can be both a definition of temperature and a law of nature.

Q13.20   A furnace raises the air temperature in a house from 10 °C to 20 °C. It does so without changing the volume of the house or the pressure of the air in the house. How can this be accomplished without violating the ideal-gas law?

Q13.21 Give an example in which the loss of internal energy by one part of a system   Section 13.5
is equal to the gain of internal energy by another part of the system, with
heat as the medium of exchange.

Q13.22 Give an example in which the total internal energy of a system increases or
decreases without a corresponding flow of heat to or from the system. Such
an example shows why the concepts of heat and internal energy are distinct.

Q13.23 An *intensive* variable is one that can be defined locally within a system; its
magnitude does not depend on the boundaries selected for the system. An
extensive variable is one that is defined for the system as a whole; its magnitude does depend on the boundaries selected for the system. Which of the
following variables are intensive and which are extensive: (a) density, (b)
pressure, (c) volume, (d) temperature, (e) mass, (f) internal energy, (g)
number of moles, and (h) molecular weight?

Q13.24 Explain the following phenomena from a *microscopic* (i.e., kinetic theory)   Section 13.6
viewpoint. (1) A gas released in free space would expand indefinitely; a solid
or liquid would not. (2) A swimmer emerging from a heated pool into warm
air feels chilly. (3) The pressure in an automobile tire increases after the
automobile has been driven awhile.

Q13.25 Imagine, as scientists once did, that the molecules of a gas occupy fixed
positions and are in contact with each other. What conclusions about
molecular diameter can you draw (a) from the law of combining volumes and
Avogadro's hypothesis and (b) from the ideal-gas law?

Q13.26 A barrier with a small hole in it separates a region containing gas at high   Section 13.7
pressure from a region containing gas at very low pressure. Is the rms speed
of molecules escaping through the hole from the high-pressure to the low-
pressure region greater than, less than, or equal to the rms speed of the
molecules left behind in the high-pressure region?

Q13.27 A radiometer consists of four vanes free to rotate about a pivot inside a bulb
containing air at very low pressure (see the figure). One side of each vane is
black and readily absorbs light; the other side is silvered and reflects most
light that strikes it. Explain why the vanes rotate when they are illuminated.
Seen from above, do the vanes in the figure rotate clockwise or counterclockwise? (Consult an outside reference if necessary.)

Q13.28 Why is *translational* kinetic energy the only form of energy that is proportional   Section 13.8
to absolute temperature? (HINT: What effect, if any, do other forms of
molecular energy have on the pressure exerted by a gas?)

Q13.29 Explain in terms of the kinetic theory why the speed of sound in air at high
altitude is nearly the same as the speed of sound at sea level despite a big
difference in air density.

Q13.30 Explain in terms of molecular speeds and molecular collisions why the speed
of sound in water is considerably greater (actually more than four times
greater) than the speed of sound in air at the same temperature.

Q13.31 (1) Can a temperature be assigned to a single molecule at one instant of time?
Why or why not? (2) Can a temperature be assigned to a single molecule
over a finite span of time? Why or why not?

Q13.32   Name one concept other than temperature that normally requires many molecules for its definition?

Q13.33   By 1900, the kinetic theory was well-tested even though the magnitude of Avogadro's number N_0 was not well-known. Discuss any one experiment that provides supporting evidence for the kinetic theory but provides no information about the mass of a single molecule or the number of molecules in a sample.

Q13.34   A sample of nitrogen and a sample of oxygen are found to conduct sound at the same speed. (1) Which gas has the higher temperature? (2) Which gas has the higher pressure?

Q13.35   Explain briefly, as if to a nonscience student, why there is a minimum temperature (absolute zero) but no maximum temperature.

Section 13.9   Q13.36   Suggest why it is easier to measure C_p than C_v for a liquid or solid.

Q13.37   Why do C_p and C_v differ very little for a liquid or a solid even though they differ very substantially for a gas?

Q13.38   (1) Explain why Equation 13.40 ($\Delta Q = CM\,\Delta T$) follows from the definition of specific heat. (2) Why is this equation strictly valid only for infinitesimal ΔQ and ΔT, but valid for finite M?

Q13.39   (1) Why is water a better coolant than most liquids? (2) Under what conditions might a different liquid be preferred as a coolant?

Q13.40   Suggest a reason in terms of molecular interactions why heats of vaporization are generally larger than heats of fusion.

Q13.41   On cold nights when the temperature falls several degrees below freezing, orange growers sometimes flood the irrigation ditches between the orange trees with water. How might this prevent the trees from freezing?

Q13.42   It is sometimes possible to melt an aluminum pan on a stove, but only after any water in the pan has boiled away. Why?

Q13.43   Home heating systems may use air, hot water, or steam to conduct energy from the furnace to living space. Why do larger buildings or clusters of buildings use only steam systems, not hot-air or hot-water systems?

Section 13.10   Q13.44   Commonly employed units for the gas constant R are J/kmole K, kcal/kmole K, and cal/gm K. (1) What is the unit of C_v in Equation 13.52 for each of these choices of unit for R? (2) For which two choices is the numerical value of C_v the same?

Section 13.11   Q13.45   In an idealized rocket nozzle, molecules of mass m move exactly parallel to each other with equal speed v. What is the temperature of the exhaust gas?

Q13.46   Let the air in a tire and in the cylinder of an attached hand pump be the system of interest. When the handle of the pump is pushed down, which, if any, of the four terms in Equation 13.55 are zero or near zero? Which are positive? Which are negative?

Q13.47   When a space vehicle is decelerated upon re-entering the atmosphere, it is heated. Discuss this phenomenon of re-entry heating in molecular terms, basing your discussion on the idea of ordered and disordered energy, the kinetic definition of temperature, and the first law of thermodynamics.

Q13.48   If the wire in Figure 13.15 is bent into a closed circle around which the bead can slide, how many degrees of freedom has the system? Explain the basis of your answer.

Section 13.12

Q13.49   Does the equipartition theorem apply to the planets?

Q13.50   For air, the ratio of specific heats C_p/C_v (usually called γ) is approximately 1.4. (1) Does this support the idea that air is composed of diatomic molecules? (2) For a monatomic gas, is γ greater or less than 1.4? (3) For a gas of complex polyatomic molecules, would you expect γ to be greater or less than 1.4?

Section 13.14

Q13.51   As hydrogen gas is heated, its specific heat (per unit mass) increases and reaches a maximum value when the gas is fully ionized. Its *molar* specific heat, however, first increases and then decreases. Explain why. (HINT: Is the number of moles constant? Is the molecular weight constant?)

Section 13.15

Q13.52   A hypothetical chamber contains a single molecule of deuterium (heavy hydrogen). Near absolute zero, this is a system that has, effectively, three degrees of freedom (the rest are frozen). Discuss the "thawing" of other degrees of freedom and the gradual increase in their number as the chamber is heated to room temperature, then to thousands, millions, and finally billions of kelvins.

EXERCISES

E13.1   Find the temperature in degrees Celsius and in kelvins to match each of the following plaints: (1) "Brrr! It's 20 below." (2) "It's 90 in the shade." (3) "The wings are beginning to ice up."

Section 13.2

E13.2   An American tourist hospitalized in a foreign land is told that his temperature is 39.5. What is his temperature in degrees Fahrenheit?

E13.3   What equation relates temperature measurements in degrees Rankine and degrees Fahrenheit?

E13.4   At what temperature do Fahrenheit and Celsius thermometers give the same numerical reading?

E13.5   In a certain constant-volume gas thermometer, the gas pressure is P_0 at the freezing point of water, which is defined to be 0 °C. At the boiling point of water at sea level, defined to be 100 °C, the gas pressure is P_1. (1) Write an equation analogous to Equation 13.1 that expresses the temperature in degrees Celsius as a function of the measured gas pressure for this thermometer. (2) Express the constant a in Equation 13.1 in terms of the reference pressures P_0 and P_1.

E13.6   In a graph in which pressure P is plotted vertically and temperature T is plotted horizontally, sketch lines of boiling and freezing for water. (Consult an outside reference if necessary. A qualitative graph suffices.) Label regions of the graph "solid," "liquid," and "gas." Identify the triple point.

E13.7   For a temperature change ΔT that is not too great, the change Δl in the linear dimension l of a piece of solid matter is given by

$$\Delta l = \alpha l \, \Delta T;$$

α is called the *linear coefficient of thermal expansion*. For iron near room temperature, $\alpha = 1.2 \times 10^{-5} \text{ K}^{-1}$. (1) By how much does the length of a 30-m section of railroad track change as its temperature is changed by 50 K? (2) For this same temperature change, what is the approximate change in the average distance between neighboring atoms in iron (the density of iron is $7.9 \times 10^3 \text{ kg/m}^3$ and its atomic weight is 56)?

Section 13.3   E13.8   (1) How many kilomoles are in 18 kg of water? (2) How many kilomoles of oxygen and hydrogen result from the dissociation of 18 kg of water ($2H_2O \rightarrow 2H_2 + O_2$)? (3) If this quantity of water is totally ionized to a gas (plasma) of electrons and bare nuclei, how many kilomoles of particles are there? (4) Is any further subdivision of the "water" possible?

E13.9   If 1 mole of radioactive atoms is distributed uniformly through the earth's atmosphere to a height of 30 km, how many of the atoms will be found in each cubic meter? (This calculation emphasizes the enormity of Avogadro's number.)

E13.10   Call the molecular weight of a substance $M.W.$ and the mass of a single molecule of the substance m. Derive a formula for m in terms of $M.W.$ and Avogadro's number N_0. (This simple formula is worth saving.)

E13.11   Let $M.W.$ represent the molecular weight of a substance, ρ its mass density in kg/m^3, and u its number density in molecules/m^3. Derive a formula for u in terms of ρ, $M.W.$, and Avogadro's number N_0. Is the formula valid for liquids and solids? (This formula is worth saving.)

E13.12   (1) One liter of hydrogen (H_2) combines with x liters of chlorine (Cl_2) to produce y liters of hydrogen chloride (HCl); all volumes are measured at the same temperature and pressure. What are x and y? (2) What are the relative volumes of each of the reacting gases and product gases (again at the same temperature and pressure) when methane (CH_4) burns in oxygen (O_2) to form carbon dioxide (CO_2) and water vapor?

Section 13.4   E13.13   Show that Avogadro's hypothesis is implied by the ideal-gas law.

E13.14   Most airplanes operate noticeably better on a cool day than on a warm day. If the air pressure is the same on a winter day at 0 °C and on a summer day at 30 °C, by what fraction does the air density differ on these two days? Which day has denser air?

E13.15   (1) What is the volume expansion factor when water turns to steam at 373 K and 1-atm pressure? (2) By what factor does the mean distance between water molecules increase? Use a water density of 10^3 kg/m^3 and an air pressure of 10^5 N/m^2 and assume that the steam behaves like an ideal gas.

E13.16   (1) A 22.4-liter container holds 10 moles of oxygen gas at 0 °C. What is the pressure of the gas? (2) A pump transfers this gas to a 10-liter container and in so doing raises the temperature of the gas to 50 °C. What is the new pressure of the gas?

E13.17   When it is released from sea level on a warm day ($P = 1$ atm, $T = 20$ °C), a meteorological balloon has a volume of 12 m^3. What is its volume when it reaches an altitude where $P = 0.4$ atm and $T = -20$ °C? (Assume the pressure inside and outside the balloon to be the same.)

E13.18   A tire gauge reads the difference between tire pressure and atmospheric pressure. Before a trip, an automobile tire containing 6 moles of air at 300 K shows a gauge pressure of 1.5 atm; this means that the pressure within the tire is 2.5 atm. Later, after running for a time, the tire shows a gauge pressure of 2.0 atm. (1) If the tire volume has not changed, what is the new temperature of the air within it? (2) If at this higher temperature the tire is deflated back to its original pressure, how many air molecules escape from the tire?

E13.19 A 1-liter flask contains nitrogen (N_2) at 20 °C and atmospheric pressure. As the flask is heated slowly to 100 °C, enough gas is allowed to escape to keep the pressure at 1 atm. Then the flask is sealed and cooled to 50 °C. (1) What mass of nitrogen escaped? (2) What is the final pressure in the flask?

E13.20 Three sealed containers of gas, all of different volume, lost their identifying tags. When found, the tags bore these labels: (a) 2 moles of helium at 300 K and 5×10^5 N/m², (b) 6×10^{23} neon atoms at 0 °C and 2 atm pressure, and (c) 7 gm of N_2 at room temperature and 20 atm pressure. Which label belongs to the largest container, which to the one of intermediate size, and which to the smallest container? Would the smallest container fit in your pocket?

E13.21 Air bubbles leaking from a submarine double in radius as they rise to the surface. If the temperature of the air in the bubbles is approximately constant, what is the depth of the submarine?

E13.22 One mole of an ideal gas occupies 22.4 liters (2.24×10^{-2} m³) at standard conditions. (1) Use the density of dry air given in Appendix 3B to calculate the mass of air in 1 mole. (2) Use the data on the composition of the atmosphere in the same appendix to find the average molecular weight of air. (NOTE: This is a *weighted* average.) (3) Compare the answers to parts 1 and 2. Does the comparison provide evidence for or against the idea that air behaves like an ideal gas?

E13.23 The *volume coefficient of thermal expansion* of a substance is defined by

$$\beta = \frac{1}{V}\frac{dV}{dT},$$

where V is volume and T is temperature; β is the fractional change in volume per unit change in temperature. (1) The linear coefficient of thermal expansion of iron near room temperature is given in Exercise 13.7. What is its volume coefficient of thermal expansion? (2) For an ideal gas at constant pressure, show that $\beta = 1/T$. What is the ratio β(ideal gas)/β(iron) at room temperature?

E13.24 Answer the questions in the footnote on page 563.

Section 13.5

E13.25 (1) A small heater dissipates 200 W (200 J/sec). How much time is needed for it to raise the temperature of 0.2 kg of water (about one cup) from 20 °C to 100 °C? (2) If the mechanical equivalent of heat were 4,184 kcal/J instead of 4,184 J/kcal, how long would it take the heater to bring the water to a boil?

E13.26 A rotund inventor ($m = 120$ kg) decides to harness the gravitational energy associated with his 3-m descent from his bedroom to his kitchen each morning. He designs a small elevator whose descent turns an electric generator that supplies power to a hot plate. If all of his change of potential energy goes into heating half a liter of coffee, by how much is the temperature of the coffee raised?

Section 13.6   E13.27   (1) For an ideal gas at standard conditions, calculate the number of molecules per cubic meter. Using this number, calculate approximately the average separation between two molecules. (2) Calculate the same two quantities for water. (3) Calculate the same two quantities for aluminum, whose density is 2.7×10^3 kg/m^3 and whose atomic weight is 27 (note that a "molecule" of Al is a single atom). (4) Discuss briefly the significance of the relative spacing of atoms or molecules in these three substances: solid, liquid, and gas?

Section 13.7   E13.28   A molecule rebounds elastically from a smooth wall (Figure 13.10). (1) Why does $p_2 = p_1$? (2) If the components p_y and p_z are unchanged in the collision, show that $(p_x)_{\text{after}} = -(p_x)_{\text{before}}$. (3) Give a vector expression for the molecule's change of momentum, $\mathbf{p}_2 - \mathbf{p}_1$.

E13.29   The interior volume of a certain house is 450 m^3; the pressure of the air in the house is 10^5 N/m^2 and its temperature is 293 K. (1) What is the total translational kinetic energy of all the molecules of air in the house? (2) Answer the same question after the house has been heated to 298 K (its pressure is unchanged). (3) Briefly discuss the eventual distribution of the energy added to the house by its furnace.

Section 13.8   E13.30   Find the rms speeds of (a) a helium atom at the liquefaction temperature of helium, 4 K, and (b) a deuterium atom in a thermonuclear fusion experiment at 2×10^7 K.

E13.31   Use Equation 13.33 to show that for a gas at room temperature (1) the average kinetic energy per molecule is about 0.04 eV and (2) the molecular kinetic energy of 1 mole is about 1 kcal.

E13.32   If hydrogen remained in molecular form (H_2) at 6,000 K (the surface temperature of the sun), at what speed would it conduct sound? Compare this speed with the speed of sound in air at normal temperature.

E13.33   An airplane flies at Mach 0.85 (85 percent of the speed of sound) at an altitude where the temperature is $-35\,°C$. What is its speed in mile/hr?

E13.34   Nitrogen molecules in the air enclosed within an orbiting space vehicle are traveling with the vehicle at a speed of 17,000 mile/hr (7.6×10^3 m/sec). What would be the temperature of a sample of nitrogen gas at rest if its molecules were moving randomly at this speed?

E13.35   What happens to the pressure of a gas in a container of fixed volume if (1) the temperature is doubled, (2) the rms speed of the molecules is doubled, or (3) a chemical reaction takes place that doubles the molecular weight of the gas (while halving the number of molecules) with no change in the total translational kinetic energy of the molecules?

E13.36   (1) Show that the rms speed of a gas molecule is given in terms of its molecular weight $M.W.$, the absolute temperature T, and the gas constant R by

$$v_{\text{rms}} = \sqrt{\frac{3{,}000\,RT}{M.W.}}$$

if T is expressed in kelvins, R in J/mole K, and v_{rms} in m/sec. (2) Find the average speed at 0 °C of the principal molecular constituents of air: nitrogen, $M.W. = 28$; oxygen, $M.W. = 32$; and argon, $M.W. = 40$.

E13.37   A molecule of water vapor ($m = 3.0 \times 10^{-26}$ kg) in a rocket exhaust nozzle has a kinetic energy of 0.2 eV. (1) Find its speed and compare this with the speed of a satellite in a low earth orbit. (2) The average kinetic energy of many water molecules is known to be 0.2 eV. Explain why the temperature of the water cannot be calculated from this piece of information. Is there a minimum temperature that the water might have? Is there a maximum temperature that it might have?

E13.38 (1) How much heat is required to raise the temperature of a 10-gm piece of copper from 0 °C to 100 °C? (2) How does this energy compare with the energy required to accelerate the same piece of copper from rest to a speed of Mach 1 (340 m/sec)?

Section 13.9

E13.39 In Yosemite Falls in California water drops 2,425 ft. If all of the potential energy of the fall were transformed into heat, by how much would the temperature of the water at the bottom of the fall be increased?

E13.40 Into a 0.2-kg saucepan initially at 20 °C is poured 0.8 kg of boiling water at 100 °C. When equilibrium is established, water and pan are at 93 °C. If half the internal energy lost by the water went into heating the pan (the other half being dissipated to the surroundings), what is the specific heat of the metal in the pan?

E13.41 One-quarter liter of water (250 gm) and its insulated 50-gm aluminum container are initially in thermal equilibrium at 20 °C. If a 100-gm piece of copper at 100 °C is placed in the water and if heat loss to the surroundings is negligible, what is the final temperature of the system?

E13.42 (1) What is the heat of vaporization of water in (a) kcal/mole? (b) eV/molecule? (2) How does the heat of vaporization of water compare with the mean translational kinetic energy of water at 373 K (either per mole or per molecule)?

E13.43 If 539 kcal, the energy required to vaporize 1 kg of water, were used instead to lift the kilogram of water in the earth's gravitational field, to what altitude could it be raised? Ignore the variation of gravitational force with height, but comment on whether it is a good approximation to do so.

E13.44 A vaporizer holds 2 liters of water and operates on 40 W of power. How long will it take to vaporize all the water?

E13.45 An insulating plastic container holds 200 gm of water at 90 °C. Ice cubes of mass 75 gm and temperature 0°C are added one at a time. What is the state of the system (a) after one cube is added? (b) after two cubes are added? (c) after three are added? (d) after four are added? (Assume that equilibrium is reached at each stage and that the heat transferred to the container and its surroundings is negligible.)

E13.46 How much ice at 0 °C must be combined with 1 kg of steam at 100 °C to produce water at 50 °C?

E13.47 Steam is pumped to the top floor of a 50-m building, where it condenses and releases its heat of vaporization. On its way back to the boiler in the basement, the water turns a waterwheel that drives a small hydroelectric generator. How does the energy supplied by the generator compare with the energy supplied by the condensing steam?

E13.48 One kg of air at 20 °C is brought into thermal contact with a quantity of

Section 13.10

helium at 10 °C; the two come to equilibrium at 15 °C. What is the mass of the helium?

E13.49   What is the volume in liters of either one of the containers mentioned in Example 2 of Section 13.10?

Section 13.11   E13.50   A 1,500-kg automobile traveling at a speed of 15 m/sec (about 33 mile/hr) is braked to a halt. As it stops, 80 percent of its energy is dissipated as heat in the brake linings and surrounding parts. (1) What is the magnitude of this heat in kilocalories? (2) If this heat is distributed uniformly in 10 kg or iron, whose specific heat is 0.11 kcal/kg K, by how much is the temperature of the iron raised? (3) What is the eventual fate of the energy that was initially in the form of bulk kinetic energy of the automobile?

E13.51   Suppose that a rocket like the one pictured in Figure 13.14(b) is propelled by an ideal monatomic gas. Initially, the gas, with all its energy in disordered form, is at 2,000 K. As it leaves the exhaust nozzle, it is at 1,000 K. Its total energy has not changed. (1) If the atomic weight of the gas is 4, what was the initial rms speed of its molecules? (2) What is the exhaust speed, that is, the speed of the ordered bulk motion of the gas leaving the nozzle?

Section 13.12   E13.52   How many degrees of freedom has each of the following systems: (a) a particle sliding on a plane; (b) a coin that can slide on a plane and turn about an axis perpendicular to the plane; (c) two charged particles sliding on a plane; (d) a pendulum pivoted to swing along a circular arc; (e) a pendulum bob free to trace a path on a spherical surface; and (f) a metal rod bent into the shape of a triangle and free to move in space?

E13.53   A cosmic-ray particle with an energy of 10^{12} eV is stopped in a tube containing 0.1 mole of neon. By how much is the temperature of the neon increased after the added energy is divided among all the molecules?

E13.54   On its way to the moon, a space vehicle moves with a speed of 5,000 m/sec. Within the cabin the temperature is 300 K. (1) As measured inside the vehicle, what is the average kinetic energy of an oxygen molecule associated with each of its three translational degrees of freedom? (2) Relative to an observer on earth, what is the average kinetic energy of the molecule associated with each of these degrees of freedom (choose one axis of a coordinate system to be parallel to the velocity of the space vehicle)?

Section 13.13   E13.55   A speck of dust in air has a mass 10^8 times greater than the mass of a molecule of nitrogen. (1) Show that the average speed of the dust speck is about 5 cm/sec. (2) Microscopic observation reveals that the displacement of the dust speck in 1 sec is much less than 5 cm. Why?

E13.56   (1) A baseball (m = 0.14 kg) being tossed around the infield has an rms speed of 20 m/sec. What is its "temperature" as calculated by setting its average kinetic energy equal to $\frac{3}{2}kT$? Why doesn't it feel hot? (2) If a baseball could survive a stellar temperature of 10^7 K, what would be the rms speed of its Brownian motion?

Section 13.14   E13.57   Derive the result $C_p' = \frac{5}{2}R$ (Equation 13.74) for the specific heat at constant pressure of a monatomic gas.

E13.58   Make the assumption (incorrect) that for ordinary water all the internal energy is in the form of translational kinetic energy of the molecules. What, then, would be the specific heat of water? Contrast your calculated value with the actual value for water and discuss the meaning of the difference.

E13.59 At sufficiently high temperature, the vibrational motion of a diatomic molecule acquires an average energy equal to kT (divided equally between kinetic energy and potential energy). Give the molar specific heats of the gas at constant volume and at constant pressure in the temperature region where the internal energy is shared among translational, rotational, and vibrational degrees of freedom.

E13.60 (1) At what temperature does $kT = 1$ eV? This number is a useful temperature-to-energy "conversion factor" that is worth saving. (2) In a nuclear explosion, $kT = 5$ keV. What is the temperature?

Section 13.15

E13.61 (1) In an outside reference find the dissociation energy of water (the energy needed for the transformation $2H_2O \rightarrow 2H_2 + O_2$) and express it in eV/molecule. (2) At about what temperature does this suggest that water vapor should "boil" into its constituent elements, hydrogen and oxygen?

PROBLEMS

The thermistor

P13.1   A thermistor is a circuit element whose resistance changes markedly with temperature; it can therefore be used as a thermometer. Consider a particular thermistor whose resistance is 150 ohms at the triple-point temperature of water. The results of comparing it with a constant-volume gas thermometer at some other temperatures are shown in the table. What is the temperature when the resistance of the thermistor is 15.2 ohms? (A graph of P vs R may be helpful. Select a suitable kind of graph paper.)

Pressure, P (atm)	Resistance, R (ohms)
0.898	239
0.966	96.8
1.034	43.4
1.102	21.2
1.171	11.2

Constant-pressure gas thermometer

P13.2   (1) Design a constant-pressure gas thermometer that will operate over a temperature range of at least several hundred kelvins (include a sketch, a discussion, and an appropriate equation). (2) Explain why the constant-pressure gas thermometer might be less convenient than a constant-volume gas thermometer for measuring a wide range of temperatures.

P13.3   An easy-to-build thermometer is shown in the figure. Through a stopper in an "empty" flask (i.e., one containing air) passes a thin tube; within the tube a few drops of ink form a visible column. (1) If the volume of the flask is 1 liter and the cross-sectional area of the column of ink is 1 mm², what change of temperature near room temperature is needed to move the column 1 mm? (2) What are some advantages and disadvantages of this thermometer?

Simplified derivation of gas
pressure

P13.4   The figure shows a highly simplified model of a gas in a cubical container of side L. All molecules move with the same speed v; one-third of them move back and forth perpendicular to each pair of walls; they move freely across the container without mutual interaction. (1) Derive a formula for the pressure exerted by this gas and show that it is the same as Formula 13.29. (2) Suggest one or more reasons why this unrealistic, oversimplified model of a gas leads to the correct result for the pressure of a confined gas.

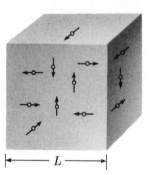

Thrust from escaping gas

P13.5   A tiny meteorite punches a hole of area A in the side of a spacecraft of mass M, and gas escapes through the hole. Inside the craft, reserve tanks and automatic valves maintain a constant gas pressure P. After time T, an astronaut discovers the leak and fixes it. What has been the change of momentum of the spacecraft?

Properties of real gases

P13.6   The important equation of the kinetic theory, Equation 13.30, is valid if the dimension of a molecule is much less than the average distance between molecules and if most of the time each molecule is free of forces exerted by other molecules. In answering the following questions, make reference to specific parts of the derivation of Equation 13.30. (1) Why does the finite size of molecules cause deviations from the results of the idealized kinetic theory? Owing to finite molecular size, is the actual gas pressure greater or less than the ideal pressure given by Equation 13.29? (HINT: Consider the limit in which the molecules are always close together.) (2) Why do forces acting between molecules cause deviations from the results of the idealized kinetic theory? Owing to intermolecular forces, is the actual gas pressure greater or less than the ideal pressure given by Equation 13.29? (HINT: Consider a solid, in which no atom is ever free of the forces of neighboring atoms.)

Force of a molecular collision

P13.7   According to Equation 13.25, the average force exerted on one wall of a container of side L by a *single* molecule of mass m is $\overline{F_1} = m\overline{v_x^2}/L$. (1) Pick reasonable values of m, v_x^2, and L and calculate a typical magnitude of this average force. (2) By any method, estimate the actual magnitude of the force exerted by this molecule on one wall during the brief instant of its collision. (3) What is the approximate ratio of the actual force in one collision to the average force over many collisions? Compare the estimated actual force with some known force, such as the weight of an object, in order to make clear how large it is. (NOTE: Only order-of-magnitude calculations are called for here.)

P13.8   At a fixed temperature T, a container of volume V contains n_1 moles of gas 1, n_2 moles of gas 2, and n_3 moles of gas 3. If the n_1 moles of gas 1 were present alone in the container, the pressure would be p_1. Similarly, with gases 1 and 3 removed, the remaining gas 2 would exert pressure p_2; and gas 3 alone at this temperature and in this volume would exert pressure p_3. These are called partial pressures. (1) Use the approach of the kinetic theory to prove that the actual pressure with all three gases present is the sum of the partial pressures: $P = p_1 + p_2 + p_3$. (2) Is this result rigorously valid for all gases or true only for ideal gases?

Law of partial pressures

P13.9   Consider the elastic collision of a helium atom and a hydrogen atom in one dimension. (1) The atoms meet head-on with equal energy. Which, if either, gains energy in the collision? (2) The atoms meet head-on with equal speed. Which, if either, gains energy in the collision? (3) The atoms meet head-on with equal magnitudes of momentum. Which if, either, gains energy in the collision? (NOTE: Since this problem does not deal with the relative probabilities of different kinds of collisions, it does not by itself reveal how energy would be shared by the atoms after many random collisions in three dimensions.)

Energy exchange in molecular collisions

P13.10   A vessel of volume V contains n_1 moles of a monatomic gas and n_2 moles of a diatomic gas. (1) What is the pressure in the vessel? (2) What is the molar specific heat at constant volume of the mixture of gases? (3) What is its molar specific heat at constant pressure?

Mixture of gases

P13.11   Suggest an experimental procedure that uses heat transfer and temperature change to measure the relative masses of different objects. Specify the quantity or quantities to be measured and the equation or equations that provide the relative masses. Is the method of any practical value?

Measuring mass by thermal means

P13.12   Starting from rest, a 1,500-kg car coasts down a hill whose vertical height is 125 m. At the bottom of the hill, the speed of the car is 30 m/sec and its temperature is the same as it was at the top of the hill. (1) Find all four terms in Equation 13.55 for the car. (2) Find all four terms in Equation 13.55 for the environment of the car (pavement, earth, and air). (3) Sum the answers to parts 1 and 2 and discuss the net transformation of energy for the combined system. Are these energy considerations consistent with the fact that the earth, air, and car together may be regarded as an isolated system?

First law of thermodynamics

P13.13   In a gas streaming with bulk flow velocity $\mathbf{v_0}$, the velocity $\mathbf{v}$ of a molecule can be written as the sum of the flow velocity and a randomly directed velocity $\mathbf{v_R}$: $\mathbf{v} = \mathbf{v_0} + \mathbf{v_R}$ (see the figure). (1) Write an expression for v^2 as a function of v_0, v_R, and the angle θ between $\mathbf{v_0}$ and $\mathbf{v_R}$. (2) Explain why the mean-square velocities are related by

$$\overline{v^2} = v_0^2 + \overline{v_R^2}.$$

(3) If $\overline{v_R^2} = 10^5 \text{ m}^2/\text{sec}^2$ and $v_0 = 200$ m/sec, what is the temperature of the gas? (4) What is the temperature of the gas in a moving frame of reference in which the bulk flow velocity is zero?

Random and bulk motion combined

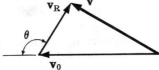

Properties of a gas related to properties of one molecule

P13.14 In a hypothetical experiment, the velocity of one molecule in a gas is measured repeatedly. Averaged over a large number of measurements, its mean-square components of velocity are found to be $\overline{v_x^2} = 4.8 \times 10^5$ m²/sec², $\overline{v_y^2} = 1.6 \times 10^5$ m²/sec², and $\overline{v_z^2} = 1.6 \times 10^5$ m²/sec². Assume that all bulk properties of the gas remain constant during the series of measurements. (1) What is the temperature of the gas? (2) What other bulk property of the gas can be deduced? (A result stated in Problem 13.13 may be useful.) (3) Give approximate magnitudes of $\overline{v_x}$, $\overline{v_y}$, and $\overline{v_z}$, the average components of velocity of the molecule studied.

Form of the internal-energy function

P13.15 For the internal energy of most gases, it is a good approximation to write $U = Nf(T)$, which states that U is proportional to the number of molecules N and otherwise is a function only of temperature, not of pressure or volume (for the ideal monatomic gas, for instance, $U = \tfrac{3}{2}NkT$). (1) Discuss the conditions under which $Nf(T)$ should accurately represent the internal-energy function. Should this form be accurate for a gas at very high density? for a gas at very low density? for solids and liquids? (2) Under what conditions for a gas is $f(T)$ a linear function of T? (HINT: Consider whether the number of degrees of freedom that share energy is constant or changing.)

Difference of specific heats

P13.16 (1) Derive the result $C_p' - C_v' = R$ (Equation 13.75) for the difference of molar specific heats of an ideal gas. Assume that the internal energy of a fixed quantity of the gas is a function only of temperature, but make no special assumption about the form of that function. (2) Explain qualitatively why C_p' is greater than C_v'.

Random vibration of a spring balance

P13.17 The force constant of a delicate spring balance is $\kappa = 0.5$ N/m ($F = -\kappa x$). Because of bombardment by air molecules, an object supported by the spring executes a random vibration (a Brownian motion). (1) If the average energy of this random motion is kT ($\tfrac{1}{2}kT$ of kinetic energy and $\tfrac{1}{2}kT$ of potential energy), what is the rms displacement of the object away from its equilibrium position at room temperature? (2) The balance is used to weigh an object whose mass is approximately 1 gm. What fractional uncertainty in its weight is contributed by the thermal fluctuations?

Internal energy of a polyatomic gas

P13.18 The internal energy of a sample of N molecules of carbon dioxide near room temperature can be written $U = a + bNkT$. (1) Use data from Table 13.2 to find b. (2) If each degree of freedom in a CO_2 molecule acquires energy $\tfrac{1}{2}kT$, what is the mean number of degrees of freedom that are excited near room temperature? (3) If U is normalized to be zero at absolute zero, the quantity a is negative. Why? (Keep in mind that the given formula for U is valid only over a limited range of temperatures.)

Work done on a gas: macroscopic and submicroscopic approaches

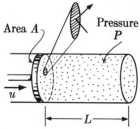

P13.19 Gas in a cylinder of cross-sectional area A is being slowly compressed by a piston moving with speed u (see the figure). (1) Using macroscopic considerations, express the rate at which work is being done on the gas (the input power). (2) Consider a single molecule rebounding from the moving piston and find its gain in kinetic energy. (NOTE: The molecule gains no energy in a frame of reference in which the piston is stationary.) (3) Apply ideas of the kinetic theory—especially the rate at which molecules collide with the wall—in order to find the rate of increase of the molecular kinetic energy of the gas. Show that the answers to parts 1 and 3 are the same. (Assume that the speed of the piston is very much less than the speed of the molecules and that thermal equilibrium prevails at all times.)

Entropy and the Second Law of Thermodynamics

As profound as any principle in physics is the second law of thermodynamics. Based on uncertainty and probability in the submicroscopic world, it accounts for specific rules of change in the macroscopic world. We shall approach this law, and a new concept, entropy, that goes with it, by considering some aspects of probability. Through the idea of probability comes the deepest understanding of spontaneous change in nature.

14.1 Probability in random events

A tray of coins can show how probability influences complex systems

We start with a system that at first glance has little to do with molecules, temperature, or heat. It is a tray of coins (Figure 14.1). For the purposes of some specific calculations, let us suppose that the tray contains just five coins. For this system we wish to conduct a hypothetical experiment and make some theoretical predictions. The experiment consists of giving the tray a sharp up-and-down motion so that all the coins flip into the air and land again in the tray, then counting how many heads and tails are displayed, and repeating this procedure many times. The theoretical problem is to predict how often a

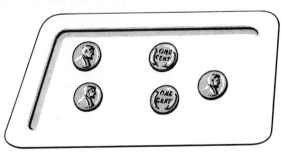

FIGURE 14.1   A tray of coins, a system governed by laws of probability.

TABLE 14.1   POSSIBLE ARRANGEMENTS OF FIVE COINS

Coin 1	Coin 2	Coin 3	Coin 4	Coin 5	
H	H	H	H	H	1 way to get 5 heads
H	H	H	H	T	
H	H	H	T	H	
H	H	T	H	H	5 ways to get 4 heads and 1 tail
H	T	H	H	H	
T	H	H	H	H	
H	H	H	T	T	
H	H	T	H	T	
H	T	H	H	T	
T	H	H	H	T	
H	H	T	T	H	
H	T	H	T	H	10 ways to get 3 heads and 2 tails
T	H	H	T	H	
H	T	T	H	H	
T	H	T	H	H	
T	T	H	H	H	
H	H	T	T	T	
H	T	H	T	T	
H	T	T	H	T	
H	T	T	T	H	
T	H	H	T	T	
T	H	T	H	T	10 ways to get 2 heads and 3 tails
T	H	T	T	H	
T	T	H	H	T	
T	T	H	T	H	
T	T	T	H	H	
H	T	T	T	T	
T	H	T	T	T	
T	T	H	T	T	5 ways to get 1 head and 4 tails
T	T	T	H	T	
T	T	T	T	H	
T	T	T	T	T	1 way to get 5 tails

particular arrangement of heads and tails will appear.

You can easily carry out the experiment yourself. Be sure that the tray is shaken vigorously enough each time so that at least some of the coins flip over. Here let us be concerned with the theory. To begin, we enumerate all possible ways in which the coins can land. This is done pictorially in Table 14.1. There are 32 possible results of a tray-shaking.* If all we do is count heads and tails

---

* Since each coin can land in two ways, the total number of ways in which five coins can land is $2 \times 2 \times 2 \times 2 \times 2 = 2^5 = 32$. Three coins could land in 8 different ways (2^3), four coins in 16 ways (2^4), and so on. In how many ways could 10 coins land?

TABLE 14.2   PROBABILITIES FOR DIFFERENT NUMBERS OF HEADS AND TAILS
WHEN FIVE COINS ARE FLIPPED

Number of Heads	Number of Tails	Probability
5	0	$\frac{1}{32} = 0.031$
4	1	$\frac{5}{32} = 0.156$
3	2	$\frac{10}{32} = 0.313$
2	3	$\frac{10}{32} = 0.313$
1	4	$\frac{5}{32} = 0.156$
0	5	$\frac{1}{32} = 0.031$

Total probability $= 1.000$

without identifying the coins, the number of possible results is 6 instead of 32 (Table 14.1).   Ten of the ways the coins can land yield three heads and two tails.   There are also ten different ways to get three tails and two heads.   Both four heads and one tail and four tails and one head can be achieved in five ways. Only one arrangement of coins yields five heads, and only one yields five tails. These numbers do not yet constitute a prediction of the results of the experiment. We need a postulate about the actual physical process, and a reasonable one is a postulate of randomness: that every coin is equally likely to land heads up or tails up and that every possible arrangement of the five coins is equally likely. This means that after very many trials, every entry in Table 14.1 should have resulted about $\frac{1}{32}$ of the time.   Note, however, that equal probability for each arrangement of coins is *not* the same as equal probability for each possible number of heads or tails.   After 3,200 trials, for example, we would expect to have seen five heads about 100 times, but three heads and two tails should have showed up ten times more frequently, or about 1,000 times.   The exact number of appearances of five heads or of three heads and two tails or of any other combination cannot be predicted with certainty.   What *can* be stated precisely (provided the postulate of randomness is correct) are probabilities of each such combination.   Shown in Table 14.2 are the basic probabilities for all the possible numbers of heads and tails that can appear in a single trial. It is interesting to present these numbers graphically also, as is done in Figure 14.2. The probability of a certain number of heads plotted vs the numbers of heads gives a bell-shaped curve, high in the middle and low in the wings.

The physical postulate:
Every arrangement is equally likely

The same kind of calculation, based on the postulate of randomness, can be carried out for any number of coins.   For ten coins, the basic probabilities are given in Table 14.3 and in Figure 14.3.   Two changes are evident.   First, the probability of all heads or all tails is greatly reduced.   Second, the bell-shaped probability curve has become relatively narrower.   The greater the number of coins, the less likely it is that the result of a single trial will be very different from an equal number of heads and tails.   To make this point clear, the probability curve for a tray of 1,000 coins is shown in Figure 14.4.   The chance of shaking all heads with this many coins would be entirely negligible even after a lifetime of trying.   As Figure 14.4 shows, there is not even much chance of

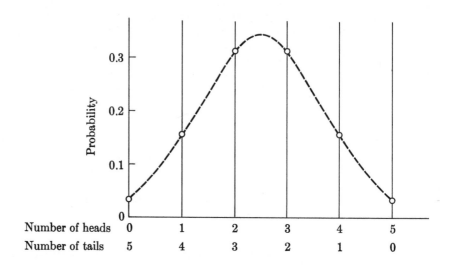

FIGURE 14.2   Probabilities for various results
of tray-shaking experiment with five coins.

TABLE 14.3   PROBABILITIES FOR DIFFERENT NUMBERS OF HEADS AND TAILS
WHEN TEN COINS ARE FLIPPED

Number of Heads	Number of Tails	Probability*
10	0	$1/1{,}024 = 0.0010$
9	1	$10/1{,}024 = 0.0098$
8	2	$45/1{,}024 = 0.0439$
7	3	$120/1{,}024 = 0.1172$
6	4	$210/1{,}024 = 0.2051$
5	5	$252/1{,}024 = 0.2461$
4	6	$210/1{,}024 = 0.2051$
3	7	$120/1{,}024 = 0.1172$
2	8	$45/1{,}024 = 0.0439$
1	9	$10/1{,}024 = 0.0098$
0	10	$1/1{,}024 = 0.0010$

Total probability $= 1.000$

* The reader familiar with binomial coefficients may be interested to know that the number of
arrangements of n coins to yield m heads is the binomial coefficient

$$\binom{n}{m} = \frac{n!}{m!\,(n-m)!}.$$

Thus the probabilities in this table are proportional to

$$\binom{10}{0}, \quad \binom{10}{1}, \quad \binom{10}{2},$$

and so on.

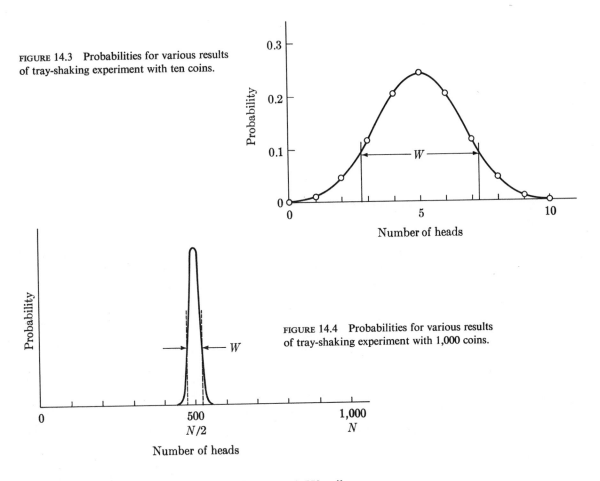

FIGURE 14.3   Probabilities for various results of tray-shaking experiment with ten coins.

FIGURE 14.4   Probabilities for various results of tray-shaking experiment with 1,000 coins.

getting a distribution as unequal as 450 heads and 550 tails.

The tendency of the probabilities to cluster near the midpoint of the graph, where the number of heads and the number of tails are nearly equal, can be characterized by a "width" of the curve. The width of the curve is defined to be the distance between a pair of points (see Figures 14.3 and 14.4) outside of which the probabilities are relatively small and inside of which the probabilities are relatively large. Exactly where these points are chosen is arbitrary. One convenient choice is the pair of points where the probability has fallen to about one-third of its central value—more exactly, to $1/e = 1/2.72$ of its central value. The reason for defining a width is this: It spans a region of highly probable results. After the tray is shaken, the number of heads and the number of tails are most likely to correspond to a point on the central part of the curve within its width. The distribution of heads and tails is unlikely to be so unequal as to correspond to a point on the curve outside of this central region. When the number of coins is reasonably large (more than 100), there is a simple formula for the width of the probability curve. If N is the number of coins, the width W of the curve between its $1/e$ points is given by

Width of a probability curve defined

$$W = \sqrt{2N}. \qquad (14.1)$$

The probability for the result of a tray-shaking to be within the width of the curve is 84 percent.*

In Figure 14.4, the number of coins is $N = 1,000$. The width W is $\sqrt{2,000}$, or roughly 44. Thus the number of heads on any trial has an 84 percent chance of lying between $500 - 22 = 478$ and $500 + 22 = 522$.

An important consequence of the so-called square-root law expressed by Equation 14.1 is a sharpening of the probability curve as the number of coins increases. The ratio of the width to the total number of coins is

$$\frac{W}{N} = \sqrt{\frac{2}{N}}. \tag{14.2}$$

As the number increases, the width-to-number ratio decreases

This ratio decreases as N increases. For 1,000 coins, the width-to-number ratio is about $1/22$. For 1,000,000 coins, it is $1/707$. If the number of coins could be increased until it equaled the number of molecules in a drop of water, say 2×10^{22}, the width-to-number ratio of the probability curve would be $1/10^{11}$. A vigorous shaking of the coins would then produce a number of heads and a number of tails unlikely to differ from equality by more than one part in one hundred billion. The probability curve would have collapsed to a narrow spike (Figure 14.5).

Two more points of interest about these head-and-tail probabilities will bring us closer to the connection between trays of coins and collections of molecules. First is the relation between probability and disorder. Ten coins arranged as all heads can be considered as perfectly orderly, as can an array of all tails. Five heads and five tails, on the other hand, arranged, for example,

Greater probability means greater disorder

as HHTHTTTHTH or as TTHTHTHHHT, form a disorderly array. Evidently a high state of order is associated with low probability, and a state of disorder

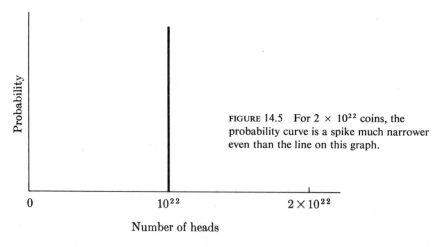

FIGURE 14.5   For 2×10^{22} coins, the probability curve is a spike much narrower even than the line on this graph.

---

* The probability curve has a simple mathematical form for large N. It is

$$P = \sqrt{\frac{2}{N\pi}}\, e^{-2(n - \frac{1}{2}N)^2/N},$$

where n is the number of heads (see Exercise 14.2).

is associated with high probability. This might be called the housewife's rule: Order is improbable; disorder is probable. The reason this is so is exactly the same for the household as for the tray of coins: There are many more ways to achieve disorder than there are to achieve order.

The second point of special interest concerns the way probabilities change in time. If a tray of 1,000 coins is carefully arranged to show all heads and is then shaken repeatedly, its arrangement will almost certainly shift in the direction of nearly equal numbers of heads and tails. The direction of spontaneous change will be from an arrangement of low probability to an arrangement of high probability, from order to disorder. The same will be true whenever the initial arrangement is an improbable one, for instance 700 tails and 300 heads. If instead we start with 498 heads and 502 tails, no amount of shaking will tend to move the distribution to a highly uneven arrangement. This can be considered an equilibrium situation. Repeated trials will then produce results not very different from the starting point. Clearly there is a general rule here—a rule of probability, to be sure, not an absolute rule: Under the action of random influences, a system tends to change from less probable arrangements to more probable arrangements, from order to disorder. The generalization of this rule from trays of coins to collections of molecules—and indeed to complex systems of any kind—is the *second law of thermodynamics*, a law with remarkably broad and important consequences, as we shall see.

Dynamic equilibrium

The second law of thermodynamics: Spontaneous change is from order to disorder

14.2 Molecular probability

Most of the large-scale properties of substances are, when examined closely enough, probabilistic in nature. Heat and temperature are purely macroscopic concepts that lose their meaning when applied to individual atoms and molecules, for any particular molecule may have more or less energy than the average or may contribute more or less than the average to a process of energy exchange. Temperature is proportional to an *average* kinetic energy; heat is equal to a *total* energy transferred by molecular collision. Because of our incomplete knowledge about the behavior of any single molecule and the consequent necessity of describing molecular motion in probabilistic terms, neither of these thermal concepts is useful except when applied to numbers so large that laws of probability become laws of near certainty. The same can be said of other concepts, such as pressure and internal energy.

Macroscopic "certainty" results from submicroscopic probability

A single molecule is characterized by position, velocity, momentum, and energy. Each of these is subject to random influences and is governed by laws of probability. Consider position, the easiest to discuss. To be specific, imagine an enclosure—such as the room you are in—divided by a screen into two equal parts. Some of the molecules of air are on one side of the room, some on the other. Common sense tells you that in a state of equilibrium, the numbers in the two halves are nearly equal.

The mathematics of molecules on two sides of a room is identical to the mathematics of coins on a tray. By the assumption of randomness, every single molecule has an equal chance to be on either side of the room, just as every coin has an equal chance to land as heads or as tails. There are many different ways to distribute the molecules in equal numbers on the two sides

Probability of position

but only one way to concentrate them all on one side. If a room contained only five molecules, it would not be surprising to find them sometimes all on a single side. The probability that they be all on the left is $\frac{1}{32}$ (see Table 14.1), and there is an equal probability that they be all on the right. The chance of a 3–2 distribution is $\frac{20}{32}$, or nearly two-thirds. Even for so small a number as five, a nearly equal division is much more likely than a very uneven division. For 10^{28} molecules, the number in a large room, the distribution is unlikely to deviate from equality by more than one part in 10^{14}. The probability for all of the 10^{28} molecules to congregate spontaneously in one half of the room is less than

$$10^{-(10^{+27})}.$$

Most probable distribution = equilibrium distribution = uniform density

This number is too small even to think about. Suddenly finding ourselves gasping for breath in one part of a room while someone in another part of the room is oversupplied with oxygen is a problem we need not be worried about.

There is a most probable distribution of molecular positions in a gas: it is a distribution of uniform density. Similarly, there is a most probable distribution of molecular speed in a gas: it is called the Maxwell-Boltzmann distribution. We present it here without proof. At temperature T, the probability per unit interval of speed v is, for molecules of mass m,

Probability of speed

The Maxwell-Boltzmann distribution is the equilibrium distribution

$$\frac{dP}{dv} = 4\pi \left(\frac{m}{2\pi kT}\right)^{3/2} v^2 e^{-mv^2/2kT}.\text{*} \qquad (14.3)$$

In Figure 14.6, the function dP/dv is plotted as a function of v for nitrogen molecules at two different temperatures. Formula 14.3 is normalized in such a way that the integral over v of the quantity on the right is equal to unity:

$$P_{\text{total}} = 4\pi \left(\frac{m}{2\pi kT}\right)^{3/2} \int_0^\infty v^2 e^{-mv^2/2kT} \, dv = 1. \qquad (14.4)$$

Regarding the "why" of the Maxwell-Boltzmann distribution, the following qualitative remarks must suffice: Equal speed for all molecules is not to be expected. Such equality would be a highly ordered and improbable situation, analogous to a clustering of all molecules at the same place. Speeds, like positions, are spread out. Since molecular kinetic energy, and therefore speed, is related to temperature, speeds can be expected to be distributed about an average speed that is low for low temperature and high for high temperature.

A mean-square speed, $\overline{v^2}$, can be defined in two ways. One is an average over time for a single molecule. This, according to Equation 13.33, is

Mean-square speed

$$\overline{v^2} = \frac{3kT}{m}. \qquad (14.5)$$

As required by the equipartition theorem, every molecule possesses this same

---

* One way to think of the meaning of dP/dv is this: If an enclosure contains a large number, N, of molecules in thermal equilibrium, the number of molecules whose speed lies in a narrow band, v to $v + \Delta v$, is $N(dP/dv)\,\Delta v$. The quantity P itself may be defined to be the probability that a molecule has any speed between 0 and v: $P(v) = \int_0^v (dP/dv)\,dv$. Equivalently, it is the fraction of the molecules whose speed is $\leq v$.

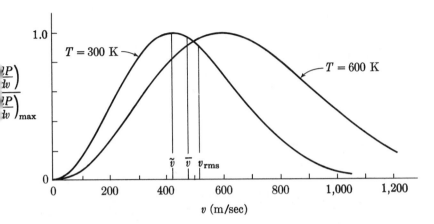

FIGURE 14.6   The Maxwell-Boltzmann speed distributions for nitrogen
molecules at two temperatures. The most probable speed is $\tilde{v} = \sqrt{2kT/m}$.
The average speed is $\bar{v} = \tilde{v}\sqrt{4/\pi}$, and the root-mean-square speed is
$v_{\mathrm{rms}} = \tilde{v}\sqrt{3/2}$. The quantity $(dP/dv)_{\max}$ is equal to $C\tilde{v}^2 e^{-1}$, where C is given
by Equation 14.8. It can also be written $(dP/dv)_{\max} = (4/e\sqrt{\pi})\tilde{v}^{-1}$.

mean-square speed in time. The other way is an average over all molecules at
an instant of time. This average can be calculated with the help of the Maxwell-
Boltzmann distribution:

$$\overline{v^2} = \int_0^\infty v^2 \frac{dP}{dv}\, dv. \tag{14.6}$$

It is left as a problem to prove that this average is also $3kT/m$.

■ EXAMPLE: What is the average speed $\bar{v}$ of a molecule at temperature T? By
how much does $\bar{v}$ differ from v_{rms}? The average speed is defined by

$$\bar{v} = \int_0^\infty v \frac{dP}{dv}\, dv. \tag{14.7}$$

This is a weighted average, with dP/dv being the weighting function. If we set

$$C = 4\pi \left(\frac{m}{2\pi kT}\right)^{3/2}, \tag{14.8}$$

Equation 14.7 reads

$$\bar{v} = C \int_0^\infty v^3 e^{-mv^2/2kT}\, dv.$$

Substituting u for $mv^2/2kT$ converts this equation to

$$\bar{v} = 2C \left(\frac{kT}{m}\right)^2 \int_0^\infty e^{-u}\, u\, du.$$

The integral is equal to 1.* Substituting the right side of Equation 14.8 for C then gives

Average speed

$$\bar{v} = \sqrt{\frac{8}{\pi}\frac{kT}{m}} .$$ (14.9)

Since v_{rms} is equal to $\sqrt{3kT/m}$ (Equation 13.38), the ratio of $\bar{v}$ to v_{rms} is

$$\frac{\bar{v}}{v_{rms}} = \sqrt{\frac{8}{3\pi}} = 0.921.$$

The average speed is about 8 percent less than the root-mean-square speed (see Figure 14.6). ∎

The second law of thermodynamics (to be pursued in the next section) is primarily a law of change. It states that the direction of spontaneous change within an isolated system is from an arrangement of lower probability to an arrangement of higher probability. Only if the arrangement is already one of maximal probability will no spontaneous change occur. Air molecules distributed uniformly in a room are (with respect to their position) in such a state of maximal probability. Similarly, the Maxwell-Boltzmann speed distribution is one of maximal probability. These are equilibrium situations, with no tendency for spontaneous change. Nevertheless, it is quite easy through external actions to depart from equilibrium and form less probable arrange-

Spontaneous change is
toward equilibrium
distributions

ments. Air can be pumped from one side of a room to another. If a barrier separating the two sides is punctured, the air rushes to equalize its distribution in space. Or particles of very high speed can be injected into a cold gas, changing the speed distribution away from the Maxwell-Boltzmann distribution. Energy exchanges quickly slow the high-speed particles and re-establish the equilibrium speed distribution.

It is worth noting that collisions and interaction play the same role for molecules as tray-shaking plays for coins. A stationary tray displaying all heads would stay that way even though the arrangement is improbable. If molecules were quiescent, once placed on one side of a room they would remain there. Or if they moved but did not interact, any improbable distribution

The role of molecular
interactions

of speeds would remain unaltered. Only because of continual molecular motion and interaction do the spontaneous changes predicted by the second law of thermodynamics actually occur.

14.3 Entropy and probability: the microscopic approach to the second law of thermodynamics

The second law in terms of
(1) probability
(2) disorder

There are a variety of ways in which the second law of thermodynamics can be stated, and we have encountered two of them so far: (1) For an isolated system, the direction of spontaneous change is from an arrangement of lesser probability

---

* It may be written $-\int_0^\infty u \, d(e^{-u})$. Integration by parts transforms it to $\int_0^\infty e^{-u} \, du$, which is equal to 1. Students with advanced training in mathematics may recognize the integral as a gamma function, $\Gamma(2)$, whose value is 1.

to an arrangement of greater probability. (2) For an isolated system, the direction of spontaneous change is from order to disorder. Like the conservation laws, the second law of thermodynamics applies only to a system free of external influences. For a system that is not isolated, there is no principle restricting its direction of change.

A third statement of the second law of thermodynamics makes use of a new concept called *entropy*. Entropy is a measure of the extent of disorder in a system or of the probability of the arrangement of the parts of a system. For greater probability, which means greater disorder, the entropy is higher. An arrangement of less probability (greater order) has less entropy. This means that the second law can be stated: (3) The entropy of an isolated system increases or remains the same.

(3) entropy

THE BOLTZMANN DEFINITION OF ENTROPY

Specifically, entropy, for which the usual symbol is S, is defined as Boltzmann's constant multiplied by the natural logarithm of the probability of any particular state of the system:

$$S = k \ln P. \tag{14.10}$$

The Boltzmann definition of entropy

The dimension of entropy is the same as the dimension of k, energy divided by temperature. Its SI unit is J/K; it is often expressed also in kcal/K. The appearance of Boltzmann's constant k as a constant of proportionality is a convenience in the mathematical theory of thermodynamics, but from a fundamental point of view, it is entirely arbitrary. The important aspect of the definition is the proportionality of the entropy to the logarithm of the probability P. To calculate P for a particular state could be very difficult. For this reason, another definition of entropy, introduced in Section 14.6, is more useful for most applications. However, the definition of Equation 14.10 is of fundamental significance because it reveals directly the role of probability in the second law of thermodynamics.

One important aspect of the entropy concept is that it is additive. For two or more systems brought together to form a single system, the entropy of the total is equal to the sum of the entropies of the parts. Probabilities, by contrast, are multiplicative. If the probability for one molecule to be in the left half of a container is $\frac{1}{2}$, the probability for two to be there is $\frac{1}{4}$, and the probability for three to congregate on one side is $\frac{1}{8}$. If two containers, each containing three molecules, are encompassed in a single system, the probability that the first three molecules are all on the left side of the first container *and* that the second three are on the left side of the second container is $\frac{1}{8} \times \frac{1}{8} = \frac{1}{64}$. On the other hand, the entropy of the combination is the sum of the entropies of the two parts. These properties of addition and multiplication are related to the logarithm appearing in Equation 14.10. For two systems,

$$S_{\text{total}} = k \ln P_1 P_2 = k \ln P_1 + k \ln P_2 = S_1 + S_2 \tag{14.11}$$

Entropies are additive

Because of this additive property, the third version of the second law stated previously can be generalized somewhat: (3') The total entropy of a set of interconnected systems increases or stays the same. If the entropy of one system decreases, the entropy of systems connected to it must increase by at least a compensating amount so that the sum of the individual entropies does not decrease.

In most applications, only *changes* of entropy are important. For this reason, it is permissible to use either absolute probability or relative probability in Equation 14.10. Let P be absolute probability and define relative probability P' by $P' = CP$, where C is any constant. Further define $S' = k \ln P'$. Then

$$S' = k \ln CP = k \ln C + k \ln P,$$

Relative probability is sufficient to define change of entropy

or

$$S' = K + S, \tag{14.12}$$

where $K = k \ln C$, another constant. Thus S and S' differ by a constant, and

$$dS' = dS. \tag{14.13}$$

Changes of entropy do not depend on the arbitrary constant C.

A PRIORI PROBABILITY

The probability appearing throughout this chapter, whether applied to coins, molecules, or complex systems, is a particular kind of probability called *a priori probability*. The exact nature of this probability must be understood if the second law is to be understood. The statement that physical systems change from less probable to more probable arrangements could seem anything but profound if the probability is regarded as an after-the-fact probability. If we decided that a uniform distribution of molecules in a box must be more probable than a nonuniform distribution because gas in a box is always observed to spread itself out evenly, the second law would be mere tautology, stating that systems tend to do what they are observed to do. In fact, the probability of the second law of thermodynamics is based on neither experience nor experiment, it is a before-the-fact (a priori) probability, based on counting the number of different ways in which a particular arrangement could be achieved. An a priori probability can be assigned to every conceivable arrangement of a system, whether or not the system or that arrangement of it has ever been observed. In practice there is no reason why the state of a system with the highest a priori probability need be the most frequently observed. Consider the case of the dedicated housewife. Almost every time an observant friend comes to call, he finds her house to be in perfect condition, nothing out of place, no dust in sight. He must conclude that for this house at least, the most probable state is a very orderly state, since that is what he most often observes. This is an after-the-fact probability. As the housewife and the student of physics know, the orderly state has a low a priori probability. Left to itself, the house will tend toward a disorderly state of higher a priori probability. A state of particularly high a priori probability for a house is one not often observed, a pile of rubble. Thus an arrangement of high probability (from here on we shall omit the modifier, a priori) need be neither frequently observed nor quickly achieved, but it is, according to the second law of thermodynamics, the inevitable destination of an isolated system.

A priori probability is determined by the number of possible arrangements of a system

■ EXAMPLE: Within a hypothetical container is a perfect vacuum. Ten molecules are admitted into the left half of the container. Later, 5 molecules are found in the left half and 5 in the right half. What has been the change of entropy from the first arrangement to the second arrangement? We may use relative probabilities taken from Table 14.3:

$$P'_2 = 252,$$
$$P'_1 = 1.$$

The change of entropy is

$$\Delta S = S'_2 - S'_1 = k \ln\left(\frac{252}{1}\right).$$

Note that the same result would be obtained using absolute probabilities, 252/1,024 and 1/1,024. Numerically, $\ln 252 = 5.53$, and

$$\Delta S = 7.6 \times 10^{-23} \text{ J/K.} \qquad ■$$

In comparison with other fundamental laws of nature, the second law of thermodynamics has two special features. First, it is not expressed by any mathematical equation. It specifies a direction of change but not a magnitude of change. The nearest we can come to an equation is the mathematical statement

$$\Delta S \geq 0. \qquad (14.14)$$

Mathematical statement of the second law

Every fundamental law of nature is characterized by remarkable generality, yet the second law of thermodynamics is unique among them (its second special feature) in that it finds direct application in a rich variety of settings: physical, biological, and human. In mentioning trays of coins, molecules of gas, and disorder in the house, we have touched only three of a myriad of applications. Entropy and the second law have contributed to discussion of the behavior of organisms, the flow of events in societies and economies, communication and information, and the history of the universe. In much of the physics and chemistry of macroscopic systems, the second law has found a use. Only at the submicroscopic level of single particles and single events is it of little importance. It is a startling and beautiful thought that an idea as simple as the natural trend from order to disorder should have such breadth of impact and power of application.

No law has wider generality

14.4   Heat flow and equipartition

The equipartition theorem and the zeroth law of thermodynamics can both be regarded as *consequences* of the second law of thermodynamics. Energy divides itself equally among the available degrees of freedom and temperatures tend toward equality because the resulting homogenized state of the molecules is the state of maximum disorder and maximum probability. The normal course of heat flow can also be understood in terms of the second law. Heat flow from a hotter to a cooler body is a process of energy transfer tending to equalize temperature, which increases disorder and thereby increases entropy. This idea will be expressed quantitatively in Section 14.6.

The second law underlies equipartition and equilibrium

The second law in terms of
(4) heat flow

Heat flow is so central to most applications of thermodynamics that the second law is sometimes stated in this restricted form: (4) Heat never flows spontaneously from a cooler to a hotter body. Notice that this is a statement about macroscopic behavior, whereas the more general and fundamental statements of the second law, which make use of the ideas of probability and disorder, refer to the submicroscopic structure of matter. Historically, the first version of the second law, advanced by Sadi Carnot in 1824, preceded the establishment of the submicroscopic basis of heat and temperature, in fact preceded the formulation of the first law of thermodynamics. Despite an incorrect view of heat and an incomplete view of energy, Carnot was able to advance the important principle that no heat engine (such as a steam engine) could operate with perfect efficiency. In modern terminology, Carnot's version of the second law is this: (5) In any device operating in a repetitive cycle heat flow out of one part of the system during one cycle cannot be transformed wholly into mechanical energy (via work) but must be accompanied by heat flow into a cooler part of the system. In brief, heat cannot be completely transformed to work by any cyclical machine.*

(5) heat engines

The consistency of Carnot's form of the second law with the general principle of entropy increase can best be appreciated by thinking in terms of order and disorder. The complete conversion of heat to work with no other change in a system would represent a transformation of disordered energy to ordered energy. This violates the second law of thermodynamics. As the discussion in Section 14.7 will show (see Figure 14.10), a *partial* conversion of heat to work is possible because a small heat flow into a cool region may increase the entropy there by more than the decrease of entropy produced by a larger heat flow out of a hot region. (At absolute zero, a collection of molecules has maximum order. Greater temperature produces greater disorder. Therefore, heat flow into a region increases its entropy, and heat flow out of a region decreases its entropy. This is expressed quantitatively by Equation 14.15.)

The reverse transformation, total conversion of work to heat, is not only possible but commonplace. Every time a moving object is brought to rest by friction, all of its ordered energy of bulk motion is converted to disordered energy of molecular motion. This is an entropy-increasing process allowed by the second law of thermodynamics. In general, the second law favors energy dissipation, the transformation of energy from available to unavailable form. Whenever we make a gain against the second law by increasing the order or the available energy in one part of a total system, we can be sure we have lost even more in another part of the system. Thanks to the constant input of energy from the sun, the earth remains a lively place, and we have nothing to fear from the homogenizing effect of the second law.

Energy dissipation increases
entropy

14.5   Perpetual motion

We have so far given five different versions of the second law and will add only

---

* In a noncyclical process, such as the flow of a hot gas through a rocket nozzle, heat *can* be transformed wholly to work. However, this is still an entropy-increasing process because of the increase of disorder associated with the net increase of volume of the gas.

one more. Worth noting in several of the formulations is the recurring emphasis on the negative. Entropy does *not* decrease. Heat does *not* flow spontaneously from a cooler to a hotter region. A cyclical device can *not* transform heat wholly to work. Our sixth version is also expressed in the negative: (6) Perpetual-motion machines cannot be constructed. This statement may sound more like a staff memorandum in the Patent Office than a fundamental law of nature. It may be both. In any event, it is certainly the latter because from it can be derived the spontaneous increase of probability, disorder, or entropy. It is specialized only in that it assumes some friction, however small, to be present to provide some energy dissipation. If we overlook the nearly frictionless motion of the planets in the solar system and the frictionless motion of single molecules in a gas, everything in between is encompassed.

The second law in terms of (6) perpetual motion

A perpetual-motion machine can be defined either as a closed system in which bulk motion persists indefinitely or as a continuously operating device whose output work provides its own input energy.* Some proposed perpetual-motion machines violate the law of energy conservation (the first law of thermodynamics). These are called perpetual-motion machines of the first kind. They can be elaborate and subtle but are less interesting than perpetual-motion machines of the second kind, hypothetical devices that conserve energy but violate the principle of entropy increase (the second law of thermodynamics).

Perpetual motion machines of the first kind violate the first law of thermodynamics

Those of the second kind violate the second law

As operating devices, perpetual-motion machines are the province of crackpot science and science fiction. As *inoperable* devices they have been of some significance in the development of science. Carnot may have been led to the second law of thermodynamics by his conviction that perpetual motion should be impossible. Arguments based on the impossibility of perpetual motion can be used to support Newton's third law of mechanics and Lenz's law of electromagnetic reaction, which will be discussed in Chapter 17. Any contemporary scientist with a speculative idea can subject it to at least one quick test: Is it consistent with the impossibility of perpetual motion?

Suppose that an inventor has just invented a handy portable coffee warmer (Figure 14.7). It takes the heat that flows from the coffee container and, by a method known only to him, converts this heat to work that is in turn expended in stirring the coffee. If the energy going back into the coffee is equal to the energy that leaks off as heat, the original temperature of the coffee will be maintained. Is it patentable? No, because it is a perpetual-motion machine of the second kind. Although it conserves energy, it performs the impossible task of maintaining a constant entropy in the face of dissipative forces that tend to increase entropy. Specifically, it violates Carnot's version of the second law (Number 5, page 622) because it is a cyclical device that converts heat wholly to work. Of course, it is also in direct violation of our sixth version of the second law.

One of the chief strengths of the second law is its power to constrain the behavior of complex systems without reference to any details. Like a corporate director, the second law rules the overall behavior of systems or interlocked sets of systems in terms of their total input and output and general function.

The global nature of the second law: Details are not required

---

* See Stanley W. Angrist, "Perpetual Motion Machines," *Scientific American*, January, 1968.

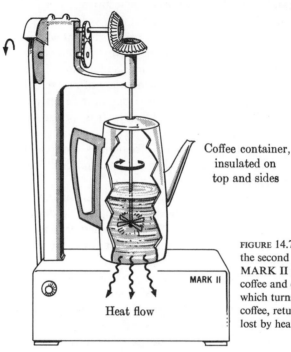

Coffee container,
insulated on
top and sides

MARK II

Heat flow

FIGURE 14.7   A perpetual-motion machine of
the second kind. The device labeled
MARK II receives heat energy from the
coffee and converts this to mechanical energy,
which turns a paddle wheel, agitating the
coffee, returning to the coffee the energy it
lost by heat flow. It is not patentable.

Given a proposed scheme for the operation of the automatic coffee warmer, it
could be quite a complicated matter to explain in terms of its detailed design
why it cannot work. Yet the second law reveals at once that no amount of
ingenuity can make it work.

14.6   Entropy and heat flow: the macroscopic approach to the second law of thermodynamics

The mathematical roots of thermodynamics go back to the work of Pierre
Laplace and other French scientists concerned with the caloric theory of heat
in the years around 1800, and even further back to the brilliant but forgotten
formulation of the kinetic theory of gases by Daniel Bernoulli in 1738. Not
until after 1850 did these and other strands come together to create the theory of
The rocky history of   thermodynamics in something like its modern form. No other great theory
thermodynamics   of physics has traveled such a rocky road to success over so many decades of
discovery, argumentation, buried insights, false turns, and rediscovery, its
paths diverging and finally rejoining in the grand synthesis of statistical mechanics that welded together the macroscopic and submicroscopic domains in
the latter part of the nineteenth century.

The first law is a pinnacle   In the long and complex history of thermodynamics, the generalization of
the principle of energy conservation to include heat stands as probably the
most significant single landmark. Joule's careful experiments on the mechanical
equivalent of heat in the 1840s not only established the first law of thermodynamics but also cleared the way for a full understanding of the second law,

provided a basis for an absolute temperature scale, and laid the groundwork for the submicroscopic mechanics of the kinetic theory. Progress in the half-century before Joule's work had been impeded by a pair of closely related difficulties: an incorrect view of the nature of heat and an incomplete understanding of the way in which heat engines provide work. To be sure, there had been important insights in this period, such as Carnot's statement of the second law of thermodynamics in 1824. But such progress as there was did not fit together into a single structure, nor did it provide a base on which to build. It was not until 1850, when the great significance of the general principle of energy conservation was appreciated by at least a few scientists, that Carnot's work was incorporated into a developing theoretical structure. The way was cleared for a decade of rapid progress. In the 1850s, the first and second laws of thermodynamics were first stated as general unifying principles, the kinetic theory was rediscovered and refined, the concepts of heat and temperature were given submicroscopic as well as macroscopic definitions, and the full significance of the ideal-gas law was understood.

Like heat and temperature, entropy was first given a macroscopic definition and then later a molecular definition. Being a much subtler concept than either heat or temperature (in that it does not directly impinge on our senses), entropy was defined only after its need in the developing theory of thermodynamics became obvious. Heat and temperature were familiar ideas refined and revised for the needs of quantitative understanding. Entropy was a wholly new idea, formally introduced and arbitrarily named when it proved to be useful in expressing the second law of thermodynamics in quantitative form. As a useful but unnamed quantity, entropy entered the writings of both Kelvin and Clausius in the early 1850s. Finally, in 1865 it was formally recognized and christened "entropy" (after a Greek word for transformation) by Clausius. Entropy, as he saw it, measured the potentiality of a system for transformation.

Entropy is not an intuitive idea

THE CLAUSIUS DEFINITION OF ENTROPY

The proportionality of entropy to the logarithm of an intrinsic probability for the arrangement of a system, as expressed by Equation 14.10, was stated first by Ludwig Boltzmann in 1877. This pinnacle of achievement in what had come to be called statistical mechanics fashioned the last great thermodynamics link between the large- and small-scale worlds. Although we now regard Boltzmann's definition based on the molecular viewpoint as the more fundamental, the earlier macroscopic definition of entropy given by Clausius is of great importance and, in most applications, of more practical value. Clausius expressed entropy in terms of the two already familiar concepts, heat and temperature. He wrote

$$dS = \frac{dQ}{T} \; ; \tag{14.15}$$

The Clausius definition of entropy

the change of entropy of any part of a system is equal to the increment of heat added to that part of the system divided by its absolute temperature at the moment the heat is added, provided the change is from one equilibrium state to another. For heat gain, dQ is positive and entropy increases. For heat loss, dQ is negative and entropy decreases. How much entropy change is produced

*Absolute temperature must
be used*

by adding or subtracting heat depends on the temperature. Since the temperature T appears in the denominator in Equation 14.15, a lower temperature enables a given increment of heat to produce a greater entropy change. Note that Equation 14.15 is correct only if the absolute temperature, not the Celsius or Fahrenheit temperature, is used.

Why a differential definition?

*1. Only entropy change
matters*

2. No such thing as total heat

Equation 14.15 defines not the entropy itself but the change of entropy. There are several reasons for this differential expression. For one reason, the absolute value of entropy is usually irrelevant. Only the change from one state to another matters. Another more important reason is that there is no such thing as "total heat." Since heat is energy transfer (by molecular collisions), it is a dynamic quantity measured only in processes of change. An increment of heat dQ can be gained or lost by part of a system, but it is meaningless to refer to the total heat Q stored in that part.* (This was the great insight about heat afforded by the discovery of the general principle of energy conservation in the 1840s.) What is stored is internal energy, a quantity that can be increased by mechanical work as well as by heat flow. Finally, it should be

3. Temperature is a variable

remarked that because of the variability of temperature, Clausius's definition necessarily refers to infinitesimal change. Since the symbol T in Equation 14.15 denotes the temperature at which heat is added, T has a fixed value only for an infinitesimal addition of heat. For finite heat flow, the entropy change is

$$\Delta S = \int \frac{dQ}{T} ; \qquad (14.16)$$

at the limits of the integration, the temperature takes on its initial and final values, T_1 and T_2.

The statement below Equation 14.15 limits the validity of this definition to changes occurring between equilibrium states. This is an important restriction, and it requires some discussion because it may at first appear that "equilibrium" and "change" are contradictory ideas. Indeed, an isolated system in equilibrium will not change, but a part of a system in equilibrium may be forced to change by outside influences. Gas in a cylinder (Figure 13.7), for example, may be in equilibrium. However, it may be forced to change its state by the

*Reconciliation of
equilibrium and change*

motion of a piston or by the addition of heat. If these outside influences act slowly enough, the change occurs through a series of equilibrium states. Imagine a slow compression of the gas, during which the gas pressure and temperature continuously adjust to the changing volume. If at any moment during the compression the piston were to stop moving, the gas would be in equilibrium at that point and have no tendency for spontaneous change. This is the idea of equilibrium during change. By contrast, if the piston were quite suddenly pulled out, thereby doubling the volume available to the gas, the change would not be through equilibrium states. After the piston stopped moving, the gas would be experiencing spontaneous change as it expanded to fill the larger volume. Only for changes through equilibrium states can the Clausius definition

---

* Since there is no heat *function* Q, there is no exact mathematical differential dQ. The quantity dQ that appears here is called an *inexact differential*. In some texts it is written $\bar{d}Q$. The subtleties of this concept are best left to more advanced texts.

of entropy be applied. There is an exception to this rule, however. If the net effect of an actual nonequilibrium change can be duplicated by a hypothetical series of equilibrium changes, the hypothetical route can be used to calculate the actual change of entropy. The meaning of this exception will be made clear by example in the next section.

★RELATIONSHIP OF THE MICROSCOPIC AND MACROSCOPIC DEFINITIONS OF ENTROPY

The two definitions of entropy, Equations 14.10 and 14.15, do not at first sight appear to have anything in common. To shed some light on their equivalence, we consider an idealized system of N molecules, each capable of vibrational motion in any of a number of equally spaced energy states. Such molecules would, in reality, also rotate and move from place to place, but for this discussion it is permissible to ignore these other modes of motion. For three such molecules, the overall state of the system can be represented by the triple-ladder diagram of Figure 14.8, in which each rung corresponds to a vibrational energy state. Dots on the three lowest rungs would indicate that the system possesses no internal energy. The dots pictured on the second, third, and bottom rungs indicate that the system has a total of five units of internal energy, two units possessed by the first molecule, three by the second, and none by the third. The intrinsic probability associated with any given total energy is proportional to the number of different ways in which that energy can be divided. This is here a probability of *energy* distribution, not a probability of spatial distribution. However, the reasoning is much the same as in Section 14.2. There the intrinsic (a priori) probability for a distribution of molecules in space was taken to be proportional to the number of different ways in which that distribution could be obtained. To give another example, the probability of throwing 7 with a pair of dice is greater than the probability of throwing 2 because there are more different ways to throw 7 than there are to throw 2.

Table 14.4 enumerates all the ways in which up to five units of energy can be divided among our three idealized molecules. The triplets of numbers in the

An example: N vibrating molecules

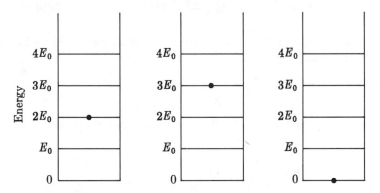

FIGURE 14.8   Idealized energy diagram for a system of three molecules, each with equally spaced energy states. Each ladder depicts the possible energies of a particular molecule, and the heavy dot specifies the actual energy of that molecule.

TABLE 14.4   INTERNAL ENERGY DISTRIBUTION FOR AN IDEALIZED SYSTEM OF THREE MOLECULES

Total Energy (E/E_0)	Distribution of Energy			Number of Ways to Distribute Energy
0	000			1
1	100	010	001	3
2	200	020	002	
	110	101	011	6
3	300	030	003	
	210	201	012	
	120	102	021	
	111			10
4	400	040	004	
	310	301	031	
	130	103	013	
	220	202	022	
	211	121	112	15
5	500	050	005	
	410	401	041	
	140	104	014	
	320	302	032	
	230	203	023	
	311	131	113	
	122	212	221	21

second column indicate the occupied rungs of the three energy ladders. Either by trial and error or by more sophisticated means, one may develop a formula for the numbers in the third column. Since these are relative probabilities, we use the notation P' and write

$$P' = \frac{1}{2}\left(\frac{E}{E_0} + 1\right)\left(\frac{E}{E_0} + 2\right).$$ (14.17)

For total energy much greater than the quantum unit of energy ($E/E_0 \gg 1$), Equation 14.17 may be approximated by

$$P' \cong \frac{1}{2}\left(\frac{E}{E_0}\right)^2.$$ (14.18)

Similar arguments show that for N molecules, the number of ways to distribute energy E, when E is much greater than E_0, is

A priori probability of energy E

$$P' \cong \frac{1}{(N-1)!}\left(\frac{E}{E_0}\right)^{N-1}.$$ (14.19)

Since only *relative* probability matters in the definition of entropy, we may drop the constant factors $(N-1)!$ and E_0^{N-1} and write

$$P = E^{N-1}$$ (14.20)

as another expression for the a priori probability associated with dividing energy E among the vibrational modes of N molecules. Therefore, the Boltzmann definition of entropy for the system yields

$$S = k \ln P = k(N - 1) \ln E. \qquad (14.21)$$

The Boltzmann entropy

To compare the Boltzmann and Clausius definitions of entropy, we must differentiate Equation 14.21. The result of the differentiation is

$$dS = \frac{k(N - 1)\, dE}{E}. \qquad (14.22)$$

Now the vibrational mode of a molecule acquires, on the average, an energy equal to kT.* For N molecules, vibrational energy and temperature are related by

$$E = NkT. \qquad (14.23)$$

Also, since we are ignoring other modes of motion, any heat is added to the energy E, and

$$dE = dQ. \qquad (14.24)$$

Substituting from Equations 14.23 and 14.24 in Equation 14.22 yields

$$dS = \frac{N - 1}{N} \frac{dQ}{T}. \qquad (14.25)$$

The Boltzmann entropy change

This differs from the Clausius definition of entropy only by the factor $(N - 1)/N$. However, Clausius's macroscopic definition is valid only for systems in which N is large. Therefore, we may replace $(N - 1)/N$ by 1 and obtain

$$dS = \frac{dQ}{T},$$

It is equivalent to the Clausius entropy for large E and large N

the Clausius definition derived from the Boltzmann definition for the simple system under study, provided (1) the total energy greatly exceeds the quantum unit of energy and (2) the number of molecules is large.

14.7   Some applications of the second law

HEAT FLOW

That heat flows spontaneously only from a warmer to a cooler place is a fact that can itself be regarded as a special form of the second law of thermodynamics. Alternatively, the direction of heat flow can be related to the general principle of entropy increase with the help of the macroscopic definition of entropy. If body 1 at temperature T_1 loses a small increment of heat ΔQ, its entropy change —a decrease—is

$$\Delta S_1 = - \frac{\Delta Q}{T_1}.$$

If this heat is wholly transferred to body 2 at temperature T_2, its entropy gain is

---

* See the discussion on page 582.

$$\Delta S_2 = \frac{\Delta Q}{T_2}.$$

The total entropy change of the system (bodies 1 and 2) is the sum of the individual entropy changes:

Entropy change in heat flow

$$\Delta S = \Delta S_1 + \Delta S_2 = \Delta Q \left(\frac{1}{T_2} - \frac{1}{T_1} \right). \qquad (14.26)$$

This entropy change must, according to the second law, be positive if the heat transfer occurs spontaneously. It is obvious, algebraically, from Equation 14.26 that this requirement implies that the temperature T_1 must be greater than the temperature T_2. In short, heat flows from the warmer to the cooler body. In the process, the cooler body gains *energy* equal to that lost by the warmer body but gains *entropy* greater than that lost by the warmer body. When equality of temperature is reached, heat flow in *either* direction would decrease the total entropy. Therefore, it does not occur.

MIXING

Suppose that a substance of mass M_1, specific heat C_1, and initial temperature T_1 is brought into thermal contact—by mixing for example—with another substance of mass M_2, specific heat C_2, and initial temperature T_2 (Figure 14.9). After thermal equilibrium is established, both are at temperature T_f. It is of interest to calculate the entropy change in the process. Let T denote the variable temperature of substance 1, and let T' denote the variable temperature of substance 2. At any time while equilibrium is being established, infinitesimal increments of heat are given by

$$dQ_1 = M_1 C_1 \, dT, \qquad (14.27)$$

$$dQ_2 = M_2 C_2 \, dT'. \qquad (14.28)$$

(For the warmer substance, losing heat, dQ is negative.) Since only heat energy is involved, the statement of energy conservation is

$$dQ_1 = -dQ_2. \qquad (14.29)$$

We assume constant specific heat so that $\Delta Q = MC \, \Delta T$ for the finite change. Then energy conservation implies the equality

$$M_1 C_1 (T_1 - T_f) = M_2 C_2 (T_f - T_2).$$

This equation may be solved for T_f:

Equilibrium temperature after mixing

$$T_f = \frac{M_1 C_1 T_1 + M_2 C_2 T_2}{M_1 C_1 + M_2 C_2}. \qquad (14.30)$$

The final temperature is a particular weighted mean of the two initial temperatures.

During the process of heat transfer, an increment of entropy change for substance 1 is

$$dS_1 = \frac{dQ_1}{T} = \frac{M_1 C_1 \, dT}{T}. \qquad (14.31)$$

FIGURE 14.9   Examples of mixing: (a) two fluids; (b) solid and fluid.

(Equation 14.27 has been used.) Similarly,

$$dS_2 = \frac{dQ_2}{T'} = \frac{M_2 C_2 \, dT'}{T'} .$$ (14.32)

The total entropy change is

$$\Delta S = \int dS_1 + \int dS_2$$

$$= M_1 C_1 \int_{T_1}^{T_f} \frac{dT}{T} + M_2 C_2 \int_{T_2}^{T_f} \frac{dT'}{T'} .$$

Entropy change in mixing

The integrals are elementary, and the final answer for the entropy change is

$$\Delta S = M_1 C_1 \ln \left(\frac{T_f}{T_1}\right) + M_2 C_2 \ln \left(\frac{T_f}{T_2}\right) .$$ (14.33)

Note that one of the two terms will be negative and one positive, because one temperature ratio will be larger than 1 and the other temperature ratio smaller than 1. The positive term will always be larger so that ΔS will be positive.

■ EXAMPLE: One kg of water at 20 °C is mixed with 2 kg of water at 80 °C. What final temperature does the mixture reach? What entropy change results from the mixing? With $M_1 = 1$ kg, $M_2 = 2$ kg, $T_1 = 293$ K, $T_2 = 353$ K, and $C_1 = C_2 = 1$ kcal/kg K, Equation 14.30 yields

$$T_f = 333 \text{ K} = 60 \,°\text{C}.$$

Although Equation 14.30 is valid for any temperature scale, it is a good idea to form the habit of using the kelvin scale. Many thermodynamic equations, such as Equations 14.31–14.33, are valid only when absolute temperature is used.   To find the entropy change for this example, substitute numbers in Equation 14.33:

$$\Delta S = 1 \text{ kcal/K} \times \ln \left(\tfrac{333}{293}\right) + 2 \text{ kcal/K} \times \ln \left(\tfrac{333}{353}\right),$$

$$= (1 \times 0.1280 - 2 \times 0.0584) \text{ kcal/K},$$

$$= 0.0112 \text{ kcal/K}.$$

Because of near cancellation of the two terms in Equation 14.33, careful numerical work is required. It is left as a problem to derive from Equation 14.33 a more useful approximate formula, one that is valid for small fractional changes of absolute temperature:

$$\Delta S = \frac{\Delta Q \, |T_2 - T_1|}{2T_f^2}, \tag{14.34}$$

where $\Delta Q = M_1 C_1 |T_1 - T_f| = M_2 C_2 |T_f - T_2| =$ heat transferred from one substance to the other. ∎

HEAT ENGINES

A heat engine is, in simplest terms, a device that transforms heat to mechanical work. Alone and without other changes in the system, such a transformation is impossible. It is an entropy-decreasing process that violates the second law of thermodynamics. This does not, of course, mean that heat engines are impossible. Gasoline engines, diesel engines, steam engines, jet engines, and rocket engines are all devices that transform heat to work. They do so by incorporating within the same system a mechanism of entropy increase that more than offsets the entropy decrease associated with the production of work. The simple example of heat flow with which this section began shows that one part of a system can easily lose entropy if another part gains more. In almost all transformations of any complexity, and in particular in those manipulated by man for some practical purpose, entropy gain and entropy loss occur side by side, with the total gain inevitably exceeding the total loss.

  The normal mechanism of entropy gain in a cyclical heat engine is heat flow. Carnot was the first to appreciate the great significance of heat flow *out* of a steam engine. Only some of the heat put into the engine can be transformed to work; the rest must be transferred from a hotter to a cooler place.* The actual mechanism of entropy increase varies from one heat engine to another and could, for some engines, be quite complicated and indirect. Here, let us

Simple assumptions define an idealized heat engine

make three simplifying assumptions: (1) The engine is cyclical. After any whole number of cycles, the engine itself is back in the same state in which it started, and its entropy is the same. This means that any entropy change of the total system, engine + environment, must occur in the environment. (The "environment" may include things sometimes considered to be part of the engine, such as the boiler of a steam engine or the exhaust manifold of a gasoline engine. For this discussion, all noncyclical parts are defined to be part of the environment.) (2) All entropy changes are associated with heat flow. This will be true, in particular, if all changes take place through equilibrium states. (3) Heat input to the engine occurs at a single fixed temperature T_1, and heat output occurs at a single fixed temperature T_2. With these assumptions, it is possible to discover, in a very simple way, what fraction of the total energy supplied by fuel can be transformed into usable work. This fraction is called the efficiency of the engine.

---

* See Riley D. Woodson, "Cooling Towers," *Scientific American*, May, 1971.

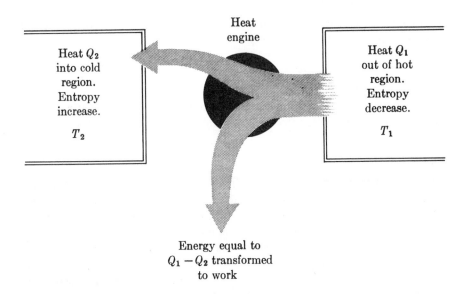

Heat
engine

Heat Q_2
into cold
region.
Entropy
increase.

T_2

Heat Q_1
out of hot
region.
Entropy
decrease.

T_1

Energy equal to
$Q_1 - Q_2$ transformed
to work

FIGURE 14.10   Schematic diagram of the functioning of a heat engine. Energy
is conserved, and entropy must not decrease.

Refer to Figure 14.10, which shows schematically the process of partial
transformation of heat to work during one cycle of the engine. The environment
consists of a hotter region, at temperature T_1, from which flows an increment of
heat Q_1, and a cooler region, at temperature T_2, into which flows heat Q_2.
The output work is W. (For notational simplicity, Δ symbols are omitted.)
The first and second laws of thermodynamics applied to this idealized heat
engine can be given simple mathematical expression:

1. Energy conservation: $Q_1 = Q_2 + W,$ (14.35)

The basic laws for this engine

2. Entropy increase: $\Delta S = \dfrac{Q_2}{T_2} - \dfrac{Q_1}{T_1} > 0.$ (14.36)

From Equation 14.36 follows the inequality

$$\frac{Q_2}{Q_1} > \frac{T_2}{T_1}.$$ (14.37)

Equation 14.35 may be rewritten in the form

$$\frac{W}{Q_1} = 1 - \frac{Q_2}{Q_1}.$$ (14.38)

The ratio on the left, (output work)/(input heat), is defined to be the efficiency η *Definition of efficiency*
of the engine. Substituting from Formula 14.37 in Equation 14.38 gives, for
the efficiency,

$$\eta < 1 - \frac{T_2}{T_1}.$$ (14.39)

If the heat engine were "perfect"—free of friction and other dissipative effects—

the entropy would remain constant rather than increase. Then Formula 14.39 would be replaced by the equality

Maximum efficiency

$$\eta_{\max} = \frac{W_{\max}}{Q_1} = 1 - \frac{T_2}{T_1}.$$
(14.40)

If the temperatures T_1 and T_2 are nearly the same, the efficiency is, at best, very low. If T_2 is near absolute zero, the theoretical efficiency can be close to 1.

Thermal pollution

Even something as complicated as a large electric power plant, whether conventional or nuclear, can be approximated as a simple heat engine of the kind just discussed. Its input heat is supplied at a fairly well-defined temperature T_1 by burning coal, oil, or gas of by fissioning uranium. Its work goes into turning electric generators. Its output heat flows into the atmosphere or into circulating water at a temperature T_2 that is greater than the normal ambient temperature of the air or water. The heat Q_2 exhausted into the environment is sometimes called "thermal pollution." Unlike the pollution of the environment by noxious substances, which can, in principle, be completely eliminated, *An unavoidable implication* thermal pollution is an inevitable concomitant of power generation—an *of the second law* unavoidable implication of the second law of thermodynamics. Heat exhausted into water is the more serious problem because of its effect on aquatic life. In the larger urban areas, heat exhausted into the atmosphere may also be of significance because of its effect on local weather.

Chemical pollution from nuclear power plants is negligible. However, the change from fossil fuel to nuclear fuel cannot circumvent the second law of thermodynamics. In fact, the nuclear power plant is a somewhat greater source of thermal pollution than is the conventional power plant. There are two reasons for this. One is that heat flow from the nuclear plant is into water instead of *Nuclear power plants have* into the air. The other reason is that the nuclear power plant is intrinsically less *lower efficiency than* efficient. The nuclear fuel "burns" at a lower temperature than fossil fuel *fossil-fuel plants* burns. Accordingly, in Equation 14.39 or 14.40, T_1 is less, the ratio T_2/T_1 is closer to 1, and the efficiency η is less for the nuclear power plant.

There is only one "cure" for thermal pollution. That is spreading the *The only cure is dilution* exhausted heat Q_2 over a sufficiently great mass of air or water that the rise of temperature of the environment above its normal level is not significant.

REFRIGERATORS

The modern marvels of technology that populate our present world—automobiles, television, airplanes, radar, pocket radios—all rest ultimately on basic principles of physics. Nevertheless, they are seldom instructive as illustrations of fundamental laws because the chain of connection from their practical function to the underlying principles is complex and sophisticated. The refrigerator is such a device. Despite its complexity of detail, however, it is worth considering in general terms. Because it transfers heat from a cooler to a warmer place, the refrigerator appears at first glance to violate the second law of thermodynamics. The fact that it must not do so allows us to draw an important conclusion about

the minimum expenditure of energy required to run it. The analysis is quite
similar to that for a heat engine. Suppose that the mechanism of the refrigerator is required to transfer heat out of the refrigerator at the rate dQ_1/dt.
If heat were added to the warmer room at only this same rate, entropy would
decrease. Some other contribution to entropy change must be occurring in
order that the total change may be positive and thereby in harmony with the
second law. This extra contribution comes from the degradation of the input
energy that powers the refrigerator. The energy supplied by electricity or by
combustion of gas eventually reaches the surrounding room as heat. Call the
external power P (energy per unit time) and the heat flow to the room dQ_2/dt.
The interior of the refrigerator is at temperature T_1 and the room is at temperature T_2. This notation is summarized in the energy flow diagram of Figure 14.11.
Note in this example that the cyclical device whose entropy does not change is
the mechanism of the refrigerator—its motor, pump, and pipes. The space
inside the refrigerator, along with the air in the room and the external power
source, is part of the environment.

*"Uphill" heat transfer alone
would decrease entropy*

The equations of energy and entropy for the refrigerator are similar to those
for the heat engine.

1. Energy conservation: $$P = \frac{dQ_2}{dt} - \frac{dQ_1}{dt}.$$ (14.41)

*Basic laws for the
refrigerator*

2. Entropy change: $$\frac{dS}{dt} = \frac{1}{T_2}\frac{dQ_2}{dt} - \frac{1}{T_1}\frac{dQ_1}{dt}.$$ (14.42)

We take both derivatives, dQ_1/dt and dQ_2/dt, to be positive. This accounts
for the negative signs on the right sides of Equations 14.41 and 14.42. Since
dS/dt must be zero or greater, Equation 14.42 implies

$$\frac{dQ_2/dt}{dQ_1/dt} \geq \frac{T_2}{T_1}.$$ (14.43)

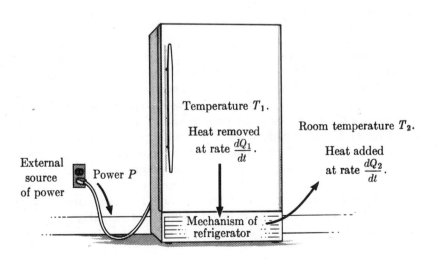

Temperature T_1.

Heat removed
at rate $\frac{dQ_1}{dt}$.

Room temperature T_2.

Heat added
at rate $\frac{dQ_2}{dt}$.

External
source
of power

Power P

Mechanism of
refrigerator

Equation 14.41 may be rewritten in the form

$$P = \frac{dQ_1}{dt}\left[\frac{dQ_2/dt}{dQ_1/dt} - 1\right].$$ (14.44)

Now substitute from Formula 14.43 in Equation 14.44, which gives

Necessary input power $$P \geq \frac{dQ_1}{dt}\left[\frac{T_2}{T_1} - 1\right].$$ (14.45)

The right side of this inequality gives the minimum external power input required to transfer heat at the rate dQ_1/dt "uphill" from temperature T_1 to temperature T_2. As might be expected, the input-power requirement increases as the temperature difference increases. If the temperature T_1 is near absolute zero, as it is in a helium liquefier, the external energy expended is much greater than the heat transferred.

The real beauty of the result expressed by Equation 14.45 is its generality for all refrigerators regardless of their construction and mode of operation. The input power P could be supplied by an electric motor, a gas flame, or a hand crank. In the small-scale world, our inability to observe precise features of individual events is one reason for the special importance of conservation laws. In the large-scale world, the elaborate complexity of many systems is one reason for the special importance of the second law of thermodynamics. Like the conservation laws, it provides an overall constraint on the system as a whole.

AVAILABLE ENERGY

Another view of the second law: Available energy decreases

In many applications of the second law, the concept of available energy* is the easiest key to understanding. In general, the trend of nature toward greater disorder is a trend toward less available energy. A jet plane before takeoff has a certain store of available energy in its fuel. While it is accelerating down the runway, a part of the energy expended is going into bulk kinetic energy (ordered energy) and another part is going into heat that is eventually dissipated into unavailable energy. As the jet climbs, part of the energy from the fuel is going into gravitational potential energy. At constant cruising speed, all of the energy of the burning fuel goes to heat the air. Thermodynamically speaking, the net result of a flight is the total loss of the available energy originally present in the fuel. A rocket in free space operates with greater efficiency. Being free of air friction, it continues to accelerate as long as the fuel is burning. When its engine stops, a certain fraction (normally a small fraction) of the original available energy in the fuel remains available in the kinetic energy of the vehicle. This energy may be "stored" indefinitely in the orbital motion of the space vehicle. If it re-enters the atmosphere, however, this energy, too, is transformed into the disordered and unavailable form of internal energy of the air. To prepare for the next launching, more rocket fuel must be manufactured. The energy expended in the chemical factory that does this job is inevitably more than the energy stored in the fuel that is produced.

---

* The phrase "available energy" is used differently here than in Section 12.6.

In general, the effect of civilization is to encourage the action of the second law of thermodynamics. Technology greatly accelerates the rate of increase of entropy in man's immediate environment. Fortunately, the available energy arriving each day from the sun exceeds by a very large factor the energy degraded by man's activity in a day. Fortunately, too, nature, with no help from man, stores in usable form some of the sun's energy—for periods of months or years in the cycle of evaporation, precipitation, and drainage; for decades or centuries in lumber; for millennia in coal and oil. In addition, the earth is richly supplied with nuclear fuel, which stores the energy of long-dead suns that burned billions of years ago. In time, if man depletes the long-term stored supply of available energy, he may have to rely more heavily on the short-term stores and perhaps also devise new storage methods to supplement those of nature.

Technology accelerates entropy increase

14.8   The behavior of gases

The expansion and compression of gases, with and without heat flow, is of importance in meteorology and also in many devices—jet engines, internal-combustion engines, vacuum pumps, and refrigeration coils, to name a few. In this section we shall examine special aspects of the behavior of gases. We assume the validity of the ideal-gas law, which is frequently an excellent approximation.

GASES AT CONSTANT VOLUME AND CONSTANT PRESSURE

For any changes of volume and internal energy of a gas (neglecting changes of bulk energy), the law of energy conservation in differential form is

$$dU = dQ + dW. \qquad (14.46)$$

This is a common form of the first law of thermodynamics (equivalent to Equation 13.56). The change in internal energy of the gas, dU, is equal to the heat flow, dQ (positive for inflow, negative for outflow), plus the increment of work (positive for work done *on* the gas, negative for work done *by* the gas). Ideal monatomic and diatomic gases were considered in Sections 13.10 and 13.14. Here we consider ideal gases in general.

If a gas is held at constant volume, no work is done ($dW = 0$), and

$$dU = dQ. \qquad (14.47)$$

The first law at constant volume

Under these conditions,

$$dQ = C_v M\, dT, \qquad (14.48)$$

where M is the mass of the gas and T is temperature. This equation is, in effect, the defining equation of C_v, the specific heat at constant volume (see Equation 13.40). Because of Equation 14.47, we may also write

$$dU = C_v M\, dT. \qquad (14.49)$$

Internal energy related to temperature

The important thing about Equation 14.49 is that it remains valid even if the volume is not constant. The internal energy per unit mass of an ideal gas depends only on its temperature, not on its pressure or volume. Equation 14.49 provides the link between internal energy and temperature, valid under all circumstances for an ideal gas.

Consideration of heating at constant pressure also leads to a useful equation of wider validity involving specific heats. For an expanding gas, $dW = -P\,dV$ (Equation 13.68), and Equation 14.46 may be rewritten as

The first law for changing volume

$$dQ = dU + P\,dV. \tag{14.50}$$

Consider in turn the three terms in this equation. If the pressure is constant,

$$dQ = C_p M\,dT, \tag{14.51}$$

the defining equation of C_p, the specific heat at constant pressure. The second term, dU, is given in general by Equation 14.49. The third term, at constant pressure, is (from the ideal-gas law)

$$P\,dV = Nk\,dT = \frac{M}{m}\,k\,dT. \tag{14.52}$$

To the right of the second equal sign, the ratio M/m of total mass to the mass of a single molecule replaces N, the number of molecules. Substituting from Equations 14.51, 14.49, and 14.52 in Equation 14.50 gives

$$C_p M\,dT = C_v M\,dT + M\,\frac{k}{m}\,dT.$$

Cancellation of common factors leaves

C_p and C_v related for an ideal gas

$$C_p = C_v + \frac{k}{m}. \tag{14.53}$$

For any ideal gas, the specific heats at constant pressure and at constant volume differ by a constant. An equivalent expression in terms of molar specific heats was stated by Equation 13.75.

ISOTHERMAL EXPANSION

Isothermal expansion is, by definition, expansion without change of temperature. For an ideal gas, constant temperature means constant internal energy. Therefore, in the isothermal expansion of an ideal gas, $dU = 0$, and

The first law if $dU = 0$

$$dQ = -dW. \tag{14.54}$$

Heat energy must be added to the gas to compensate for the work done by the gas (see Figure 14.12). In the process, the entropy of the gas increases. The total entropy change is

$$\Delta S = \int \frac{dQ}{T} = \frac{\Delta Q}{T}, \tag{14.55}$$

where ΔQ is the total heat added during the expansion. The integral in Equation 14.55 may be evaluated at once because T is constant. Note that the positive value of ΔS does not follow directly from the second law of thermodynamics, for the expanding gas is not an isolated system. For isothermal compression, the entropy of the gas decreases.

The submicroscopic view affords insight into the reason for the change of entropy. At constant temperature, the expanding gas experiences no change of a

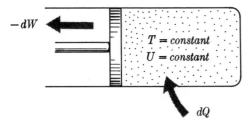

FIGURE 14.12   Isothermal expansion of an ideal gas. The heat input, dQ, is equal to the work output, $-dW$.

priori probability associated with the energy or velocity of its molecules. However, there is a change of position probability because of the changing volume. Larger volume means greater disorder of position and, therefore, greater entropy. Compression to smaller volume means greater order of position and, therefore, less entropy.

For constant temperature, the ideal-gas law gives Boyle's law:

$$PV = NkT = constant. \tag{14.56}$$

A graph of pressure vs volume [Figure 14.13(a)] is a hyperbola, $P \sim V^{-1}$. To evaluate the entropy change, we must relate the added heat to the properties of the gas. From Equation 14.54, the total heat and total work are equal in magnitude:

$$\Delta Q = -\Delta W. \tag{14.57}$$

The total work is given by

$$\Delta W = -\int P \, dV. \tag{14.58}$$

Making use of Equation 14.56, we then have, for the total added heat,

$$\Delta Q = NkT \int \frac{dV}{V}. \tag{14.59}$$

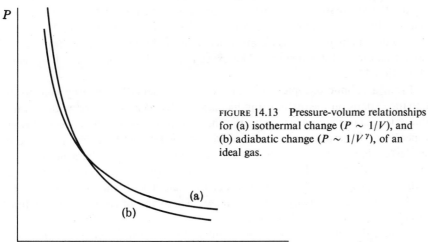

FIGURE 14.13   Pressure-volume relationships for (a) isothermal change ($P \sim 1/V$), and (b) adiabatic change ($P \sim 1/V^{\gamma}$), of an ideal gas.

The constant factor NkT is taken outside the integral. The limits of integration are the initial volume V_1 and the final volume V_2. Evaluation of the integral yields

*Heat added in isothermal
expansion*

$$\Delta Q = NkT \ln \left(\frac{V_2}{V_1}\right). \tag{14.60}$$

Finally, substituting this expression for ΔQ in Equation 14.55 gives, for the change of entropy,

$$\Delta S = Nk \ln \left(\frac{V_2}{V_1}\right). \tag{14.61}$$

*Entropy change in isothermal
expansion*

Because of Boyle's law, the change of entropy may also be written

$$\Delta S = Nk \ln \left(\frac{P_1}{P_2}\right). \tag{14.62}$$

Note, too, that in either of these expressions, Nk could be replaced by nR, the number of moles times the gas constant.

ADIABATIC EXPANSION

In adiabatic change (Figure 14.14), there is no heat flow. Such change is approximated if a system is well insulated or if the change occurs quickly enough that there is not time for much heat flow. The change must not, however, be abrupt, for we assume, as we did for isothermal expansion, that the change occurs through equilibrium states, making the Clausius formula, $dS = dQ/T$, valid.

Since $dQ = 0$, adiabatic expansion is characterized by no entropy change:

$$\Delta S = 0. \tag{14.63}$$

Without heat flow, the energy-conservation equation, Equation 14.46, becomes

The first law if $dQ = 0$

$$dU = dW. \tag{14.64}$$

The internal energy decreases as work is done by the expanding gas. Accompanying the decrease of internal energy is a decrease of temperature (see Equation 14.49). Therefore, the product of pressure and volume decreases. Since volume increases, pressure must decrease, and by a greater factor than it does for isothermal expansion. (The exact relation between P and V appears in Equation 14.72.)

*Adiabatic change: insight
from the submicroscopic view*

From a submicroscopic point of view, the absence of entropy change in adiabatic expansion means that the increase of *disorder* associated with greater volume is exactly compensated by the increase in *order* associated with lower temperature. If for a given increase in volume, the temperature were to decrease even faster than it does for adiabatic expansion, there would be a net gain in order and a decrease of entropy. If the temperature were to decrease more slowly (or not at all), the extra disorder associated with the volume increase would win out, and entropy would increase. These are, of course, only qualitative guides, not rules of calculation.

To find the relation between pressure and volume in adiabatic change, we

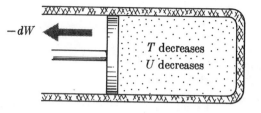

FIGURE 14.14   Adiabatic expansion. There is no heat transfer. The output work is equal to the decrease of internal energy (Equation 14.64).

begin with the energy equality, Equation 14.64. In this we may set

$$dU = C_v N m\ dT, \tag{14.65}$$

which is the same as Equation 14.49 except for the replacement of the total mass M by Nm, the number of molecules times the mass of a molecule; and

$$dW = -P\ dV.$$

With these substitutions, the energy equation reads

$$C_v N m\ dT + P\ dV = 0. \tag{14.66}$$

To eliminate the variable T in favor of the variables P and V, differentiate the ideal-gas equation $PV = NkT$. The result is

$$P\ dV + V\ dP = Nk\ dT. \tag{14.67}$$

Substituting from Equation 14.67 for dT in Equation 14.66 gives

$$\frac{C_v m}{k}(P\ dV + V\ dP) + P\ dV = 0. \tag{14.68}$$

From Equation 14.53,

$$\frac{k}{m} = C_p - C_v,$$

so the combination $C_v m/k$ can be written

$$\frac{C_v m}{k} = \frac{C_v}{C_p - C_v}. \tag{14.69}$$

For the dimensionless ratio of specific heats at constant pressure and at constant volume the symbol γ is used:

$$\gamma = \frac{C_p}{C_v}. \tag{14.70}$$

With this notation, after some algebraic manipulation, Equation 14.68 can be written

$$V\ dP + \gamma P\ dV = 0,$$

or

$$\frac{dP}{P} + \gamma\frac{dV}{V} = 0. \tag{14.71}$$

Integration gives

$$\ln P + \gamma \ln V = constant,$$

from which it follows that

Pressure-volume relationship
for adiabatic change of an
ideal gas

$$PV^\gamma = constant. \tag{14.72}$$

Recall that γ is greater than 1; for example, $\gamma = \frac{7}{5}$ for a diatomic gas at normal temperature. A graph of pressure vs volume for this mathematical relationship appears in Figure 14.13(b). It is left as an exercise to find the relationships between P and T and between V and T for adiabatic change.

FREE EXPANSION

If a gas is confined in one half of a container whose other half is evacuated and if the barrier separating the two halves is abruptly removed, the resulting redistribution of the gas to fill the whole container is referred to as free expansion (Figure 14.15). In this process, no heat flows to or from the gas, and no work is done. Therefore, there is no change in the internal energy of the gas (Equation 14.46):

Conditions of free expansion

$$\Delta Q = \Delta W = \Delta U = 0. \tag{14.73}$$

If the gas is an ideal gas, its temperature also remains unchanged. If, incorrectly, we assumed the validity of the Clausius formula for entropy, we would predict no change of entropy: $\Delta S = \Delta Q/T = 0$. In fact, as the submicroscopic view would suggest, there *is* a change of entropy. However, the Clausius formula cannot be applied directly because the process of free expansion proceeds through nonequilibrium states.

$\Delta Q = 0$, *but* ΔS *is* <u>*not*</u> *zero*

One way to find the entropy change is to visualize a change through equilibrium states, the final result of which is the same as the final result of free expansion. Such a change is the isothermal expansion discussed earlier (page 638). The free expansion of the gas after the abrupt removal of a barrier results in the gas occupying a larger volume at the same temperature; exactly the

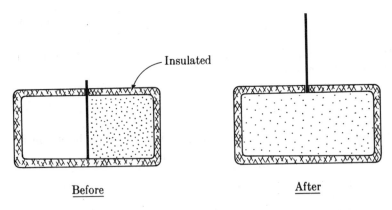

Before   After

FIGURE 14.15   Free expansion. Although the process occurs without heat transfer or work and, for an ideal gas, without change of internal energy or temperature, the entropy of the gas does increase.

same final state would be reached if the gas expanded slowly against a receding piston, with heat being supplied to compensate for the work done. The entropy change for free expansion is, therefore, the same as for isothermal expansion. It is given by Equation 14.61.

Equivalent process is slow isothermal expansion

The entropy change for free expansion may also be calculated directly from the Boltzmann definition of entropy, $S = k \ln P$. Entropy change from state 1 to state 2 is

Direct application of the Boltzmann definition

$$S = k \ln P_2 - k \ln P_1 = k \ln \left(\frac{P_2}{P_1}\right) \qquad (14.74)$$

(here P designates probability, not pressure). In this process, only probability of position is relevant since the internal energy and the temperature of the gas do not change. Recalling that position probabilities for a container divided into two equal parts follow the same rules as probabilities of heads and tails for coins in a tray, we can use Tables 14.2 and 14.3 as a guide. The total probability P_T for *some* distribution of molecules in the total volume V_T is unity:

$$P_T = 1. \qquad (14.75)$$

The probability of finding all of five molecules in the volume $V = \frac{1}{2}V_T$ is, from Table 14.2,

$$P = (\tfrac{1}{2})^5 = \tfrac{1}{32}.$$

The probability of finding all of ten molecules in the volume $V = \frac{1}{2}V_T$ is, from Table 14.3,

$$P = (\tfrac{1}{2})^{10} = \tfrac{1}{1,024}.$$

Evidently, for N molecules, the probability of concentration in half the total volume must be

$$P = (\tfrac{1}{2})^N. \qquad (14.76)$$

It is not hard to prove the further generalization that the probability for concentration in one-third or one-fourth of the total volume is $(\tfrac{1}{3})^N$ or $(\tfrac{1}{4})^N$; or, in general,

$$\frac{P}{P_T} = \left(\frac{V}{V_T}\right)^N. \qquad (14.77)$$

Probability of position, $P \sim V^N$

The a priori probability of position for N molecules in volume V varies in proportion to V raised to the Nth power. The result expressed by Equation 14.77 may be used in Equation 14.74 to find the entropy change in free expansion. It is

$$\Delta S = k \ln \left(\frac{V_2^N}{V_1^N}\right).$$

Because of a basic property of logarithms, this is the same as

$$\Delta S = Nk \ln \left(\frac{V_2}{V_1}\right), \qquad (14.78)$$

Entropy change in free expansion of an ideal gas

which is identical to Equation 14.61. Working from the Boltzmann definition of entropy, we have no need to postulate alternative paths of change through equilibrium states nor any need to consider heat flow. In only a few such simple processes, however, is it convenient to use the Boltzmann definition for a practical calculation.

★14.9   Cyclical processes

THE CARNOT CYCLE

In Section 14.7, we described an idealized heat engine in overall functional terms (see Figure 14.10), without any reference to a specific device or mode of operation. A device that meets the conditions of that discussion is the so-called Carnot engine. Its mode of operation is called a *Carnot cycle*, which is an alternating sequence of isothermal and adiabatic changes. A variety of systems can be made to execute a Carnot cycle. One example of a Carnot engine, utilizing gas in a cylinder, is shown in Figure 14.16. The corresponding pressure-volume diagram

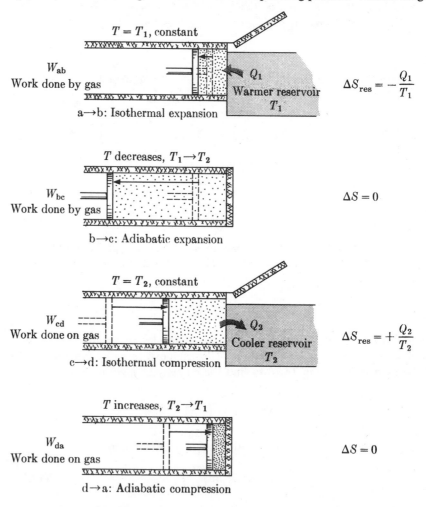

FIGURE 14.16   A Carnot cycle, executed by gas in a cylinder. Details of the figure are explained in the text.

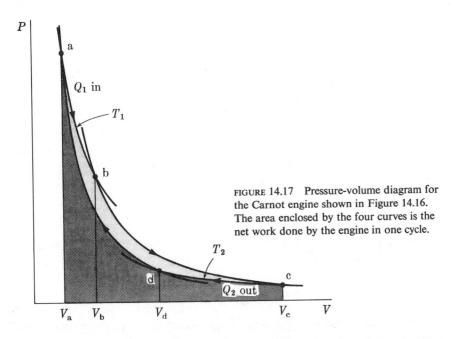

FIGURE 14.17   Pressure-volume diagram for the Carnot engine shown in Figure 14.16. The area enclosed by the four curves is the net work done by the engine in one cycle.

for the gas appears in Figure 14.17. The gas—called the "working substance"—need not be an ideal gas. In other ways, however, this engine *is* idealized. We postulate perfect isothermal and adiabatic processes, all changes occurring through equilibrium states. There are no dissipative effects, and the net change of entropy of the engine and its environment is zero.

Let us enumerate the four steps of the Carnot cycle, beginning with the gas at its maximum pressure and minimum volume (point a in Figure 14.17). Its temperature at this point is T_1.

1. a → b: The gas expands isothermally. Heat Q_1 from a reservoir at temperature T_1 flows into the gas to keep its temperature constant as it does work W_{ab} on its environment. (For convenience, we choose positive magnitudes for all increments of heat and work; we also omit Δ symbols.)

2. b → c: The gas expands further, now adiabatically. As it does so, its internal energy decreases, and its temperature falls from T_1 to T_2. It does work W_{bc} on its environment.

3. c → d: The gas is compressed isothermally. Heat Q_2 flows from the gas into a reservoir at temperature T_2 as work W_{cd} is done on the gas.

4. d → a: The gas is compressed further, adiabatically. Its internal energy increases, and its temperature rises from T_2 to T_1. Work W_{da} is done on the gas.

The four steps of the Carnot cycle

Equation 14.58 gives an expression for the work done on a gas whose volume changes. The integral ∫ $P\ dV$ has a simple graphical interpretation. It is the area under a curve in a PV diagram. In Figure 14.17, for example, the area under the curve ab from volume V_a to volume V_b is the work W_{ab} associated with the first step of the Carnot cycle. During this isothermal expansion, the work done *on* the gas is $-W_{ab}$, and the work done *by* the gas is $+W_{ab}$. Similarly,

Graphical interpretation of work in a PV diagram

the area under the curve bc from V_b to V_c is the work W_{bc}. For a decreasing volume (moving right to left in the PV diagram), the sign conventions are reversed. Thus the magnitude of the shaded area under curve cd is the positive work done *on* the gas in step 3 of the cycle.* The net work done by the gas on its environment during the full cycle is

$$W = W_{ab} + W_{bc} - W_{cd} - W_{da}. \tag{14.79}$$

Interpreting the four increments of work graphically, we can see that this net work W is the same as the lightly shaded area bounded by the four curves in Figure 14.17. Because of energy conservation, it must also be equal to the difference of heat flow in and heat flow out:

Energy conservation for the cycle

$$W = Q_1 - Q_2, \tag{14.80}$$

which is equivalent to Equation 14.35.

During step 1 of the cycle, the warmer reservoir suffers a decrease of entropy (see Figure 14.16):

$$\Delta S_{res} = -\frac{Q_1}{T_1} \quad (a \rightarrow b).$$

Since the gas in the cylinder gains the same heat at the same temperature, its change of entropy in step 1 is equal and opposite to that of the reservoir:

$$\Delta S_{gas} = +\frac{Q_1}{T_1}.$$

In steps 2 and 4, with no heat flow, neither the gas nor its environment experiences a change of entropy. In step 3, since gas temperature and reservoir temperature are again postulated to be equal,

$$\Delta S_{res} = +\frac{Q_2}{T_2} = -\Delta S_{gas}.$$

From these simple equations we gain expressions for the total changes of entropy during a full cycle:

$$\Delta S_{gas} = \frac{Q_1}{T_1} - \frac{Q_2}{T_2}, \tag{14.81}$$

$$\Delta S_{environment} = -\frac{Q_1}{T_1} + \frac{Q_2}{T_2}. \tag{14.82}$$

For the gas, because it returns to its initial state after one cycle there is no net change of entropy: $\Delta S_{gas} = 0$. According to Equations 14.81 and 14.82, this means that $\Delta S_{environment}$ is also equal to zero. From either of these conditions, it follows that

Consequence of zero entropy change for gas and environment

$$\frac{Q_1}{T_1} = \frac{Q_2}{T_2}, \tag{14.83}$$

---

* This comes about because of the mathematical rule $-\int_{V_c}^{V_d} P\, dv = +\int_{V_d}^{V_c} P\, dV$.

which is equivalent to Formula 14.36 with the inequality replaced by an equality.

The efficiency of the Carnot engine is defined to be $\eta = W/Q_1$. From Equations 14.80 and 14.83, it is

$$\eta = 1 - \frac{T_2}{T_1}. \tag{14.84}$$

The Carnot engine is a realization of the schematic engine in Figure 14.10

Compare this with Equation 14.40. The mathematics of the Carnot engine is evidently identical to the mathematics of the idealized heat engine discussed in Section 14.7, with zero entropy change.

THE THERMODYNAMIC TEMPERATURE SCALE

From Equation 14.83, the ratio of heat flows into and out of the Carnot engine is the same as the ratio of the temperatures of the two reservoirs:

$$\frac{Q_1}{Q_2} = \frac{T_1}{T_2}. \tag{14.85}$$

This fact can be used to *define* a temperature scale, the so-called thermodynamic temperature scale. The ratio of the temperatures of two reservoirs can in principle be determined by using these reservoirs to drive a Carnot engine, then measuring the heat flow into and out of the engine. Standardization can be achieved by bringing one reservoir into thermal equilibrium with water at its triple-point and defining this temperature to be 273.16 K.

Heat flow in and out of a Carnot engine can define temperature

The thermodynamic temperature scale in fact proves to be identical to the scale defined by an ideal gas in a gas thermometer. However, it is an interesting, different approach to temperature, resting, as it does, on the second law of thermodynamics. The thermodynamic scale does not require that the working substance in the Carnot engine be an ideal gas, or even that it be a gas. This means that the definition is usable below the liquefaction point of all gases. On the thermodynamic scale, absolute zero can be defined as the exhaust temperature for which no heat flows from an ideal Carnot engine. Phrasing it differently, it is the exhaust temperature that permits a Carnot engine to convert all input heat to work ($\eta = 1$).

Merits of the thermodynamic scale

Although the thermodynamic temperature scale does not require the abstraction of an ideal gas, it is, of course, idealized in other ways. In particular, it requires a perfect Carnot engine, one that operates without increasing the entropy of its environment.

THE GASOLINE ENGINE AND THE DIESEL ENGINE*

The pressure-volume diagrams in Figure 14.18 represent, in simplified and approximate form, the cycles of the gasoline engine and the diesel engine. Consider first the cycle of Figure 14.18(a).

---

* For historical background, see the following two articles by Lynwood Bryant in *Scientific American*: "The Origin of the Automobile Engine," March, 1967; and "Rudolph Diesel and His Rational Engine," August, 1969.

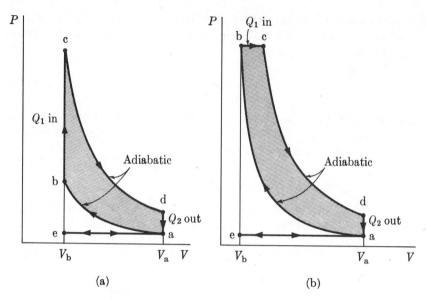

FIGURE 14.18   Pressure-volume diagrams for idealized cycles of (a) gasoline engine and (b) diesel engine.

Steps of idealized gasoline-engine cycle

   1. $a \to b$:   A fuel-air mixture is compressed adiabatically from volume V_a to volume V_b. Its temperature increases from T_a to T_b. Work, equal to the area under the curve ab, is done on the gas.

   2. $b \to c$:   Combustion takes place, adding heat Q_1 to the gas. During this rapid process, temperature and pressure rise, but the increase of volume is negligible.

   3. $c \to d$:   The gas expands adiabatically, doing work on its environment equal to the area under the curve cd. Temperature falls from T_c to T_d.

   4. $d \to a$:   Heat Q_2 flows from the gas as its pressure falls at constant volume. (In an actual engine, this drop of pressure and loss of heat are achieved by opening an exhaust valve; here we postulate that the mechanism is heat conduction from a constant mass of gas.)

   5. $a \to e$:   Combustion products are exhausted at constant pressure.

   6. $e \to a$:   A fresh fuel-air mixture is admitted to the cylinder as its volume expands at constant pressure.

   In this idealized gasoline-engine cycle, the net work done in steps 5 and 6 is zero. The work done by the engine in one cycle is the shaded area bounded by the lines ab, bc, cd, and da. Just as in the Carnot engine, this work is equal to the heat added minus the heat exhausted:

$$W = Q_1 - Q_2 .$$

The efficiency of the engine is

$$\eta = \frac{W}{Q_1} = 1 - \frac{Q_2}{Q_1} . \tag{14.86}$$

With the help of some simplifying assumptions, it is possible to express this efficiency in terms of temperatures in different parts of the cycle. Let us suppose that the entropy change has its limiting value, zero, and that both before and after combustion the gas is an ideal gas with constant specific heats. Since heat flow takes place at constant volume, we have, using Equation 13.40,

$$Q_1 = C_v M \cdot (T_c - T_b),$$

$$Q_2 = C_v M \cdot (T_d - T_a).$$

Heat flow at constant volume

The efficiency is, therefore,

$$\eta = 1 - \frac{Q_2}{Q_1} = 1 - \frac{T_d - T_a}{T_c - T_b}. \tag{14.87}$$

The adiabatic curves ab and cd are both described by Equation 14.72, $PV^\gamma = $ *constant*. This relationship, combined with the ideal-gas law, $PV = nRT$, implies that the combination $TV^{\gamma-1}$ is also constant for the adiabatic change of an ideal gas. In particular,

$$T_a V_a^{\gamma-1} = T_b V_b^{\gamma-1}, \tag{14.88}$$

$$T_d V_a^{\gamma-1} = T_c V_b^{\gamma-1} \tag{14.89}$$

Conditions of adiabatic change

(we use the facts that $V_c = V_b$ and $V_d = V_a$). Equations 14.88 and 14.89 combine to yield both

$$\frac{T_d - T_a}{T_c - T_b} = \left(\frac{V_b}{V_a}\right)^{\gamma-1} \tag{14.90}$$

and

$$\left(\frac{V_b}{V_a}\right)^{\gamma-1} = \frac{T_a}{T_b} = \frac{T_d}{T_c}. \tag{14.91}$$

Using Equation 14.90 to substitute in Equation 14.87 gives

$$\eta = 1 - \left(\frac{V_b}{V_a}\right)^{\gamma-1}. \tag{14.92}$$

Efficiency in terms of compression ratio

Because of Equation 14.91, the efficiency may also be written in either of the following forms:

$$\eta = 1 - \frac{T_a}{T_b}, \tag{14.93}$$

$$\eta = 1 - \frac{T_d}{T_c}. \tag{14.94}$$

Efficiency in terms of temperatures

The highest temperature reached during the cycle is T_c; the lowest temperature is T_a. It therefore follows from either Equation 14.93 or 14.94 that

$$\eta < 1 - \frac{T_a}{T_c}. \tag{14.95}$$

Even for this idealized engine with $\Delta S = 0$, the efficiency is less than $1 - (T_{min}/T_{max})$ and, therefore, less than the efficiency of a Carnot engine operating between these same limiting temperatures (see Equation 14.84). This is a special

For given T_{max} and T_{min}, the Carnot engine is the most efficient

case of a general theorem: Given a maximum temperature T_1 at which heat is added and a minimum temperature T_2 at which heat is exhausted, the Carnot engine, with efficiency $1 - (T_2/T_1)$, is the engine with the greatest possible efficiency.

■ EXAMPLE: What is the efficiency of an ideal gasoline engine if its working substance is approximated as a diatomic gas and its compression ratio is 8? For a diatomic gas, $\gamma = C_p/C_v = \frac{7}{5} = 1.4$. In Equation 14.92 use this value of γ and $V_b/V_a = \frac{1}{8}$ to get

$$\eta = 1 - (\tfrac{1}{8})^{0.4} = 0.565.$$

The efficiency of an actual engine is, of course, considerably less than this value; it is typically 0.15 to 0.20.   ■

Diesel engines are more efficient than gasoline engines

The diesel engine differs from the gasoline engine in its mode of combustion. Fuel is added gradually beginning at the point of maximum compression [point b in Figure 14.18(b)]. The combustion proceeds during an expansion phase (b → c), which can be approximated as a constant-pressure process. Otherwise, the cycle is like that of the gasoline engine. Because of higher compression ratios and higher combustion temperatures, diesel engines, in practice, achieve higher efficiencies than gasoline engines.

14.10   The arrow of time

The ability to take a fresh look at the familiar and to contrast it with what would be the familiar in a different universe is a skill worth cultivating. For the scientist as well as the student, useful insights come from looking at the familiar as if it were unfamiliar.

The second law attaches an arrow to time

Consider the second law of thermodynamics. We need not go to the laboratory or a machine or even the kitchen to witness its impact on events. It is unlikely that anyone could get through any five minutes of his waking life without seeing the second law at work. The way to appreciate this fact is by thinking backward. Imagine a motion picture of any scene of ordinary life being run backward. One might watch a student untyping a paper, each keystroke erasing another letter as the keys become cleaner and the ribbon fresher. Or bits of hair clippings on a barber-shop floor rising to join the hair on a customer's head as the barber unclips. Or a pair of mangled automobiles undergoing instantaneous repair as they back apart. Or a dead rabbit rising to scamper backward into the woods as a crushed bullet reforms and flies backward into a rifle while some gunpowder is miraculously manufactured out of hot gas. Or something as simple as a cup of coffee on a table gradually becoming warmer as it draws heat from its cooler surroundings. All of these backward-in-time views and the myriad more that spring to mind are ludicrous and impossible for one reason only—they violate the second law of thermodynamics. In the

Events unfold in one direction

actual sequence of events, entropy is increasing. In the time-reversed view, entropy is decreasing. We recognize at once the obvious impossibility of the process in which entropy decreases, even though we may never have thought about entropy increase in the everyday world. In a certain sense everyone "knows" the second law of thermodynamics. It distinguishes the possible from the impossible in ordinary affairs.

In some of the examples just cited the action of the second law is obvious, as in the increasing disorder produced by an automobile collision or the increasing entropy associated with heat flow from a cup of coffee. In others it is less obvious. But whether or not we can clearly identify the increasing entropy, we can be very confident that whenever a sequence of events occurs in our world in one order and not in the opposite order, it is because entropy increase is associated with the possible order and entropy decrease with the impossible order. The reason for this confidence is quite simple. We know of no law other than the second law of thermodynamics that assigns to processes of change in the large-scale world a preferred direction in time. In the submicroscopic world, too, time-reversal invariance is a principle governing most fundamental processes.* Here we have an apparent paradox. In order to understand the paradox and its resolution, we must first understand exactly what is meant by time-reversal invariance.

A paradox: one-way time and time-reversal invariance

The principle of time-reversal invariance can be simply stated in terms of hypothetical moving pictures. If the filmed version of any physical process or sequence of events is shown backward, the viewer sees a picture of something that could have happened. In slightly more technical language, any sequence of events, if executed in the opposite order, is a physically possible sequence of events. This leads to the rather startling conclusion that it is, in fact, impossible to tell by watching a moving picture of events in nature whether the film is running backward or forward. How can this principle be reconciled with the gross violations of common sense contained in the backward view of a barber cutting hair, a hunter firing a gun, a child breaking a plate, or the President signing his name? Does it mean that time-reversal invariance is not a valid law in the macroscopic world? No. As far as we know, time-reversal invariance governs every interaction that underlies processes of change in the large-scale world. The key to resolving the paradox is to recognize that possibility does not mean probability. Although the spontaneous reassembly of the fragments of an exploded bomb into a whole, unexploded bomb is wildly improbable, it is not, from the most fundamental point of view, impossible.

Resolution of the paradox: The seemingly impossible is only improbable

At every important point where the macroscopic and submicroscopic descriptions of matter touch, the concept of probability is crucial. The second law of thermodynamics is basically a probabilistic law whose approach to absolute validity increases as the complexity of the systems it describes increases. For a system of a half-dozen molecules, entropy decrease is not only possible, it is quite likely, at least some of the time. All six molecules might cluster in one corner of their container, or the three less energetic molecules might lose energy via collisions to the three more energetic molecules ("uphill" heat flow). For a system of 10^{20} molecules, on the other hand, entropy decrease becomes so

---

* For the first time in 1964, in an experiment concerned with the decay of neutral kaons, some doubt was cast on the universal validity of time-reversal invariance, which had previously been supposed to be an absolute law of nature. If, as now seems likely, the principle is imperfect, it will remain valid to a high degree of approximation since it has already been tested in many situations. In particular, all interactions that have any effect on the large-scale world do obey the principle of time-reversal invariance. For further discussion, see Section 27.7.

improbable that it deserves to be called impossible. We could wait a billion times the known lifetime of the universe and still never expect to see the time-reversed view of something as simple as a piece of paper being torn in half. Nevertheless, it is important to realize that a time-reversed process is possible in principle.

Even in the world of particles, a sequence of events may occur with much higher probability in one direction than in the opposite direction. In the world of human experience, the imbalance of probabilities is so enormous that it no longer makes sense to speak of the more probable direction and the less probable direction. Instead, we speak of the possible and the impossible. The action of molecular probabilities gives to the flow of events in the large-scale world a unique direction. The (almost complete) violation of time-reversal invariance by the second law of thermodynamics attaches an arrow to time, a one-way sign for the unfolding of events. Through this idea, thermodynamics impinges on philosophy.

Two aspects of the arrow of time

In the latter part of the nineteenth century, long before time-reversal invariance was appreciated as a fundamental law of submicroscopic nature, physicists realized that the second law had something quite general to say about our passage through time. There are two aspects of the idea of the arrow of time: first, that the universe, like a wound-up clock, is running down, its supply of available energy ever dwindling; second, that the spontaneous tendency of nature toward greater entropy is what gives man a conception of the unique one-way direction of time.

The second law of thermodynamics had not long been formulated in a general way before men reflected on its implications for the universe at large. In 1865, Clausius wrote, without fanfare, as grand a pair of statements about the world as any produced by science: "[W]e can express the fundamental laws of the universe which correspond to the two fundamental laws of the mechanical theory of heat in the following simple form.

Grand generalization of the first and second laws

"1. The energy of the universe is constant.
"2. The entropy of the universe tends toward a maximum."*

These are the first and second laws of thermodynamics extended to encompass all of nature. Are the extensions justifiable? If so, what are their implications? We know in fact no more than Clausius about the constancy of energy and the steady increase of entropy in the universe at large. We do know that energy conservation has withstood every test since he wrote and that entropy increase is founded on the very solid principle of change from arrangements of lesser probability to those of greater probability. Nevertheless, all that we have learned of nature in the century since Clausius leaped boldly to the edge of existence should make us cautious about so great a step. In 1865, the single theory of Newtonian mechanics seemed to be valid in every extremity of nature, from the molecular to the planetary. A century later we know instead that it fails in every extremity—in the domain of small sizes, where quantum mechanics rules; in

Reasons to be less bold

---

* See W. F. Magie, ed., *A Source Book in Physics* (Cambridge, Massachusetts: Harvard University Press, 1965), p. 236.

the domain of high speed, where special relativity changes the rules; and in the domain of the very large, where general relativity warps space and time.

The logical terminus of the universe, assuming it to be a system obeying the same laws as the macroscopic systems accessible to experiment, is known as the "heat death," a universal soup of uniform density and uniform temperature, devoid of available energy, incapable of further change, a perfect and featureless final disorder. If this is where the universe is headed, we have had no hints of it as yet. Over a time span of ten billion years or more, the universe has been a vigorously active place, with new stars still being born as old ones are dying. It is quite possible that the long-range fate of the universe will be settled within science and need not remain forever a topic of pure speculation. At present, however, we have no evidence at all to confirm or contradict the applicability of thermodynamics to the universe as a whole. Even if we choose to postulate its applicability, we need not be led inevitably to the idea of the ultimate heat death. The existence of a law of time-reversal invariance and the essential probabilistic nature of the second law leave open the possibility that one grand improbable reversal of probability could occur in which disorder is restored to order. Finally, we can come back to the second aspect of the arrow of time, the uniqueness of the direction of man's course through time, with this challenging thought. If it is the second law that gives man his sense of time's direction, the very construction of the human machine forces us to see the universe running down. In a world that we might look in upon from the outside to see order being built from disorder, the less probable from the more probable, we would see creatures who remembered their future and not their past. For them the trend of events would seem to be toward disorder and greater probability, and it would be ourselves who seemed to be turned around.

In the three centuries since Newton, time has evolved from the obvious to the mysterious. In the *Principia*, Newton wrote, "Absolute, true, and mathematical time, of itself, and from its own nature flows equably without regard to anything external, and by another name is called duration." This view of time as something flowing constantly and inexorably forward, carrying man with it, persisted largely intact until the revolution of relativity at the beginning of this century. The nineteenth century brought only hints of a deeper insight, when it was appreciated that the second law of thermodynamics differentiated between forward and backward in time, as the laws of mechanics had failed to do. If time were run backward, the reversed planetary orbits would be reasonable and possible, obeying the same laws as the actual forward-in-time orbits. But the reversal of any entropy-changing transformation would be neither reasonable nor possible. The second law of thermodynamics points the way for Newton's equable flow.

Relativity had the most profound effect on our conception of time. The merger of space and time made a temporal arrow unreasonable when there was no spatial arrow. More recently, time-reversal invariance has confirmed the equal status of both directions in time. Relativity also brought time to a stop. It is more consistent with the viewpoint of modern physics to think of man and matter moving through time (as they move through space) than to think of time itself as flowing.

All the new insights about time make clear that we must think about it in very human terms—its definition, its measurement, its apparently unique direction stem not from "absolute, true and mathematical time" but from psychological time. These insights also reinforce the idea that the second law of thermodynamics must ultimately account for our sense of time.

It is a stimulating idea that the only reason man is aware of the past and not the future is that he is a complicated and highly organized structure. Unfortunately, simpler creatures are no better off. They equalize future and past by remembering neither. An electron, being precisely identical with every other electron, is totally unmarked by its past or by its future. Man is intelligent enough to be scarred by his past. But the same complexity that gives him a memory at all is what keeps his future a mystery.

Summary of ideas and definitions

A basic physical postulate for a system subject to random influences is that every arrangement accessible to the system is equally likely.

The a priori probability for a system to have some property (such as definite energy or a definite number of molecules in one part of a container) is proportional to the number of different arrangements of the system that have this property.

Greater a priori probability means greater disorder.

Greater complexity of a system means smaller spontaneous fluctuations away from its most probable states.

The most probable spatial distribution of molecules is a distribution of uniform density.

The most probable speed distribution of molecules is the Maxwell-Boltzmann distribution (Equation 14.3).

In thermal equilibrium, the average properties of all molecules at one time are the same as the average properties of one molecule over a long time.

The Boltzmann definition of entropy is
$$S = k \ln P, \tag{14.10}$$
where P is the probability for a state of the system.

The Clausius definition of entropy is
$$dS = dQ/T, \tag{14.15}$$
applicable for change from one equilibrium state to another.

The entropy of a system is the sum of the entropies of its parts.

Alternative statements of the second law of thermodynamics:

1. Spontaneous change is from states of lesser probability to states of greater probability.
2. Spontaneous change is from order to disorder.
3. $\Delta S \geq 0$: The entropy of an isolated system increases or remains the same. *This is the most basic statement.*
4. Heat does not flow spontaneously from a cooler to a hotter body.
5. In a cyclical device, heat cannot be transformed wholly to work.
6. Perpetual-motion machines are impossible (dissipative mechanisms decrease available energy).

No law of physics has wider generality than the second law of thermodynamics.

Equipartition and the zeroth law are consequences of the second law.

"Downhill" heat flow increases entropy (Equation 14.26).

Equilibrium established by mixing increases entropy (Equations 14.33 and 14.34).

The efficiency of a heat engine is defined to be
$$\eta = \frac{W}{Q_1} = 1 - \frac{Q_2}{Q_1}. \tag{14.38, 14.86}$$

The efficiency of a Carnot engine driven by reservoirs at temperatures T_1 and T_2 is
$$\eta = 1 - \frac{T_2}{T_1}. \tag{14.84}$$

Any other engine operating between the same two temperatures has a lower efficiency than that of a Carnot engine.

Thermal pollution, an inescapable consequence of the second law, is somewhat greater for nuclear power plants than for fossil-fuel plants.

A refrigerator requires input power in order to transfer heat from a cooler to a warmer place (Equation 14.45).

Some important results for ideal gases:

1. Internal energy: $dU = C_v M \, dT.$ (14.49)

2. Specific heats: $C_p = C_v + \dfrac{k}{m}.$ (14.53)

3. Isothermal change: $\Delta S = Nk \ln \left(\dfrac{V_2}{V_1}\right).$ (14.61)

4. Adiabatic change: $PV^\gamma = constant.$ (14.72)

5. Free expansion: $\Delta S = Nk \ln \left(\dfrac{V_2}{V_1}\right).$ (14.78)

Work done by a gas is equal to the area under a curve in a PV diagram.

The Carnot cycle is defined by alternating isothermal and adiabatic changes. Its working substance need not be an ideal gas.

Heat flow in and out of an ideal Carnot engine can be used to define the thermodynamic temperature scale (Equation 14.85). The thermodynamic scale and the ideal-gas-thermometer scale are the same.

The gasoline engine and the diesel engine can be approximately represented by simple PV diagrams (Figure 14.18). For practical reasons, the diesel engine has the greater efficiency.

A law of time-reversal invariance underlies macroscopic phenomena. At the same time, the second law of thermodynamics determines a one-way flow of events. The idea of probability resolves the paradox.

Applied to the universe as a whole, the second law implies a dwindling supply of available energy and an eventual "heat death."

Generalization of the first and second laws to the entire universe goes beyond the bounds of contemporary science.

Time is a deep and in some ways mysterious concept that is tied to human perception and memory.

QUESTIONS

Section 14.1

Q14.1   (1) Some systems, once put into an orderly state and left alone, remain that way. Name one such system. (2) What is required to make a system in an orderly (improbable) state follow its "natural" trend toward disorder?

Q14.2   (1) A student is investigating probability concepts by carrying out the tray-shaking experiment described in the text. Unknown to him, his roommate has replaced one of his genuine coins by a two-headed coin. Is he likely to discover the counterfeit sooner working with few coins or working with many coins? (2) If one out of every ten coins in a tray is a two-headed coin, will the distribution of heads reveal this fact sooner with few coins or with many coins?

Q14.3   A formula for the probability of n heads among N coins (if N is large) is given in Exercise 14.2. Explain in qualitative terms why $P(\tfrac{1}{2}N)$ *decreases* as N increases even though the probability curve becomes more sharply spiked near $n = \tfrac{1}{2}N$ as N increases.

Q14.4   Each of the three following situations is characterized by a different kind of uncertainty. Comment on the differences. Which of the three is governed by thermodynamic probability (the probability of atomic multitudes)? (1) A pion of known energy enters a bubble chamber. The number of bubbles formed along its first centimeter of track is measured. The number of bubbles along its second centimeter of track can then be predicted approximately, but not exactly. (2) Another pion is created in the chamber. How long it will live before decaying is uncertain. (3) Still another pion, of energy higher than any previously studied, strikes a nucleus. The result of the collision is uncertain.

Section 14.2 Q14.5 What if the number of air molecules in a room were much smaller than usual, perhaps totaling only a few thousand? Describe any interesting effects that might occur.

Section 14.3 Q14.6 The probability of throwing "snake eyes" (a pair of ones) with a pair of dice is $\frac{1}{36}$. Is this an a priori probability? Why or why not?

Q14.7 (1) What is meant by the "state" of a tray of coins? (NOTE: In general, the state of a system is defined by specifying a limited number of its properties, leaving other properties unspecified.) (2) Give a brief definition of the a priori probability that a tray of coins will be found in a certain state.

Q14.8 Generalize the answer to the previous question: Give a brief definition of the a priori probability that a system will be found in a certain state. Is this an operational definition?

Q14.9 It was once widely believed that living organisms might be exempt from the second law of thermodynamics. What is your opinion? Can you cite any specific evidence in support of your opinion?

Q14.10 A house is in complete disarray. A housewife spends the day straightening it up—creating order out of disorder, converting a more probable arrangement to a less probable arrangement. Explain how she can do this without violating the second law of thermodynamics.

Q14.11 Each of the following events is possible but unlikely. (1) A glass of water in a warm room freezes, and the room gets warmer. (2) A judge believes the testimony of a convicted criminal when it conflicts with the testimony of a police officer. (3) After being shaken, a tray of coins that previously showed 50 heads and 50 tails shows 65 heads and 35 tails. (4) Heat flows spontaneously in interstellar space from a cool region containing 1,000 atoms to a warm region containing 1,000 atoms. (5) A pion lives 10 min. Which of these events violate the second law of thermodynamics? Which of them stand a reasonable chance of actually occurring? Explain briefly the reasons for each of your answers. (HINT: An event that violates the second law of thermodynamics *can* occur.)

Section 14.4 Q14.12 On a hot summer day, a man closes the doors and windows of his small apartment and opens his refrigerator door. Is this a good way to keep cool without investing in an air conditioner?

Q14.13 A proton approaches the earth from outer space. It experiences the earth's magnetic force and gravitational force, enters the atmosphere, and is slowed down. Discuss the energy exchanges involved in this sequence of events. How is the initial energy of the proton finally distributed? Does the proton finally come to rest? Does entropy increase?

Section 14.5 Q14.14 If the entropy of a device were exactly constant, could the device exhibit perpetual motion? Illustrate your answer with an example.

Q14.15 Suppose that Newton's third law were not valid. Explain how this might lead to a spontaneous *decrease* of entropy—changing disorder to order.

Q14.16 A satellite experiencing a small drag force in the thin outer reaches of the atmosphere may *gain* kinetic energy as a result of this friction. (1) Does this violate the second law of thermodynamics? Explain. (2) Is the air heated or cooled by the satellite?

Q14.17 An inventor designs an engine that takes in air, extracts heat from the air, converts some of this heat to work, and exhausts the chilled air back into the environment. He argues that the engine need not violate the second law of thermodynamics because only some of the heat taken from the air is transformed to work. Refute this argument.

Q14.18 Name any system not isolated from outside influences whose entropy "spontaneously" decreases. For the system you have named, where and how does a more-than-compensating increase of entropy take place? **Section 14.6**

Q14.19 (1) Explain from a *microscopic* point of view why the melting of ice in a pan is an entropy-increasing process for the ice. (2) Explain from a *macroscopic* point of view why placing a pan of water in a suitable environment can cause the entropy of the water either to increase or to decrease.

Q14.20 Explain why Equation 14.30 is valid for any temperature scale. **Section 14.7**

Q14.21 What are some of the noncyclical parts of a gasoline engine? What are its cyclical parts?

Q14.22 Consider an idealized heat engine that exhausts its excess heat to a reservoir whose temperature is very close to absolute zero. Explain in your own words why this makes possible a theoretical efficiency of almost 1, that is, an almost total conversion of heat to work.

Q14.23 In a power plant would it be advantageous to refrigerate the water used for cooling in order to increase the efficiency of the plant? *Optional:* Investigate this question quantitatively, using formulas developed in Section 14.7 for heat engines and refrigerators.

Q14.24 In outside references, find the amount of solar energy that reaches the earth per second (see also Exercise 10.6) and the rate at which man uses energy. Compare the two.

Q14.25 A wet bathing suit spontaneously chills itself (and its occupant). How can this happen without violating the second law of thermodynamics?

Q14.26 In idealized adiabatic change, $\Delta S = 0$. Give an example of an almost adiabatic change in practice, point out its mechanism of actual entropy change, and indicate why this mechanism produces a small *increase* of entropy. **Section 14.8**

Q14.27 As shown in Figure 13.7, gas in a cylinder is heated by a Bunsen flame. Explain why the entropy change of the gas can be calculated from the formula $\Delta S = \int dQ/T$ if the heating is slow but not if the heating takes place rapidly at one point on the cylinder.

Q14.28 How many isothermal and how many adiabatic curves pass through a single point in a PV diagram? Compare the slopes of the curves.

Q14.29 A nonideal gas may experience a change of temperature when it expands freely. Suggest a reason for this in terms of molecular interactions. Would you expect the temperature to rise or fall?

P

Section 14.9

Q14.30 (1) Describe qualitatively how the temperature of a gas varies if the changes of the gas are described by a rectangle in a *PV* diagram (see the figure). (2) For the direction of change indicated by the arrows in the figure, is net work done *by* the gas or *on* the gas?

V

Q14.31 The cycle of a Carnot engine consists of four processes in sequence. (1) Describe an idealized cyclic engine that uses fewer than four processes per cycle. (2) Sketch a *PV* diagram for this engine if its working substance is a gas. (3) What is the minimum number of sequential processes required in a heat engine?

Section 14.10

Q14.32 Why can the second law of thermodynamics be regarded, on the one hand, as one of the most general and profound laws of nature and, on the other hand, as not a fundamental law at all?

Q14.33 Give two examples from everyday life (other than those cited in the text) that illustrate the action of the second law of thermodynamics. For each, indicate how disorder or entropy is increased.

Q14.34 (1) A baseball player catches a ball moving with velocity **v**. If he throws it from exactly the spot where he caught it with exactly the velocity −**v**, will it exactly retrace its path through the air? Why or why not? (2) Answer the same question for a ball caught and thrown back on the airless moon. (Assume both earth and moon to be inertial frames of reference.) (3) What is the relevance of these answers to time-reversal invariance and the second law of thermodynamics?

EXERCISES

Section 14.1

E14.1 Suppose that a small cylinder (see the figure) could be so nearly perfectly evacuated that only 100 molecules remained within it. (1) Using Figures 14.3 and 14.4 and Equation 14.1 as guides, sketch a curve of relative probability for any number of these molecules to be found in region A, which is half the container. (2) If you placed a bet at even money that a measurement would reveal exactly 50 molecules in region A, would this be a good bet or a poor bet from your point of view? (3) If you bet, again at even money, that a series of measurements would show less than 60 molecules in region A more often than not, would you be making a good bet or a poor bet?

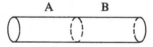

E14.2 For a large number N of coins in a tray, the probability that n of them will show heads is

$$P(n) = \sqrt{\frac{2}{N\pi}}\, e^{-2(n-\frac{1}{2}N)^2/N}.$$

(1) Verify that the width of the probability curve as defined in Section 14.1 is given by $W = \sqrt{2N}$. (2) For $N = 1,000$, what is $P(500)$? (3) With the help of a table of definite integrals, show that $\int_{-\infty}^{\infty} P\, dn = 1$. *Optional:* Find a table of probability integrals and use it to show that

$$\int_{\frac{1}{2}N-\frac{1}{2}W}^{\frac{1}{2}N+\frac{1}{2}W} P \, dn \cong 0.84.$$

E14.3   (1) Construct a table of all the possible combinations of numbers that can be thrown with two dice. (2) From the table, deduce the probabilities of throwing all sums from 2 to 12. Sketch a graph of this probability vs the sum showing on the dice. (3) What is the probability of throwing 7 and *then* 11? What is the probability of getting 7 *or* 11 in a single throw?

E14.4   Within the left half of a container are $10^{24} + 10^{12}$ molecules, and within its right half are $10^{24} - 10^{12}$ molecules—an imbalance of 1 part in a million million. By what factor is this arrangement less probable than an arrangement of equal division: 10^{24} molecules in each half? (Use the formula given in Exercise 14.2.)   Section 14.2

E14.5   The most probable speed of a molecule in a gas, written $\tilde{v}$, is the speed for which dP/dv (Equation 14.3) takes on its maximum value. (1) Show that $\tilde{v} = \sqrt{2kT/m}$. (2) By what percent is $\tilde{v}$ less than v_{rms}?

E14.6   The average time for a molecule in a gas to move a distance l is

$$\bar{t} = \overline{\left(\frac{l}{v}\right)} = l\overline{v^{-1}};$$

it involves the average of the inverse speed. Following the pattern of Equations 14.6 and 14.7, evaluate $\overline{v^{-1}}$. Express the answer in terms of kT and in terms of v_{rms}.

E14.7   (1) For nitrogen gas at standard conditions find the number N of molecules in a $1-m^3$ container. (2) Approximately how many of these molecules have speeds between 300 and 310 m/sec? (See the footnote on page 616.) (3) Approximately how many have speeds between 3,000 and 3,010 m/sec?

E14.8   A room contains N molecules. The probability that n of them are in one half of the room is the quantity $P(n)$ given in Exercise 14.2. (1) Give an expression for $k \ln P$, the entropy of a particular arrangement. (2) What is the entropy difference between a state with $n = 0$ and a state with $n = \frac{1}{2}N$? (3) Evaluate this entropy difference numerically for $N = 6 \times 10^{23}$.   Section 14.3

E14.9   An air table is divided into three regions of equal area. Three pucks are placed in region 1. Later, region 1 is observed to be empty, two pucks are in region 2, and one puck is in region 3. (1) What has been the increase of entropy of the system of three pucks? (2) Will the entropy of this system continue to increase indefinitely, will it approach a maximum and remain constant, or will it alternately decrease and increase?

E14.10   Find the change of entropy—including the sign—for each of these processes: (1) 1 kg of ice at 0 °C melts; (2) 1 kg of steam at 100 °C condenses.   Section 14.6

E14.11   If the probabilities of two events are 0.15 and 0.35, their *relative* probabilities are 15 and 35, or 3 and 7, or any other pair of numbers with the same ratio. Except as a matter of convenience for dealing with phenomena near absolute zero, only relative probabilities are important in thermodynamics. Explain how the irrelevance of the absolute value of entropy stated in connection with Equation 14.15 is equivalent to a statement that only relative probability plays a role in the definition expressed by Equation 14.10.

E14.12   Derive Equation 14.17 for the number of ways to distribute energy E among 3 molecules. (SUGGESTION: Assume P' to be a quadratic function of n, where $n = E/E_0$; find the coefficients of the quadratic expression by using the first few entries in Table 14.4, and check the result by calculating P' for $n = 5$ or 6.)

Section 14.7   E14.13   To keep the temperature in an oven at a steady 470 K, a heating element is dissipating 100 W of power. The temperature of the air surrounding the oven is 300 K. (1) What is the entropy change per second associated with the leakage of heat from the oven to the surrounding air? (2) Does keeping the oven warm involve any other changes of entropy?

E14.14   Prove that the final temperature T_f of a mixture, as given by Equation 14.30, lies between the initial temperatures T_1 and T_2 of the materials that are mixed.

E14.15   Fifty gm of ice at 0 °C are mixed with 100 gm of water at 80 °C. Find (1) the final temperature of the mixture and (2) the total change of entropy.

E14.16   Equal masses of water at initial temperatures T_1 and T_2 are mixed and come to thermal equilibrium. Prove that the entropy change ΔS, as given by Equation 14.33, is positive.

E14.17   (1) Half a liter of water at 30 °C is placed in contact with a large block of ice at 0 °C until the temperature of the water falls to 20 °C. Another half liter of water at 30 °C is placed in contact with a large block of matter at 60 °C until the temperature of the water rises to 40 °C. What is the total entropy change? (HINT: Four entropy changes must be considered.) (2) The two half liters of water are mixed and reach thermal equilibrium at their original temperature of 30 °C. Compare the entropy change in this process with the entropy change in part 1.

E14.18   A heat engine, represented schematically in Figure 14.10, takes in heat at 800 K and gives out heat at 300 K. (1) What is its maximum theoretical efficiency? (2) If its actual efficiency is half this theoretical limit, how many joules of work does it produce for each calorie of input heat?

E14.19   (1) For an idealized heat engine (Figure 14.10), show that the maximum work can be written

$$W_{max} = Q_2 \left(\frac{T_1}{T_2} - 1 \right)$$

(compare this with Equation 14.40). (2) If the source of heat is at temperature $T_1 = 500$ K, for what range of exhaust temperatures T_2 will the "wasted" energy Q_2 be no greater than the useful work W_{max}?

E14.20   A power station generates 10^8 W of mechanical power to turn electric generators. Its overall efficiency is 0.4. (1) At what rate (kcal/sec) does it exhaust heat to the environment? (2) What is the rate of flow of water through the station if the temperature of the water is raised by 3 C°? Express the answer in kg/sec and in gallon/hr.

E14.21   A helium liquifier with an inside temperature of 4 K operates in an environment at 300 K. For each joule of energy extracted from the helium at 4 K, how many joules of energy (at least) must be added to the environment as heat?

E14.22   To freeze a tray of water, a household refrigerator extracts 40 kcal of heat from the freezing compartment at 260 K. The temperature of the room is 295 K. (1) To do this, what is the minimum energy input in joules required from an outside power source? (2) If this refrigerator is able to extract heat from its freezing compartment at the rate 3 kcal/min and if it operates at near maximum efficiency, what is its electric power requirement in watts?

E14.23   A gas does 100 J of work on its surroundings while 50 cal of heat are being added to it. (1) What is the change of its internal energy? (2) Name one other way in which the same change of internal energy could have been brought about. Would the final state of the gas be the same in both cases?

Section 14.8

E14.24   The initial temperature of the gas in the preceding exercise is 350 K. Its mass is 100 gm and its specific heat is 0.17 cal/gm K. (1) What is its change of temperature? (2) What is its change of entropy?

E14.25   Show that the expressions $C_p = C_v + (k/m)$ and $C_p' = C_v' + R$ (Equations 14.53 and 13.75) are equivalent.

E14.26   One mole of air initially at standard conditions is isothermally compressed to a pressure of 2 atm. (1) What is its final volume? (2) What is its final temperature? (3) What is its change of entropy?

E14.27   One mole of air initially at standard conditions is adiabatically compressed to a pressure of 2 atm. (1) What is its final volume? (2) What is its final temperature? (3) What is its change of entropy?

E14.28   From Equation 14.72 and the ideal-gas law, derive relationships (1) between pressure and temperature and (2) between volume and temperature valid for adiabatic change.

E14.29   One liter of air at standard conditions undergoes free expansion to occupy 2 liters. It is then adiabatically compressed back to a volume of 1 liter. For this cycle, find the net change of (1) pressure, (2) temperature, and (3) entropy.

E14.30   (1) Beginning at pressure P_0 and volume V_0, a gas doubles its volume isothermally. What work is done by the gas? (2) Beginning with the same initial conditions P_0 and V_0, a gas doubles its volume adiabatically. What work is done by the gas? (3) For which process is the work greater?

Section 14.9

E14.31   An ideal diatomic gas ($\gamma = 1.40$) is the working substance in a Carnot engine operating between temperatures of 300 K and 1,200 K. Show that the ratio of the maximum to the minimum volume occupied by the gas during the cycle must be at least 32.

E14.32   Suppose that the temperatures at points a, b, and c in the gasoline-engine cycle of Figure 14.18(a) are related by $T_c = 2T_b = 4T_a$. (1) If the working substance is a diatomic gas, what is the compression ratio of the engine? (2) What is its theoretical efficiency? (3) What is the efficiency of a Carnot engine operating between the same minimum and maximum temperatures?

E14.33   Show that the efficiency of the idealized diesel engine represented by the diagram in Figure 14.18(b) can be written

$$\eta = 1 - \frac{1}{\gamma} \frac{T_d - T_a}{T_c - T_b},$$

where T_a, T_b, T_c, and T_d are the temperatures at points a, b, c, and d in the diagram and $\gamma = C_p/C_v$.

PROBLEMS

Computing probabilities   **P14.1**   Each of three wheels in a carnival game has an equal number of red, yellow, and green squares around its edge. A customer puts down a dime and wins a prize if all three wheels stop at the same color after they are spun. (1) What is the probability of winning? (2) If the carnival owner pays 30 cents for each prize that he awards, what part of the dime spent by each customer can the owner reckon as profit?

P14.2   In a certain population, the probability that a newborn child will be male is 0.53 and the probability that it will be female is 0.47. Assume that these probabilities are valid for every woman individually. (1) What is the probability that a woman who has borne three children has produced only sons? (2) What is the probability that a woman who has borne four children has produced only sons? (3) What is the probability that the pregnant mother of three sons will bear a fourth son?

P14.3   A candy packer pulls out three pieces of candy at a time from a large bin containing twice as many chocolate candies as butterscotch candies. If he is random in his selection, what is the probability that he will select (a) three chocolate candies? (b) three butterscotch? (c) two chocolate and one butterscotch? (d) two butterscotch and one chocolate? Check that your four probabilities sum to one.

P14.4   Drops of honey are placed at points A, B, C, and D on a trellis; then 1,000 ants are released at point O (see the figure). Observation shows that 122 ants reach A, 390 reach B, 370 reach C, and 118 reach D. (1) If each ant goes left or right with equal probability at each intersection, what are the probabilities that an ant reaches points A, B, C, and D? (2) Do the observations support the assumption that the ants go left or right with equal probability? (A qualitative and somewhat intuitive answer suffices.)

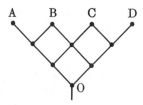

One-dimensional random walk   **P14.5**   An inebriate leaves a corner bar and starts walking along an east-west street. At every corner there is an equal probability that he will continue in the same direction or will turn and walk back in the direction from which he has just come. (1) After he has walked 5 blocks, what are the probabilities that he is at any corner from 5 blocks west to 5 blocks east of his starting point? (2) If he repeats this performance every night, what is his average distance from the bar after 5 blocks of walking? *Optional:* Express the probabilities of part 1 in terms of binomial coefficients.

P14.6   The binomial series for integer q is

$$(1 + x)^q = \sum_{n=0}^{q} \binom{q}{n} x^n ;$$

Property of binomial coefficients

the binomial coefficient is defined in a footnote in Section 14.1 (see also Appendix 6C). (1) Prove the following property of binomial coefficients:

$$2^{-q} \sum_{n=0}^{q} \binom{q}{n} = 1.$$

(2) What is the relevance of this formula to the probability considerations in Section 14.1?

P14.7   One end of a container, called region A, comprises $\frac{1}{5}$ of the container's volume; the rest of the container, called region B, comprises $\frac{4}{5}$ of its volume. (1) What is the probability that all N molecules in the container are in region A? (2) What is the probability that all N molecules are in region B? (3) Evaluate these probabilities for $N = 5$ and $N = 10$. (4) For both $N = 5$ and $N = 10$, find the difference in entropy between the state with region A empty and the state with region B empty.

Probability of position

P14.8   Use Equation 14.6 and the Maxwell-Boltzmann speed distribution to show that the mean-square speed of molecules in a gas is $\overline{v^2} = 3kT/m$, the same result that is required by the equipartition theorem.

Mean-square molecular speed

P14.9   A gas moves through a pipe with constant flow velocity v_0. (1) Show that the energy of the gas is the sum of the internal energy in a frame of reference moving with the gas and a bulk energy calculated as if the gas were a rigid body. (2) If the flow is in the x direction, by how much do v_x^2 and v_y^2 differ? Does the distribution of speeds follow the Maxwell-Boltzmann distribution?

Gas with bulk motion

P14.10   Let $P(v)$ be the probability that a molecule has any speed less than or equal to v. (1) What is the significance of $1 - P$? (2) What is the meaning of $P(v + \Delta v) - P(v)$? (3) What is the meaning of dP/dv? (4) If there are N molecules in a sample, what is the meaning of $N(dP/dv) \Delta v$? (Note that this combination can be written approximately as $N \cdot P(v + \Delta v) - N \cdot P(v)$.) (5) Explain carefully why the average speed of a molecule is given by Equation 14.7. (SUGGESTION: Set up the average as a sum and use the definition of a definite integral as the limit of a sum.)

Concept of probability per unit speed

P14.11   Consider N molecules among which are distributed n quantum units of energy. Show that for $n \gg 1$, the number of ways to distribute the energy is proportional to n^{N-1} (see Equations 14.19 and 14.20). (An inductive method using intuitive arguments and working upward from small numbers is acceptable. Alternatively, consult an outside reference on combinatorial analysis.)

A priori probability of energy distribution

P14.12   One kg of steam experiences the following changes. For each process, calculate the entropy change of the steam, paying attention to sign. (1) The steam is heated from 375 K to 385 K with the input of 4.8 kcal of heat as it expands under constant pressure. (2) It is maintained at a temperature of 385 K by the addition of further heat as it continues to expand, doing 10^4 J of work. (3) By means of 100 J of external work without heat flow, the steam is compressed to a smaller volume. (Its temperature is increased by much less than 1 K in this process.) (4) Extraction of 4.8 kcal of heat from the steam at constant pressure lowers its temperature from 385 K to 375 K. Sum the

Entropy changes of gas in noncyclic processes

entropy changes of the steam and explain why the sum is not zero. How does the steam at the end differ from the steam at the beginning?

Entropy change in mixing   **P14.13**   One kg of ice at $-20\,°C$ is mixed with 2 kg of water at $20\,°C$. (1) What is the final state of the system? (2) What is the net change of entropy? (For the ice, use $C_p = 0.5$ kcal/kg K.)

                          P14.14   Equation 14.33 gives the entropy change resulting from mixing if no changes of phase are involved. Prove that this equation can be approximated by Equation 14.34 if the fractional changes of absolute temperature are small.

Heat engines in series   **P14.15**   As indicated schematically in the figure, two heat engines are run in series. Engine 1 takes heat Q_1 from a source at temperature T_1 and exhausts heat Q_2 at a temperature T_2. The input of engine 2 is the heat Q_2 at temperature T_2; it exhausts heat Q_3 at temperature T_3. If engine 1 does work W_1 and engine 2 does work W_2, calculate the maximum possible efficiency of these two engines working together—that is, the maximum value of $(W_1 + W_2)/Q_1$. How does it compare with the maximum efficiency of a single engine operating between temperatures T_1 and T_3?

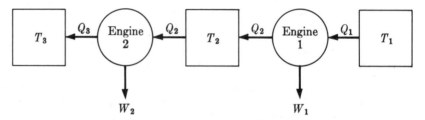

Engine-refrigerator combination   **P14.16**   (1) Prove that the engine-refrigerator combination indicated schematically in the figure is possible if both the engine and the refrigerator operate at maximum efficiency (zero entropy change). The energy W required to operate the refrigerator is supplied by the engine. The heat Q_2 exhausted by the engine into the region at temperature T_2 is the same as the heat removed from that region by the refrigerator. (Take note of the notational differences between this figure and Figure 14.11.) (2) Prove that $Q_3 = Q_1$. (3) State in general terms how reality must differ from the idealization considered here.

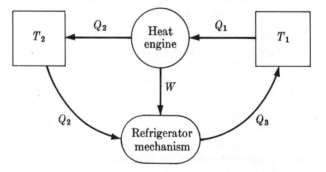

Adiabatic change   **P14.17**   (1) During adiabatic change, how does the rms molecular speed depend on volume? (2) What adiabatic volume change of an ideal monatomic gas is required to double the rms speed of its molecules? (3) Answer the second question for an ideal diatomic gas.

P14.18 One mole of an ideal monatomic gas initially occupies volume V_0 at temperature T_0 and pressure P_0. It is (a) adiabatically compressed to volume $\frac{1}{2}V_0$ and then (b) isothermally expanded to volume V_0. (1) What are the temperature and pressure of the gas after its compression? (2) What are its temperature and pressure when it again occupies volume V_0? (3) What are the changes of internal energy in the compression and the expansion? (4) What are the changes of entropy in the compression and the expansion? (5) Display the changes of the gas in a PV diagram. (6) Calculate the entropy change of the gas if it had moved from its initial to its final state along the line $V = V_0$ in the PV diagram. How does this compare with the sum of the two entropy changes in part 4?

Transformations of an ideal monatomic gas

P14.19 On one side of a piston of area A is air at constant atmospheric pressure P_0 and fixed temperature T_0. On the other side, confined in the end of a cylinder, is air at pressure P. The displacement of the piston away from its equilibrium position is s. Other notation is indicated in the figure. (1) For isothermal change and for $s \ll L$, show that the piston acts as a Hooke's law spring ($F = -\kappa s$). Find its force constant κ. (2) Show that the piston also obeys Hooke's law for adiabatic change and for $s \ll L$, and demonstrate that the force constant κ' for adiabatic change is related to κ for isothermal change by $\kappa' = \gamma \kappa$, where $\gamma = C_p/C_v$.

Air spring

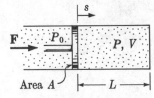

P14.20 (1) For the isothermal air spring defined in the preceding problem, sketch a graph of the restoring force F as a function of the displacement s, and discuss the deviations from Hooke's law for $s > 0$ and $s < 0$. (2) Discuss in some detail the behavior of this "spring" if a finite force is applied to it so suddenly that the air on one side of the piston is momentarily left behind and must undergo free expansion to catch up with the piston. Is Hooke's law still obeyed? If so, is the force constant the same as for slow change?

P14.21 All the processes in the Carnot cycle are reversible, so the cycle itself is reversible. For the reversed engine, work is done on the gas in the cycle, heat is removed from the low-temperature reservoir, and a greater amount of heat is delivered to the high-temperature reservoir; it acts as a refrigerator. Show that no engine operating between temperatures T_1 and T_2 can be more efficient than the Carnot engine; do so by imagining a situation in which a more efficient engine delivers its work to a Carnot refrigerator operating between the same two temperature reservoirs. Consider the net flow of heat into or out of each reservoir and show that the combination of the two engines constitutes a device that violates the second law of thermodynamics.

Proof that a Carnot engine has maximum efficiency

PART FIVE

Electromagnetism

15 Electricity

*Electrical science a century
behind mechanics*

More than a century elapsed between Newton's discovery of the law of gravitational force and Coulomb's determination of the law of electric force. In retrospect, this seems a very long time, once the spirit and methods of modern science had come alive. However, it is not difficult to find some reasons for the lag of electricity behind mechanics. Mechanics was concerned with the grand sweep of the cosmos and linked earthly laws with universal laws. Electricity, thought at first to be an attribute of only certain substances, seemed to be less general and less important. As a practical matter, electrical phenomena, in spite of ready accessibility, were not easy to deal with quantitatively. An electrified object gradually lost its charge; charges in metals moved about in a manner the experimenter could not control; electric currents persisted only for a moment. Planetary motion was not subject to such vagaries. Whatever the reasons, the fact is that while mathematicians and scientists were perfecting the techniques and the tests of mechanics, electricity remained, literally, a sideshow attraction. Around the middle of the eighteenth century, the sparks and shocks of electricity were more often used by entertainers seeking personal profit than by scientists seeking knowledge.

This is not to say that electricity had been completely ignored by men of science. By about 1750, a date roughly marking the beginning of electricity and magnetism as serious branches of science, a certain amount of rudimentary knowledge about electricity had been accumulated. That a mineral called amber could be electrified—or, in modern terminology, charged—had been known to the Greeks. Since electrification was for many centuries believed to be a property exclusively of this one substance, the Greek word for amber, *elektron*, has furnished the root of our "electricity." Not until the time of Brahe and Kepler did knowledge of electricity take a significant step forward from the Greeks of

2,000 years earlier. A treatise by William Gilbert, *De Magnete*,* published in England in 1600, revealed a number of new facts about electricity (and magnetism), setting the stage for true scientific studies of these fields. In particular, Gilbert discovered that electrification is by no means limited to amber but is a general phenomenon. So the middle of the eighteenth century marks not so much the time when studies in electricity were initiated as the time when the tempo of effort and exchange of ideas had reached a jumping-off point to rapid progress.

15.1 Basic properties of electric force

We can summarize most of what was known of electricity in the mid-eighteenth century in terms of the following simple experiments, which may easily be performed by the reader. The only equipment required is a few small rubber balloons, a few feet of string, and some wool or fur (Figure 15.1). A balloon rubbed with wool (or fur or any of numerous other materials) becomes "electrified." What exactly does this mean? If we pretend that we know nothing of electric charge and proceed only on the basis of our experimental findings, we can say only that this process called electrification has altered the properties of the balloon in some way. Before electrification, it had no properties of attraction for anything else. After electrification, it will readily stick to a wall or a ceiling, and it will attract to itself bits of paper or dust. Next we might discover that

A primitive approach to electricity

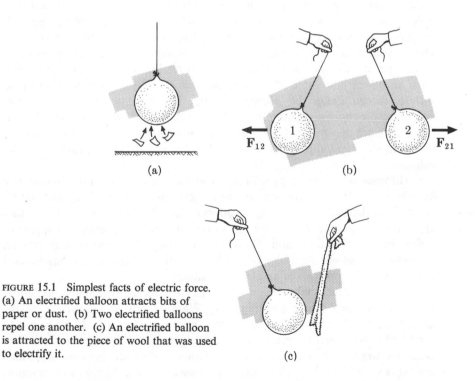

FIGURE 15.1 Simplest facts of electric force.
(a) An electrified balloon attracts bits of paper or dust. (b) Two electrified balloons repel one another. (c) An electrified balloon is attracted to the piece of wool that was used to electrify it.

* Gilbert's book is available in paperback (New York: Dover Publications, Inc., 1958).

electrification can give rise to repulsion as well as attraction. Two electrified balloons suspended from threads and held not too far apart will repel one another, as evidenced by the fact that the strings take up a slanting position instead of hanging vertically. If the balloons are held a great distance apart, there seems to be little or no force; if they are brought closer together, the force gradually increases in intensity. Moreover, Newton's third law can be verified for this new kind of force. Regardless of the degree of electrification of the balloons or their distance apart, the force of the first on the second is equal and opposite to the force of the second on the first. In a similar way the attractive electric force, say between a balloon and the piece of wool used to electrify it, can be studied and found to have the same properties.

Attraction and repulsion

The fact that an electrified object is attracted to almost any other object led at first to the erroneous conclusion that electric forces are always attractive. Not until 1733 was it discovered (by Charles Du Fay) that electrification can lead both to attraction and to repulsion.

The direction of the electric force is of interest as well as its magnitude. We find that it acts along the line joining the electrified objects. It is, like the gravitational force, a central force. (This fact could, of course, be more accurately verified using objects much smaller than balloons.) Also, the electric force—again like the gravitational force—can act through a vacuum. It requires no material medium for its transmission. One very vital fact about electric force, yet a fact readily overlooked, is that the electric force is exceedingly powerful. Since a balloon sticking to a wall can readily be pulled off by a child, it is not so obvious that the force is strong. Yet if it is compared with the gravitational force, it becomes obvious that the electric force is enormous. The gravitational force between a pair of balloons is entirely negligible compared with the electric force. Finally we can readily discover that the electric force an object is capable of exerting or feeling seemingly has nothing to do with the mechanical or the geometrical properties of the object. The electrification of a balloon depends on how much it is rubbed and what it is rubbed with, but it does not depend on the size or shape or weight or color or orientation of the balloon. It is apparently an entirely new and different property of the balloon.

Simple facts of electric force

Through such simple experiments can one gain considerable qualitative knowledge of electric force, knowledge roughly the same as that possessed by scientists in the middle of the eighteenth century. The electric force is (1) either attractive or repulsive, (2) central, (3) weaker at greater distance, (4) capable of acting through a vacuum, and (5) exceedingly powerful compared with gravity. It (6) obeys Newton's third law, and (7) its strength is independent of mechanical or geometrical properties of an electrified object.

With this much knowledge about electric force assimilated, scientists began to ask two major questions: (1) What exactly is the nature of the electrification phenomenon? That is, can the property of a body causing it to exert and to feel electric force be quantitatively defined and measured? (2) How does the strength of electric force vary as the distance between electrified objects is varied? Both of these questions were answered together with scientific precision in the latter half of the eighteenth century. Before that, the concept of electric charge evolved gradually as a qualitative idea.

15.2 The concept of charge: its conservation and quantization

Early studies of electricity involved not only electric force, but also—indeed to a greater extent—the phenomenon of electrification itself. Gilbert proposed in 1600 that electrical effects arise from an electric fluid. With some substantial modifications, the doctrine of the electric fluid held sway until late in the nineteenth century. Even our present concept of charge does not differ very drastically from old ideas about the electric fluid.

Basically, the idea of the electric fluid is very simple. Matter was supposed to contain, besides its material constituents, an ethereal fluid. According to Gilbert, friction could release a part of the fluid into the space surrounding an object, and the gradual flow of the fluid back to its parent object accounted for electrical attraction. According to this view, a neutral piece of amber contained its normal quota of electric fluid. After being rubbed with wool, it suffered a deficiency of the fluid, the lost fluid being distributed in the space around the amber. A bit of paper drawn to the amber was being borne on the tide of returning fluid. The eventual neutralization of the piece of amber occurred as soon as all the fluid had returned to it.

The idea of an electric fluid

It was in terms of a modified electric fluid theory that Benjamin Franklin proposed the law of charge conservation. After the discovery of the conduction of electricity through metals in 1729, Gilbert's idea of a separate electric fluid attached to each material object gave way to the idea of a single electric fluid that could flow from one body to another. The discovery of electric repulsion soon led to the introduction of a two-fluid theory that rivaled the one-fluid theory. The two fluids corresponded to what we now call positive and negative charge. Charges of like sign repel; those of unlike sign attract. In 1747, Franklin, still holding to the one-fluid theory, made the inspired suggestion that the total amount of electric fluid remained forever constant, any loss of fluid by one body being exactly compensated by an equal gain of fluid by another body. In his view, neutrality represented a "normal" amount of fluid, what we now call positive charge represented an excess of fluid, and what we now call negative charge represented a deficiency of fluid.

Franklin's postulate of charge conservation

Not much later (1759), experiments of Franz Aepinus (Figure 15.2) showed that there was, in fact, no evidence that any electric fluid occupied the space outside an electrified body. At this point the fluid, having retreated to the interior of material objects (except in certain phenomena such as sparks), scarcely differed from our modern idea of charge. Toward the end of the eighteenth century the two-fluid theory gradually re-emerged as the dominant theory of electricity, in part because it proved to be more convenient in calculations of electric force, in part because it was championed by influential scientists, such as Charles Coulomb. The two fluids came to be called charge, and for a century the source of all electrical (and magnetic) phenomena was successfully described as a pair of fluids that could flow through some materials, that could be held fast on other materials, that acted as the source of electric force, and that, when present in equal quantities, canceled each other's effects.

The idea that electric charge was not a continuous fluid, but that instead fixed amounts of charge were associated with each atom, was suggested by Michael Faraday as early as 1840. That charge is indeed concentrated in

Charge quantization

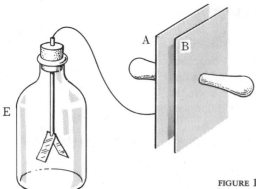

FIGURE 15.2   Schematic representation of an early experiment (Aepinus, 1759) that suggested that charge (or electric fluid) exists only within matter, not in the space surrounding an object. The rate at which plate A loses its electric charge is unaffected by the presence of plate B. The mutual repulsion of the metal foil leaves in the electroscope E provides a measure of the degree of electrification of plate A.

quantized lumps on individual particles was finally verified beyond doubt by J. J. Thomson's discovery of the electron in 1897. Concerning our view of charge, the most important consequence of this discovery is that it rendered irrelevant the idea of a *separate* fluid, distinct from the material basis of the substance. Charge becomes a property of matter, not an additional substance added to matter. Yet, viewed more carefully, our modern idea of charge is perhaps not significantly different from the old idea of an electric fluid. Our mental image of charge is still an image of something extra, a "substance" carried by charged particles, a substance that neutral particles lack. At the deepest level, charge remains a mystery. The fact that we "understand" electrical and magnetic phenomena—that we can support a vast range of experimental results on a simple and powerful theoretical framework and can successfully predict new phenomena—should not delude us into thinking that we really understand electric charge.

Charge still mysterious

In 1747 Franklin had an accurate "feeling" for the nature of charge, and he could make a brilliant guess about its conservation. However, his law of conservation must be recognized as a guess. At the time, there was no definition or measurement of charge as a quantitative concept. An operational definition that could convert a qualitative idea into a quantitative concept had to await the discovery of the exact law of force between electrified objects several decades later.

15.3   Coulomb's law of electric force

In his monumental work begun in 1666, Newton discovered three vital facts about the gravitational force: First, the strength of the force varies inversely as the square of the distance between objects. Second, the force can act through empty space. Third, the gravitational force exerted by an object (and experienced by an object) is proportional to its mass. A century went by before it was discovered that the electric force shares with the gravitational force the first two of these fundamental properties. It must be remembered that in the

Electricity and gravity compared

manifestations most evident to man, these two kinds of force seemed then to have nothing whatever in common. Gravity acted over interplanetary distance; electricity was known only to act over short distances within the laboratory. The source of gravity, mass, was an invariable property of an object that no amount of heating, distorting, or rubbing could alter; the source of electric force, charge, on the other hand, could easily be altered on a given object in a variety of ways.

The inverse-square law of electric force was accurately established in 1785 by Coulomb* (Figure 15.3). Expressed as a proportionality, it is

$$F \sim \frac{1}{r^2}, \tag{15.1}$$

Dependence on distance

where F is the magnitude of the force exerted by either of a pair of electrified objects on the other (by Newton's third law, they must be equal) and r is the distance between the two objects, if the separation of the objects is much greater than their size. For uniformly charged spheres, r is the distance between their centers. The discovery of this law marked a turning point in the history of electromagnetism. It provided for the first time a way to define and measure charge exactly. Equally important, by demonstrating that electric and gravitational forces vary in the same way with distance, it suggested that the electric force is perhaps also a fundamental force of nature and worthy of as much attention as gravitation had received. Over laboratory scales of distance—millimeters to meters—the dependence on distance given by Formula 15.1 is now known to be correct to within a few parts in 10^{16}.†

By itself, Formula 15.1 reveals only the dependence of electric force on distance, not the magnitude of the force. The successful assumption that leads to a formula for the magnitude is as simple an assumption as one could imagine: that the force exerted by or experienced by a body depends on only a single scalar property of that body, its charge. Moreover, the force is proportional to the charge. It is independent of the mass, size, shape, composition,

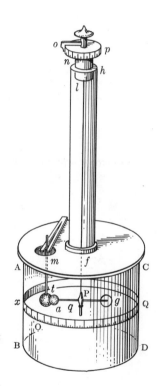

FIGURE 15.3   Torsion balance used by Charles Coulomb (1785) to establish the inverse square law of electric force. The force between two charged balls in the lower left part of the apparatus twists the long fiber. The neutral position of the fiber is varied by manually twisting its upper support. [Illustration adapted from W. F. Magie, *A Source Book in Physics* (Cambridge: Harvard University Press, 1965), p. 410.]

* The law had been suggested on a number of earlier occasions: for example, by Joseph Priestley in 1767. Coulomb's achievement was the measuring of the dependence of the electric force on distance to a previously unobtainable precision. (Cavendish had actually made an accurate determination before Coulomb, but he did not publish his result.)

† Experimental confirmation of the precise quantum theory of the hydrogen atom shows the inverse-square law of electric force to be valid to distances as small as 10^{-15} m. Indirect evidence from studies of the earth's magnetic field extends the validity of the law to a few thousand kilometers. There is no sure support for it over astronomical distances. For research reports on this topic, see A. S. Goldhaber and M. M. Nieto, *Physical Review Letters* **21**, 567 (1968), and E. R. Williams, J. E. Faller, and H. A. Hill, ibid. **26**, 721 (1971).

temperature, and all other properties of the body. Since the electric force acting between two objects is the same for both objects, the force must be proportional to each charge if it is proportional to either. The law of force (which we call Coulomb's law) is written

Dependence on charge

$$F_{12} = k_e \frac{q_1 q_2}{r^2},$$ (15.2)

where q_1 and q_2 are the charges of the objects and k_e is a constant of proportionality. The notation F_{12} means the force experienced by object 1 arising from the presence of object 2. Evidently,

$$F_{12} = F_{21},$$ (15.3)

in keeping with Newton's third law. Also implicit in Equation 15.2 is a law of superposition (Section 15.5).

DEFINITION OF CHARGE

Coulomb's law contains, then, not only the inverse-square dependence on distance but also the basic assumption of the proportionality of electric force to charge (and to no other intrinsic properties of bodies). It constitutes, in effect, a definition of charge. It may also be used to define a unit charge. In the cgs system of units, the proportionality constant k_e is arbitrarily set equal to 1, so that the law reads

Cgs version defines the esu

$$F_{12} = \frac{q_1 q_2}{r^2} \quad \text{(cgs)}.$$ (15.4)

Then the unit charge is, by definition, the charge that exerts a force of 1 dyne on an equal charge 1 cm away. This unit charge is called the electrostatic unit (esu), or the statcoulomb.

The SI unit of charge, the coulomb (C), is defined differently. Electric currents exert magnetic forces on one another. Such forces (discussed in Chapter 16) are easier to measure with precision than electrostatic forces. Consequently, it is preferable to define a unit current by direct reference to magnetic force than to define a unit charge by direct reference to electric force. The unit current, defined by a magnetic-force experiment (Section 16.9), is called the ampere (A). Since current is charge per unit time,

$$I = \frac{dq}{dt},$$ (15.5)

Definition of the coulomb

the ampere and the second define the coulomb:

$$1 \text{ C} = 1 \text{ A sec}$$ (15.6)

(this repeats Equation 2.14). In a wire carrying a steady current of 1 A, a charge of 1 C is conducted past a given point in 1 sec. Or, if a variable current, $I(t)$, flows to an object where charge is accumulating, the charge accumulated in time t is defined by an integral:

$$q = \int_0^t I(t') \, dt'.$$ (15.7)

Again, if I is measured in amperes and t in seconds, then q is expressed in coulombs. The conversion factor linking the cgs and SI units of charge is

$$3.0 \times 10^9 \text{ esu/C}. \tag{15.8}$$

The quantum unit of charge is given by Equation 2.15 (see also Appendix 3). Even in the macroscopic domain, the coulomb is a very large unit of charge. An electrified balloon, for instance, might possess a net negative charge of only about 10^{-6} C.

With the SI unit of charge defined via a magnetic force measurement, the constant k_e in Equation 15.2 is not arbitrary. It must be determined experimentally; for example, by measuring the force between known charges a known distance apart. It is standard, with SI units, to write $k_e = 1/4\pi\epsilon_0$; then Coulomb's law takes the form

$$F_{12} = \frac{1}{4\pi\epsilon_0} \frac{q_1 q_2}{r^2} \quad \text{(SI)}. \tag{15.9} \qquad \textit{SI version}$$

The quantity ϵ_0, known as the permittivity of free space, has the value

$$\epsilon_0 = 8.8542 \times 10^{-12} \text{ C}^2/\text{N m}^2. \tag{15.10}$$

The inverse of $4\pi\epsilon_0$ is, to close approximation.

$$\frac{1}{4\pi\epsilon_0} = 9.00 \times 10^9 \text{ N m}^2/\text{C}^2. \tag{15.11}$$

VECTOR FORM OF COULOMB'S LAW

Force is, of course, a vector quantity; Equation 15.9 gives only the magnitude* of the electrostatic force. To provide a vector expression, we may define the position vectors of two charged particles to be $\mathbf{r}_1$ and $\mathbf{r}_2$ and the displacement vector from particle 2 to particle 1 to be (Figure 15.4)

$$\mathbf{r}_{12} = \mathbf{r}_1 - \mathbf{r}_2. \tag{15.12}$$

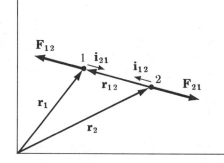

FIGURE 15.4   Vector diagram for interacting charged particles.

---

* Strictly speaking, F_{12} as given by Equation 15.9 is a component, not a magnitude; it can be either positive or negative, depending on the relative sign of q_1 and q_2. A positive sign means repulsion; a negative sign means attraction.

This vector may also be described as the position of particle 1 relative to particle 2. With this notation, the force acting on particle 1 contributed by particle 2 is

Coulomb's law in vector form

$$\mathbf{F}_{12} = \frac{1}{4\pi\epsilon_0} \frac{q_1 q_2 \mathbf{r}_{12}}{r^3},$$ (15.13)

where r is defined as the magnitude of $\mathbf{r}_{12}$ (or of $\mathbf{r}_{21}$):

$$r = |\mathbf{r}_{12}| = |\mathbf{r}_{21}|.$$ (15.14)

Since $\mathbf{r}_{12} = -\mathbf{r}_{21}$, it follows from Equation 15.13 that $\mathbf{F}_{12} = -\mathbf{F}_{21}$. The force $\mathbf{F}_{12}$ is repulsive (parallel to $\mathbf{r}_{12}$) for charges of the same sign, such that the product $q_1 q_2$ is positive; it is attractive (antiparallel to $\mathbf{r}_{12}$) for charges of opposite sign, such that $q_1 q_2$ is negative. Another, often more convenient way to write Equation 15.13 is

The unit-vector form is convenient

$$\mathbf{F}_{12} = \frac{1}{4\pi\epsilon_0} \frac{q_1 q_2 \mathbf{i}_{12}}{r^2},$$ (15.15)

where $\mathbf{i}_{12}$ is a unit vector parallel to $\mathbf{r}_{12}$ (Figure 15.4).

Note that Equation 15.9 or 15.15 is valid if SI units are used but is *not* valid with cgs units (compare Equation 15.4). It is characteristic of electromagnetic theory that many equations are valid only for some sets of units and not for others. In what follows, all equations are written in a form valid for SI units, unless explicit notation to the contrary is made. Eventually, the student of physics must be at home with cgs as well as SI (or mks) units. In first studying electromagnetic theory, however, it is an unnecessary distraction to keep track of two sets of units and two forms of many equations. We shall consistently use SI units, with only occasional reference to cgs units. Some basic equations of electromagnetism for both sets of units are summarized in Appendix 5.

■ EXAMPLE: Particles of equal charge, $q_1 = q_2 = q_3 = 2 \times 10^{-6}$ C, are located at three corners of a square with sides of 0.1 m, as shown in Figure 15.5. What is the total force $\mathbf{F}_2$ acting on particle 2? For convenience, choose axes as shown in the figure. The magnitudes of forces $\mathbf{F}_{23}$ and $\mathbf{F}_{21}$ are equal. From Equation 15.9,

$$F_{23} = F_{21} = 9.0 \times 10^9 \frac{\text{N m}^2}{\text{C}^2} \times \frac{(2 \times 10^{-6} \text{ C})^2}{(0.1 \text{ m})^2} = 3.6 \text{ N}.$$

In vector notation,

$$\mathbf{F}_{21} = 3.6\mathbf{i} \text{ N},$$

$$\mathbf{F}_{23} = 3.6\mathbf{j} \text{ N}.$$

Their sum is

$$\mathbf{F}_2 = \mathbf{F}_{21} + \mathbf{F}_{23} = (3.6\mathbf{i} + 3.6\mathbf{j}) \text{ N}.$$

The magnitude of $\mathbf{F}_2$ is $F_2 = 5.1$ N. It is directed at 45 deg above the x axis. ■

It is worth drawing attention to the fact that in order to approach an understanding of a new phenomenon—electricity—we rely on the already well-established mechanical concept of force. Attempts to understand electricity

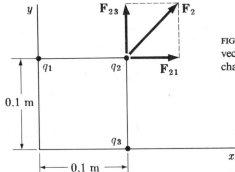

FIGURE 15.5   The force on charge q_2 is the vector sum of the forces contributed by charges q_1 and q_3.

by studying "purely" electrical phenomena—sparks jumping between electrified objects, for example, or shocks administered to human subjects—would not fare nearly so well. Electricity has now developed into a complete and self-consistent theory with an independent status. Even so, the theory preserves its ties with mechanics. Force, energy, and momentum remain essential concepts of electromagnetism. No theory stands entirely alone, simply because no part of nature is wholly independent of any other part.

Electricity is tied to mechanics

15.4   Electric field

Occasionally, a new concept makes its way into physics with a deceptively simple definition but remarkably fruitful consequences. Electric field is a concept of this type. The electric field at a point is defined operationally as the electric force on a test charge placed at that point divided by the magnitude of the test charge—provided that other charges, which give rise to the field, remain undisturbed. In symbols,

$$\mathbf{E} = \frac{\mathbf{F}}{q'},\qquad(15.16)$$

Electric field is defined as force per unit charge

$\mathbf{E}$ being the usual symbol for electric field*; $\mathbf{F}$ designates force, and q' designates charge. As a notational device, we shall sometimes add a prime to the symbol q if the passive role of charge is being emphasized—charge *experiencing* a force or *responding* to an electric field. Without a prime, the symbol q will usually indicate charge in its active role, *exerting* a force or *creating* an electric field. The assertion "There is an electric field at the center of this room" could be tested by placing a suitably small charge at the center of the room and observing whether or not it experienced a force. If it did, we would say that by definition an electric field exists at that point. The magnitude and direction of the field could then be measured by measuring the force and dividing by the magnitude

---

* The symbol for the magnitude of electric field is E, the same as the symbol for energy. This duplication is too well-established to alter. It should cause no problem for the student who is alert to the context surrounding equations. In the following text, the meaning of the symbol is stated explicitly when there is any possibility of ambiguity.

*The test charge must be
stationary*

of the test charge (presumed already known). In the definition, it is essential that the test charge be stationary. In any frame of reference in which a stationary charge experiences a force, there exists, by definition, an electric field. Note that the electric field is a vector quantity. It is chosen to point in the direction that a positive charge would be pushed. The dimension of electric field is evidently force divided by charge. Its SI unit is newton/coulomb. As will be made clear later, this unit is the same as volt/meter:

$$\text{unit of } \mathbf{E} = \text{N/C} = \text{V/m}. \tag{15.17}$$

The definition of electric field poses no conceptual problem. Whenever a stationary charged particle experiences a force, we are quite free to divide the force by the charge and give this quotient a new name, "electric field." The important thing to understand is why this arbitrarily defined quantity is useful. Several reasons can be given here; others will emerge in later developments in this chapter and the next two. One merit of the electric field concept is that it

The field exists in empty space

can be said to exist at a point in space, whether or not a charge is located at that point and whether or not any force is being experienced at that point. The field can be thought of as a latent force, or potential force, describing the force that would act at any point if a charge were placed there. Moreover, the field, one single quantity, can provide information about the force that would act on *any* charged particle placed at the given point. If the charge q' is placed where the electric field is equal to $\mathbf{E}$ and if q' does not disturb the sources of $\mathbf{E}$,* the force acting on the charge will be

$$\mathbf{F} = q'\mathbf{E}. \tag{15.18}$$

*Meaning of field:
a continuously distributed
quantity*

If the electric field can be defined at any particular point in space, it can, of course, be defined at all points in space. It can be regarded as a continuous distributed property over any region of space or over all of space. This is what "field" means in physics: a quantity defined at all points throughout a region of space. We may, for example, speak of the temperature field in a room; at every point in the room, there exists a temperature, a continuously distributed scalar quantity.

LINES OF FIELD

Related to the idea of the distributed electric field is the great pictorial convenience resulting from use of the field concept. Consider a single isolated positive charge q at a fixed point. What is the electric field in the space surrounding this charge? To answer this question, we imagine a second test charge q' moved about from place to place in the neighborhood of the fixed charge q. Wherever it is placed, q' (presumed to be positive) will experience a force directed away from q; this force determines the electric field. If at each point in space we imagine an arrow representing the electric field at that point, all of the arrows will be pointing outward, like the spines of a porcupine, away

---

* This restriction is necessary in order that $\mathbf{E}$ be the same with the test charge present and with it absent. If $\mathbf{E}$ is taken to mean only the field with the charge q' present, Equation 15.18 is valid without restriction.

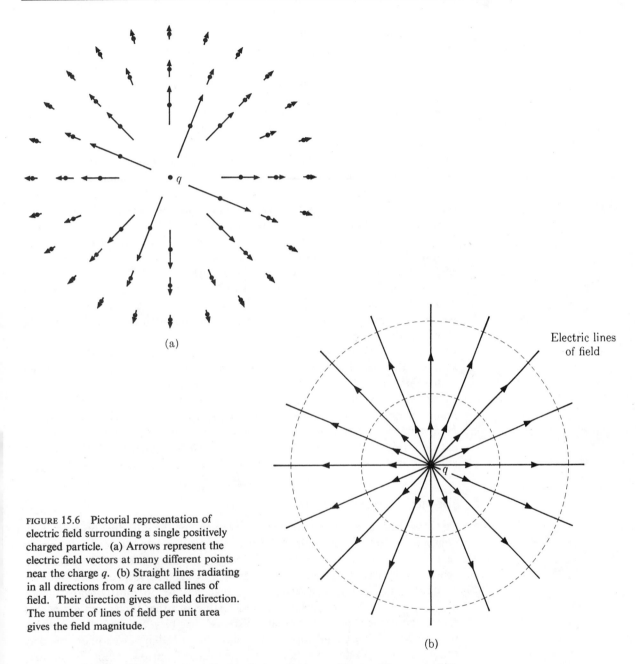

(a)

Electric lines
of field

FIGURE 15.6   Pictorial representation of
electric field surrounding a single positively
charged particle. (a) Arrows represent the
electric field vectors at many different points
near the charge q. (b) Straight lines radiating
in all directions from q are called lines of
field. Their direction gives the field direction.
The number of lines of field per unit area
gives the field magnitude.

(b)

from the charge q [Figure 15.6(a)]. Now that the test charge q' has served its
purpose to define the electric field, we take it away, leaving the single charge q
surrounded by its electric field. If the separate arrows are joined together by
straight lines radiating outward from q, the resulting porcupine quills, extending
on to infinity, provide a three-dimensional "picture" of the electric field created
by a single charged particle. As in Figure 15.6(b), we may attach arrowheads
to the radiating lines to indicate the direction of the field, the direction of force
that would be exerted on a positively charged particle.

Lines of field portray field direction

The lines constructed in this way are called "lines of field," or "lines of force." They conveniently pictorialize the electric field. Actually, they do even more than this. If interpreted in the right way, they provide information on the strength of the field as well as its direction. In the example just cited, with straight lines of field radiating from a point, imagine two concentric spheres, one with twice the radius of the other, each being pierced by the lines of field radiating from their common center [Figure 15.6(b)]. The larger sphere, with twice the radius of the smaller, has four times the surface area of the smaller. Since the number of lines piercing each sphere is the same, the number of lines per unit area is four times less for the larger than for the smaller sphere. The electric field at the outer sphere is also four times less than at the inner sphere (see Equation 15.20). As a general rule, in a field-line diagram, the magnitude of the electric field is proportional to the number of lines per unit area crossing a hypothetical surface normal to the direction of the field lines. Note in Figure 15.6(b) that the number of lines per unit area approaches infinity at the location of the charge q, where the field becomes infinite.

Lines per unit area give field magnitude

As illustrated by several examples in Figure 15.7, the lines of field are of great help in visualizing distributions of electric field. It is left as an exercise to show that the fields created by two like charges and two unlike charges are as shown in this figure. The last example in Figure 15.7 shows a possible distribution of electric field inside a "black box." It illustrates the fact that the field idea and the pictorial representation of fields can be very useful even when the sources of the field are unknown. In this example, there may be charge distributed over the walls of the box and other charge outside it. Regardless of how many charges may be contributing to the field at a point within the box, the field at that point is still one single quantity, determining the net force that would act on a test charge placed at that point. The field "automatically" sums and summarizes the many contributions of outside charges contributing to the force.

THE FIELD CONCEPT AND LOCAL ACTION

So far we have considered two advantages attending the introduction of the new concept of electric field. First, the field describes a latent force that may be regarded as existing in empty space. Second, the field, distributed throughout space, lends itself to graphic presentation through the idea of lines of field. A third, and no less significant, advantage has to do mostly with human psychology. Despite the clear and inescapable fact that forces can act across empty space, the idea of "action at a distance" has been consistently repugnant to scientists. Through the introduction of one intermediary or another, man has sought to account for the transmission of force from one point to another, without embracing the idea of action at a distance. Newton regarded as obviously absurd the idea that the sun's gravitational force could act on the earth without an intermediate agent to transmit the force. This agent was given the name "ether"; it persisted in scientific thought until early in this century. With similar motivation, Gilbert had introduced the idea of the electric fluid flowing out into the space surrounding an electrified body to transmit the electric force to neighboring objects. After the electric fluid was forced by the weight of experimental evidence of the mid-eighteenth century to retreat back

Idea of the ether

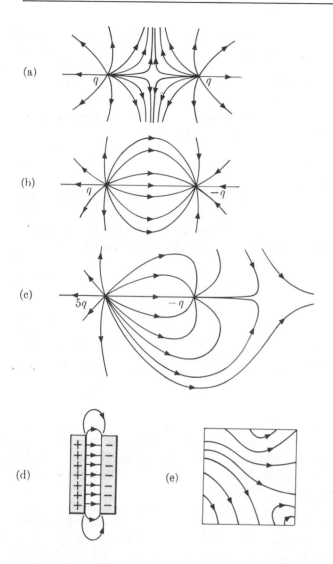

FIGURE 15.7   Lines of field associated with various distributions of electric charge. (a) Two equal positive charges. (b) A pair of equal and opposite charges. This combination is called a dipole. (c) Charges $+5q$ and $-q$. (d) Two parallel metal plates, as in a capacitor, one charged positively, the other with equal negative charge. (e) A "black box," a field distribution within an enclosure that can be defined and measured even if the sources of the field are unknown.

into the electrified body, the doctrine of electrical action at a distance gained a partial, though temporary, victory. The victory was partial because although no electric fluid occupied the space between charged objects, the ether was still there and could be assigned the job of transmitting electric force as it was supposed to transmit gravitational force. Alternatively, in the view of some, two ethers could coexist in space, one to transmit gravitational force and one to transmit electric force.   The victory was temporary because the concept of electric field, introduced in the nineteenth century, again replaced the idea of distant action by the idea of local action.   It is this view that prevails today.

According to this view of the electric field, the force exerted by one charge on another can be regarded as a two-stage process.   Consider a charge q located at point A and a charge q' at point B, a distance r away (Figure 15.8).   The force experienced by q' resulting from the presence of q is

$$F_E = \frac{1}{4\pi\epsilon_0} \frac{qq'i_r}{r^2}, \tag{15.19}$$

where i_r is a unit vector directed from A toward B.   Coulomb's law in this form may be regarded as a statement of distant action.   With the help of the field concept, it may be broken into two pieces, one a statement of the creation of a field, and one a statement of the action of the field.   These statements are

$$E = \frac{1}{4\pi\epsilon_0} \frac{qi_r}{r^2} \tag{15.20}$$

Two-stage view of electric force   and

$$F_E = q'E. \tag{15.21}$$

The first says that at a distance r away from itself the charge q creates an electric field E.   The radial component of this field is

$$E = \frac{1}{4\pi\epsilon_0} \frac{q}{r^2}.^* \tag{15.22}$$

The second statement says that this electric field causes the charge q' to experience a force F_E.   Evidently, if Equation 15.20 is substituted in Equation 15.21, Equation 15.19 is the result.   What the field idea has effected is not any change in Coulomb's law, nor in the calculated force; it has only altered the way man looks at the phenomenon of electric force.

The "reality" of the electric field   Is the field "real"?   Logically speaking, it is as real as any other quantitative concept in physics.   It is operationally defined; it has an unambiguous and measurable magnitude and direction.   But this is an unsatisfying answer; it says no more than that scientists have defined the electric field in a logically self-consistent way.   And endless series of useless concepts could be defined just as accurately.   The significant question is not whether the field is real, but whether it is useful.   In the end, the reality of nature—that is, the image of the physical world to which scientific discovery leads us—is based on those concepts that have proved useful in science.   We quite naturally attribute a deeper reality to the few most useful concepts of science than we do to numerous

---

* Equations 15.20 and 15.22 are valid if the charge q is at rest; for a moving charge, the electric field is given by

$$E = \frac{1}{4\pi\epsilon_0} \frac{q}{r^2} \frac{[1 - (v^2/c^2)]}{[1 - (v^2 \sin^2 \theta/c^2)]^{3/2}},$$

where θ is the angle between the velocity v of the particle and the radial vector r from the particle to the point of observation, and c is the speed of light.   So long as v is much smaller than c, Equations 15.20 and 15.22 remain excellent approximations.

FIGURE 15.8   The two-stage view of electric force. (a) A charge q at point A creates a field at point B. (b) A charge q' at B experiences a force because of the existence of the field at that point.

peripheral concepts, even though the latter may be equally "real" from a logical point of view.   Even though the definition of electric field as force per unit charge may at first appear to add little to one's understanding of electrical phenomena, in fact, from our present perspective we can say without doubt that the electric field has been an exceedingly useful and fruitful concept in science. Including value judgments as well as mere logic, then, we must conclude that the electric field represents reality.

15.5   The law of superposition

The law of superposition, concerned with two or more forces or fields, is often taken for granted.   Actually, it deserves special notice as a particularly important statement about fields.   We proceed by example.   Suppose that a charge q_A is located at point A and that a charge q'_C is located at point C and that this pair of charges is far removed from all others [Figure 15.9(a)].   The charge q'_C will experience a force F_{CA} because of the neighboring charge q_A.   Now remove charge q_A to a great distance, and bring up another charge q_B to a point B near C.   The force on q'_C will now be contributed by q_B; call the new force F_{CB}. Finally, leaving the charges q_B and q'_C at their locations B and C, return charge q_A to its original location A.   Now what will be the force exerted on charge q'_C?

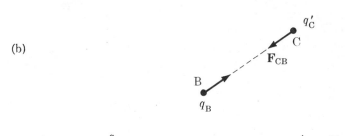

FIGURE 15.9   Illustration of the law of superposition for electric forces.   In the presence of charges q_A and q_B together, charge q'_C feels a force equal to the vector sum of the forces that would act if the charges q_A and q_B were separately present one at a time.

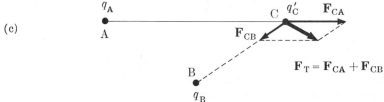

$$F_T = F_{CA} + F_{CB}$$

The superposition of forces

Experiment shows that the combined force is the vector sum of the forces $\mathbf{F}_{CA}$ and $\mathbf{F}_{CB}$ contributed by the two other charges separately. The result holds true for any number of contributing forces. The fact that individual contributions may simply be summed (as vectors) to give the total force is what is called the law of superposition.

It may seem self-evident that if a charge is being pushed by two other charges, the force it feels is the sum of the forces it would feel if each of the other charges were present one at a time. Actually, this superposition is an extremely important fact about electric forces that has no right at all to be called self-evident. Elsewhere in the physical world, the idea of superposition is not

Examples of nonsuperposition

always valid. If a pint of water is added to a pint of alcohol, the total volume of liquid turns out to be less than two pints. If a neutron and a proton join to form a deuteron, the mass of the deuteron is less than the sum of the masses of the neutron and proton. If three nuclear particles are close together, the force on one of them is not equal to the sum of the forces that would be exerted by the other two separately. Perhaps the best proof that the superposition law of electric forces is not self-evident is the fact that it is not precisely true. In recent years we have learned that electric forces are not exactly additive. Even in the atomic world, the deviation from additivity—that is, the extent to which the law of superposition is "violated"—is exceedingly small. In the large-scale world, the effect is entirely negligible, and the law of superposition is precisely correct to within the limits of human skill in measurement. The almost exact validity of this law for electric (and magnetic) forces further affirms our faith in the simplicity of nature. It is difficult to imagine any simpler way to combine two forces than by adding them together.

If electric (and magnetic) forces obey the law of superposition, then electric (and magnetic) fields do, too. Indeed, the significance of the law can better be appreciated in terms of its meaning for fields. Imagine two charges q_A and q_B at the points A and B, this time without a third charge present (Figure 15.10). If either q_A or q_B were present alone, it would establish in its neighborhood a

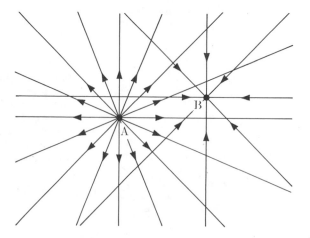

FIGURE 15.10 Superposition in terms of fields. Fields created by different particles coexist in space without mutual interaction.

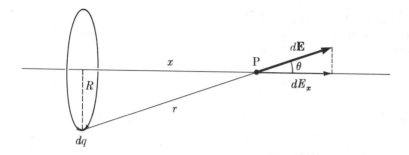

FIGURE 15.11   At point P, the electric field contributed by the increment of charge dq is $d\mathbf{E}$, and its component along the axis of the loop is dE_x.

"Coulomb field," directed away from itself (for positive charge) and diminishing in strength as the inverse square of the distance.   According to the law of superposition, the field in space with both charges present is the vector sum of the two different Coulomb fields centered at the points A and B.   This means that we may think of the two fields as coexisting in space, each wholly uninfluenced by the presence of the other.   The physical meaning of the law of superposition is that the field created by a given charge depends not at all on how many other fields may also be present in the same space.   In light of our modern view of the field as a "substance," the possibility of superposing fields in the same space without mutual interaction is a remarkable fact, one that clearly illustrates the simplicity that the law of superposition has contributed to our view of nature.

Fields coexist without interaction

■ EXAMPLE: A total charge q is spread uniformly around a hoop of radius R. What is the electric field created on the axis of the hoop a distance x from the center of the hoop?   We may sum the contributions from infinitesimal increments of charge dq around the circumference of the hoop.   One such contribution, $d\mathbf{E}$, is shown in Figure 15.11.   Point P, where the field is evaluated, is at distance x from the center of the hoop and distance r from its edge.   From Equation 15.22, the magnitude of $d\mathbf{E}$ is

$$dE = \frac{1}{4\pi\epsilon_0} \frac{dq}{r^2}. \qquad (15.23)$$

Other contributions to the total field at P lie on the surface of a cone so that their components perpendicular to the axis of the hoop cancel and their components along the axis add.   One component along the axis is

$$dE_x = dE \cos\theta = dE\left(\frac{x}{r}\right). \qquad (15.24)$$

Since $r^2 = x^2 + R^2$, Equations 15.23 and 15.24 combine to yield

$$dE_x = \frac{1}{4\pi\epsilon_0} \frac{dq\, x}{(x^2 + R^2)^{3/2}}. \qquad (15.25)$$

The magnitude of the total field is

$$E_x = \int dE_x.$$

The integral sums the increments of charge around the circumference of the hoop. Since all factors multiplying dq on the right side of Equation 15.25 are constant for this integration, the result is simply

Field of a loop of charge

$$E_x = \frac{1}{4\pi\epsilon_0} \frac{qx}{(x^2 + R^2)^{3/2}} \,. \tag{15.26}$$

What approximate form does this equation take for x much greater than R? What is its value at $x = 0$?   ∎

15.6   Electric flux; Gauss's law

Imagine a sphere of radius R centered at a point charge q [Figure 15.6(b)]. The product of the field strength E at the spherical surface and the area A of the sphere is independent of R:

$$EA = \frac{1}{4\pi\epsilon_0} \frac{q}{R^2} \times 4\pi R^2 = \frac{q}{\epsilon_0} \,. \tag{15.27}$$

This product is called the *flux* of the electric field, or simply the electric flux, for which the symbol Φ_E is used. Electric flux is proportional to the number of lines of field penetrating a given surface. A precise definition of flux is given as a differential statement. Imagine any infinitesimal area dS (Figure 15.12). Arbitrarily choose either of the two directions normal to the surface as the positive direction. Then the area can be represented by a vector $d\mathbf{S}$ with magnitude dS and direction along the chosen positive normal direction. If an electric field exists in the vicinity of the area element $d\mathbf{S}$, the electric flux penetrating the area element is defined by

$$d\Phi_E = \mathbf{E} \cdot d\mathbf{S}. \tag{15.28}$$

Definition of electric flux   This may also be written

$$d\Phi_E = E \, dS \cos\theta, \tag{15.29}$$

where θ is the angle between the vectors $\mathbf{E}$ and $d\mathbf{S}$. If $d\Phi_E$ is positive, the field lines come out of the surface on the side chosen as the positive normal; a negative value of $d\Phi_E$ means that the field lines enter this side. The increment of flux $d\Phi_E$ may be zero if $\mathbf{E}$ is zero or if the lines of field run parallel to the surface area, not cutting it from either side.

FIGURE 15.12   The electric flux through the element of area $d\mathbf{S}$ is defined to be $d\Phi_E = \mathbf{E} \cdot d\mathbf{S} = E \, dS \cos\theta.$

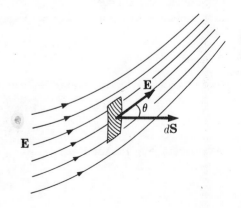

Electric flux is, by definition, a scalar quantity. The total flux penetrating a finite surface may be written as an integral:

$$\Phi_E = \int \mathbf{E} \cdot d\mathbf{S}. \qquad (15.30)$$ *Flux as a surface integral*

This is an example of a *surface integral*. Figure 15.13 helps to make its meaning clear. The surface of interest is divided into infinitesimal elements of area $d\mathbf{S}$. For each element, the scalar product $\mathbf{E} \cdot d\mathbf{S}$ is formed, and these quantities are summed algebraically over the whole surface. This is the meaning of the surface integral. Techniques for its practical evaluation depend on the particular geometry of the surface.

The unit of flux is clearly the unit of field multiplied by the unit of area:

$$\text{unit of electric flux} = \text{N m}^2/\text{C} = \text{V m}. \qquad (15.31)$$

■ EXAMPLE 1: A square surface of side L is parallel to the xz plane and intercepts the y axis at y_0 (Figure 15.14). What is a general expression for the electric flux cutting this surface? What is the flux if $\mathbf{E}$ is constant? As shown in the figure, we may write the element of surface area

$$d\mathbf{S} = dx\,dz\,\mathbf{j}.$$

The scalar product $\mathbf{E} \cdot d\mathbf{S}$ is

$$\mathbf{E} \cdot d\mathbf{S} = E_y\,dx\,dz.$$

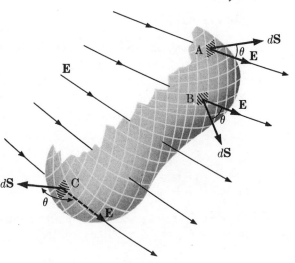

FIGURE 15.13   The idea of a surface integral. The infinitesimal contributions $\mathbf{E} \cdot d\mathbf{S}$ are summed over the surface. In this figure, $\mathbf{E} \cdot d\mathbf{S}$ is positive at points A and B, negative at point C.

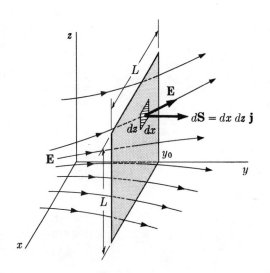

FIGURE 15.14   Flux crossing a square surface. The positive direction of area is chosen to be to the right.

The components E_x and E_z do not contribute. If E_y depends on x, y, and z, the surface of interest is specified by setting $y = y_0$. The flux is

$$\Phi_E = \int \mathbf{E} \cdot d\mathbf{S} = \int E_y(x, y_0, z) \, dx \, dz.$$

More explicitly, this is written as a double integral,

$$\Phi_E = \int_{z=0}^{L} \int_{x=0}^{L} E_y(x, y_0, z) \, dx \, dz. \tag{15.32}$$

For the special case, $E_y = constant$, the factor E_y may be taken outside the integral. Integrations over x and over z then separately give factors L, so that the flux is

Flux of constant field across a plane

$$\Phi_E = E_y L^2 = E_y A; \tag{15.33}$$

where A is the area of the square surface. An alternative approach, for constant $\mathbf{E}$, is to return to Equation 15.30 and write

$$\Phi_E = \mathbf{E} \cdot \int d\mathbf{S}. \tag{15.34}$$

The integral $\int d\mathbf{S}$ is the (vector) area of the whole plane surface, $L^2 \mathbf{j}$. The scalar product in Equation 15.34 is therefore $E_y L^2$, the same result as obtained above. ∎

If flux is to be calculated across a closed surface, as in the example of the sphere that opened this section, we write

$$\Phi_E{}^c = \oint \mathbf{E} \cdot d\mathbf{S}. \tag{15.35}$$

The superscript c and the circle superimposed on the integral sign are both notational devices to indicate a closed surface. For such a closed surface, the positive normal to the surface is chosen, by standard convention, to point outward, away from the enclosed volume.

GAUSS'S LAW

For a spherical surface centered on a point charge, the total flux is

$$\oint \mathbf{E} \cdot d\mathbf{S} = EA,$$

where E is the radial component of $\mathbf{E}$ at the sphere and A is the area of the sphere. (The proof of this statement is left as a problem.) Equation 15.27 may, therefore, be rewritten

$$\oint \mathbf{E} \cdot d\mathbf{S} = \frac{q}{\epsilon_0}, \tag{15.36}$$

Gauss's law: flux related to enclosed charge

or

$$\Phi_E{}^c = \frac{q}{\epsilon_0}. \tag{15.37}$$

These equations prove to be far more general than is indicated by the context of this discussion. Their generality is a fact we state without proof. Equation 15.36 (or 15.37) is called *Gauss's law*. It is valid for any shape of surface and any

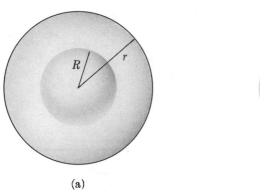

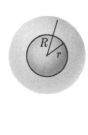

(a)   (b)

FIGURE 15.15   For a uniformly charged sphere, convenient Gaussian surfaces are concentric spheres (a) outside and (b) inside the charged sphere.

distribution of charge; it remains valid if magnetic field is also present and if the charges are in motion. In the general case, the symbol q on the right side of the equation represents the total charge contained within the closed surface. In words: The total electric flux emanating from a closed surface is equal to the total charge contained within the surface divided by ϵ_0. If no charge is contained within a closed surface, there may, of course, be lines of field crossing the surface, but the contributions of inward and outward flux over the surface must cancel to produce zero total flux.

There is a simple pictorial way to understand the meaning of Gauss's law. A positive charge may be regarded as a "source" of electric field lines because lines fan out from the charge. A negative charge is a "sink" of field lines; field lines vanish into it. Thus if a closed surface surrounds a positive charge, field lines must emerge outward from the surface; the flux is positive. A net negative flux implies that more field lines are entering the enclosed volume than are leaving it. Therefore, some lines must be terminating on negative charge within the volume. If as many lines cross a given surface one way as the other way (zero total flux), there is no net source or sink of lines within the enclosed volume and therefore no net charge.

Sources and sinks of field lines

As the following examples will make clear, Gauss's law is a simple and powerful tool for finding distributions of electric field when a high degree of geometrical symmetry prevails.

■ EXAMPLE 2:   What is the electric field outside a uniformly charged sphere? As a Gaussian surface, choose a larger sphere of radius r concentric with the charged sphere, whose radius is R [Figure 15.15(a)]. The symmetry of the situation implies that the field must be directed radially outward (or inward) and that it must be a function of radius only—therefore, of constant magnitude over the surface of the Gaussian sphere. The radial direction of **E** means that for the surface in question,

$$\mathbf{E} \cdot d\mathbf{S} = E_r \, dS.$$

Because of the constancy of E_r over the spherical surface, the flux integral is elementary:

$$\oint \mathbf{E} \cdot d\mathbf{S} = E_r \oint dS = E_r A,$$

where $A = 4\pi r^2$. Gauss's law therefore takes the form

$$E_r A = \frac{q}{\epsilon_0}. \tag{15.38}$$

Here q is the total charge contained on the sphere of radius R. From Equation 15.38, with $A = 4\pi r^2$,

$$E_r = \frac{1}{4\pi\epsilon_0} \frac{q}{r^2} \quad (r > R). \tag{15.39}$$

The vector result is

Field outside a uniformly charged sphere

$$\mathbf{E} = \frac{1}{4\pi\epsilon_0} \frac{q}{r^2} \mathbf{i}_r \quad (r > R). \tag{15.40}$$

The field outside a uniformly charge sphere is indistinguishable from the field of a point charge.   ∎

■ EXAMPLE 3:   What is the electric field within a uniformly charged spherical shell? This time construct the Gaussian sphere of radius r inside the charged spherical shell of radius R [Figure 15.15(b)]. Symmetry arguments like those in Example 2 apply. Now, since the charge within the Gaussian sphere is zero, Equation 15.38 is replaced by $E_r A = 0$. Therefore, $E_r = 0$ and

Field inside a uniformly charged spherical shell

$$\mathbf{E} = 0 \quad (r < R). \tag{15.41}$$

There is no electric field within a uniformly charged spherical shell. A graph of E_r vs r for a spherical shell of charge is shown in Figure 15.16. Note the discontinuity at $r = R$.   ∎

■ EXAMPLE 4:   On a plane metal surface, approximated as an infinite plane, there is a uniform surface charge density σ (C/m^2). There is no charge and no field within the metal. What is the electric field outside the metal surface? A convenient Gaussian surface for this problem is a cylinder, as shown in Figure 15.17, its sides perpendicular to the metal surface, its ends parallel to the surface, one end within the metal and one end outside. As in the preceding examples, symmetry can be invoked. Here it requires that the field be directed normal to the surface. Accordingly, for the sides of the cylinder, $\mathbf{E} \cdot d\mathbf{S} = 0$; $\mathbf{E}$ and $d\mathbf{S}$ are perpendicular. Since there is no field within the metal, the only contribution to

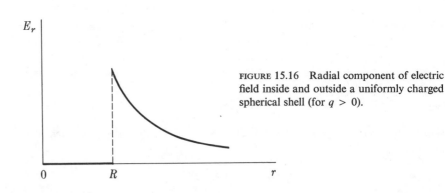

FIGURE 15.16   Radial component of electric field inside and outside a uniformly charged spherical shell (for $q > 0$).

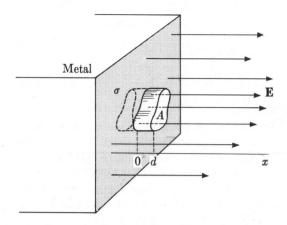

FIGURE 15.17   A cylindrical Gaussian surface is used to find the field outside
a uniformly charged plane metal surface.

the total flux through the closed surface is the flux at the end of the cylinder
outside the metal. This contribution is

$$\int \mathbf{E} \cdot d\mathbf{S} = E_x A, \tag{15.42}$$

where A is the area of the end of the cylinder and E_x is the outward component
of the field at the distance d from the metal. The charge contained within the
cylinder is

$$q = \sigma A, \tag{15.43}$$

since the area of metal surface enclosed is also A. Setting the total flux equal to
q/ϵ_0, we have

$$E_x A = \sigma \frac{A}{\epsilon_0},$$

which implies

$$E_x = \frac{\sigma}{\epsilon_0}. \tag{15.44}$$

*Field outside a plane
uniformly charged metal
surface*

The electric field, directed normal to the metal surface, depends only on the
surface density of charge and not on the distance from the surface; it is a
uniform field.   ∎

15.7   Potential

As a charged particle moves from place to place in an electric field, its energy
changes. If, for instance, it is allowed to move freely under the action of the
field, it gains kinetic energy. If an external force is applied to cause it to move
"uphill" against the electric force, it gains potential energy. In either case, work
is associated with its change of position. For an infinitesimal displacement $d\mathbf{s}$,
the work done by the field on the particle of charge q' is

$$dW = \mathbf{F} \cdot d\mathbf{s} = q'\mathbf{E} \cdot d\mathbf{s}. \tag{15.45}$$

The first equality is the fundamental definition of work (Equation 10.22). The second makes use of Equation 15.18, $\mathbf{F} = q'\mathbf{E}$. For a finite displacement from position $\mathbf{r}_1$ to position $\mathbf{r}_2$, the work done on the particle is

Work done by an electric force

$$W_{12} = q' \int_{\mathbf{r}_1}^{\mathbf{r}_2} \mathbf{E} \cdot d\mathbf{s}. \tag{15.46}$$

The line integral on the right follows the path of the particle (see Figure 10.8 and the discussion on page 386). An important property of this integral, which we state without proof, is this: For *static* fields, the integral depends only on the end points, not on the path. This means that the static electric force is a *conservative* force and that a potential-energy function can be associated with it. The difference of potential energy between two points is the negative of the work done by the force as a particle moves from one point to the other*:

Static electric forces are conservative

$$\Delta U = U(\mathbf{r}_2) - U(\mathbf{r}_1) = -W_{12}. \tag{15.47}$$

Electric potential, often called simply *potential*, is defined as electric potential energy per unit charge:

$$\Delta V = \frac{\Delta U}{q'} = -\frac{W_{12}}{q'}.$$

Definition of potential

The standard symbol for potential is V. In terms of field, it is defined by

$$V(\mathbf{r}_2) - V(\mathbf{r}_1) = -\int_{\mathbf{r}_1}^{\mathbf{r}_2} \mathbf{E} \cdot d\mathbf{s} \qquad \text{(static field).} \tag{15.48}$$

A static field $\mathbf{E}$ is a *conservative field*.

The concept of emf

If the field is not static, a quantity called electromotive force, or emf, for which we use the symbol $\mathscr{V}$, is defined by

$$\mathscr{V} = \int_{\mathbf{r}_1}^{\mathbf{r}_2} \mathbf{E} \cdot d\mathbf{s} \qquad \text{(general).} \tag{15.49}$$

Electromotive force, like potential, is energy per unit charge (it is *not*, as its unfortunately chosen name might suggest, a force). The only difference (apart from sign) is that emf may depend on the path as well as the end points, whereas potential depends only on the end points. In many texts, emf is defined more generally to include the energy per unit charge generated by batteries or other devices whose action cannot be described solely in terms of macroscopic electric fields. We shall instead think of a battery simply as a source of potential (which it is), without investigating its inner workings. We shall return in Chapter 17 to the concept of emf as defined by Equation 15.49.

Potential is, by its definition, a scalar quantity. Its SI unit is the volt (V). Since potential is energy per unit charge, the volt is related to the joule and the coulomb by

The volt

$$1 \text{ V} = 1 \text{ J/C.} \tag{15.50}$$

We already gave the SI unit of electric field as volt/meter; the definition of potential, Equation 15.48, now makes clear why this is correct. The relation of

---

* This was expressed in one dimension by Equation 10.71 and in three dimensions by Equation 10.118. To review the fundamental idea of potential energy, refer back to the discussions near these equations.

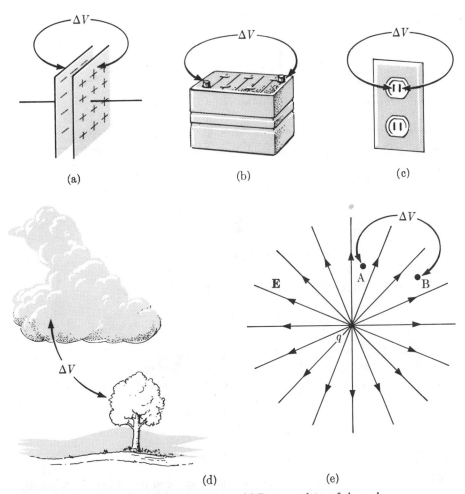

FIGURE 15.18   Examples of potential difference. (a) Between plates of charged capacitor. (b) Between terminals of storage battery. (c) Between slots of household outlet. (d) Between storm cloud and tree. (e) Between two points in space near a charged particle.

the volt to the cgs (Gaussian) unit of potential, the statvolt, is given in Appendix 4.

An analogy between potential and electric field is worth noting. Electric field was defined as *force* per unit charge (a vector quantity). Potential is defined as *energy* per unit charge (a scalar quantity). The simple act of dividing force by charge led to a powerful new concept because the field could be associated with a point in space whether or not any charged object was there to experience a force. Dividing potential energy by charge performs very much the same function. We may assign a potential difference to two points in space whether or not a particle actually moves between the two points to release or expend energy. It is important to notice that potential is defined for a pair of points, whereas a field can be defined at one point. Only potential *difference* has meaning. Some examples of potential difference are illustrated in Figure 15.18.

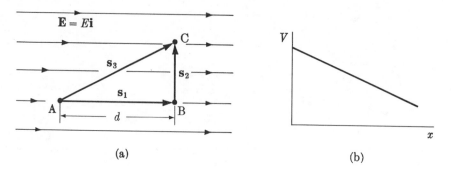

FIGURE 15.19   (a) Displacements in a uniform field used to find the potential.
(b) The potential is a linear function of x with slope $dV/dx = -E$.

UNIFORM FIELD

The relationship between potential and field is particularly simple in a uniform
field.* Then the constant $\mathbf{E}$ can be removed from the integral defining potential.
The potential difference between two points is

$$\Delta V = -\mathbf{E} \cdot \int_{\mathbf{r}_1}^{\mathbf{r}_2} d\mathbf{s} = -\mathbf{E} \cdot (\mathbf{r}_2 - \mathbf{r}_1). \tag{15.51}$$

Consider three points A, B, and C in a uniform field, as shown in Figure 15.19(a),
the displacement $\mathbf{s}_1$ from A to B being along the field direction, the displacement
$\mathbf{s}_2$ from B to C being perpendicular to $\mathbf{E}$. Potential differences are

$$V_B - V_A = -\mathbf{E} \cdot \mathbf{s}_1 = -Ed,$$
$$V_C - V_B = -\mathbf{E} \cdot \mathbf{s}_2 = 0,$$
$$V_C - V_A = -\mathbf{E} \cdot \mathbf{s}_3 = -Ed.$$

Clearly, potentials depend only on distance measured parallel to $\mathbf{E}$. A graph of
potential V vs x, with the x axis chosen to be along the field direction, is shown
in Figure 15.19(b). The absolute magnitude of V is irrelevant. Its zero could be
chosen at any convenient point x_0. The function is written

Potential of a uniform field

$$V = -E \cdot (x - x_0). \tag{15.52}$$

Potential differences are given by

$$V_2 - V_1 = -E \cdot (x_2 - x_1). \tag{15.53}$$

There is an easy way to interpret the negative slope in the graph of Figure
15.19(b). A positive charge gains energy from the field in moving "downhill" to
lower potential. Thus the downhill direction is the direction of the force on a
positive particle. For a negative particle, the sign is, of course, reversed. The
magnitude of the slope is the electric field E.

In a wire conducting current, there is an approximately uniform electric

---

* A proof of path-independence of the work done by a constant force appears in Section 10.10.

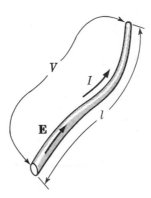

FIGURE 15.20   A wire of length *l*. The potential difference *V* between its ends is proportional to the field *E* in the wire. Conventional current is directed parallel to **E**.

field directed along the wire. The potential difference between the ends of the wire is equal to this field multiplied by the length of the wire (Figure 15.20):

$$V = El. \tag{15.54}$$

Potential and field in a wire

By convention, the positive direction of current flow is the direction of the field, from higher to lower potential. The negative electrons conducting the current actually move the other way. We shall use the standard convention, saying that the direction of the current is the direction in which positive charge would move if it were free to move. (In liquids and gases, positive ions may indeed contribute to the current flow.)

ELECTRIC ENERGY AND POWER

Potential energy *U* and potential *V* are related by

$$U = qV. \tag{15.55}$$

In practice, when charge moves from one point to another, the potential energy may be converted to other forms of energy. More generally,

$$\text{energy} = qV. \tag{15.56}$$

This electric energy may manifest itself in many ways—in the heat of an electric iron, the light and heat of an electric bulb, the mechanical work of a motor, the kinetic energy of an electron flying between two points in a vacuum tube. Or it may be external work performed against electric force. When energy is released by the steady flow of current between points of different potential, a formula derivable from Equation 15.56 is useful:

Energy and power simply related to potential

$$P = IV. \tag{15.57}$$

On the left side is power, or energy per unit time. On the right the potential is multiplied by the current *I*, or charge per unit time. Differentiation of Equation 15.56 with respect to time yields Equation 15.57, if *V* is constant. Since the SI unit of power is the watt (W), a connection among units implied by Equation 15.57 is

$$1 \text{ J/sec} = 1 \text{ W} = 1 \text{ A} \times 1 \text{ V.} \tag{15.58}$$

The reason potential (or voltage, as it is sometimes called) is a particularly important concept in the practical utilization of electricity is that very often the generators of electric current develop a particular fixed potential that depends very little on how much current, if any, flows. This applies both to chemical cells and to mechanical generators. Between the terminals of an automobile battery there might exist a potential difference of 12 V. This potential difference remains very nearly constant whether or not charge moves from one terminal to the other. Depending on what is connected between them, anything from 0 to perhaps 25 A can flow between the terminals without much change in the potential. Likewise, the generators supplying household circuits supply nearly the same alternating potential at all times. Current and power vary according to what is switched on or plugged in by the users.

The electron volt

The connection between energy and potential has led to the introduction of a new energy unit, the electron volt, now the most commonly used energy unit in the small-scale world. Despite the word "volt" appearing in its name, the electron volt (eV) is a unit of energy, not potential (see Section 2.9, and also Tables 3.1 [mass energy in eV] and 13.4 [thermal energies in eV]). Since 1 eV is the energy gained or lost by an electron (or any other particle with the same magnitude of charge) in moving between two points with a potential difference of 1 V, its magnitude expressed in joules may easily be calculated from the fundamental relation between energy and potential, Equation 15.56. Use $e = 1.602 \times 10^{-19}$ C and $V = 1$ V to obtain

$$1 \text{ eV} = 1.602 \times 10^{-19} \text{ J}.$$

SPHERICALLY SYMMETRIC POTENTIALS

A potential of fundamental importance is that associated with a single point charge. For definiteness, consider a positive charge q, such as that of an atomic nucleus. We seek the potential difference between points A and B, one a distance

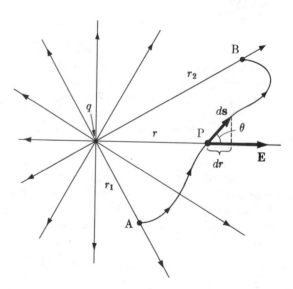

FIGURE 15.21   Arbitrary path used to find the potential of a point charge.

r_1 from the nucleus, the other a distance r_2 from the nucleus (Figure 15.21). This problem was treated in Section 10.10 (see Equations 10.127–10.132 and Figure 10.27). Here let us choose a more general path from A to B in order to demonstrate the path-independence of the integral defining the potential. Consider a point P anywhere along the path (Figure 15.21). It is a distance r from the charge q; at this point, the increment of displacement along the path, $d\mathbf{s}$, makes angle θ with the radially directed field $\mathbf{E}$. The scalar product $\mathbf{E} \cdot d\mathbf{s}$ is $E \, ds \cos \theta$, or

$$\mathbf{E} \cdot d\mathbf{s} = \frac{1}{4\pi\epsilon_0} \frac{q}{r^2} \, ds \cos \theta.$$

Since $ds \cos \theta = dr$, this can be written

$$\mathbf{E} \cdot d\mathbf{s} = \frac{q}{4\pi\epsilon_0} \frac{dr}{r^2} .$$

Equation 15.48 becomes

$$V(\mathbf{r}_2) - V(\mathbf{r}_1) = -\frac{q}{4\pi\epsilon_0} \int_{r_1}^{r_2} \frac{dr}{r^2} . \tag{15.59}$$

Path-independent potential difference

We see that regardless of the path, the line integral reduces to a simple one-dimensional integral over the radial coordinate. (This simplicity is preserved if the path is such that r increases and then decreases or even if the path executes loops. Why?) The integral in Equation 15.59 is elementary and depends only on the end points. It leads to the formula

$$V(r_2) - V(r_1) = \frac{q}{4\pi\epsilon_0} \left(\frac{1}{r_2} - \frac{1}{r_1} \right) .$$

With the conventional choice, $V(\infty) = 0$ (see the discussion preceding Equation 10.132), the potential associated with a point charge is

$$V(r) = \frac{1}{4\pi\epsilon_0} \frac{q}{r} . \tag{15.60}$$

The potential of a point charge

It is important to remember that this is still a potential *difference*—between r and ∞. In Figure 15.22 are shown graphs of this potential function, and of the associated potential-energy functions for positive and negative charges in the field of a nucleus.

Because of the law of superposition, the potentials contributed by two or more charged particles are additive. If, for example, the two protons in a hydrogen molecule (each with charge e) are located at $x = -a/2$ and $x = +a/2$ (Figure 15.23), the potential at some point P may be written as a sum:

Potentials are additive

$$V_P = \frac{1}{4\pi\epsilon_0} \left(\frac{e}{r_1} + \frac{e}{r_2} \right) . \tag{15.61}$$

where r_1 and r_2 are the distances of P from the protons. If an electron (charge $-e$) is located at P, its potential energy is

$$U_P = -eV_P .$$

FIGURE 15.22   (a) Potential V vs distance r from center of nucleus to point in space, if the potential at infinite distance is defined to be zero. (b) Potential energy curves for nucleus interacting separately with proton and with electron.

(a)

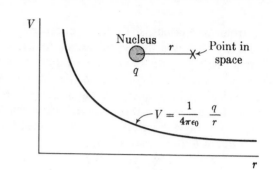

(b)

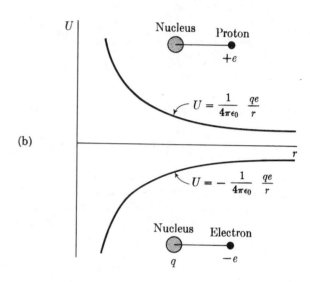

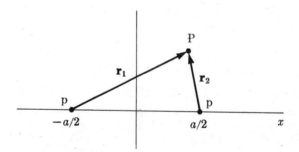

FIGURE 15.23   Potentials are additive. The potential at P is the sum of the potentials contributed by the two protons.

■ EXAMPLE 1:   What is the potential of a uniformly charged spherical shell of radius R? (a) Outside the shell, the field **E** is the same as that of a point charge. The potential is therefore also the same (if $V(\infty) = 0$). It is

Potential outside a spherical
shell of charge

$$V(r) = \frac{1}{4\pi\epsilon_0}\frac{q}{r} \qquad (r > R). \qquad (15.62)$$

where q is the total charge on the shell. (b) Inside the shell, $\mathbf{E} = 0$ (Equation 15.41). Equation 15.48 therefore implies $V(\mathbf{r}_2) - V(\mathbf{r}_1) = 0$ for any two points $\mathbf{r}_1$ and $\mathbf{r}_2$ within the shell. We conclude

$$V = constant \qquad (r < R).$$

The constant is arbitrary if an arbitrary new zero of potential is chosen. This is not convenient. It is preferable to measure the potential both inside and outside the shell relative to zero potential at $r = \infty$. Then, for *all* points Equation 15.48 can be written (for this example)

$$V(r) = - \int_\infty^r E_r \, dr = + \int_r^\infty E_r \, dr.$$

For $r > R$, $E_r = q/4\pi\epsilon_0 r^2$, and Equation 15.62 results. For $r < R$, the integral must be divided into two parts: one from r to R, which is zero, and one from R to ∞, which gives $q/4\pi\epsilon_0 R$. We therefore conclude that

$$V(r) = \frac{1}{4\pi\epsilon_0}\frac{q}{R} \qquad (r \le R). \tag{15.63}$$

Potential inside the shell

A graph of V vs r for the spherical shell appears in Figure 15.24. ∎

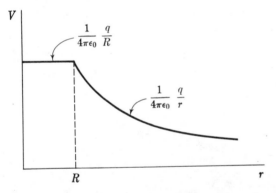

FIGURE 15.24   The potential of a spherical shell of charge. The constant value of V within the shell means that no work is required to move a charged particle from one place to another within the shell. The work to move it from any place within the shell to infinity is the same as the work to move it from $r = R$ to $r = \infty$.

★GRADIENT OF THE POTENTIAL

As stated by Equation 10.78, the relation between force and potential energy in one dimension is

$$F_x = -\frac{dU}{dx}.$$

The force is the negative gradient of the potential energy. The generalization of this relationship to three dimensions is given by Equations 10.120–10.122, which make use of partial derivatives. If we consider these equations in particular for a static electric force acting on a charged particle, we may divide both sides of each equation by the charge on the particle and thereby relate force per unit charge (electric field) to energy per unit charge (potential). The resulting equations are

E derived from V

$$E_x = - \frac{\partial V}{\partial x}, \tag{15.64}$$

$$E_y = - \frac{\partial V}{\partial y}, \tag{15.65}$$

$$E_z = - \frac{\partial V}{\partial z}. \tag{15.66}$$

These three equations together comprise what is called the three-dimensional gradient; they are summarized using vector notation by (see the footnote on page 418)

$$\mathbf{E} = -\nabla V, \tag{15.67}$$

sometimes written $\mathbf{E} = -\mathbf{grad}\ V$. Equation 15.67 (or Equations 15.64–15.66) may be looked upon as the "inverse" of Equation 15.48. One involves differentiation, the other integration.

■ EXAMPLE 2: A potential function is given by $V = -E \cdot (x - x_0)$, where E and x_0 are constants (Equation 15.52). What is the electric field? Differentiation with respect to x (Equation 15.64) gives

$$E_x = E.$$

Since V does not depend on y or z, the partial derivatives $\partial V/\partial y$ and $\partial V/\partial z$ are both zero. Therefore,

$$E_y = E_z = 0.$$

In summary,

$$\mathbf{E} = E\mathbf{i}.$$

The field is constant and in the x direction.   ■

■ EXAMPLE 3: Find the z component of the electric field whose potential function is

$$V = \frac{1}{4\pi\epsilon_0} \frac{q}{r}$$

(that of a point charge or a uniformly charged sphere). To apply Equations 15.64–15.66, we must express V as a function of x, y, and z:

Potential of a point charge

$$V = \frac{q}{4\pi\epsilon_0} \frac{1}{\sqrt{x^2 + y^2 + z^2}}. \tag{15.68}$$

To find $\partial V/\partial z$, regard x and y as constants and differentiate with respect to z. This procedure gives

$$\frac{\partial V}{\partial z} = -\frac{q}{4\pi\epsilon_0} \frac{z}{(x^2 + y^2 + x^2)^{3/2}}.$$

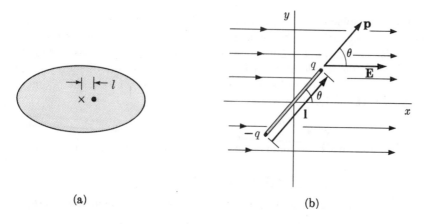

FIGURE 15.25   Electric dipoles. (a) In a polarized molecule, the average position of the positive charge (shown by the dot) is displaced from the average position of the negative charge (shown by the cross), causing the molecule to have a dipole moment. (b) An idealized dipole consists of equal and opposite charges, q and $-q$, separated by displacement **l**. Its dipole moment is $\mathbf{p} = q\mathbf{l}$.

The combination $x^2 + y^2 + z^2$ may be re-expressed as r^2 so that Equation 15.66 gives

$$E_z = -\frac{\partial V}{\partial z} = \frac{q}{4\pi\epsilon_0}\frac{z}{r^3}.\tag{15.69}$$

z component of the field

Note that the field of a point charge (Equation 15.20) can be written

$$\mathbf{E} = \frac{q}{4\pi\epsilon_0}\frac{\mathbf{r}}{r^3}.\tag{15.70}$$

Its z component is indeed the same as that given by the gradient of the potential.   ■

★15.8   The electric dipole

Often in nature, a system may have zero total charge yet exhibit a separation of charge, with an excess of positive charge on one side and an excess of negative charge on the other side. A molecule, for example, may be "polarized," such that the average position of its negative charge and the average position of its positive charge are spatially separated [Figure 15.25(a)]. Such a system is called an electric dipole. It is said to possess a *dipole moment.**

The simplest example of an electric dipole is a pair of equal and opposite point charges, q and $-q$, separated by distance l [Figure 15.25(b)]. The dipole moment of this system is, by definition, a vector quantity given by

$$\mathbf{p} = q\mathbf{l},\tag{15.71}$$

Electric dipole moment for equal and opposite charge pair

---

* A system with a nonzero total charge may also possess a dipole moment.

where $\mathbf{l}$ is the displacement vector from $-q$ to $q*$ (the context should prevent any confusion between dipole moment $\mathbf{p}$ and momentum $\mathbf{p}$). Let us consider the potential energy of a dipole in a uniform electric field if, as shown in Figure 15.25(b), the dipole moment makes an angle θ with the direction of the field. Choosing the x axis to be parallel to the field, we can take the potential function to be (Equation 15.52)

$$V = -E \cdot (x - x_0).$$

The charge q has an x coordinate given by $x_1 = \frac{1}{2}l \cos \theta$ and a potential energy given by

$$U_1 = qV(x_1) = -qE \cdot (\tfrac{1}{2}l \cos \theta - x_0).$$

The x coordinate of the charge $-q$ is $x_2 = -\frac{1}{2}l \cos \theta$, and its potential energy is

$$U_2 = qV(x_2) = +qE \cdot (-\tfrac{1}{2}l \cos \theta - x_0).$$

The sum of these two potential energies is the potential energy of the system:

$$U = U_1 + U_2 = -qEl \cos \theta. \tag{15.72}$$

By taking advantage of the vector definition of dipole moment, we can write this as a scalar product:

Potential energy of a dipole

$$U = -\mathbf{p} \cdot \mathbf{E}. \tag{15.73}$$

(An additive constant is also permissible.) The potential energy is minimum for $\mathbf{p}$ parallel to $\mathbf{E}$ and maximum for $\mathbf{p}$ antiparallel to $\mathbf{E}$. The work required to rotate the dipole from parallel to antiparallel orientation is

$$W = 2pE. \tag{15.74}$$

■ EXAMPLE: It has been postulated that elementary particles might possess electric dipole moments, although none have so far been observed. Suppose that the neutron has a dipole moment corresponding to the separation of charges e and $-e$ by a distance of 10^{-25} m. What is the energy in eV required to reverse its orientation in the electric field of a proton at a distance of 1 A from the proton? This electric field is

$$E = \frac{1}{4\pi\epsilon_0} \frac{e}{r^2} = 9 \times 10^9 \frac{\text{N m}^2}{\text{C}^2} \times \frac{1.60 \times 10^{-19} \text{ C}}{(10^{-10} \text{ m})^2}$$

$$= 1.44 \times 10^{11} \text{ V/m}.$$

(Notice the large magnitude of this field by macroscopic standards.) The hypothesized dipole moment is

$$p = el = 1.60 \times 10^{-19} \text{ C} \times 10^{-25} \text{ m}$$

$$= 1.60 \times 10^{-44} \text{ C m}.$$

According to Equation 15.74, the work required to reverse the dipole is

---

* For a set of point particles with charges q_i and position vectors $\mathbf{r}_i$, the dipole moment is defined by $\mathbf{p} = \sum_i q_i \mathbf{r}_i$.

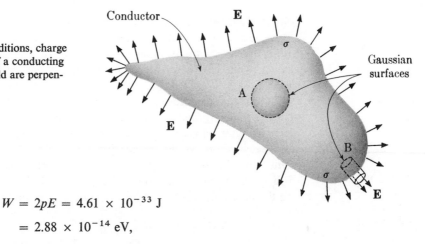

FIGURE 15.26 For static conditions, charge resides only on the surface of a conducting body, and lines of electric field are perpendicular to its surface.

$$W = 2pE = 4.61 \times 10^{-33} \text{ J}$$
$$= 2.88 \times 10^{-14} \text{ eV},$$

exceedingly small compared with typical energies in the atomic domain. ∎

No net *force* acts on the dipole in Figure 15.25(b) because its two charges experience equal and opposite forces. However, a *torque* (or couple) acts on the dipole. Inspection of the figure shows that the field is "trying" to rotate the dipole clockwise, so the torque acts into the page. It is left as a problem to show that this torque is given by

$$\mathbf{T} = \mathbf{p} \times \mathbf{E}. \qquad (15.75)$$

Torque exerted on a dipole

15.9 Conductors in static fields

Conductors such as metals have a number of notably simple properties when influenced by static electric fields; these properties all arise from the fact that the conductor contains charge carriers (normally electrons) that are free to move in response to electric forces. Let us suppose that the only forces acting on the charge carriers are electric forces and dissipative (frictional) forces arising from their interaction with atoms or ions as they move through the conductor.* This means that so long as an electric field exists within the conductor, charge will move. The only *static* situation is one in which there is no electric field within the conductor.

Definition of an idealized conductor

These considerations, together with Gauss's law, enable us to prove an important theorem: *Any net static charge on a conducting body must reside on the surface of the body.* Consider an arbitrary Gaussian surface contained entirely within a conducting body (surface A in Figure 15.26), and suppose that no charge is in motion.† Then the electric *field* is zero at all points on the Gaussian surface. This means that the electric *flux* across the surface is zero. Therefore, according to Gauss's law, there is no net charge within the enclosed volume. Since the

Theorem: no static charge within a conductor

Proof: $\mathbf{E} = 0$
$\Phi_E = 0$
$q = 0$

---

* This assumption is not necessarily valid for certain conductors—the liquid electrolyte in a storage battery, for example. However, it is valid to excellent approximation for a metal.

† At the atomic level, electrons may be moving in all directions at high speed. However, if there is no *net* motion in any direction, we can say, at the macroscopic level, that charge is at rest.

volume enclosed can be chosen arbitrarily small (it must still contain many atoms; remember that this is a classical discussion) and can be placed anywhere within the conductor, we conclude that the net charge is zero throughout the interior of the conductor. If the body has any net charge, it must reside on the surface.

If a Gaussian surface (such as B in Figure 15.26) encloses part of the surface of the conducting body, a net charge may be contained. Then a net flux must pierce the Gaussian surface outside the conducting body. An infinite plane metal surface with surface charge density σ was considered in Section 15.6. The result obtained there remains valid in the immediate vicinity of *any* metal surface. Adjacent to the surface, the electric field is perpendicular to the surface (see the next paragraph) and has a magnitude given by Equation 15.44:

Field near any conducting surface

$$E = \frac{\sigma}{\varepsilon_0}. \tag{15.76}$$

The requirement that the charge distribution be static limits the net charge, if any, to the surface of a conducting body. The same requirement can reveal two interesting facts about the surface. First, the electric field just outside the surface must be perpendicular to the surface. If there were a nonzero component of **E** parallel to the surface, it would cause charge to move along the surface, in violation of our requirement that the distribution be static. Second, the potential must be constant everywhere on the surface. Consider a path along the surface joining two points A and B (Figure 15.27). Everywhere along this line, $\mathbf{E} \cdot d\mathbf{s} = 0$. The potential difference is therefore zero. From Equation 15.48,

E *perpendicular to surface*

$$V_B - V_A = - \int_A^B \mathbf{E} \cdot d\mathbf{s} = 0.$$

Since this holds true for any pair of points on the surface, we conclude that

The surface of a conductor is an equipotential

$$V = constant \tag{15.77}$$

everywhere on the surface. The surface of a conducting body (for static conditions) is called an equipotential surface.

The entire volume of a conducting body is in fact an equipotential region. Consider a path AC from a point on the surface of a body to any point within the body. Since $\mathbf{E} = 0$ along this path, $V_C - V_A = 0$. All points within the body have the same potential as the surface.

FIGURE 15.27   (a) Along any line on the surface of a conductor—for static conditions —the integral $\int \mathbf{E} \cdot d\mathbf{s}$ is zero because **E** is perpendicular to $d\mathbf{s}$ at all points on the path. (b) Along any line from the surface to an interior point in the conductor, $\int \mathbf{E} \cdot d\mathbf{s} = 0$ because $\mathbf{E} = 0$.

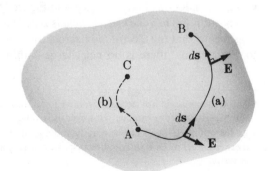

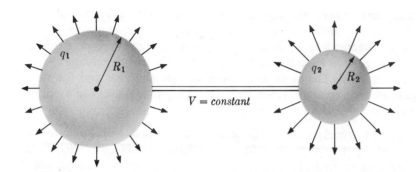

FIGURE 15.28   Two metal spheres connected by a long thin rod form a single conducting body. In static equilibrium, both spheres have the same potential. The field is greater near the smaller sphere.

CHARGED SPHERES

For an isolated charged spherical conductor—it does not matter whether it is solid or hollow—the charge distributes itself uniformly over the outside surface so that the surface charge density is

$$\sigma = \frac{q}{4\pi R^2}, \tag{15.78}$$

where q is the net charge on the sphere and R is its radius. According to Equation 15.63, the potential of the sphere is (for the choice $V = 0$ at $r = \infty$)

$$V = \frac{1}{4\pi\epsilon_0} \frac{q}{R}. \tag{15.79}$$

Potential of an isolated spherical conductor

Because of Equation 15.78, this may also be written

$$V = \frac{R\sigma}{\epsilon_0}. \tag{15.80}$$

If two widely separated spheres are joined by a conducting link (Figure 15.28), they form a single conducting body; accordingly, the total charge will distribute itself over the spheres in such a way that both have the same potential. From Equation 15.79, we conclude that the charge on each must be proportional to the radius of the sphere:

$$\frac{q_1}{R_1} = \frac{q_2}{R_2}. \tag{15.81}$$

If in this equation we replace q_1 by $4\pi R_1{}^2\sigma_1$ and q_2 by $4\pi R_2{}^2\sigma_2$, we see that the surface charge densities are *inversely* proportional to the radii:

Conditions on two spheres of equal potential

$$\frac{\sigma_1}{\sigma_2} = \frac{R_2}{R_1}. \tag{15.82}$$

As indicated in Figure 15.28, the electric field, being proportional to the surface charge density, is greater near the smaller sphere.

This effect, the proportionality of E to $1/R$, is relevant also for conducting bodies of arbitrary shape. More surface charge accumulates at regions of small radius of curvature, and the electric field is greater there (see Figure 15.26). For a charged conductor in air, neutralization of the charge occurs primarily by the flow of charge to or from the sharpest points on the body where the electric field is greatest. This fact is used in designing lightning rods and the static discharge brushes on some airplanes, both of which help to prevent an excessive build-up of static charge on the structure being protected.

■ EXAMPLE: Two concentric metal spheres have equal and opposite net charges, q and $-q$ (Figure 15.29). How is the charge distributed? What is the potential difference between the two spheres? Because of the spherical symmetry of the situation, the zero total charge on the spheres tells us that the electric field outside the outer sphere is zero. This in turn means that there is no charge on the outer surface of the outer sphere. The inner surface of the inner sphere is likewise free of charge; otherwise, this charge would create a field within the conducting material. We conclude that charge q resides on the outer surface of the inner sphere (radius R_1) and charge $-q$ resides on the inner surface of the outer sphere (radius R_2). A concentric spherical Gaussian surface between the two spheres encloses charge q. In this region, the field is the same as that of a point charge,

$$\mathbf{E} = \frac{1}{4\pi\epsilon_0} \frac{q\mathbf{i}_r}{r^2}.$$

The potential difference between radii R_1 and R_2 is, therefore, the same as for a point charge q at the center:

Potential difference of oppositely charged concentric spheres

$$V_2 - V_1 = \frac{q}{4\pi\epsilon_0} \left(\frac{1}{R_2} - \frac{1}{R_1} \right). \tag{15.83}$$

If the potential at $r = \infty$ is zero, what are the individual potentials V_1 and V_2? ■

To illustrate a more complicated situation (one for which no simple mathematical expressions for field and potential exist), Figure 15.30 shows the lines of field and the equipotential surfaces near two conducting spheres, one bearing no net charge. Notice that the uncharged sphere does have nonzero surface charge density, as indicated by the field lines beginning and ending on this sphere. Another thing to notice: Field lines and equipotential surfaces are always perpendicular, not only at the boundaries of the conductors but also elsewhere in space.

15.10   Ohm's law

Prior to Alessandro Volta's discovery of the chemical battery in 1800, very little had been learned about the flow of current through material substances. So long as charge could be caused to flow only in momentary pulses as electrified objects were discharged, the difficulties of measurement were too great to permit any accurate quantitative results. It was known only that different materials had vastly different conducting properties. Metals allowed charge to flow readily from point to point and, accordingly, were called conductors. Through some other substances, called insulators, the flow of charge was so greatly

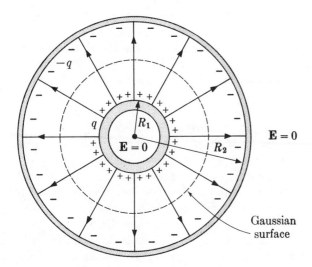

FIGURE 15.29   Concentric metal spheres with equal and opposite net charge.
The field is nonzero only in the space between the two spheres.

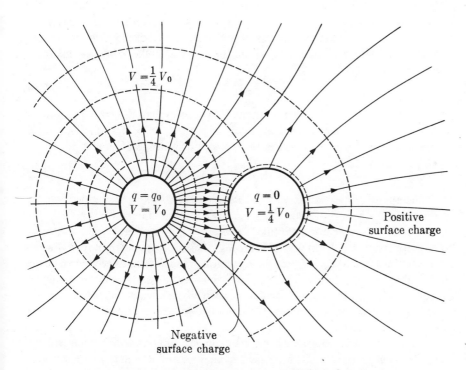

FIGURE 15.30   Distribution of electric field near two conducting spheres, one
with a net positive charge, one with no net charge. Solid lines are field lines.
Dashed lines represent equipotential surfaces. [Diagram from Berkeley
Physics Course, Volume 2, *Electricity and Magnetism,* by Edward M. Purcell
(New York: McGraw-Hill Book Co., 1964); with permission of Education
Development Center, Inc.]

inhibited that it was not possible to detect any current at all. Substances of intermediate conducting power, such as salt water, were also known.

Historical significance of the battery

Volta's battery made possible for the first time* the creation of steady currents of long duration, a technical advance of very great significance. Probably the most important consequence of the generation of steady currents was that it opened the way to the discovery of the link between electricity and magnetism. Secondarily, it made possible a study of the nature of current flow itself, a necessary first step toward the practical utilization of electricity.

From 1800 to the present time, the flow of current in circuits has continued to be a subject of substantial research interest. In electrical terminology, a "circuit" is any continuous path or array of paths along which current may flow. A circuit usually contains a battery or other source of potential to create the current. In addition, it may contain anything from a single wire to a complicated collection of wires, tubes, transistors, capacitors, and other "circuit elements." The path from one terminal of a flashlight cell through the lamp and back to the other terminal of the cell is a simple circuit. A string of Christmas-tree lights plugged into a wall socket forms part of a circuit, or it may be considered a circuit by itself. The maze of parts within a television receiver is formed into a circuit.

We wish to consider here only simple circuits consisting of a battery whose terminals are joined by wires or other pieces of solid matter. Such circuits were the first to be studied. A remarkably simple law of current flow in solids was discovered by Georg Ohm in 1826. He found that current density (defined below) is proportional to the electric field within the material. Ohm's law, in this form, may be written

Ohm's law: Current density is proportional to electric field

$$\mathbf{J} = \sigma \mathbf{E}. \tag{15.84}$$

The current density $\mathbf{J}$ is a vector quantity whose direction is the direction of current flow and whose magnitude is current per unit area. It is the amount of charge crossing unit area in unit time. Its SI unit is ampere/(meter)^2:

$$\text{unit of } \mathbf{J} = \text{A/m}^2 = \text{C/sec m}^2. \tag{15.85}$$

The constant of proportionality, σ, is called the *conductivity* of the medium. Its unit is given in Equation 15.90. Ohm's law is not a fundamental law because it is not precisely valid for any material. Nevertheless, it is exceedingly useful, as it holds approximately for many substances. Table 15.1 lists conductivities of some common materials. Notice the enormous range of conductivities revealed in the table—more than a factor of 10^{20} between a good conductor, such as copper or silver, and a good insulator, such as porcelain. Germanium and silicon, with intermediate values of conductivity, are examples of substances called semiconductors.

The conductivity σ varies widely

For a particular wire or circuit element, the potential difference between its two ends is proportional to the electric field within it (Equation 15.54); also, the current flowing through it is proportional to the current density within it.

---

* The single chemical cell, or Galvanic cell, although available before 1800, became a practical research tool only when combined by Volta into the multicell battery.

TABLE 15.1   CONDUCTIVITIES OF SOME COMMON MATERIALS AT ROOM TEMPERATURE

Material	Conductivity, σ (1/ohm m)*
Silver	6.2×10^7
Copper	5.9×10^7
Gold	4.1×10^7
Iron	1.0×10^7
Lead	5×10^6
Tin	3×10^5
Sea water	5
Germanium	2
Silicon	1.6×10^{-3}
Porcelain	About 10^{-13}
Glass	Typically 10^{-13}–10^{-15}

* The unit of conductivity is sometimes written mho/m. One mho is defined as the inverse of 1 ohm.

In symbols, $V \sim E$ and $I \sim J$. For such a circuit element, therefore, an alternative form of Ohm's law is

$$I \sim V; \tag{15.86}$$

current is proportional to potential difference (Figure 15.31). A simple way to look at this form of the law is to think of the potential as the "motive power" (the British word for potential, "tension," suggests the sense) and the current as the resulting effect. Doubling the potential across a circuit element causes a doubling of the amount of charge that flows through it in 1 sec. This assignment of cause and effect, of course, is only an aid to visualization and has no deep meaning.

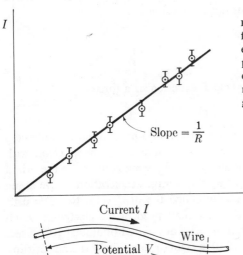

Slope = $\dfrac{1}{R}$

Current I

Potential V

Wire

FIGURE 15.31   Ohm's law. If the current I flowing through a wire or other circuit element is directly proportional to the potential difference V across the circuit element, the material obeys Ohm's law. Its resistance is the inverse of the slope of the graph of I vs V.

The proportionality of Formula 15.86 is transformed to an equation by introducing a constant of proportionality, written $1/R$. Then

$$I = \frac{1}{R} V.$$
(15.87)

Alternatively, the same equation may be re-expressed in the form

Another form of Ohm's law
$$V = IR.$$
(15.88)

This is the form of Ohm's law most frequently encountered. The quantity R, called the resistance of the circuit element, has the dimension of potential divided by current. Its SI unit is volt/ampere. This particular combination has been given a new name, the ohm (symbol Ω):

$$\text{unit of resistance} = \text{ohm} \ (\Omega) = \text{V/A}.$$
(15.89)

In terms of this unit, the unit of conductivity σ may be expressed:

$$\text{unit of conductivity} = 1/\Omega \ \text{m} = (\Omega \ \text{m})^{-1}.$$
(15.90)

It is left as a problem to relate the resistance of a wire to its conductivity, its length, and its cross-sectional area.

A short length of ordinary wire has a resistance much less than 1 Ω. A typical light bulb has a resistance of about 100 Ω; an iron or electric toaster, a resistance of 15 or 20 Ω. Inside radio and television receivers are used many circuits elements called resistors whose resistance varies from a few ohms to millions of ohms.

Ohm's law is approximately valid for most materials as long as they are not subjected to extremes of temperature. The resistance of metals decreases at low temperature. Near absolute zero, some metals become superconductors; their resistance vanishes and current can flow with zero potential difference. Most materials also show significant change of resistance when they become very hot. A circuit element that obeys Ohm's law is called a linear resistor because of the appearance of the graph of Figure 15.31. A nonlinear resistor (sometimes called a nonohmic resistor) is one that does not obey Ohm's law.

MOTION OF ELECTRONS IN WIRES

An electron ($q = -e$) in an electric field $\mathbf{E}$ experiences a force

$$\mathbf{F} = -e\mathbf{E}.$$

Drift velocity
Within a wire conducting current, this force is balanced by an oppositely directed "frictional" force arising from the frequent encounters of the electron with crystal imperfections and with individual ions. These encounters are the origin of resistance. The electrons, experiencing no average acceleration, move along the wire with a constant average velocity called the drift velocity. The drift velocity is quite small compared with the actual speed of the electrons. Each electron darts this way and that within the wire at a speed of almost 10^6 m/sec. Its drift velocity is perhaps 1 cm/sec (0.01 m/sec) or less. Only the net drifting motion contributes to the current flow and to the transmission of power.

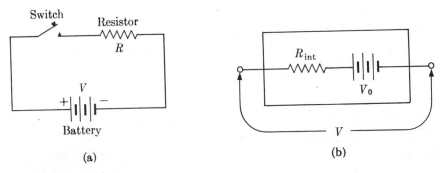

FIGURE 15.32   (a) Simple circuit. (b) Model of a battery. Because of the internal resistance, the potential at the terminals depends on the current flow.

15.11   Simple circuits

In this section we shall consider only linear resistors. If the terminals of a battery of potential V are connected through a resistor of resistance R, Ohm's law tells us that the current flow will be given by the formula

$$I = \frac{V}{R}.$$

This simple circuit is diagrammed in Figure 15.32(a); this figure also illustrates the symbols that are commonly used to indicate a battery, a resistor, and a switch in circuit diagrams.

    The battery itself is a device—fairly complicated at the atomic level—that adds energy to charge through chemical reactions. In effect it "pumps" electrons from a lower to a higher potential energy, opposite to the direction in which they would otherwise spontaneously flow. For steady current flow, chemical energy generated in the battery is exactly equal to energy dissipated in the circuit in heat or other forms. A reasonably good model for a battery [see Figure 15.32(b)] is a fixed source of potential V_0 in series with an internal resistance R_{int}. If the external resistance R is much greater than R_{int}, the actual potential V across the terminals of the battery will not be much less than V_0.

A battery transforms chemical energy to electric energy

SERIES CIRCUITS: KIRCHHOFF'S RULES

The simplest series circuit consists of two resistors, the first with resistance R_1 and the second with resistance R_2, joined together in series and then connected to a battery (Figure 15.33). We can apply Ohm's law to each of the resistors separately:

$$V_1 = I_1 R_1, \tag{15.91}$$

$$V_2 = I_2 R_2. \tag{15.92}$$

A little fundamental thinking about the nature of current and potential reveals two useful facts about the series circuit. First, the currents through the two resistors are equal:

$$I_1 = I_2. \tag{15.93}$$

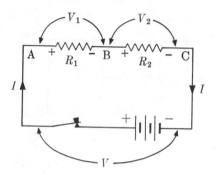

FIGURE 15.33   Series circuit.

Second, the potential difference across the pair of resistors is equal to the sum of the potential differences across each one:

$$V = V_1 + V_2. \tag{15.94}$$

These two equations are actually applications of two fundamental conservation laws, the conservation of charge and the conservation of energy. They are worth discussing carefully, even if they do seem obvious. For steady flow, the current into any point in a circuit must equal the current out of that point. Otherwise, charge would be growing or diminishing at that point, thereby violating the assumption of steady flow; or else charge would be coming into or going out of existence, thereby violating a fundamental conservation law. This implication of charge conservation is one of two rules called *Kirchhoff's rules*, which are useful in analyzing direct-current circuits. One way to state Kirchhoff's first rule is this: *The total current flowing into any point in a circuit is zero.* Applied to point B in Figure 15.33, the rule simply means $I_1 = I_2$ (Equation 15.93).

Kirchhoff's first rule expresses charge conservation

Kirchhoff's second rule expresses energy conservation

Kirchhoff's second rule states that *the sum of the potentials around any closed loop in a circuit is zero.* This means that the gains and losses of energy of an electron going once around the loop cancel, so it suffers no net gain or loss of energy in completing the loop. If it were otherwise, energy in the circuit would be increasing or decreasing, which would violate either the assumption of steady flow or the law of energy conservation. The very fact that each point in the circuit can be assigned a definite potential requires the validity of Kirchhoff's second rule. Applied to the simple circuit of Figure 15.33, this rule gives

$$V_{AB} + V_{BC} + V_{CA} = 0. \tag{15.95}$$

One must pay close attention to signs.* In the figure the relative polarities are labeled. We have $V_{AB} = V_1$, $V_{BC} = V_2$, and $V_{CA} = -V$, so Equation 15.95 is equivalent to Equation 15.94.

Now we may assemble the facts summarized by Equations 15.91–15.94. Since $I_1 = I_2$, we may drop the subscripts and call the current simply I. With substitutions from Equations 15.91 and 15.92, Equation 15.94 becomes

$$V = IR_1 + IR_2 = I(R_1 + R_2).$$

---

* See also the discussion on page 715.

This may be written

$$V = IR, \tag{15.96}$$

where R, the effective resistance, or "total resistance," of the circuit, is given by

$$R = R_1 + R_2. \tag{15.97}$$

This result could have been guessed, but our way of deriving it uses methods that may be applied to more complicated situations. For any number of resistors in series, similar reasoning leads to the result

Resistors in series

$$R = R_1 + R_2 + R_3 + \cdots. \tag{15.98}$$

RESISTORS IN PARALLEL

The analysis of resistors in parallel makes use of the same principles. Figure 15.34 shows the simplest example of a parallel circuit, in which two resistors are joined in parallel, their ends being connected to a battery. The summing of potentials around any of the three possible closed loops shows the magnitudes of three potentials to be equal:

$$V = V_1 = V_2. \tag{15.99}$$

Application of Kirchhoff's first rule to the junction A gives

$$I = I_1 + I_2. \tag{15.100}$$

Next, apply Ohm's law separately to the two resistors (making use at the same time of Equation 15.99):

$$I_1 = \frac{V_1}{R_1} = \frac{V}{R_1},$$

$$I_2 = \frac{V_2}{R_2} = \frac{V}{R_2}.$$

Substituting these expressions for I_1 and I_2 in Equation 15.100 gives

$$I = V \left(\frac{1}{R_1} + \frac{1}{R_2} \right),$$

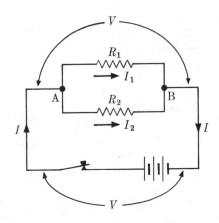

FIGURE 15.34   Parallel circuit.

an equation that may be written

$$I = \frac{V}{R}.$$ (15.101)

The effective resistance, or "total resistance," R (most conveniently written as an inverse), is given by

$$\frac{1}{R} = \frac{1}{R_1} + \frac{1}{R_2}.$$ (15.102)

Resistors in parallel   For any number of parallel resistors, similar reasoning gives

$$\frac{1}{R} = \frac{1}{R_1} + \frac{1}{R_2} + \frac{1}{R_3} + \cdots.$$ (15.103)

Notice that this result implies that the total resistance R is always less than the least resistance of the parallel resistors. Ordinary household circuits are always parallel circuits. The lamps, motors, and heaters plugged into sockets in a house are all in parallel with each other. The potential across each lamp or appliance is then always the same, and the current flowing through it does not depend on what else is connected. As more things are turned on or connected, the total resistance of the entire household circuit decreases and the total current increases, the potential remaining unchanged.

■ EXAMPLE 1:   What is the total resistance of the combination of six resistors shown in Figure 15.35(a)? We note first that a physically equivalent arrangement is that of Figure 15.35(b), which is more evidently a series and parallel combination. The $R_2 R_3$ pair can be replaced by a single resistance R' defined by

$$\frac{1}{R'} = \frac{1}{R_2} + \frac{1}{R_3}.$$

Its value is $R' = 2\ \Omega$. Similarly, the $R_4 R_5$ pair can be replaced by $R'' = 2.5\ \Omega$. These steps give, as an equivalent circuit, four resistors in series [Figure 15.35(c)], whose total resistance is

$$R = R_1 + R' + R'' + R_6 = 9\ \Omega.$$

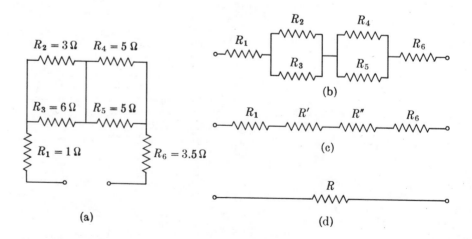

FIGURE 15.35   (a) A combination of resistors. (b)–(d) Successive reductions to an equivalent single resistor.

The original combination is equivalent to a single 9-Ω resistor [Figure 15.35(d)]. ■

■ EXAMPLE 2:   Two batteries and three resistors are connected as shown in Figure 15.36.   What are the implications of charge conservation and energy conservation (Kirchhoff's rules) for this circuit? We choose arbitrary directions for the currents I_1, I_2, and I_3, as shown by the arrows in the figure. If these directions prove wrong, the currents will simply turn out to be negative. Correct answers will still be obtained. Charge conservation at point A gives

$$I_2 = I_1 + I_3. \tag{15.104}$$

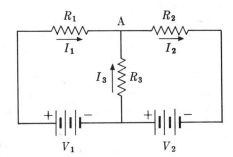

FIGURE 15.36   A circuit that can be analyzed with the help of Kirchhoff's rules.

Energy conservation around the loop containing R_1 and R_3 and around the loop containing R_3 and R_2 give

$$V_1 = I_1 R_1 - I_3 R_3, \tag{15.105}$$

$$V_2 = I_3 R_3 + I_2 R_2. \tag{15.106}$$

Each of the potentials across a resistor has been replaced by current × resistance, with signs chosen to match the assumed direction of current flow. From these three equations, the three unknowns, I_1, I_2, and I_3, may be found in terms of the knowns, V_1, V_2, R_1, R_2, and R_3. It is left as an exercise to find the currents. ■

As this example shows, applying Kirchhoff's second rule requires care in the choice of signs. To avoid errors, it is probably best to use a simple recipe, such as the following one: (1) Assign a current direction to every branch of a circuit. (A branch is a single path from one junction to another, such as the path through battery 1 and resistor 1 in Figure 15.36.) (2) Choose a direction to follow around every loop in the circuit (for example, clockwise around the $V_1 R_1 R_3$ loop in Figure 15.36). (3) Pick the signs of the potentials from the following table.

Circuit Element	Chosen Loop Direction *through* the Circuit Element	Potential
Resistor	Same as the assigned current direction	Positive
	Opposite to the assigned current direction	Negative
Battery	From the positive to the negative terminal	Positive
	From the negative to the positive terminal	Negative

(4) Set the sum of the potentials around a loop equal to zero. For example, choosing to move clockwise around the $V_1 R_1 R_3$ loop in Figure 15.36 leads to the equation

$$-V_1 + I_1 R_1 - I_3 R_3 = 0,$$

which is equivalent to Equation 15.105. Going counterclockwise around the $V_2 R_2 R_3$ loop in the same circuit leads to the equation

$$V_2 - I_2 R_2 - I_3 R_3 = 0,$$

which is equivalent to Equation 15.106.

RESISTANCE AND POWER

According to Equation 15.57, power is given by the product of potential difference and current:

A precise equation for steady current flow

$$P = VI.$$

This is a precise equation because it depends simply on the definition of potential.* Since, according to Ohm's law, $V = IR$, power may also be expressed as

$$P = I^2 R. \tag{15.107}$$

Approximate equations when Ohm's law is valid

Another equivalent expression is

$$P = \frac{V^2}{R}. \tag{15.108}$$

These two equations are valid whenever Ohm's law is valid. They may be applied either to a circuit as a whole or to any part of a circuit.

15.12   Capacitance

A capacitor is a device that stores charge. In simplest form, it consists of parallel metal plates separated by air or by other insulating material (Figure 15.37). No charge can flow through it, but charge can, for a time, flow onto one side of the capacitor and away from its other side, until it has accumulated charge $+q$ on one plate and charge $-q$ on the other plate. A potential difference of magnitude V then exists between its plates. The capacitance C of the capacitor (always a positive quantity) is defined by

Definition of capacitance

$$C = \frac{q}{V}. \tag{15.109}$$

Since the potential generated between the plates is proportional to the stored charge, the ratio q/V is a constant for any particular capacitor. Larger capacitance means that more charge can be stored for a given potential difference.

---

* Equation 15.57 is precisely valid for d.c. circuits, and is also valid for a.c. circuits if potential and current alternate in phase and if root-mean-square values of V and I are used. In either case, it does not depend on the linearity of resistors.

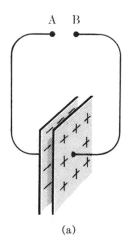

A   B

(a)

(b)

(c)

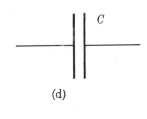

C

(d)

FIGURE 15.37   Capacitors. (a) Idealized version of capacitor. Equal and opposite charges are stored on parallel metal plates. (b) Early version of capacitor, the "Leyden jar," invented in 1745. Glass separates layers of metal foil. (c) Actual capacitor used in radio-frequency oscillator. Other capacitors vary enormously in size and in physical construction. (d) Standard representation of a capacitor in circuit diagrams.

The SI unit of capacitance is called the farad, in honor of Michael Faraday. From Equation 15.109, it must be equal to 1 coulomb per volt:

$$\text{unit of capacitance} = \text{farad (F)} = \text{C/V}. \qquad (15.110)$$

In practice, the farad is a very large unit of capacitance. Most capacitors are rated in microfarads, μF (10^{-6} farad) or in picofarads, pF (10^{-12} farad).

The capacitance of an idealized parallel-plate capacitor can be related to the area A of its plates and their separation d. Between the plates of such a capacitor is an approximately uniform electric field $\mathbf{E}$ (Figure 15.38). According

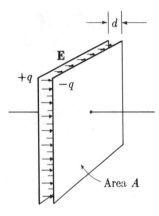

FIGURE 15.38 The electric field between closely spaced charged plates is nearly uniform and is simply related to the charge on the plates and the potential difference between them.

to a result derived in Section 15.6 (Equation 15.44), the magnitude of the field between the plates is

Field between parallel plates

$$E = \frac{\sigma}{\epsilon_0},$$ (15.111)

where σ is the charge per unit area on the metal plate. The potential difference, equal to Ed, is

$$V = \frac{\sigma d}{\epsilon_0}.$$

For σ we may substitute q/A, where A is the area of one plate. Then

$$V = \frac{qd}{\epsilon_0 A}.$$

Substituting this result for V in Equation 15.109 gives, for the capacitance of a parallel plate capacitor,

Capacitance of parallel-plate capacitor

$$C = \frac{\epsilon_0 A}{d}.$$ (15.112)

For a pair of capacitors in parallel (Figure 15.39), the potential is the same across both: $V_1 = V_2 = V$. The sum of the stored charges is

$$q_1 + q_2 = C_1 V + C_2 V.$$

This may be written

$$q_T = (C_1 + C_2)V,$$

where q_T is the total stored charge, $q_1 + q_2$. The capacitance of the combination is therefore

Capacitors in parallel

$$C = C_1 + C_2.$$ (15.113)

It is left as an exercise to prove that the inverse capacitance of two capacitors in series is given by

Capacitors in series

$$\frac{1}{C} = \frac{1}{C_1} + \frac{1}{C_2}.$$ (15.114)

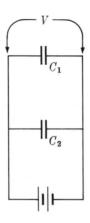

FIGURE 15.39 Capacitors connected in parallel to a source of potential. Capacitance is additive.

■ EXAMPLE 1: What is the capacitance of a pair of concentric metal spheres of radii $R_1 = 10$ cm and $R_2 = 11$ cm (see Figure 15.29)? According to Equation 15.83, the magnitude of their potential difference is

$$V = \frac{q}{4\pi\epsilon_0} \frac{R_2 - R_1}{R_1 R_2}.$$

Substituting this expression for V in Equation 15.109, gives, for the capacitance,

$$C = \frac{4\pi\epsilon_0 R_1 R_2}{R_2 - R_1}. \tag{15.115}$$

Capacitance of concentric spheres

For the given dimensions, this formula yields

$$C = \frac{0.10 \text{ m} \times 0.11 \text{ m}}{9 \times 10^9 \text{ N m}^2/\text{C}^2 \times 0.01 \text{ m}}$$

$$= 1.22 \times 10^{-10} \text{ F}$$

$$= 122 \text{ pF}.$$

It is of interest to consider also the limit $R_2 \rightarrow \infty$. Then, with R_1 replaced by R,

$$C = 4\pi\epsilon_0 R. \tag{15.116}$$

Capacitance of a single sphere

This is the capacitance of a single sphere. For $R = 0.1$ m, for example,

$$C = 11.1 \text{ pF}.$$

In general, the capacitance of a single conducting body may be defined by Equation 15.109 if q is the magnitude of charge on the body and if V is the magnitude of its potential with the zero of potential at infinity. ■

The capacitor, a repository of stored charge, is also a repository of stored energy—energy that can be regained by allowing the capacitor to discharge through a resistor or other circuit element. The stored energy can be calculated by considering the process of adding charge to the capacitor. If charge dq' is added to a capacitor whose potential is V', the added increment of potential energy is

$$dU = V' \, dq'.$$

Since V' is related to the charge q' already on the capacitor by $V' = q'/C$, this relation may also be written

$$dU = \frac{1}{C} q' \, dq'.$$ (15.117)

Consider now a capacitor, initially uncharged, to which a total charge q is added (for a two-plate capacitor, this means charge q on one plate and charge $-q$ on the other plate). The stored potential energy is, from Equation 15.117,

$$U = \frac{1}{C} \int_0^q q' \, dq' = \frac{q^2}{2C}.$$ (15.118)

Energy stored in a capacitor   An alternative expression for the same result, obtained by setting $q = CV$, is

$$U = \tfrac{1}{2}CV^2.$$ (15.119)

With q in coulombs, V in volts, and C in farads, U is in joules.

★THE RC CIRCUIT

A simple circuit containing a capacitor is shown in Figure 15.40. When the switch is closed, a steady current flows through the resistor, and a potential V_0 is applied across the capacitor, which, therefore, gains a charge $q_0 = CV_0$. When the switch is opened, the capacitor begins to discharge through the resistor. At any time during the discharge, let the potential across the capacitor (and across the resistor) be V, let the current through the resistor be I, and let the charge remaining on the capacitor be q. There exist several simple relations among these quantities. First, the definition of capacitance gives

$$V = \frac{q}{C}.$$ (15.120)

Ohm's law for the resistor gives

$$V = IR.$$ (15.121)

And because of the conservation of charge, the rate of decrease of charge on the capacitor must be equal to the current in the resistor:

$$I = -\frac{dq}{dt}.$$ (15.122)

Substituting from Equations 15.120 and 15.122 for V and I in Equation 15.121 gives

$$\frac{q}{C} = -R \frac{dq}{dt},$$

or, after slight rearrangement,

Equation of discharging
capacitor

$$\frac{dq}{dt} = -\frac{1}{RC} q.$$ (15.123)

This relates the charge to its rate of change. It is a differential equation asking the mathematical question: For what function $q(t)$ is the derivative dq/dt

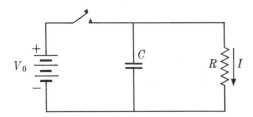

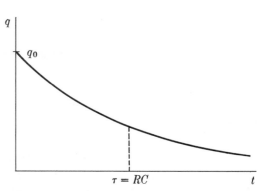

FIGURE 15.40   Circuit used to study the discharge of a capacitor through a resistor.

FIGURE 15.41   The charge on a capacitor discharging through a resistor falls exponentially to zero.

proportional to $-q$? The decreasing exponential is such a function—indeed the only such function. The solution to this differential equation may be written

$$q(t) = q_0 e^{-t/RC}. \qquad (15.124) \qquad \textit{Its solution}$$

The correctness of this solution is easily verified by substituting it back in Equation 15.123. The one arbitrary constant, q_0, is chosen to be equal to the given initial charge at $t = 0$.

According to Equation 15.124, the discharge of the RC circuit follows an exponential law (Figure 15.41), with the charge falling to $1/e$ of its initial value in a characteristic time τ given by

$$\tau = RC \qquad (15.125) \qquad \textit{The RC time constant}$$

(ohms × farads = seconds). Alternatively, the half life for the discharge is

$$t_{1/2} = \tau \ln 2 = 0.693 RC. \qquad (15.126)$$

The quantity τ is called the RC time constant of the circuit. It is easy to choose circuit elements such that RC has any value from less than a microsecond to more than an hour. The reader may verify that potential and current also follow the same exponential law of decrease,

$$V = V_0 e^{-t/RC}, \qquad (15.127)$$

$$I = I_0 e^{-t/RC}, \qquad (15.128)$$

where $V_0 = q_0 C$ and $I_0 = V_0/R$.

■ EXAMPLE 2:   How much energy is dissipated in the resistor during the discharge of the capacitor? The energy is the time integral of the power (since $P = dE/dt$):

$$E = \int_0^\infty P \, dt. \qquad (15.129)$$

A convenient expression for the power is $P = V^2/R$ (Equation 15.108). Using this expression for P and using Equation 15.127 for V, we get

$$E = \left(\frac{V_0^2}{R}\right) \int_0^\infty e^{-2t/RC} \, dt.$$

In the integral, set $2t/RC = u$; then

$$E = \frac{V_0{}^2}{R}\frac{RC}{2}\int_0^\infty e^{-u}\,du.$$

This integral is equal to 1. The total energy dissipated is therefore

$$E = \tfrac{1}{2}CV_0{}^2.$$

This is equal, as it should be, to the energy initially stored in the capacitor (see Equation 15.119). ∎

★15.13   Dielectrics

Polarization

A dielectric is a material that can be *polarized*. This means that at the atomic level, its positive and negative charges can be slightly separated [see Figure 15.25(a)] by the influence of an applied electric field. It then behaves roughly as an electric dipole. More exactly, it can be considered a myriad of individual molecular dipoles. If the molecules of the material possess electric dipole moments even when no field acts on them (water is an example), they are called *polar molecules*. A material composed of such molecules is polarized by partial alignment of its molecules. A *nonpolar molecule* possesses no permanent dipole moment but can experience some separation of charge and acquire a dipole moment in the presence of an electric field.

Polarization and static induction

One of the simplest phenomena of electrostatics, the attraction of an uncharged bit of matter to a charged body [Figure 15.1(a)], is explained in terms of polarization. As shown in Figure 15.42, a piece of paper near a negatively charged comb is polarized in such a way that a slight excess of positive charge accumulates at the end nearest the comb and a slight excess of negative charge accumulates at the other end. Since the field is weaker at greater distance from the comb, the positive charge experiences a greater force, and there is a net attraction. This phenomenon is sometimes called *static induction*. The excess

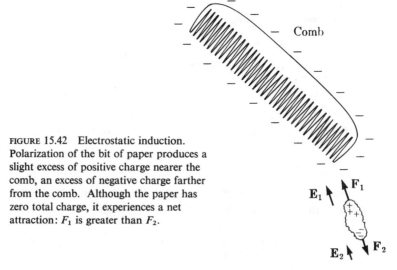

FIGURE 15.42   Electrostatic induction. Polarization of the bit of paper produces a slight excess of positive charge nearer the comb, an excess of negative charge farther from the comb. Although the paper has zero total charge, it experiences a net attraction: F_1 is greater than F_2.

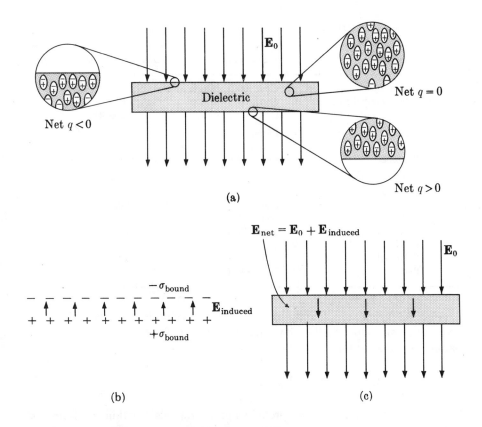

FIGURE 15.43   (a) Polarization of molecules in a dielectric produces a net
excess of positive charge at one surface and a net excess of negative charge at
the other surface. (b) The effect of the dielectric can be duplicated by means
of two sheets of charge, called bound charge, which produce a field $\mathbf{E}_{induced}$.
(c) The actual net field within the dielectric is parallel to, but weaker than, the
external field.

charge is called *induced charge*. From a macroscopic point of view, much the
same phenomenon occurs—also with a net attraction—if the paper is replaced by
a conducting body, such as a piece of aluminum foil. The physical mechanism,
however, is very different in the two cases. The paper is a good insulator with
no free charge. Its induced charge results from the displacement of charge in
each molecule by much less than a single atomic diameter. In the aluminum
foil, on the other hand, free electrons actually move macroscopic distances.

   Now consider a slab of dielectric material in a uniform electric field
(Figure 15.43). Each molecule in the material possesses a dipole moment that,
averaged over time, is aligned with the applied field. As shown in Figure 15.43(a),
any small region—infinitesimal by macroscopic standards but large enough to
encompass many molecules—is electrically neutral if it lies entirely within the
dielectric. However, if it includes either surface, it contains a net charge, positive
on one surface and negative on the other. This means that the entire electrical
effect of the dielectric can be represented by two sheets of charge, one positive
and one negative, as shown in Figure 15.43(b). The induced surface charge

*A polarized slab is
represented by surface sheets
of charge*

TABLE 15.2   DIELECTRIC CONSTANTS OF SOME MATERIALS

Substance	Conditions	Dielectric Constant
Steam	Gas, 100 °C, 1 atm	1.0126
Ethanol (ethyl alcohol)	Gas, 100 °C, 1 atm	1.0061
Air	Gas, 20 °C, 1 atm	1.00054
Water	Liquid, 20 °C	80
Ethanol	Liquid, 25 °C	24
Benzene	Liquid, 20 °C	2.28
Lead chloride	Solid, 20 °C	33.5
Bakelite	Solid, 25 °C	7
Porcelain	Solid, 20 °C	6–8
Sodium chloride	Solid, 20 °C	5.6
Pyrex glasses	Solid, 20 °C	4–5
Nylon	Solid, 20 °C	3.5
Polyethylene	Solid, 20 °C	2.3
Paraffin	Solid, 20 °C	2.0–2.5

densities (C/m^2) are σ_{bound} and $-\sigma_{bound}$. It is left as a problem to show that they give rise to an induced field within the dielectric that is the same as that of a parallel-plate capacitor (Equation 15.111):

$$E_{induced} = \frac{\sigma_{bound}}{\epsilon_0}. \tag{15.130}$$

This induced field is to be interpreted as an average field within the dielectric over a volume containing many molecules. There is a similarly averaged *net* field within the dielectric [Figure 15.43(c)] that is the vector sum of the originally applied field and the induced field:

$$\mathbf{E}_{net} = \mathbf{E}_0 + \mathbf{E}_{induced}. \tag{15.131}$$

The net field is diminished   Since $\mathbf{E}_0$ and $\mathbf{E}_{induced}$ are oppositely directed, $\mathbf{E}_{net}$ is smaller in magnitude than $\mathbf{E}_0$. (Why is $\mathbf{E}_{net}$ always in the same direction as $\mathbf{E}_0$?)

A useful measure of the effectiveness of a dielectric is the *dielectric constant* κ_e, defined as the factor by which the field is reduced within the dielectric:*

The dielectric constant

$$\kappa_e = \frac{E_0}{E_{net}}. \tag{15.132}$$

The dielectric constants of various materials are shown in Table 15.2. The remarkable substance water, so ubiquitous and so essential for man, shows itself here, as in many other ways, to be unusual.

CAPACITOR WITH DIELECTRIC

Suppose now that a dielectric slab is placed between the metal plates of a capacitor (Figure 15.44). The surface charge densities on the metal plates we

---

* A related quantity, called the *permittivity* of the material, is defined by $\epsilon = \kappa_e \epsilon_0$.

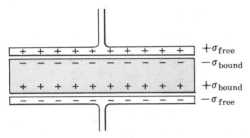

FIGURE 15.44   A dielectric slab in a capacitor.
Its effect is to increase the capacitance.

may call σ_{free} and $-\sigma_{\text{free}}$ (the subscript indicates the fact that this charge is
free to move). Adjacent to the plates are the induced surface charge densities
$-\sigma_{\text{bound}}$ and σ_{bound}. The net charge per unit area at one plate is $\sigma_{\text{free}} - \sigma_{\text{bound}}$,
and this is what determines the net field between the plates. It is

$$E_{\text{net}} = \frac{\sigma_{\text{free}} - \sigma_{\text{bound}}}{\epsilon_0} = E_0 - E_{\text{induced}}. \tag{15.133}$$

where $E_0 = \sigma_{\text{free}}/\epsilon_0$, the field created by the free charge, and where $E_{\text{induced}} = \sigma_{\text{bound}}/\epsilon_0$, the field created by the bound (or induced) charge. (Why do the signs
on the right sides of Equations 15.131 and 15.133 differ?)

For a capacitor containing a dielectric, the definition of capacitance,
Equation 15.109, is rewritten as

$$C = \frac{q_{\text{free}}}{V}. \tag{15.134}$$

*Revised definition of
capacitance*

In the numerator,

$$q_{\text{free}} = \sigma_{\text{free}} A, \tag{15.135}$$

where A is the area of the plates. In the denominator, $V = E_{\text{net}} d = E_0 d / \kappa_e$.
Since $E_0 = \sigma_{\text{free}}/\epsilon_0$, this potential can be written as

$$V = \frac{\sigma_{\text{free}} d}{\epsilon_0 \kappa_e}. \tag{15.136}$$

Substituting these formulas for q_{free} and V in Equation 15.134 yields

$$C = \frac{\kappa_e \epsilon_0 A}{d}$$

$$= \kappa_e C_{\text{vac}}, \tag{15.137}$$

*Capacitance of parallel-plate
capacitor with dielectric*

where $C_{\text{vac}} = \epsilon_0 A/d$, the capacitance if no dielectric is present (Equation 15.112).
This result is easy to understand. The induced charge on the dielectric weakens
the field between the plates by a factor κ_e and therefore diminishes the potential
difference between the plates by the same factor. The capacitance goes up by
this factor. The same charge is stored at lower potential, or greater charge is
stored at the same potential.

15.14   Electric acceleration of charged particles

In this section we shall consider the acceleration of charged particles by electric fields in a vacuum. (A simple example appears also in Section 7.9.)

THE CATHODE-RAY TUBE

The principle of the cathode-ray tube (often abbreviated CRT) is illustrated in Figure 15.45. Electrons boiling off the hot cathode are accelerated a short distance down the neck of the tube by an electric field existing between the cathode and the anode. If the potential difference between anode and cathode is called V_a (the accelerating potential), the kinetic energy acquired by the electrons is

$$K = eV_a. \tag{15.138}$$

Those electrons that fly through a hole in the center of the anode enter a region nearly free of electric field and complete their journey to the tube face at nearly constant speed. A typical value of V_a is about 10^3 V, giving to the electrons an energy of 10^3 eV.

As early as 1897, J. J. Thomson constructed a cathode-ray tube that provided electric acceleration of electrons perpendicular as well as parallel to the axis of the tube. His method is still in use in oscilloscopes, devices that use cathode-ray tubes to graphically display a potential that varies rapidly with time. The bare essentials of a tube arranged to give transverse acceleration are shown in Figure 15.46. An electron reaches the deflection plates with horizontal component of velocity v_x determined by

$$\tfrac{1}{2}mv_x^2 = eV_a, \tag{15.139}$$

and then spends between the plates a time given by

$$t = \frac{l}{v_x},$$

where l is the length of the deflection plates. During this time the electron experiences a vertical force (upward in the illustrated example) given by

$$F_y = eE_y = \frac{eV_d}{d}, \tag{15.140}$$

where V_d is the deflection potential existing between the plates and d is the separation of the plates. The upward acceleration of the electron between the plates is therefore

$$a_y = \frac{F_y}{m} = \frac{e}{m}\frac{V_d}{d}, \tag{15.141}$$

where m is the mass of the electron. This acceleration, acting for time t, gives to the electron an upward component of velocity

$$v_y = a_y t = \frac{e}{m}\frac{l}{d}\frac{V_d}{v_x}. \tag{15.142}$$

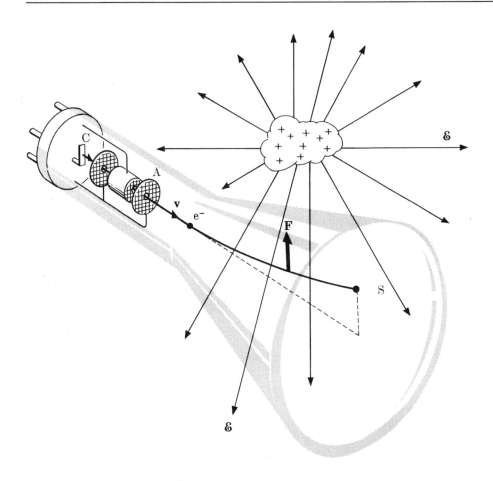

FIGURE 15.45   The cathode-ray tube (simplified, with inessential detail omitted).
Electrons boil from the hot cathode (C) and are attracted to the positively
charged anode (A). Those passing through the central hole in the anode fly
on to cause a fluorescent spot (S) on the tube face. Illustrated is an upward
deflection produced by a positively charged object above the beam.

FIGURE 15.46   Cathode-ray tube with internal
plates to provide electric deflection
(idealized and not to scale). Between C and
A, electrons acquire a horizontal component
of velocity v_x. Passing between deflection
plates D, they are accelerated vertically by a
deflection potential V_d and acquire a vertical
component of velocity v_y. A second pair of
plates to provide deflection left and right on
the screen is not shown.

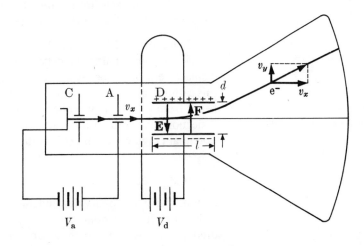

Continuing toward the screen, the electron moves at an angle θ to the horizontal, with

$$\tan \theta = \frac{v_y}{v_x} = \frac{elV_d}{dmv_x^2} .$$

From Equation 15.139, $mv_x^2 = 2eV_a$, so the expression for $\tan \theta$ can be simplified:

Electric deflection in a CRT

$$\tan \theta = \frac{l}{2d} \frac{V_d}{V_a} . \qquad (15.143)$$

The electron deflection depends on the ratio of two lengths and the ratio of two potentials.

■ EXAMPLE: It is of interest to calculate typical physical magnitudes within a CRT.   Let us choose $V_a = 1,000$ V, $V_d = 100$ V, $l = 3$ cm, and $d = 0.6$ cm. From Equation 15.143,

$$\tan \theta = \left(\frac{3}{1.2}\right)\left(\frac{100}{1,000}\right) = 0.25,$$

giving an angle of about 14 deg. From Equation 15.139, the speed of the electron before it enters the deflection plates is

$$v_x = \sqrt{\frac{2eV_a}{m}} = \sqrt{\frac{2 \times 1.60 \times 10^{-19} \text{ C} \times 10^3 \text{ V}}{9.1 \times 10^{-31} \text{ kg}}},$$

which works out to be

$$v_x = 1.88 \times 10^7 \text{ m/sec},$$

about $\frac{1}{16}$ the speed of light.   Between the plates, the electron spends a time $t = 1.6 \times 10^{-9}$ sec and there experiences an acceleration

$$a_y = \frac{eV_d}{md} = \frac{1.60 \times 10^{-19} \text{ C} \times 100 \text{ V}}{9.1 \times 10^{-31} \text{ kg} \times 0.006 \text{ m}} = 2.9 \times 10^{15} \text{ m/sec}^2,$$

or about $3 \times 10^{14}g$.   One must marvel at the fact that laws of force and laws of motion discovered in the sluggish macroscopic world remain valid in the frenetic domain of electron motion (provided, as we now know, that the electron speed is not too close to the speed of light).   ■

Equation 15.142 shows that the electron gains a vertical component of velocity proportional to the deflection potential V_d. This means in turn that the displacement of the beam spot on the tube face is proportional to V_d. In effect, this cathode-ray tube is a pictorial voltmeter. If another pair of plates swings the beam from left to right while an unknown potential is applied to the vertical

Principle of the oscilloscope

deflection plates, the beam traces out on the tube face a graph of the unknown potential (Figure 15.47). This is the principle of the oscilloscope.

VACUUM TUBES

Among the evolutionary descendants of the early cathode-ray tubes are vacuum tubes, which serve quite different purposes. The simplest vacuum tube, the diode, contains only a cathode and an anode, separated by empty space. The

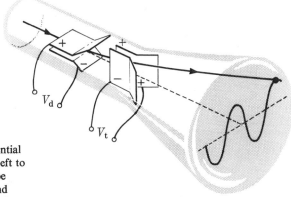

FIGURE 15.47   The principle of the oscilloscope. While a "time-base" potential V_t is swinging the electron beam from left to right at a steady rate, the potential to be studied, V_d, is swinging the beam up and down. As a result, the moving spot of the beam on the tube face traces out a graph of V_d vs time.

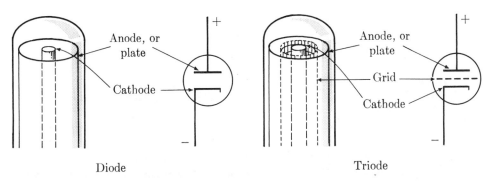

FIGURE 15.48   The diode and the triode, simple vacuum tubes used to control current flow. Not shown in either the pictorial or schematic representations of the tubes are the filament wires used to heat the cathode.

next most complicated vacuum tube, the triode, contains three elements—a cathode, an anode, and between them a screen called a grid. Figure 15.48 shows the actual typical construction of diodes and triodes, together with the schematic representations of diode and triode used in circuit diagrams.

In a diode the hot cathode boils off electrons into the space around it. If the anode is positively charged, these electrons are accelerated to the anode and current flows through the tube. If the anode is negatively charged, the electric field forces the electrons back toward the cathode and no current flows. In Great Britain a vacuum tube is called, more descriptively, a valve because it can be used to turn on or shut off the flow of current. One common use of the diode is to "rectify" alternating current—that is, to convert alternating current to direct current. The anode is alternately charged positively and negatively with respect to the cathode. Half the time (when the anode is negative) no current flows, and half the time (when the anode is positive) current does flow through the tube. Although the resulting direct current is not steady, it flows in only one direction.

The diode

It can rectify current

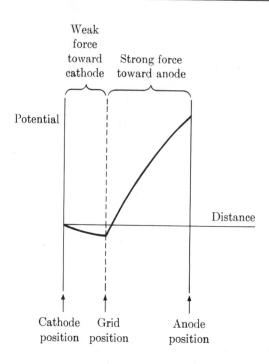

FIGURE 15.49   Idealized potential diagram for triode. What appears here as a small valley appears to the negatively charged electron as a small hill. The choice of zero potential at the cathode is arbitrary.

The triode   The triode finds its chief applications in control and amplification. Typically, the grid of the triode is maintained at a small negative potential with respect to the cathode, whereas the anode potential is large and positive with respect to the cathode. This means that electrons between cathode and grid feel a weak force repelling them back toward the cathode. Any electron beyond the grid, on the other hand, feels a strong force attracting it to the anode. The repulsive electric force prevents most of the electrons boiling off the cathode from reaching the grid. A few emerge from the cathode with sufficient energy to overcome the repulsive force and make their way past the grid, where they are drawn on to the anode. Now, if the grid potential is made slightly more negative, far fewer electrons will be able to penetrate past the grid, and the current flow through the tube will be greatly reduced. If the grid potential is made slightly less negative, more electrons will surmount the repulsive force between cathode and grid, and the current through the tube will increase. This situation can be pictorialized by a potential diagram like that in Figure 15.49. The grid represents —for the negative electrons—a small hill between cathode and anode. A small change in the height of this hill can result in a large change in the flow of electrons reaching the anode.

It can amplify potential   The triode can be used most simply as a switch. A flow of current through the tube can be turned on or off by adjusting the potential on the grid. More often the triode serves as an amplifier. The grid potential is varied up and down about some prechosen neutral value that permits a moderate flow of current through the tube. As the grid potential increases, the tube current increases; as the potential decreases, the tube current decreases. For each alternation of the grid potential there is a corresponding alternation of the current through the tube. This current in turn may be allowed to flow through a resistor attached in series to the tube (Figure 15.50). Because of Ohm's law, the potential across this resistor, given by

$$V = IR,$$

will be proportional to the current through the tube (the same as the current through the resistor). Hence every change of grid potential will be reflected in an exactly corresponding, but usually much larger, change of potential across the series resistor: the triode has acted to amplify potential. One or more triodes form the heart of many phonograph amplifiers. In such an amplifier, the potential fed to the grid oscillates rapidly in synchronism with the vibrations of sound that were recorded. If the amplified potential is precisely proportional to the input potential, the amplifier is said to be linear. A high-fidelity amplifier is one that is very nearly linear.

In many applications, vacuum tubes have been largely supplanted by transistors. These so-called "solid-state devices" are composed of semiconductors. A description of semiconductors will be found in Section 24.11.

15.15 Field energy

The field concept brought to electromagnetic theory many valuable dividends beyond ease of visualization: it made possible a local theory without action at a distance; it generated a deeper understanding of the links between electricity and magnetism; it provided a basis for a concise mathematical theory of electromagnetism; and it introduced a way of thinking about nature that proved fruitful in the development of modern theories of relativity and quantum mechanics. Finally, the fields provided a seat of electromagnetic energy. To the question "Where is the electrostatic energy?" we can now give the answer: "Wherever there is electric field." The field is literally a physical repository for energy.

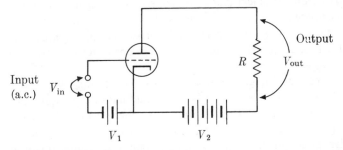

FIGURE 15.50 Simple amplifier. Relative to cathode, the grid of a triode is held at a slightly negative potential V_1, and the anode is held at a high positive potential by a battery of potential V_2. Additional small alternations of potential V_{in} at the grid control the current flow and produce larger but proportional changes in the potential V_{out} across the resistor. (The circuit to heat the cathode is not shown.)

*Energy density of the
electric field*

Theory beyond the scope of this text predicts that the energy density of the electric field, for which we use the symbol u, is given by

$$u = \tfrac{1}{2}\epsilon_0 E^2. \tag{15.144}$$

The SI unit of u is J/m³. Consider, for example, an idealized parallel-plate capacitor (Figure 15.38) whose uniform field **E** is confined in a volume Ad (A = area of plate, d = distance between plates). From Equation 15.111, the magnitude of the field is $E = \sigma/\epsilon_0$, which can also be written

$$E = \frac{q}{A\epsilon_0}$$

(q = charge on one plate). If the stored energy per unit volume is $\tfrac{1}{2}\epsilon_0 E^2$, the total stored energy in the field is

$$U = uAd = \frac{1}{2}\,\epsilon_0 \left(\frac{q}{A\epsilon_0}\right)^2 Ad,$$

which simplifies to

$$U = \frac{q^2 d}{2\epsilon_0 A}. \tag{15.145}$$

According to Equation 15.112, the capacitance of the parallel plate capacitor is

$$C = \frac{\epsilon_0 A}{d}.$$

Therefore, Equation 15.145 may be rewritten as

$$U = \frac{q^2}{2C}, \tag{15.146}$$

*Two ways to look at the
energy stored in a capacitor*

the same as Equation 15.118. The earlier result was calculated by considering the energy required to charge the capacitor. In general, the total energy calculated by assigning an energy per unit volume of $\tfrac{1}{2}\epsilon_0 E^2$ is always the same as the potential energy calculated from the work required to move the charges and create the field distribution. It is legitimate and consistent to regard the stored energy as being distributed through space as field energy. When magnetic field is also present, another energy-density term proportional to the square of the magnetic field is also necessary. The magnetic energy-density term is given in Section 16.2.

For a point charge, the integrated stored energy is infinite. What this means physically is that an infinite amount of work would have been required to assemble a finite charge at a point from infinitesimal charges brought to the point. Yet nature presents us with units of charge that do not appear to be divisible into smaller units and that seem to be point charges. The problem of the point charge has been a troublesome one in both classical theory and quantum theory. Although some aspects of the problem have been solved, the problem remains, and it may hold hidden clues of a deeper structure of space, time, and matter. In most practical calculations, the infinite self-energy of point charges may be ignored.

Summary of ideas and definitions

Electric charge is a scalar quantity that may be positive or negative; it is a quantized property of particles and obeys a conservation law; its unit, the coulomb (C), is defined as 1 A sec.

The law of force between charged particles (Coulomb's law) may be written

$$\mathbf{F}_{12} = \frac{1}{4\pi\epsilon_0} \frac{q_1 q_2 \mathbf{i}_{12}}{r^2}; \qquad (15.15)$$

the "permittivity of free space," ϵ_0, is an experimentally determined constant.

Electric field, expressed in newton/coulomb, or volt/meter, is defined as the force per unit charge acting on a stationary test charge ($\mathbf{F} = q'\mathbf{E}$).

The electric field created by a point charge is

$$\mathbf{E} = \frac{1}{4\pi\epsilon_0} \frac{q\mathbf{i}_r}{r^2}. \qquad (15.20)$$

Fields created by several charges obey a law of superposition.

Lines of field originate at positive charge and terminate at negative charge; field strength is proportional to the number of lines per unit area.

Electric flux is defined either by $d\Phi_E = \mathbf{E} \cdot d\mathbf{S}$ or as a surface integral (Equation 15.30); it is proportional to the number of lines of field crossing an area.

Gauss's law relates the flux through a closed surface to the charge enclosed by the surface:

$$\oint \mathbf{E} \cdot d\mathbf{S} = \frac{q}{\epsilon_0}. \qquad (15.36)$$

The field outside a uniformly charged spherical shell is the same as that of a point charge; inside the shell, $\mathbf{E} = 0$.

The field near a charged metal surface is perpendicular to the surface and has magnitude $E = \sigma/\epsilon_0$.

Static electric forces are conservative; electric potential energy per unit charge is called potential (or voltage) and is measured in volts. It is expressed as a line integral of the electric field (Equation 15.48).

The potential of a uniform field in the x direction is
$$V = -E \cdot (x - x_0). \qquad (15.52)$$

The potential of a point charge (or outside a uniformly charged sphere) is

$$V = \frac{1}{4\pi\epsilon_0} \frac{q}{r}. \qquad (15.60)$$

Power is related to potential by $P = IV$.

In a field $\mathbf{E}$, an electric dipole has potential energy $U = -\mathbf{p} \cdot \mathbf{E}$ (Equation 15.73) and experiences torque $\mathbf{T} = \mathbf{p} \times \mathbf{E}$ (Equation 15.75).

When static conditions prevail, a conductor is an equipotential; net charge, if any, resides only on its surface.

On a charged conductor, the maximum accumulation of charge occurs at points of maximum curvature.

An approximate law governing current flow in many substances is Ohm's law, written $\mathbf{J} = \sigma\mathbf{E}$ (Equation 15.84), or

$$V = IR. \qquad (15.88)$$

Kirchhoff's first rule expresses charge conservation: The total current flowing into any point in a circuit is zero (if conditions are steady).

Kirchhoff's second rule expresses energy conservation: The sum of the potentials around any closed loop in a circuit is zero (if conditions are steady).

For series resistors, the total resistance is
$$R = R_1 + R_2 + R_3 + \cdots; \qquad (15.98)$$
for parallel resistors, the total resistance is given by
$$\frac{1}{R} = \frac{1}{R_1} + \frac{1}{R_2} + \frac{1}{R_3} + \cdots. \qquad (15.103)$$

When Ohm's law is valid, power is related to resistance by

$$P = I^2 R = \frac{V^2}{R}. \qquad (15.107, 15.108)$$

Capacitance is defined by

$$C = \frac{q}{V} \quad \text{or} \quad \frac{q_{\text{free}}}{V}. \qquad (15.109, 15.134)$$

The capacitance of a parallel plate capacitor is
$$C = \frac{\epsilon_0 A}{d} \quad \text{or} \quad \frac{\kappa_e \epsilon_0 A}{d}. \qquad (15.112, 15.137)$$

The energy stored in a capacitor is

$$U = \frac{q^2}{2C} = \frac{1}{2} CV^2. \quad (15.118, \ 15.119)$$

If a charged capacitor is connected to a resistor, the charge decreases exponentially with a time constant that is equal to RC (Equation 15.124).

A polarized dielectric can be represented by sheets of bound (or induced) surface charge. The field in the dielectric is reduced by a factor κ_e (the dielectric constant):

$$E_{net} = \frac{E_0}{\kappa_e}. \quad (15.132)$$

The effect of a dielectric in a capacitor is to increase the capacitance by a factor κ_e.

An oscilloscope uses a cathode-ray tube to act as a pictorial voltmeter.

A diode can act as a switch or a rectifier (transforming alternating current to pulsed direct current).

A triode can act as an amplifier.

The energy density in space where there is electric field is

$$u = \tfrac{1}{2}\epsilon_0 E^2. \quad (15.144)$$

QUESTIONS

Section 15.1

Q15.1   In the dry climate of Los Alamos, New Mexico, a physicist is likely to receive a mild electric shock when he walks up to a friend and shakes hands. When he travels to a humid climate and greets another friend, he receives no shock. Why the difference?

Q15.2   Suggest a simple experiment to show that the electric force experienced by an object does not depend on its mass.

Section 15.2

Q15.3   An electrified rubber balloon has an excess of negative charge. It is attracted to most objects (walls, tables, blackboards, people, etc.). Does this mean that most objects are positively charged? If so, why this imbalance that favors positive charge? If not, why is the balloon more often attracted than repelled?

Q15.4   What tests could you perform on a small pellet to find out (a) whether it is charged or not and (b) if it is charged, what the sign of its charge is? (HINT: Being attracted by another object known to be charged does not prove that the pellet is charged.)

Q15.5   A rubber balloon is initially neutral. After being rubbed with wool it is electrically charged. Describe an experimental procedure (it need not be very practical) that could test the conservation of charge in this process.

Q15.6   Suppose that a scientist who wished to re-introduce the one-fluid theory increased the charge assigned to every elementary particle by 1 quantum unit. In his scheme, the electron has zero charge, the neutron has a charge of $+1$ unit, and the proton has a charge of $+2$ units. Is the redefined charge conserved? Explain why it is or is not.

Q15.7   Briefly describe the meaning of charge as you might explain it to someone with no training in science.

Q15.8 In thermonuclear reactions, atomic nuclei at high temperature collide and interact. Suggest a reason why experimenters attempting to produce controlled thermonuclear power limit themselves to working with isotopes of hydrogen.

Section 15.3

Q15.9 Explain how Newton's third law is "automatically" incorporated in Equations 15.13 and 15.15.

Q15.10 An enterprising student of physics, unwilling to follow the crowd, defines charge (for which he uses the symbol ξ) in such a way that the law of electric force takes the form

$$F = K\frac{\xi_1^2\xi_2^2}{r^2},$$

where K is a constant of proportionality. (1) Explain why this law of force is perfectly compatible with experiment. (2) Is there still a conservation law analogous to the law of charge conservation? If so, what is the conserved quantity? (On purely logical grounds this law of force and Coulomb's law are equally acceptable. Yet it is easy to see why scientists prefer Coulomb's law.)

Q15.11 Can lines of electric field intersect? Why or why not?

Section 15.4

Q15.12 (1) Give one example of a scalar field quantity other than temperature. (2) Give one example of a vector field quantity other than electric field.

Q15.13 Describe qualitatively a distribution of charge on the walls of a box that could give rise to the lines of field pictured in Figure 15.7(e).

Q15.14 Sketch the field line pattern surrounding a long thin rod that carries a net negative charge distributed uniformly over its surface. (HINTS: 1. Symmetry requires that certain of the field lines be straight lines. 2. At a great distance from the rod, the pattern of field lines must resemble the pattern surrounding a point charge.)

Q15.15 Sketch qualitatively the field line pattern created by four equal positive charges at the corners of a square. Take advantage of the symmetry of the situation.

Q15.16 Particle 1 bearing charge q_1 and particle 2 bearing charge q_2 occupy a certain region. (1) To calculate the force on particle 1, what electric field is used? (2) To calculate the force on particle 2, what electric field is used? (3) If a third charged particle is added to the region, what electric field is used to find the force on the new particle?

Section 15.5

Q15.17 Give an example of a surface (not a closed surface) near a point charge *across* which the electric *flux* is zero but *on* which the electric *field* is not zero.

Section 15.6

Q15.18 Give an example of a closed surface that is cut by lines of electric field and across which the total electric flux is zero.

Q15.19 The electric field **E** is zero everywhere on a certain closed surface. Can this surface enclose any charged bodies? Can it enclose any net charge?

Q15.20 Explain why the field of a point charge must be spherically symmetric—its direction along a radial line and its magnitude dependent only on radial distance from the charge. (SUGGESTION: Examine the implications of the contrary assumption that the field is *not* spherically symmetric.)

Q15.21   In Section 15.6 Gauss's law is used to prove that $\mathbf{E} = 0$ inside a uniformly charged spherical shell. In Section 11.2 a different method was used to prove that the gravitational force inside a uniform spherical shell is zero (see Figure 11.3). Could the method of Section 11.2 be applied to the uniformly charged spherical shell? Explain.

Q15.22   An electron moves through a region of space containing a distribution of charge. (1) If the distribution of charge (excluding the electron) is spherically symmetric with respect to some origin, will the angular momentum of the electron be constant with respect to that origin? Why or why not?

Section 15.7   Q15.23   (1) If the potential is zero at a point, must the electric field be zero at that point? (2) If the electric field is zero at a point, must the potential be zero at that point?

Q15.24   From Equation 15.59 and the argument preceding it one may conclude that the line integral $\int_{\mathbf{r}_1}^{\mathbf{r}_2} \mathbf{E} \cdot d\mathbf{s}$ is independent of path if $\mathbf{E}$ is the field of a single point charge. What law allows you to conclude immediately that this line integral is path-independent in the field of an arbitrary static distribution of charge?

Q15.25   (1) Can the electric field be calculated at a point if the potential is known at that point? (2) Can the electric field be calculated at a point if the potential is known throughout a small region near that point?

Q15.26   As an electron moves between points of different potential in a wire, why does the average kinetic energy of the electron not change?

Section 15.8   Q15.27   A dipole such as the one pictured in Figure 15.25(b) is pivoted at its center and is located in a uniform electric field $\mathbf{E}$. (1) For what orientation is it in unstable equilibrium? (2) For what orientation is it in stable equilibrium? (3) Explain why it will execute simple harmonic oscillation if it is displaced slightly from the latter orientation and released.

Q15.28   Does a dipole in a *non*uniform electric field experience a net force? If so, in what direction? Answer with the help of a diagram.

Q15.29   Is there any point (other than at infinite distance) where the electric field produced by a dipole is zero? If so, what is the approximate location of that point?

Q15.30   Charges q and $-q$ are held a fixed distance apart to form a dipole. Explain why no net work is required to bring a third charge from a great distance to the midpoint of the dipole.

Section 15.9   Q15.31   Would the static electric field within a conductor be zero if electric forces did not obey an inverse-square law? Explain.

Q15.32   Why are lines of static electric field always perpendicular to equipotential surfaces (in empty space as well as in matter)?

Q15.33   Why is it possible to shield an apparatus or a laboratory room against electric forces but not against gravitational forces?

Section 15.10   Q15.34   A lead wire of length l and cross-sectional area A is melted and then formed into a new wire of length $2l$ and cross-sectional area $\frac{1}{2}A$. (1) Does the conductivity of the wire increase, decrease, or remain unchanged? (2) Does the resistance of the wire increase, decrease, or remain unchanged? Give reasons for your answers.

Q15.35 Estimate approximately (1) the resistance of an electric iron designed to operate at 110 V, (2) the total current being supplied to an apartment with half a dozen lights burning and a hot plate operating, and (3) the power available in a laboratory designed to accommodate 20 students. Explain how you arrive at each answer.

Section 15.11

Q15.36 Why is high voltage preferred to low voltage for the long-distance transmission of electric power?

Q15.37 Christmas wire A has 8 light sockets connected in series; wire B has 8 sockets connected in parallel. Both are plugged into a 120-V line. Describe what would happen if the bulbs intended for wire A were used in wire B and those intended for wire B were used in wire A.

Q15.38 Why do some electric power companies reduce voltage in times of heavy demand? What do they "save"?

Q15.39 Why do lights in a house sometimes dim when an appliance is turned on? Would you expect your appliance to cause a neighbor's lights to dim?

Q15.40 In a graph of the potential V vs the charge q of a capacitor, what is the significance of the slope, dV/dq?

Section 15.12

Q15.41 If the charge stored in a capacitor is doubled, how do (a) the potential, (b) the electric field, and (c) the capacitance change?

Q15.42 Any two conducting objects bearing equal and opposite charges form a capacitor. Explain why the potential difference between the "plates" of any capacitor is proportional to the stored charge.

Q15.43 Why is the magnitude of the induced electric field within a dielectric always less than—although sometimes only slightly less than—the magnitude of the applied field? Explain in terms of molecular polarization (see Figure 15.43).

Section 15.13

Q15.44 Why is water, despite its high dielectric constant and its low price, not used as a dielectric material in capacitors?

Q15.45 An experimenter has enough dielectric material to fill half the volume between two concentric metal spheres. How should he place the material in order to maximize the capacitance of the spheres?

Q15.46 A particle of mass m and charge q is released from rest in a nonuniform electric field (one in which the lines of field are curved). Explain carefully why the particle will *not* follow a line of field.

Section 15.14

Q15.47 A negatively charged muon (heavier than an electron) is released from the cathode C in Figure 15.46. Will it strike the screen of the CRT above, below, or at the same point where electrons strike the screen?

EXERCISES

E15.1 (1) Use Equation 15.9 to verify that $C^2/N\,m^2$ is the correct SI unit of the permittivity constant ϵ_0. (2) Show that $C^2/N\,m^2$ and $A^2\,sec^4/kg\,m^3$ are equivalent units.

Section 15.3

E15.2 Equal charges separated by 1 cm repel each other with a force of 10^{-5} N. What is the magnitude of each charge?

+10 μC   +3 μC   −10 μC
1 ●   2 ●   3 ●

|←—2 cm—→|←—2 cm—→|

E15.3   Three pellets with charges of $+10\ \mu$C, $+3\ \mu$C, and $-10\ \mu$C are arranged as shown in the figure. Find the magnitude and direction of the force on each.

E15.4   The charged pellets of the preceding exercise are rearranged to lie at the corners of an equilateral triangle of side 2 cm. (1) Which pellet experiences the greatest magnitude of force? (2) Find the magnitude and direction of the force on pellet 2. (Include a diagram with your answer.)

E15.5   Suppose that both of the strings supporting balloons 1 and 2 in Figure 15.1(b) make an angle of 30 deg with the vertical. Prove that if the hands supporting the strings are moved apart until the distance between the centers of the balloons is doubled, the new inclination of each string to the vertical will be 8.2 deg.

E15.6   The charge of a proton is 1.60×10^{-19} C; the charge of a lead nucleus is 82 times as great. (1) When a proton is 10^{-10} m from a lead nucleus, what electric force does the proton experience? (2) If the proton, initially at rest, experienced approximately this force for 10^{-16} sec, what momentum would it acquire? What speed?

E15.7   A uranium nucleus splits into two equal fragments, each with 46 quantum units of charge. (1) When these fragments are separated by 2×10^{-14} m as they start to fly apart, what electric force acts on one of them? (2) What electric force does this fragment feel an instant later after each fragment has moved 2×10^{-14} m and they are separated by 6×10^{-14} m? (3) Multiply the approximate average force experienced by one of the fragments by the distance it has moved to obtain the work done on it (roughly). Express this energy in MeV. *Optional:* Perform an integration in order to answer part 3 exactly.

E15.8   A charge q_1 is located at the origin of a coordinate system. Another charge q_2 is located at (x, y) and experiences a force $\mathbf{F}_2$ produced by the charge q_1. Show that the components of $\mathbf{F}_2$ can be written

$$F_{2x} = \frac{1}{4\pi\epsilon_0} \frac{q_1 q_2 x}{(x^2 + y^2)^{3/2}} \quad \text{and} \quad F_{2y} = \frac{1}{4\pi\epsilon_0} \frac{q_1 q_2 y}{(x^2 + y^2)^{3/2}}.$$

E15.9   The current flowing to a metal sphere is given by

$$I(t) = I_0 e^{-t/\tau},$$

where $I_0 = 3$ A and $\tau = 10^{-4}$ sec. If the sphere is initially neutral, what is its final charge?

E15.10 Bodies of masses m_1 and m_2 carry charges of q_1 and q_2 respectively and are separated by distance r. (1) Obtain an algebraic expression for the ratio F_e/F_g of the electric force to the gravitational force acting between these bodies. (2) For a pair of protons verify that F_e/F_g is approximately equal to 1.2×10^{36}.

E15.11 If all the electrons could be magically removed from a 1-gm pellet of frozen hydrogen, the total charge of the 6×10^{23} protons remaining behind would be 96,500 C (1 faraday). Imagine two such hypothetical bodies (composed entirely of protons) separated by 0.1 m. What electric force would act on one of them? Compare this force with your weight or with some other easily visualized force.

E15.12 At what distance from a proton in empty space is the electric field equal to 10^6 V/m?

Section 15.4

E15.13 An electron is drawn toward a proton with a force of 0.92×10^{-7} N. (1) What are the magnitude and direction of the electric field that the electron "feels"? (2) What are the magnitude and direction of the electric field produced by the electron at the location of the proton? (3) What is the distance between the particles?

E15.14 In an experiment a vertically directed electric field of 10^5 V/m is found to be just sufficient to support the weight of a tiny charged pellet. What is the charge-to-mass ratio of the pellet? How does this compare with the charge-to-mass ratio of an electron (given in Appendix 3)?

E15.15 A charge of 4×10^{-8} C is located at the point $x = 0.04$ m, $y = 0.03$ m; all other charges are far away. Find the components of the electric field at the origin.

E15.16 Two charges q_1 and q_2 known to have equal magnitude are separated by 0.1 m. Midway between them the electric field is found to be directed toward the charge q_2 and to have magnitude 4.8×10^4 V/m. Find q_1 and q_2.

E15.17 Three charges, q_1, q_2, and q_3, are arranged at three corners of a square as shown in the figure. The first two charges are known to be $q_1 = 10$ nC and $q_2 = 28$ nC (1 nC $= 10^{-9}$ C); the electric field at the fourth corner of the square is known to be directed horizontally to the right as shown. (1) What is the charge q_3? (2) What is the magnitude of the total electric field **E** at the fourth corner?

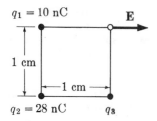

E15.18 A proton in an evacuated container is pulled downward by the earth's gravity. (1) What magnitude of electric field would be required to counter this gravitational force? (2) Show that the required electric field could be provided by a single electron about 12 cm away.

E15.19 Work out the field line diagrams for (a) two equal positive charges and (b) two charges of equal magnitude and opposite sign [Figures 15.7(a) and 15.7(b)]. Method: At each of a number of points sketch the magnitudes and directions of the two contributing fields and complete a vector sum diagram ($\mathbf{E} = \mathbf{E}_1 + \mathbf{E}_2$). Do this as accurately as you can by eye without precise measurement. The resulting pattern of arrows will suggest how to draw the smooth field lines.

E15.20 The electric field on the axis of a uniformly charged hoop is given by Equation 15.26. (1) Give approximate expressions for this field for (a) $x \ll R$ and (b) $x \gg R$. (2) At what distance x from the center of the hoop is E_x maximum? (3) What is this maximum value of E_x if $q = 10^{-7}$ C and $R = 0.05$ m?

Section 15.5

E15.21   The semicircular hoop of radius R shown in the figure is uniformly charged; its charge per unit length is $\tau_0 = q/\pi R$ and its charge in length ds is $dq = \tau_0\,ds$. Show that the net electric field at point O (the center of the semicircle) is

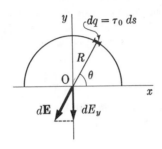

$$E = -\frac{1}{4\pi\epsilon_0}\frac{2}{\pi}\frac{q}{R^2}\,\mathbf{j}.$$

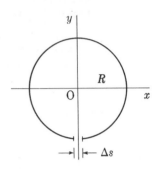

E15.22   A uniformly charged thin rod is bent into the form of a circle of radius R with a small gap of length Δs in it (see the figure). If the charge per unit length along the arc is τ_0 and if $\Delta s \ll R$, what is the electric field (magnitude and direction) at the central point O?

E15.23   If *gravitational field* is defined as gravitational force per unit mass, what is the gravitational field of the earth at its surface (a) algebraically, in terms of the gravitational constant G and properties of the earth, and (b) numerically?

Section 15.6   **E15.24**   If gravitational field is gravitational force per unit mass (see the preceding exercise) and gravitational flux is the surface integral of the gravitational field, show that the gravitational flux over a spherical surface surrounding the earth is $\Phi_G = -4\pi G M_E$ (the positive direction of a surface element is radially outward).

E15.25   What is the electric flux through the section of a spherical surface shown in the figure if a point charge q is located at the origin?

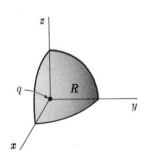

E15.26   Show that Gauss's law together with symmetry considerations leads to the formula

$$\mathbf{E} = \frac{1}{4\pi\epsilon_0}\frac{q}{r^2}\,\mathbf{i}_r$$

for the electric field surrounding a point charge. (This means that Coulomb's law can be considered to be a *consequence* of Gauss's law.)

E15.27   For a sphere,

$$\oint dS = 4\pi R^2,$$

which states that the sum of infinitesimal magnitudes of area over the entire surface of the sphere is the total area $4\pi R^2$. What is the corresponding integral of the *vector* increments of area, $\oint d\mathbf{S}$?

E15.28   The nucleus of an oxygen atom contains 8 protons confined within a spherical volume of radius about 4 fm (4×10^{-15} m). Find the magnitude of the electric field of the nucleus at (a) a distance of 5 fm from the center of the nucleus and (b) at the "edge" of the atom, about 10^{-10} m from the nucleus.

E15.29 A total charge q is spread uniformly through a sphere of radius R; the charge density within the sphere (C/m^3) is therefore $\rho_0 = q/(\frac{4}{3}\pi R^3)$. Show that the electric field within the sphere is given by

$$ \mathbf{E} = \frac{\rho_0}{3\epsilon_0} r \mathbf{i}_r = \frac{1}{4\pi\epsilon_0} \frac{qr}{R^3} \mathbf{i}_r, $$

where r is radial distance measured from the center of the sphere and $\mathbf{i}_r$ is a unit vector in the radial direction.

E15.30 The electric field near a charged metal plate is measured to be 10^5 V/m and is directed toward the plate. Find the surface charge density σ on the plate in (a) C/m^2 and (b) number of excess electrons per m^2.

E15.31 The figure shows a thin sheet of plastic that contains a uniformly distributed charge per unit area σ. Imagine the sheet to be infinite in extent. (1) Show that on both sides of the sheet the magnitude of the electric field $\mathbf{E}$ is $\sigma/(2\epsilon_0)$. (2) Sketch a graph of E_x vs x for $\sigma > 0$ (the coordinate x is defined in the figure).

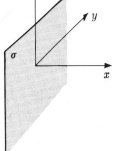

E15.32 Charge per unit length τ_0 lies along an idealized infinite straight line. (1) Find the electric field at distance r from the line. (2) Suggest a reason why the magnitude of the field is not proportional to $1/r^2$. Does the field fall off more slowly or more rapidly than the field of a point charge?

E15.33 In a long circular cylinder of radius a there is a constant density of charge ρ_0 (C/m^3). Using Gauss's law, find the electric field inside and outside the cylinder. (Idealize the cylinder as being of infinite length.)

E15.34 In a certain television tube electrons "fall" through a potential of 20,000 V on their way to the screen. (1) What energy do the electrons acquire in eV? (2) With what speed do they strike the screen? (3) If the acceleration is accomplished in a distance of 0.04 m, what average force acts on the electrons as they are being accelerated?

Section 15.7

E15.35 As it moves a distance l through the uniform electric field $\mathbf{E}$ shown in the figure, an electron experiences a lateral displacement Δy. (1) What is the potential difference between points A and B? (2) What is the change of kinetic energy of the electron as it moves from A to B?

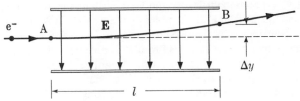

E15.36 A proton is located at the origin. (1) What are the potential differences $V(r_1) - V(r_2)$ and $V(r_2) - V(r_3)$ for $r_1 = 1$ Å (10^{-10} m), $r_2 = 2$ Å, and $r_3 = \infty$? (2) In moving from a great distance to within 1 Å of a proton, does an electron move to a region of higher or lower potential? (3) Does it gain or lose potential energy? How much? Express the answer in eV.

E15.37 A positive charge q is spread uniformly over the surface of a sphere of radius R. From this surface a small particle of mass m and negative charge $-q'$ is ejected upward. Show that the minimum initial speed that the particle must have if it is to escape from the sphere is

$$v_{esc} = \sqrt{\frac{1}{2\pi\epsilon_0} \frac{qq'}{mR}} \; .$$

(It is instructive to compare this formula for electrical escape speed with the formula for gravitational escape speed given by Equation 11.21.)

E15.38 Suppose that an electron is approximated as a spherical shell of mass m, radius r_e, and charge $-e$. (1) What is the potential at the surface of this hypothetical entity? (2) If this potential is set equal to $-mc^2/e$, the rest energy of the electron divided by its charge, what is r_e (a) algebraically and (b) numerically? This distance is called the "classical electron radius."

E15.39 When plugged into a 110-V outlet, an electric space heater dissipates 1,460 W. What current flows through the heater? (NOTE: The answer is the same for a d.c. circuit and for rms values of an a.c. circuit.)

E15.40 A 12-V storage battery is advertised as a 100 ampere-hour battery. (1) What total charge can the battery deliver? (2) What is the total stored energy in the battery? (3) For how long could this battery light a pair of headlamps, each of 60 W?

E15.41 A giant spark is created by bringing near together two metal spheres with a potential difference of 10^6 V. The spark carries a current of 10^{-3} A and persists for 0.5 sec. (1) What is the power of the spark? (2) What total energy is associated with the spark? (3) How many electrons pass from one sphere to the other?

E15.42 Show that the law of superposition of electric fields implies a law of superposition of potentials: The potential associated with several charges is the sum of the potentials that would exist if each charge were present alone.

Section 15.8 E15.43 Charges $+10^{-8}$ C and -10^{-8} C are located at opposite ends of a small rod of length 0.02 m. (1) What is the dipole moment of the rod? (2) In an electric field of 10^5 V/m, what work is required to turn the rod from an orientation perpendicular to the field to an orientation parallel to the field?

E15.44 Charges q and $-q$ are located on the x axis at $x = \frac{1}{2}l$ and $x = -\frac{1}{2}l$ respectively. (1) Sum the fields $\mathbf{E}_1$ and $\mathbf{E}_2$ contributed by the two charges in order to find the net field $\mathbf{E}$ at any point on the x axis. (2) Sum the potentials V_1 and V_2 contributed by the two charges in order to find the net potential $V(x)$ at any point on the x axis. (3) From $V(x)$ obtain the field component E_x on the x axis. Compare this answer with the answer to part 1. (4) What is the approximate form of $V(x)$ at large x? In what important way does this approximate form differ from the potential of a single point charge?

E15.45 With respect to an arbitrarily chosen origin let the charge q in Figure 15.25(b) be at $\mathbf{r}_1$ and the charge $-q$ be at $\mathbf{r}_2$. Show that for this pair of charges, the general definition of dipole moment, $\mathbf{p} = \sum_i q_i\mathbf{r}_i$, gives $\mathbf{p} = q\mathbf{l}$ (Equation 15.71).

Section 15.9 E15.46 Sphere A, whose radius is 1 cm, and sphere B, whose radius is 2 cm, are well separated from each other. Initially each sphere carries a net charge of

+1 nC (10^{-9} C). Then the spheres are joined by a conducting wire. (1) Show that the potentials of the spheres *before* they are joined by the wire are $V_A \cong 900$ V and $V_B \cong 450$ V (if $V(\infty) = 0$). (2) How much charge flows through the wire from one sphere to the other? (3) Show that the final potential of the spheres is $V_A = V_B \cong 600$ V.

E15.47 In Figure 15.29, charge q is distributed over the outer surface of the inner sphere (radius R_1) and charge $-q$ is distributed over the inner surface of the outer sphere (radius R_2). Let the outer radius of the outer sphere be R_3. (1) Find the electric field $\mathbf{E}$ for (a) $r < R_1$, (b) $R_1 < r < R_2$, (c) $R_2 < r < R_3$, and (d) $r > R_3$. (2) Find the potential V for the same four regions if $V(\infty) = 0$.

E15.48 (1) If a charge of -1 C could be put on a metal sphere of radius 0.1 m, what would be the electric field in the vicinity of the metal surface? (2) If each atom in the surface layer of the metal occupies an area of 1 Å^2, how would the number of extra electrons on the sphere compare with the number of atoms in the surface layer? (3) In moving a distance of 1 Å in the field just outside the surface, what energy would an electron gain? Express the answer in eV and compare it with the few eV required to dislodge an electron from an uncharged metal surface.

E15.49 Within a piece of copper, the electric field is $E = 0.03$ V/m. (1) What is the current density in the copper? (2) What is the potential difference between two points separated by 5 cm along the direction of the field? (3) If this field and this current density exist in a mile-long copper cable of cross-sectional area 10^{-4} m^2, (a) what current flows in the cable and (b) what power is dissipated in the cable?

Section 15.10

E15.50 In a wire of length l and constant cross-sectional area A there exists an electric field $\mathbf{E}$ directed along the wire. A current I flows in the wire, and the potential difference between its ends is V. (1) Show that if the current density is proportional to the electric field (Equation 15.84), the current is proportional to the potential difference (Equation 15.87). (2) Derive the following formula that relates the resistance R and the conductivity σ of the wire:

$$R = \frac{l}{\sigma A}.$$

E15.51 Using the formula given in the preceding exercise, find the resistance of (a) a silver wire and (b) a germanium wire, both of length 5 cm and cross-sectional area 10^{-6} m^2.

E15.52 An electric heater has a resistance of 20 Ω. How many such heaters can be connected to a 120-V household circuit without activating a 25-A circuit breaker?

E15.53 Which of the following has the least resistance: (a) a 60-W automobile headlight connected to a 12-V battery; (b) a 1,200-W hot plate conducting a current of 10 A; or (c) a small 3-V battery that provides a current of 2 A when its terminals are joined by a wire of negligible resistance?

Section 15.11

E15.54 One light bulb whose resistance is 100 Ω and another light bulb whose resistance is 200 Ω (both resistances being measured when the bulbs are hot) are connected in parallel across a 120-V d.c. line. Find (1) the current in each bulb, (2) the power dissipated by each bulb, and (3) the number of electrons passing through each bulb in 1 sec.

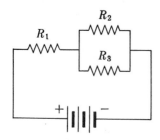

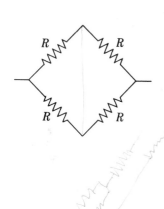

E15.55 The battery potential in the circuit shown in the diagram is 12 V. The resistances are $R_1 = 10\,\Omega$, $R_2 = 5\,\Omega$, and $R_3 = 20\,\Omega$. (1) Find (a) the current in each resistor and (b) the power dissipated by each resistor. (2) How long must this circuit operate before 1 kW-hr of energy has been supplied by the battery?

E15.56 Use two kinds of reasoning to prove that the total resistance of a set of parallel resistors is less than the least resistance in the set. (1) Working from Equation 15.103, give a mathematical proof. (2) Use a physical argument based on the fact that the total current through the set of resistors is greater than the current through any single resistor.

E15.57 (1) Prove that the combination of four identical resistors shown in the figure has the same total resistance R as one of the resistors alone. (2) In what other way can these resistors be joined to form a combination of total resistance R?

E15.58 (1) If three appliances having resistances of 10, 20, and 30 Ω respectively are plugged into a 120-V line and all turned on, what total power do they use? (2) If the appliances are accidentally connected in series across the 120-V line instead of being correctly connected in parallel, what is their total power consumption?

E15.59 Two heating elements, one of resistance 10 Ω and one of 20 Ω, are used in a heater that is plugged into a 120-V line. By taking advantage of all possible combinations of the elements, what power dissipations are possible? (Exclude the open circuit, for which $P = 0$, and the short circuit, for which —in principal— $P = \infty$.)

E15.60 In the circuit shown in the accompanying diagram, $R_1 = 1\,\Omega$, $R_2 = 2\,\Omega$, $R_3 = 3\,\Omega$, and $R_4 = 4\,\Omega$. The ammeters labeled A measure currents $I_1 = 2$ A and $I_3 = 5$ A. Find the battery potentials V_1 and V_2.

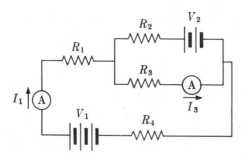

E15.61 A certain battery acts as a fixed source of potential $V_0 = 6$ V in series with a resistor of resistance $R_{\text{int}} = 0.1\,\Omega$ [see Figure 15.32(b)]. Joining the terminals of the battery is a resistor of variable resistance R; the potential across this external resistor is V and the current through it is I. (1) (a) Express V as a function of I. (b) Sketch a graph of V vs I. (c) What is the maximum possible value of I? (2) (a) Express V as a function of R. (b) Sketch a graph of V vs R for $0 \le R \le 20\,\Omega$. (3) For what value of R is the heat generated in the external resistor four times greater than the heat generated within the battery?

E15.62 (1) Complete Example 2 in Section 15.11 by showing that the currents I_1, I_2, and I_3 in the circuit shown in Figure 15.36 are given by

$$I_1 = [(R_2 + R_3)V_1 + R_3V_2]/D,$$

$$I_2 = [R_3V_1 + (R_1 + R_3)V_2]/D,$$

$$I_3 = [-R_2V_1 + R_1V_2]/D,$$

where $D = R_1R_2 + R_2R_3 + R_3R_1$. (2) Discuss the limit $R_3 \to \infty$.

E15.63 One plate of a capacitor has a charge of 10^{-8} C; the other plate has a charge of -10^{-8} C. If the potential between the plates is 50 V, what is the capacitance of the capacitor?

Section 15.12

E15.64 The potential between the plates of a capacitor separated by 0.2 cm is 300 V. (1) What is the magnitude of the electric field in this region? (2) What is C/A, the capacitance per unit area (F/m^2) of the capacitor?

E15.65 The figure shows two capacitors connected in series. (1) If the plates of both capacitors are initially neutral and if current then flows for a time in the circuit, explain why the two capacitors accumulate equal charge. (2) Show that the inverse capacitance of the combination is given by

$$\frac{1}{C} = \frac{1}{C_1} + \frac{1}{C_2}.$$

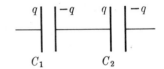

E15.66 (1) Using the definition $C = q/V$ and the fact that the potential outside a uniformly charged sphere is the same as the potential of a point charge, derive the formula $C = 4\pi\epsilon_0 R$ (Equation 15.116) for the capacitance of a single isolated sphere. (2) What is the capacitance of the earth in farads?

E15.67 A capacitor has plates of area 0.002 m^2 separated by an air gap of 3 mm. Stored in the electric field between the plates is an energy of 2×10^{-7} J. What is the potential between the plates?

E15.68 As a capacitor discharges through a resistor, its charge decreases exponentially (Equation 15.124). Verify that the potential across the resistor and the current through it also decrease exponentially (Equations 15.127 and 15.128).

E15.69 A vial of water is placed in an applied electric field of 10^5 V/m. (1) What is the induced electric field within the water? (2) What is the net electric field within the water?

Section 15.13

E15.70 A 20-pF capacitor consists of two parallel plates, each of area 10^{-3} m^2, separated by a layer of polyethylene. What is the distance between the plates?

E15.71 Electrons in the cathode-ray tube of Figure 15.46 are accelerated through a potential $V_a = 1,000$ V, then pass between deflection plates of length $l = 3$ cm and separation $d = 0.3$ cm. If the distance from deflection plates to screen is 20 cm, what deflecting potential V_d is required to move the electron beam spot 5 cm away from the center of the tube face?

Section 15.14

E15.72 In a region containing an arbitrary electric field, different particles start from the same point with the same initial velocity. Explain why all particles with the same charge-to-mass ratio (q/m) will follow the same trajectory.

E15.73 In a diode, anode and cathode have a potential difference of 500 V and are separated by 0.6 cm. A current of 3 mA flows through the tube, which is evacuated. (1) With what speed do electrons strike the anode? (2) If the electron energy is transformed to heat at the anode, what is the rate of production of heat in watts?

E15.74 Through the triode in Figure 15.50 flows a current of 1 mA. The resistance R is equal to 50 kΩ, and the potential V_2 is 450 V. (1) What is the potential V_{out} across the resistor? (2) What is the effective resistance of the vacuum tube (the ratio of its potential to its current)? (3) An increase of the input potential V_{in} by 1 V causes the current flowing through the triode to double. What is the amplification factor $\Delta V_{out}/\Delta V_{in}$?

Section 15.15

E15.75 At a distance of 1 Å from a proton, what is the energy density of the electric field (a) in J/m^3? (b) in $eV/Å^3$?

E15.76 In the space between a pair of capacitor plates is stored 10^{-6} J of energy in an electric field that is nearly constant over a volume of 3×10^{-5} m^3. What is the magnitude of the electric field in this region?

PROBLEMS

Ratio of electric and gravitational forces

P15.1 Suppose that the two balloons shown in Figure 15.1(b) have equal mass m, that their centers are separated by distance r, and that each of the strings supporting the balloons makes an angle of 45 deg with the vertical. Balloon 1 exerts on balloon 2 an electric force $\mathbf{F}_e$ (the same as $\mathbf{F}_{21}$ in Figure 15.1) and a gravitational force $\mathbf{F}_g$ (*not* the weight of the balloon). (1) Show that

$$\frac{F_e}{F_g} = \frac{M_E}{m} \left(\frac{r}{R_E} \right)^2,$$

where M_E is the mass of the earth and R_E is the radius of the earth. (2) Insert reasonable values of m and r into this formula and evaluate the ratio F_e/F_g numerically. Comment on the significance of the answer.

Dependence of electric force on the product of two charges

P15.2 Two charges are near one another and isolated from the rest of the universe. If the force experienced by the first is proportional to its own charge ($F_1 \sim q_1$), prove, using Newton's third law and the assumption that the law of force is valid for any charge, that this force must also be proportional to the second charge ($F_1 \sim q_2$) and therefore that it is proportional to the product of both charges ($F_1 \sim q_1 q_2$).

Superposition: Finding a total field by integrating infinitesimal contributions

P15.3 A thin rod of length $2L$ is uniformly charged. Its charge per unit length is τ_0; as indicated in the figure, this means that its charge in an increment of length dx is $dq = \tau_0\, dx$. (1) Using symmetry arguments (no calculations required), find the direction of the net electric field $\mathbf{E}$ at point P on the perpendicular bisector of the rod at a distance y from the rod. (2) Calculate the magnitude of the net field $\mathbf{E}$ at P. (A table of integrals may be needed.) (3) Obtain an approximate expression for E that is valid for $y \gg L$. Give a simple argument for the "reasonableness" of this expression. (Examining an answer in a limiting situation is often a good way to check for possible error.)

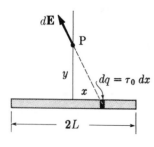

P15.4 A semicircular ring of radius a has a charge per unit length given by $\tau = \tau_0 \sin 2\theta$ (the angle θ is defined in the figure). (1) What is the net charge on the ring? Describe qualitatively the distribution of the charge. (2) What is the direction of the net field $\mathbf{E}$ at point O, the center of the semicircle? (3) Show that the magnitude of $\mathbf{E}$ at point O is

$$E = \frac{1}{4\pi\epsilon_0} \frac{4\,\tau_0}{3\,a}.$$

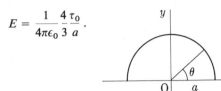

P15.5 A circular ring of radius a has a charge per unit length given by $\tau = \tau_0 \sin \theta$ (the angle θ is defined in the figure). (1) Describe qualitatively the distribution of charge on the ring. What is the total charge? (2) What is the direction of the net field $\mathbf{E}$ at point O, the center of the circle? (3) Show that the magnitude of $\mathbf{E}$ at point O is

$$E = \frac{\tau_0}{4\epsilon_0 a}.$$

(A table of definite integrals may be needed.)

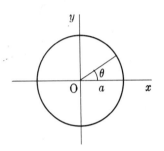

P15.6 Suppose that the hoop in Figure 15.11 is replaced by a disk having the same radius R and bearing the same charge q (the charge per unit area on the disk is then $\sigma = q/\pi R^2$). Find the electric field at point P on the axis of the disk at distance x from the disk.

P15.7 Suppose that a thin insulating fiber is stretched along the axis of the uniformly charged hoop shown in Figure 15.11 and that a bead can slide without friction along the fiber. (1) If the hoop has radius R and positive charge q and the bead has mass m and negative charge $-q'$, obtain an expression for the period of oscillation of the bead as it executes vibrations of small amplitude ($x \ll R$) about the center of the hoop. (2) Evaluate the period for $R = 10^{-2}$ m, $m = 10^{-3}$ kg, and $q = q' = 10^{-8}$ C.

Harmonic oscillation in electric fields

P15.8 The electric field within a uniform ball of charge centered at the origin is given in Exercise 15.29. (1) What is the potential within this ball of charge (a) if $V = 0$ at the center of the ball? (b) if $V = 0$ at infinity? (2) What is the frequency of oscillation of a particle of mass m and negative charge q' moving along a radial line within a ball of radius R and positive charge q? (3) Evaluate this frequency numerically for an electron within a lead nucleus, for which $q = 82e$ and $R = 7 \times 10^{-15}$ m.

P15.9 This problem uses a result of the preceding problem. What kinetic energy would an electron have to have in the center of a lead nucleus in order to escape from the nucleus and reach infinite distance with negligible kinetic energy? Express the answer in eV.

Escape of an electron from an atomic nucleus

P15.10 In a sphere of radius R centered at the origin, the density of charge is given by $\rho = (q/\pi R^4)r$, where r is the radial coordinate. (1) Verify that the total charge of the sphere is q. (2) Find the electric field inside and outside the sphere. (3) Find the potential inside and outside the sphere if the potential is adjusted to be zero at infinity and to have no discontinuity at $r = R$.

Spherically symmetric distribution of charge

P15.11   In a sphere of radius R centered at the origin, the density of charge is given by

$$\rho = A \left[\frac{1}{r^2} - \frac{3}{R^2} \right] ,$$

where r is the radial coordinate and A is a constant. (1) What is the SI unit of A? (2) Find the electric field inside and outside the sphere. (3) Find the potential inside and outside the sphere if the potential is adjusted to be zero at infinity and to have no discontinuity at $r = R$.

Displacement vector expressed as an integral

P15.12   Prove that

$$\int_{\mathbf{r}_1}^{\mathbf{r}_2} d\mathbf{s} = \mathbf{r}_2 - \mathbf{r}_1 ,$$

independent of path. (This result is used in Equation 15.51).

Field of two equal charges

P15.13   As shown in the figure, two particles of equal charge q are located at the points $(a, 0)$ and $(-a, 0)$. (1) What is the potential V at the arbitrary point P? (2) What is the electric field $\mathbf{E}$ at point P? (3) What is the approximate form of V at large distance $(r \gg a)$?

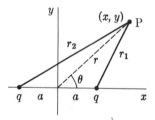

Field of a dipole

P15.14   Answer the three parts of the preceding problem if the particle of charge q at the point $(-a, 0)$ is replaced by a particle of charge $-q$. Show that the answer to part 3 can be written

$$V \cong \frac{1}{4\pi\epsilon_0} \frac{p \cos \theta}{r^2} \qquad (r \gg a),$$

where p is the magnitude of the dipole moment ($p = 2qa$).

Interaction of two dipoles

P15.15   The centers of two identical electric dipoles are located a fixed distance L apart; the distance L is much larger than the length l of each dipole. (1) For what orientations of the dipoles is their total potential energy (a) greatest and (b) least? (2) What is the energy difference between these two states of greatest and least energy?

Torque on a dipole

P15.16   Show that the torque on a dipole of dipole moment $\mathbf{p}$ in an electric field $\mathbf{E}$ is $\mathbf{T} = \mathbf{p} \times \mathbf{E}$ (Equation 15.75).

Oscillation of a dipole

P15.17   Show that for small vibrations about its orientation of stable equilibrium, a dipole in an electric field $\mathbf{E}$ vibrates harmonically with frequency ν given by

$$\nu = \frac{1}{2\pi} \sqrt{\frac{pE}{I}} ,$$

where I is the moment of inertia of the dipole and p is the magnitude of its dipole moment.

P15.18 (1) The total charge of the particles shown in the figure is zero. What is their total dipole moment? (2) Find approximate expressions for the potential of this combination of charges (a) on the x axis for $x \gg a$ and (b) on the y axis for $y \gg a$. This combination is called an electric quadrupole.

Electric quadrupole

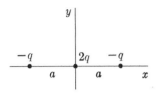

P15.19 (1) Inside an isolated spherical shell of matter, the gravitational field is zero; inside a hollow metal sphere, the electric field is zero. Explain the reason for the similarity. (2) If the spherical shell of matter is distorted, the gravitational field within it is no longer zero; if the metal sphere is distorted, the electric field within it remains zero. Explain the reason for the difference.

Gravity and electricity: points of similarity and difference

P15.20 A conducting body contains a hollow cavity of arbitrary shape (see the figure). Prove that if the cavity contains charge q, charge $-q$ must reside on the surface S that bounds the cavity, regardless of the total charge of the body. Assume static conditions. (Note the obvious implication that if the cavity is free of charge, the inner surface S must also be free of charge.)

Cavity in a conductor

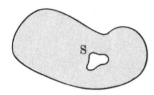

P15.21 As shown in the figure, a cylindrical metal shell of inner radius b and outer radius c surrounds a coaxial metal rod of radius a. The inner rod has surface charge density σ_0 (C/m^2); the outer cylinder has no net charge. (1) Find the electric field for (a) $a < r < b$ and (b) $r > c$. (2) What is the potential difference between the inner rod and the outer cylinder? (3) What is the calculated potential difference between the outer cylinder and an infinitely distant point? Why is this answer "unphysical"?

Coaxial conducting cylinders

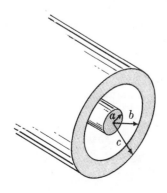

Drift velocity   **P15.22** The electrons that are free to move over large distances in a metal are called conduction electrons. Suppose that there are n conduction electrons per unit volume in a wire and that the drift velocity of these electrons—their average component of velocity along the wire—is v_d. (1) Show that the current in the wire is

$$I = neAv_d,$$

where e is the magnitude of the electron charge and A is the cross-sectional area of the wire. (2) Evaluate v_d numerically if $I = 1$ A, $n = 10^{28}$ m^{-3}, and $A = 10^{-6}$ m^2.

Effect of gravity on   **P15.23** The static electric field within a conductor is zero if the charge carriers
conduction electrons   (normally electrons) experience only electric forces. (1) Treat the conduction electrons in a metal as free particles and show that the static electric field in a metal is *not* zero if gravity is taken into account. (2) What is the direction and magnitude of the electric field? What is the potential difference between two points separated vertically by 1 m in a block of metal? (3) Describe the distribution of charge in a vertical metal rod whose total charge is zero. (4) Could this rod be used as a battery—that is, as a source of potential?

Wire of nonconstant cross   **P15.24** The radius of a wire varies linearly with distance: $r = a + \alpha x$. As shown
section   in the figure, $r = a$ at $x = 0$ and $r = b$ at $x = l$. (1) Express α in terms of a, b, and l. (2) For the steady flow of charge through the wire, why is it current and not current density that is constant (independent of x)? (3) Prove that the resistance of the wire between $x = 0$ and $x = l$ is given by

$$R = \frac{l}{\sigma \pi a b},$$

where σ is the conductivity of the wire.

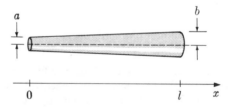

Power loss in a transmission   **P15.25** The diagram represents schematically a long-distance power-transmission
line   line joining a generating station to a city. If the potential at the generating station is $V_1 = 50{,}000$ V, the current is $I = 2{,}000$ A, and the resistance of each wire of the transmission line is 0.3 Ω, (1) what power is dissipated in the transmission line? (2) What fraction is this of the total power supplied by the generating station? (3) What is the potential V_2 at the city? (4) If the potential V_1 is doubled and the current I halved, so that the total power supplied by the generating station is unchanged, how does the power loss in the transmission line change?

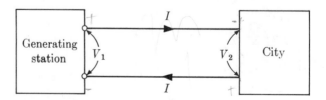

P15.26 (1) Show that the current through the ammeter A in the accompanying circuit diagram is zero if $R_1/R_2 = R_3/R_4$. (This is a Wheatstone bridge circuit. Since the condition of zero current can be established precisely, the circuit provides a useful way to measure an unknown resistance R_1 in terms of known resistances R_2, R_3, and R_4.) (2) Apply Kirchhoff's rules in order to find the total resistance of the combination of five resistors if $R_1 = R_2 = R_3 = R_5 = 1\,\Omega$ and $R_4 = 2\,\Omega$. (Note that this circuit, in contrast to the one shown in Figure 15.35, does not consist simply of series and parallel combinations of resistors.)

Wheatstone bridge circuit

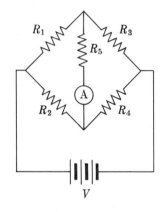

P15.27 Two coaxial conducting cylindrical shells form a capacitor. The inner shell has radius a and the outer one has radius b; both are of length l. (1) Show that the capacitance of this capacitor is

Cylindrical capacitor

$$C = \frac{2\pi\epsilon_0 l}{\ln(b/a)}.$$

(2) Show that for $b - a \ll a$, this is the same as the capacitance of a parallel-plate capacitor of the same plate area.

P15.28 The diagram shows a circuit used for charging a capacitor. At $t = 0$, when the capacitor is uncharged, the switch is closed. This problem refers to the properties of the circuit for $t > 0$. (1) Using the fact that the sum of the potentials around the loop is zero (Kirchhoff's second rule), set up a differential equation for the variable charge q on the capacitor. (2) Verify that

Charging a capacitor

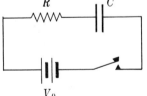

$$q(t) = V_0 C\left[1 - e^{-t/RC}\right]$$

is a solution to this equation (for the given initial condition, it is in fact *the* solution). (3) Sketch a graph of q vs t. (4) Explain why the final charge ($q_0 = V_0 C$) does not depend on the resistance R in the circuit. (5) For $R = 1\,\text{M}\Omega$ and $C = 1\,\mu\text{F}$, how long does it take for half the final charge to accumulate on the capacitor?

P15.29 A capacitor is charged in the manner described in the preceding problem. Prove that half the energy supplied by the battery is stored in the capacitor and half is dissipated as heat in the resistor.

Effect of temperature on capacitance

P15.30 A capacitor is constructed of parallel plates of aluminum of area A held a distance x apart by plastic spacers (see the figure). As temperature T changes, both A and x change. (1) Show that the rate of change of capacitance with temperature is given by

$$\frac{dC}{dT} = C\left[\frac{1}{A}\frac{dA}{dT} - \frac{1}{x}\frac{dx}{dT}\right].$$

(Neglect the dielectric effect of the plastic). (2) If the linear coefficients of thermal expansion (see Exercise 13.7) of both the aluminum and the plastic are equal to $2.4 \times 10^{-5}\ \text{K}^{-1}$, what is the change of capacitance for a temperature change of 10 K? (3) If the capacitance is to be nearly temperature-independent, what should be the linear coefficient of thermal expansion of the material chosen for the spacers?

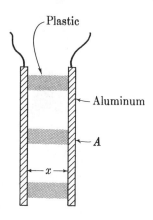

Forces on plates of a capacitor

P15.31 As indicated in the figure, the plates of a charged isolated capacitor ($q = constant$) attract each other, whereas the plates of a capacitor connected to a source of potential ($V = constant$) repel each other. (1) Explain qualitatively why the forces have these directions. (SUGGESTION: Consider the work required to separate the plates in the two cases.) (2) To find the force F_x acting on one plate of a capacitor, use the equation $F_x\,dx = -dU$, where dx is a displacement of the plate and dU is the change of stored potential energy. Verify the properties of attraction and repulsion stated above and show that in both cases the magnitude of the force is $|F_x| = \frac{1}{2}qE$, where q is the magnitude of the charge on one plate and E is the magnitude of the electric field between the plates.

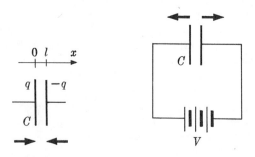

P15.32 Two sheets of charge, one with surface charge density σ (C/m²) and one with surface charge density $-\sigma$, are parallel to one another and separated by a distance x, which is small compared with their linear dimension l (see the figure). (1) Find the electric fields at points A, B, C, and D (let the positive x direction be to the right). (2) If the negatively charged sheet is replaced by a sheet with surface charge density σ, what are the electric fields at A, B, C, and D? (3) If the sheet on the right is removed, what are the electric fields at A and B?

Sheet charges

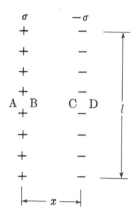

P15.33 A dielectric layer of thickness x is inserted between parallel metal plates of area A and separation d (see the figure). Show that the capacitance of this capacitor is independent of the location of the layer (whether it is adjacent to one plate or is parallel to but not touching either plate) and is given by

Effects of dielectric layers

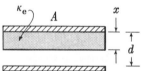

$$C = \frac{\epsilon_0 A}{d - x[1 - (1/\kappa_e)]}.$$

P15.34 A conducting sphere of radius a is imbedded in a concentric dielectric sphere extending from $r = a$ to $r = b$ (see the figure). (1) Show that the capacitance of the sphere is given by

$$C = \frac{4\pi\epsilon_0 \kappa_e a}{1 + (a/b)(\kappa_e - 1)}.$$

(2) Give approximate expressions for C that are valid for (a) $(b/a) \gg \kappa_e$ and (b) $\kappa_e \gg (b/a)$. Explain physically the reason for the form of C in these two limits.

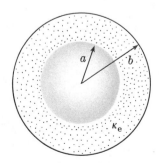

Energy and force associated with dielectric

P15.35 As shown in the figure, a dielectric slab is removed from between the plates of a parallel-plate capacitor. (1) Show that the change of stored energy in the capacitor is (a) $\Delta U = -(\kappa_e - 1)U_{vac}$ if the plates remain connected to a source of constant potential and (b) $\Delta U = [1 - (1/\kappa_e)]U_{vac}$ if the capacitor is isolated so that the charge on its plates remains constant. In these expressions, κ_e is the dielectric constant of the slab and U_{vac} is the stored potential energy when the slab is fully removed. (2) In which case does the slab push upward on the hand? In which case does it pull downward on the hand? (3) Is the force exerted by the slab on the hand likely to be appreciable in either case? Justify your answer with an approximate calculation.

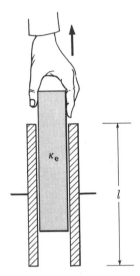

Gauss's law in a dielectric

P15.36 In general, Gauss's law can be written

$$\oint \mathbf{E}_{net} \cdot d\mathbf{S} = q_{net}/\epsilon_0 .$$

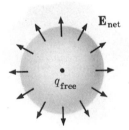

Within a dielectric, however, this is not a convenient form of the law. (1) By considering the flux of electric field through a sphere surrounding a free charge q_{free} in a dielectric (see the figure), obtain a modified form of Gauss's law that relates $\mathbf{E}_{net}$ and q_{free}. Express the law both in terms of the dielectric constant κ_e and in terms of the permittivity ϵ (see the footnote on page 724). (2) What is the relationship between q_{net} and q_{free} within the sphere in the figure? Explain physically why q_{net} is less in magnitude than q_{free}. (3) Use the modified form of Gauss's law to find the net electric field in a dielectric near a uniformly charged conducting plane.

Field energy of a charged sphere

P15.37 A total charge q is spread uniformly over the surface of a sphere of radius R. (1) What is the energy density $u(r)$ in the field surrounding the sphere $(r \geq R)$? (2) By integrating over the volume outside the sphere, show that the total energy stored in the field is $U = q^2/(8\pi\epsilon_0 R)$. Express this result also in terms of the capacitance of the sphere. (3) Imagine an electron to be a spherical shell of charge. If the total energy in the field of the electron is equal to the rest energy $m_e c^2$, what is the electron's radius R_e? Express the answer algebraically and also numerically in fm. This radius is half the so-called "classical radius" of the electron.

16

Electromagnetism

For centuries, the study of magnetism was limited to the effects of attraction and repulsion that exist between lodestones and other natural magnets, including the earth. Then came the momentous discovery of a connection between magnetism and electricity. Now all known magnetism is established as electrical in nature: magnetism *is* electromagnetism. Nevertheless, scientists have kept alive their interest in the hypothetical magnetic pole or magnetic charge, which, if it existed, would be an elementary seat of magnetism in the same sense that electric charge is the seat of electricity. Recent searches for a magnetically charged particle have not succeeded.

We begin this chapter by considering magnets and magnetic poles, an old-fashioned approach with a modern flavor. Then, in Section 16.3, a historical survey of key discoveries linking electricity and magnetism will introduce the ideas to be developed in the remainder of this chapter and in Chapter 17.

16.1 Magnets and magnetic force

Stationary charges and magnets do not interact

The qualitative facts of natural magnetism can be stated briefly. Certain objects called magnets, usually (but not necessarily) containing iron, can attract and repel other magnets and can attract pieces of iron that are not magnets. Unmagnetized iron, placed near a magnet or touched by a magnet, can itself become magnetized. That magnetism is distinct from electricity is demonstrated simply by the fact that a charge and a magnet placed near one another exert no mutual forces on each other. Magnets influence magnets and charges influence charges, but magnets and charges at rest coexist without interaction. A typical magnet acts as if it had two centers of force. The two centers of force of a long, thin magnet may be near the ends of the magnet, well separated from each other (Figure 16.1). These are called the "poles" of the magnet, and poles are

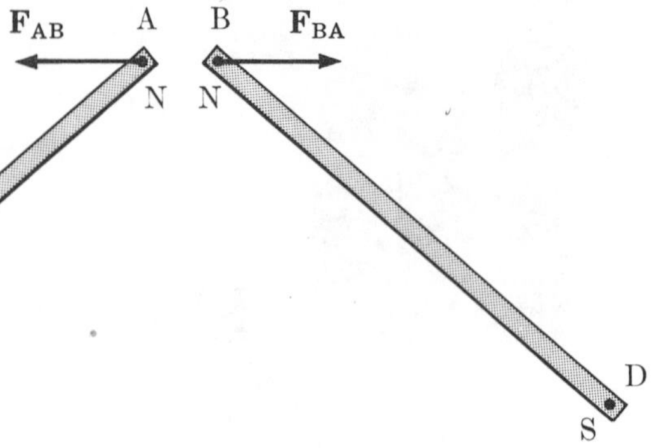

FIGURE 16.1   Long thin magnets act as if they have two well-separated centers of force, called north and south poles. In the arrangement shown here two north poles repel one another, following an inverse-square law of force. The more distant south poles experience weaker forces.

found to attract or repel other poles according to an inverse-square law, in exact analogy to Coulomb's law of electric force (or Newton's law of gravitational force). A "pole strength" P may be defined such that the force between two poles is proportional to the product of their pole strengths* and inversely proportional to the square of the distance between them:

$$F_M \sim \frac{P_1 P_2}{r^2}.$$

(16.1)

With SI units, pole strength is so defined that the law of force is written

Force between poles

$$F_M = \frac{\mu_0}{4\pi} \frac{P_1 P_2}{r^2}.$$

(16.2)

The quantity μ_0 is a constant, called the permeability constant, chosen arbitrarily to have the precise numerical value

$$\mu_0 = 4\pi \times 10^{-7} \text{ N/A}^2.$$

(16.3)

The reason for its unit, with the dimension of force/(current)^2, will become clear later. Since the concept of pole strength is not often used in fundamental applications of electromagnetism, its SI unit has not acquired a separate name. We may coin for it the name "michell," in honor of John Michell, who in 1750 first accurately established the inverse-square law of force for poles (Formula 16.1):

unit of pole strength = michell = A m.

(16.4)

The unit, ampere meter, follows from Equations 16.2 and 16.3.

Isolated poles have not been found

If isolated poles existed in the form of elementary particles, Equation 16.2 would express a precisely valid fundamental law of force. Since there is no evidence for such entities, however, it is only an approximate law, obeyed by the poles of magnets to a greater or lesser degree of accuracy, depending on the size and shape of the magnets and the way they are magnetized. Experimentally, the poles of a magnet can never be isolated. If a magnet, such as one of those

---

* To avoid confusion with ordinary, or electric, charge, we shall not use the designation "magnetic charge," which some authors prefer to "pole strength."

pictured in Figure 16.1, is broken, each piece displays equal and opposite pole strengths. The total pole strength of any object, magnetized or not, is always found to be exactly zero. By convention, the pole of a magnet attracted to the northern part of the earth is called a north pole, and its pole strength is called positive. The opposite pole, attracted to the southern part of the earth, is called a south pole; its pole strength is called negative. Since the earth itself is a magnet, its south pole is actually located in a northern region and its north pole in a southern region. This unfortunately confused notation can be alleviated somewhat by using the words "north-seeking pole" rather than "north pole" to describe the end of a magnet drawn toward northern latitudes.

Magnetism, like electricity, was known to the Greeks. As they attributed electricity to a single substance, amber (*elektron*), they also attributed magnetism to a single substance, magnetite (*e lithos magnetis*). Magnetite is a form of iron ore frequently found to be magnetized in its natural state. A magnet, unlike a charged object, does not lose its power to exert forces after a short time. A magnet may remain magnetized indefinitely. This fortunate property makes it well suited to serve as a compass. The year Earth's magnetism was first tapped for navigational aid is unknown. It seems likely that the tendency of one end of a pivoted magnet to swing to the north was discovered in China and that this knowledge was transmitted to Europe as early as the twelfth century. It remained for Gilbert in 1600 to point out that this property of magnets could be understood as arising simply from the fact that the earth itself is a giant magnet. It is interesting that in the twentieth century, the captain of an ocean liner or airliner still relies heavily on the magnetic compass as a primary source of information on his direction of motion.

Natural magnets

16.2 Magnetic field

Conceptually, magnetic field and electric field have much in common. Nevertheless, it is important to realize that they are distinct; both are necessary for describing electromagnetic phenomena. The magnetic field may be thought of as a potentiality for exerting a force on a magnetic pole. Provisionally, we define it as force per unit pole strength:

$$\mathbf{B} = \frac{\mathbf{F}}{P'} .$$ (16.5)

Preliminary definition of magnetic field

(This definition helps to make clear the meaning of magnetic field, but it is not a practical definition for scientific purposes, since isolated poles have not been found to exist. Better definitions, which involve practical force measurements, will be given in Sections 16.4 and 16.7. The contemporary definition incorporated in the International System will be given in Section 17.1.) Conventionally, the symbol **B** represents magnetic field (a vector quantity). The magnetic field created by a stationary pole of strength P is

$$\mathbf{B} = \frac{\mu_0}{4\pi} \frac{P}{r^3} \mathbf{r} = \frac{\mu_0}{4\pi} \frac{P}{r^2} \mathbf{i_r} ,$$ (16.6)

where **r** is the displacement vector from the location of the pole to the place where the field is measured, and where $\mathbf{i_r}$ is a unit vector parallel to **r**. Combining

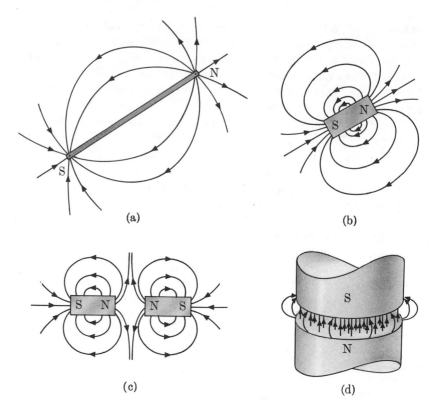

FIGURE 16.2 Examples of magnetic field distributions. (a) Long skinny magnet. The field near each end approximates the field of an isolated pole. (b) Short fat magnet. The field differs significantly from the field of two simple poles. (c) Two magnets repelling one another. (d) A nearly uniform field in the space between a pair of large flat parallel pole faces.

this equation with the statement of magnetic force,

$$\mathbf{F} = P'\mathbf{B},\tag{16.7}$$

one obtains, after some minor changes of notation, an expression for the force acting between poles,

$$\mathbf{F}_{12} = \frac{\mu_0}{4\pi}\frac{P_1 P_2 \mathbf{i}_{12}}{r^2}.\tag{16.8}$$

Here $\mathbf{i}_{12}$ is a unit vector parallel to $\mathbf{r}_{12}$, the displacement vector from pole 1 to pole 2; and $r = |\mathbf{r}_{12}|$. This result is equivalent to Equation 16.2. Compare it with Equation 15.15.

The SI unit of magnetic field is called the weber/m^2 (Wb/m^2) or tesla (T):

$$\text{unit of } \mathbf{B} = \text{Wb/m}^2 = \text{T} = \text{N/A m.}\tag{16.9}$$

1 Wb/m^2 = 1 T = 10^4 G   The cgs unit, the gauss (G), is also commonly encountered. The conversion factor is

$$10^4 \text{ gauss/tesla (G/T).}\tag{16.10}$$

The earth's field near the surface is about 0.5 G, or 5×10^{-5} T. The field near a small hand magnet might be about 100 G, or 10^{-2} T. Fields of 1 to 10 T (10^4 to 10^5 G) or more can be generated by powerful electromagnets.

The direction of the magnetic field is taken to be the direction in which a north pole would be pushed. Since a north pole is one drawn to the northern part of the earth, the earth's lines of magnetic field point in a generally northerly direction (see Figure 16.16). Several other examples of lines of magnetic field are shown in Figure 16.2.

THE MAGNETIC DIPOLE

As indicated in Figure 16.3, a small pivoted magnet, or compass, can serve to map lines of field. When the compass needle is aligned with the field, it is in equilibrium, experiencing neither force nor torque. When it lies across the lines of field, it does experience a torque, which tends to align it with the field. An idealized compass needle, or bar magnet, consisting of equal and opposite poles of strength P and $-P$ separated by distance l, is called a dipole. Its magnetic dipole moment (or simply magnetic moment) μ is defined as the vector

$$\mu = P\mathbf{l}, \tag{16.11}$$

Magnetic dipole moment

where $\mathbf{l}$ is the displacement vector from the south pole to the north pole (Figure 16.4). In a magnetic field $\mathbf{B}$ the two poles experience forces

$$\mathbf{F}_N = P\mathbf{B}, \tag{16.12}$$

$$\mathbf{F}_S = -P\mathbf{B}. \tag{16.13}$$

Thus the total force on the magnet, regardless of its orientation, is zero. As inspection of Figure 16.4 makes clear, the total torque does not vanish. Taking the midpoint O of the magnet as a reference point (any other would do as well), we have for the torque (using $\mathbf{T} = \mathbf{r} \times \mathbf{F}$),

$$\mathbf{T} = \tfrac{1}{2}\mathbf{l} \times \mathbf{F}_N - \tfrac{1}{2}\mathbf{l} \times \mathbf{F}_S.$$

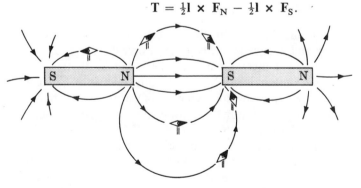

FIGURE 16.3   A pivoted dipole magnet (a compass) can serve to map lines of magnetic field.

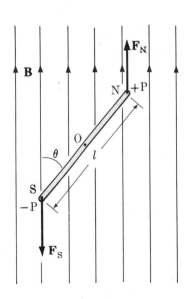

FIGURE 16.4   A magnetic dipole in a uniform field.

Using Equations 16.12 and 16.13 leads to

$$\mathbf{T} = Pl \times \mathbf{B}.$$

In terms of the magnetic moment μ, this result may be written

Torque on a dipole
$$\mathbf{T} = \mu \times \mathbf{B}. \tag{16.14}$$

In the example shown in Figure 16.4, the torque has magnitude

$$T = PlB \sin\theta = \mu B \sin\theta \tag{16.15}$$

and is directed upward from the page. More generally, Equation 16.14 may be used to *define* magnetic moment. Any object that in a magnetic field experiences a torque is said to have a magnetic moment; its magnetic moment is then determined with the help of Equation 16.14. In every way, the behavior of a magnetic dipole in a magnetic field is identical to the behavior of an electric dipole in an electric field. All results of Section 15.8 can be translated to the magnetic dipole. For example, its potential energy is

Energy of a dipole
$$U = -\mu \cdot \mathbf{B}, \tag{16.16}$$

and the work required to invert it from alignment parallel to the field to alignment antiparallel to the field is

$$W = 2\mu B. \tag{16.17}$$

SOME BASIC PROPERTIES OF THE MAGNETIC FIELD

The magnetic field shares several basic properties with the electric field. Among other things:

1. It obeys a law of superposition.
2. It obeys a form of Gauss's law.
3. It possesses an energy density proportional to the square of the field strength.

Superposition of magnetic fields and forces
(1) Superposition means the same for the magnetic field as for the electric field. Magnetic forces and magnetic fields from different sources combine by simple vector addition. Different magnetic fields can be thought of as coexisting in space without interaction. More generally, electric and magnetic fields together obey a law of superposition. Our use of the airwaves is crucially dependent on this fact. The space near the earth is filled with electromagnetic radiation carrying radio and television programs, navigational signals, telephone conversation, military intelligence, ham-radio chatter, and a myriad of other messages. Each wave makes its way undisturbed through a space it shares with thousands of other waves. Only because of the law of superposition for electric and magnetic fields does a listener hear the same modulation that left a single antenna instead of a meaningless cacophony of sound.

(2) An increment of magnetic flux is defined, in exact analogy to the definition of electric flux, as the component of the field normal to a surface multiplied by the increment of surface area:

$$d\Phi_B = \mathbf{B} \cdot d\mathbf{S}. \tag{16.18}$$

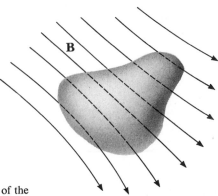

FIGURE 16.5   The solenoidal nature of the
magnetic field. In the absence of isolated
poles, lines of magnetic field never end. The
flux of **B** through a closed surface is zero.

Recall that $d\mathbf{S}$ is a vector normal to the surface. Its positive direction, which is arbitrary, defines the direction of positive flux. For a finite area, the magnetic flux is written as an integral over the surface:

$$\Phi_B = \int \mathbf{B} \cdot d\mathbf{S}. \qquad (16.19)$$ *Magnetic flux*

In the International System,

$$\text{unit of magnetic flux} = \text{weber (Wb)} = \text{T m}^2. \qquad (16.20)$$

The cgs unit, the G cm^2, is much smaller. The conversion factor is

$$10^8 \text{ G cm}^2/\text{Wb}. \qquad (16.21)$$

If magnetic poles existed, the magnetic flux emerging from a closed surface would be proportional to the net pole strength contained within the volume. The magnetic version of Gauss's law has the form

$$\oint \mathbf{B} \cdot d\mathbf{S} = \mu_0 P \qquad \text{(if free poles)}, \qquad (16.22)$$

where P is the total pole strength within the volume. (Compare this equation with Equation 15.36.) Since experiment so far gives $P = 0$ for every closed volume, the law may be written

$$\oint \mathbf{B} \cdot d\mathbf{S} = 0 \qquad \text{(no poles)}. \qquad (16.23)$$ *Magnetic version of Gauss's law*

This statement about magnetic field is sometimes called the *solenoidal rule*. Magnetic field lines are called "solenoidal" because they loop around and never end. The integral of Equation 16.23 is zero because as many field lines enter as leave every closed volume; none terminate (Figure 16.5).

(3) The energy stored in a magnetic field may be considered to be distributed through space with an energy density u (J/m^3) given by

$$u = \frac{1}{2\mu_0} B^2. \qquad (16.24)$$ *Magnetic energy density*

Equation 16.24 and Equation 15.144 may be combined to give an expression for the total energy density in the electromagnetic field:

$$u = \frac{1}{2}\left(\epsilon_0 E^2 + \frac{1}{\mu_0}B^2\right).$$ (16.25)

This formula could be used, for instance, to find the energy density within a laser, where intense electric and magnetic fields exist.

How exactly do the electric field and the magnetic field differ? Operationally, it is easy to distinguish them: A stationary charge experiences a force in an electric field but is uninfluenced by a magnetic field; a stationary magnet feels no torque in an electric field but is twisted by a magnetic field. We may say that an electric field is that which can exert a force on a charge, and a magnetic field is that which can exert forces on a magnet. So long as no motion is involved, electrical and magnetic phenomena are totally independent; electric and magnetic fields coexist in space without mutual effect. With motion or change, they do mingle. Even then, however, electric and magnetic fields retain their identity as two distinct concepts. Actually, the theory of relativity has merged the ideas of electric field and magnetic field into the single concept of electromagnetic field. But the two ideas have not lost their individuality and distinctness through the merger, any more than man and wife cease to be individuals when married. To draw a simpler physical analogy, we may say that the ideas of "east" and "north" and "up" may be merged into the single idea of "displacement in space." The three directions are obviously closely related ideas, but they are still distinct and distinguishable. In the same way, electric and magnetic fields remain distinct concepts, even though they have been drawn together into a larger whole.

E *and* **B**: *interrelated but distinct concepts*

16.3   Key discoveries in electromagnetism

In this section, we shall, by means of a historical survey of key discoveries, preview the essential ideas that will be developed and expanded in the sections that follow.

A definite connection between electricity and magnetism was first established in 1820 by Hans Christian Oersted, a professor of natural philosophy in Copenhagen. At the end of a lecture on the subjects of electricity and magnetism, he placed a compass needle near a wire carrying an electric current. The compass needle swung to a new direction, indicating the existence of a magnetic torque, a torque that could be attributed only to the nearby electric current. Whether this experiment was carried out by chance or by design is uncertain. In any case, Oersted was prepared to capitalize on the discovery. As the subjects of his lecture suggest, he was already convinced of the existence of a connection between electricity and magnetism. Having discovered the connection, he quickly established the pattern of what we now call the lines of magnetic field. They trace circular paths about a current-carrying wire (Figure 16.6), very different indeed from the radial lines of magnetic field emanating from a magnetic pole at rest. Other scientists, especially in France, were drawn to investigate Oersted's discovery. Through the efforts of Jean Baptiste Biot,

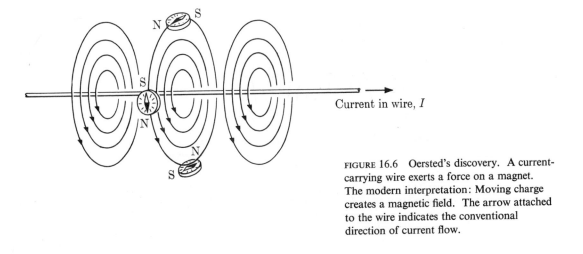

FIGURE 16.6   Oersted's discovery. A current-carrying wire exerts a force on a magnet. The modern interpretation: Moving charge creates a magnetic field. The arrow attached to the wire indicates the conventional direction of current flow.

Felix Savart, and André Marie Ampère, many aspects of the link between electric currents and magnets were worked out in mathematical detail within a few months of the arrival in Paris of the news of Oersted's discovery.

What exactly is the content of Oersted's discovery? We can best express it from a modern point of view. (1) A moving charge or, equivalently, an electric current, creates a magnetic field. Therefore, a magnet placed near a current will experience a force.* Because of Newton's third law—verified to be valid for this new effect—the magnet in turn must cause the moving charge or current to experience a force, equal and opposite to that felt by the magnet. Thus a corollary to the creation of a magnetic field by a moving charge is: (2) A magnetic field exerts a force on a moving charge (Figure 16.7). Finally, since a moving charge

Three links between magnetic field and moving charge or current

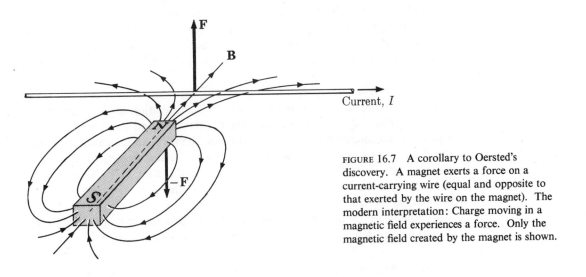

FIGURE 16.7   A corollary to Oersted's discovery. A magnet exerts a force on a current-carrying wire (equal and opposite to that exerted by the wire on the magnet). The modern interpretation: Charge moving in a magnetic field experiences a force. Only the magnetic field created by the magnet is shown.

---

* In a nonuniform field, a magnet will experience a net force as well as, possibly, a net torque.

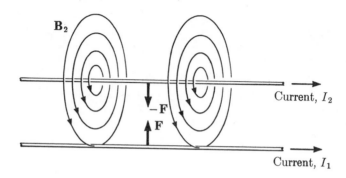

FIGURE 16.8 Ampère's discovery based on Oersted's work. One current-carrying wire exerts a force on another. The modern interpretation: Each current creates a magnetic field; each current experiences a force in the field created by the other. Only the magnetic field created by current I_2 is shown.

both creates a magnetic field and feels a force in a magnetic field, no magnets at all are necessary to demonstrate the new effect: (3) One current will exert a force on another current (Figure 16.8). Since a wire carrying current contains moving charge but normally has no net electrification, any force exerted by one current-carrying wire on another wire is necessarily distinct from the electrostatic force of Coulomb. These were the important new discoveries of 1820 (with a modern interpretation*) that launched the combined science of electromagnetism.

Magnetic induction:
A changing magnetic field
induces a current

Another giant stride occurred in 1831, when Michael Faraday in England and Joseph Henry in the United States independently discovered that a moving magnet generates a current in a nearby wire. One of Faraday's experiments was the following (Figure 16.9): A magnet is moved near a coil of wire, which is closed through a current-sensitive meter. When the magnet moves, a current is observed to flow in the wire. The current is proportional to the speed of the magnet. It also has the properties of being greater if the magnet is more powerful and greater if the magnet is moved closer to the wire. When the magnet stops moving, the current stops flowing. This effect is called *induction*. The moving magnet "induces" a current.

To describe the new phenomenon, Faraday introduced the idea of magnetic lines of force and moved toward our modern interpretation of magnetic induction. He imagined lines of force penetrating the wire and there being able to induce current whenever the lines moved across the wire. In the modern description, his idea of local action persists. We now say that a moving (or changing) magnetic field creates an electric field. Within the wire, this electric field—which exists only so long as the magnetic field is changing—accelerates charge and thereby induces current.

Faraday's lines of force—precursors of the field concept—proved fruitful in unifying the description of several forms of magnetic induction. As Faraday

---

* The equivalence of electric current and charge in motion was established much later. Early results concerning electromagnetism were all expressed in terms of currents.

verified, current is induced in one wire if another current-carrying wire is moved near it or if, even without motion, current in a neighboring wire is started or stopped (Figure 16.10). Each example of the induction of current is associated with a changing magnetic field.

The discovery of electromagnetic induction revealed that mechanical energy could be transformed directly to electrical energy. All modern generators are based on this principle; they derive current from the relative motion of conducting wires and magnetic fields. Faraday saw clearly the important implications for man of his discovery, but he chose to continue to pursue fundamental research rather than devote his talents to the development of practical generators.

Practical implications of induction

In the decades following Faraday's discovery, insight into electromagnetism deepened as new implications of the electromagnetic laws were worked out mathematically and as new applications were discovered. Long-distance telegraphy, initiated in 1844, set off the communications revolution that is still in process. Motors and generators, which directly harness the bonds between electricity and magnetism, evolved into practical devices of commerce in the

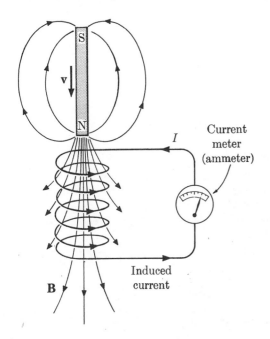

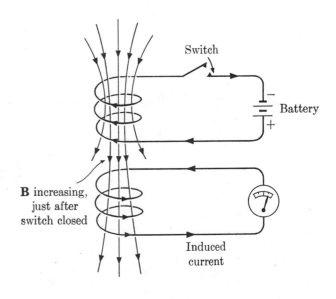

FIGURE 16.9   A discovery of Faraday and Henry. A moving magnet generates a current in a nearby wire. The modern interpretation: The changing magnetic field creates an electric field that accelerates charge within the wire to cause the current. Arrows attached to the wire show the direction of conventional current flow, opposite to the actual direction of motion of electrons through the wire.

FIGURE 16.10   Induction without motion. A changing current in one wire creates a current in another wire. Closing the switch in the upper circuit influences the lower circuit in much the same way that a moving magnet would influence it (compare Figure 16.9).

period 1850–1880. In this period of consolidation and application, the electric and magnetic fields moved gradually to a more central position in the theory of electromagnetism. Both fields showed up as important concepts in the work of James Clerk Maxwell in the 1860s. By 1885, Oliver Heaviside had cast the equations governing the fields into a form that revealed the beautiful symmetry that exists in nature between electricity and magnetism.

Maxwell's unification of electromagnetism

Three of Maxwell's achievements deserve special mention. First is his unification of all of electromagnetism. He drew together the loose ends of past work into a single theoretical structure. From his equations could be derived all that was already known of the subject, plus much that was still to be learned. Second, he discovered (theoretically, not experimentally) a new connecting link between electric and magnetic fields. The nature of this link is illustrated in Figure 16.11. Current flowing toward one metal plate and away from another produces an increasing electric field between the plates. Surrounding this region of growing field appears a magnetic field, much like the field created by a current—even though the region between the plates contains neither current nor charge. Maxwell thought of the region between the plates as containing something he called a displacement current. Now, however, we simply describe the

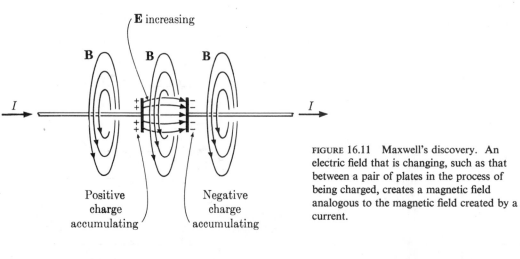

FIGURE 16.11   Maxwell's discovery. An electric field that is changing, such as that between a pair of plates in the process of being charged, creates a magnetic field analogous to the magnetic field created by a current.

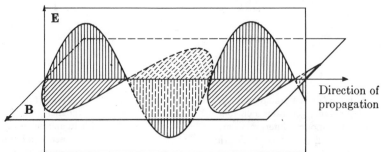

FIGURE 16.12   Maxwell's prediction. Electromagnetic waves, far removed from charges or currents, should be able to propagate through space. We understand these waves now to consist of oscillating electric and magnetic fields of equal energy density.

phenomenon in this way: A changing electric field creates a magnetic field. This makes Maxwell's law an exact parallel of the law discovered by Faraday and Henry, which, in modern terms, is: A changing magnetic field creates an electric field.

Another kind of induction

Third, Maxwell predicted the existence of electromagnetic waves, and suggested that light is an example of electromagnetic radiation.   Now we understand such radiation to consist of electric and magnetic fields in a perfect state of balance, each field continually changing and continually interacting with the other field (Figure 16.12).   The wave requires the oscillatory motion of charge for its creation, but once created, it propagates without further stimulus from charge or matter.   The continually changing electric field in the wave creates a magnetic field; the continually changing magnetic field in turn creates an electric field.   Like two freezing trappers in the wilds who huddle together to stay alive, the electric and magnetic fields hang together and keep each other alive through the laws linking electricity and magnetism.   The wave terminates only when it meets another charge that can be set into motion and absorb the energy in the wave.   Ordinary light is "atom-made" electromagnetic radiation.   The first "man-made" radiation was achieved in the 1880s.

Balanced oscillation of **E** *and* **B** *in electromagnetic waves*

16.4   The magnetic force on a moving charge

The cathode-ray tube (Figure 15.45) is a device that can be conveniently used to illustrate the nature of the magnetic force on a moving charged particle.   Consider the effect of a bar magnet held near the CRT (Figure 16.13).   If the magnet is held above the tube, with its north pole nearer the electron beam, the spot on the tube face is deflected neither toward nor away from the magnet.   Instead, it swings to its own right (to the left side of the tube face from the vantage point of a viewer).   The force is at right angles to a line joining the magnet and an electron. If the magnet is swung around to the viewer's left, the spot will move downward. For any position of the magnet, the electrons are observed to experience a force perpendicular to their direction of flight (their velocity vector) and perpendicular to the direction of the magnetic field.

If the magnet is turned around, exchanging the positions of its north and south poles, the direction of the electron deflection is reversed.   If the magnet is moved closer, the deflection is greater.   If the electrons are caused to move more rapidly, the force is found to be greater.   A series of experiments with electrons of various speeds moving through known magnetic fields would lead to the following law:

$$\mathbf{F}_M \sim q'\mathbf{v} \times \mathbf{B}. \tag{16.26}$$

The magnetic force on a moving charge is proportional to the magnitude of the charge and to the vector product of its velocity and the magnetic field.   With SI units the constant of proportionality is set equal to 1, and the law of force reads

$$\mathbf{F}_M = q'\mathbf{v} \times \mathbf{B}. \tag{16.27}$$

Magnetic force on a charged particle

The magnitude of the force is given by

$$F_M = q'vB \sin \theta, \tag{16.28}$$

where θ is the angle between **v** and **B**.   A charge cutting transversely across lines

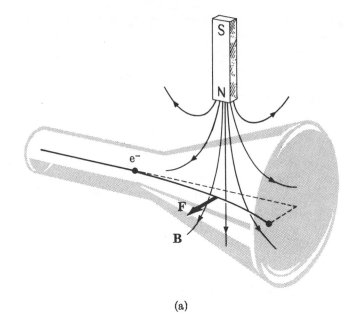

(a)

FIGURE 16.13   Deflection of moving electrons by a magnet. (a) With magnetic field lines running downward through the tube, electrons are deflected toward the right as shown. (b) With a horizontal field as shown in the tube, the beam is deflected downward. (c) Reversing the magnet polarity and changing its distance from the tube reverses the direction of the force and changes its magnitude.

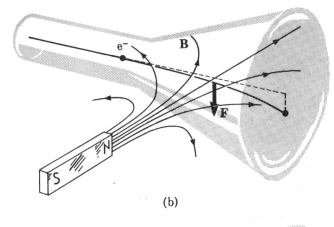

(b)

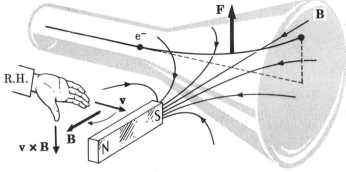

(c)

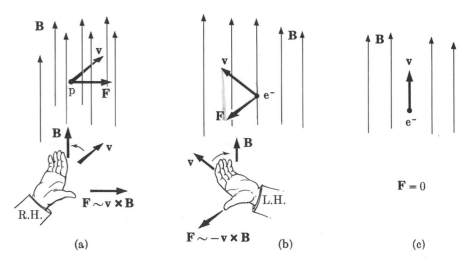

FIGURE 16.14   The vector character of magnetic force. (a) For a positively
charged particle, a right-hand rule determines the direction of the force, which
is perpendicular both to **B** and to **v**. (b) For a negatively charged particle, a
left-hand rule serves. (c) If **v** is parallel to **B**, the force vanishes (since
v × **B** = 0).

of field experiences the maximum force. A charge moving along a line of field
experiences no force. Experimentally, the direction of the force obeys the same
rules as the mathematically defined vector product. A right-hand rule determines
the direction along a line perpendicular to **v** and **B** (Figure 16.14). To find the
direction of the force acting on a negative particle, use either a right-hand rule
and then reverse the direction, as is indicated in Figure 16.13(c), or use the
left-hand rule without a reversal, as shown in Figure 16.14(b).

Equation 16.27 provides a *definition* of the concept of magnetic field
independent of the magnetic-pole concept. All other concepts in the equation
—force, charge, and velocity—are independently defined by reference to other
experiments. Roughly speaking (overlooking the vector relationships), magnetic
field may be said to be force per unit charge per unit speed.

A definition of magnetic field

It is instructive to compare Equation 16.27 with Equation 15.18, which we
may write

$$\mathbf{F_E} = q'\mathbf{E}.$$

Both can be considered to define fields. In both, a force is proportional to
charge and to a field. The all-important differences are two: (1) The magnetic
force is proportional to velocity; the electric force is not. (2) The electric force
is in the direction of the field; the magnetic force is perpendicular to the field.
Comparison of these equations also reveals an interesting difference in the
vector character of **E** and **B**: the magnetic field is an axial vector, whereas the
electric field is a polar vector (see Section 6.8).*   Finally, **E** and **B** differ in

Electric and magnetic force laws compared

---

* These assignments rest on the arbitrary convention that charge is a scalar quantity, an
assumption that requires pole strength to be a pseudoscalar quantity. An equally acceptable
alternative set of assignments would be the following: q, pseudoscalar; P, scalar; E, axial
vector; **B,** polar vector.

physical dimension. Electric field is force per unit charge. Magnetic field has the dimension of (force × time)/(charge × distance), or force/(current × distance) (see Equation 16.9). The ratio E/B has the dimension of speed. These particular relationships are peculiar to SI units; they do not hold for cgs units.

16.5 Magnetic deflection of charged particles

In a number of ways in nature, but more especially in man-made devices, the magnetic force on moving charges is at work. It is a guiding principle in every electric motor and in every television set. In the electric motor, a current-carrying wire in a magnetic field experiences a force; since the wire is rigidly attached in a coil to a rotor, the force causes the rotor to turn. In a television tube, precisely controlled rapidly changing magnetic fields deflect the electron beam according to a schedule, drawing its end-point in successive horizontal sweeps across the tube face,* making (in the U.S.A.) 525 sweeps per picture and 30 pictures per second.

   Two important results concerning the motion of charged particles in magnetic fields were proved in Section 7.9: (1) In *any* magnetic field, a particle moves with constant speed. (2) In a *uniform* magnetic field, a particle moves in a helical path—a combination of constant speed motion along the field and uniform circular motion transverse to the field. The radius of its circular path is

Radius of particle trajectory in uniform magnetic field

$$r = \frac{mv_\perp}{q'B}, \qquad (16.29)$$

where $v_\perp$ is the component of its velocity perpendicular to **B**. A slightly different form of this equation proves to be valid for relativistic particles as well as for nonrelativistic particles:

A form that remains valid near the speed of light

$$r = \frac{p_\perp}{q'B}. \qquad (16.30)$$

   Among many other applications, Equation 16.30 finds a use in the analysis of bubble-chamber photographs (Figure 16.15). For elementary particles leaving observable tracks in a bubble chamber, the magnitude of q' is always the same: 1.60×10^{-19} C. The known field strength is typically about 1 T (10^4 G). The direction in which the particle is deflected reveals the sign of its charge, its radius of curvature determines $p_\perp$, and the angle of its track to the magnetic field relates $p_\perp$ to its total momentum **p**. Sometimes the combination p/q' of a moving charged particle is known as the "magnetic rigidity" of the particle, for it is a measure of the difficulty of bending the trajectory. Particles of high rigidity are barely deflected as they pass through the bubble chamber; particles of low rigidity may be deflected into a full circle within the chamber.

   If a particle executing approximately helical motion in a magnetic field encounters a more intense field, its motion will tighten into a smaller helix, and its drifting motion along the field will be slowed. Enough intensification of the field will cause the drifting motion to reverse its course. The particle is said

---

* The television beam intensity, which makes possible a picture instead of a uniformly illuminated screen, is controlled electrically, not magnetically.

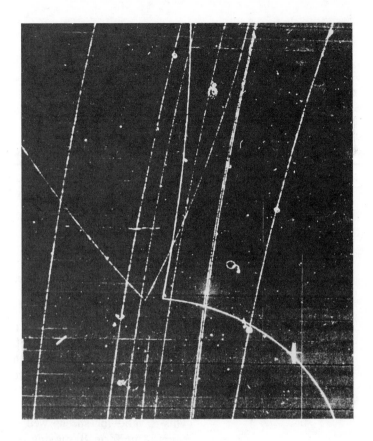

FIGURE 16.15 Magnetic deflection of charged particles in a bubble chamber. The magnetic field in this chamber was directed inward, away from the camera. The incoming particles are flying upward, and two new pairs of charged particles are created in the chamber. Can you determine the sign of the charge on each particle? Assuming that the magnitude of the charge is the same on all the particles, why are some tracks curved more than others? (Photograph courtesy of Lawrence Radiation Laboratory, University of California, Berkeley.)

to have encountered a "magnetic mirror." It spirals toward the region of stronger field, then away from it. A so-called "magnetic bottle" has a magnetic mirror at both ends.

The earth's magnetic field provides a natural "magnetic bottle" in the space outside the earth's atmosphere. The Van Allen radiation belt consists of protons and electrons trapped in this "bottle" (Figure 16.16). As calculated in Section 7.9 (Equation 7.117), a typical proton in the Van Allen belt, with an energy of 1 MeV, experiencing a magnetic field of 10^{-5} T, has a maximum radius of curvature of about 15 km, or 9 miles. This seems a great deal, but it is small compared with the size of the Van Allen belt. (What would be the maximum radius of curvature of this same proton in a laboratory field of 1 T?)

The earth's magnetic bottle

THE CHARGE-TO-MASS RATIO OF THE ELECTRON

A combination of electric and magnetic acceleration of electrons in a cathode-ray tube provides a way to find the ratio of the charge and mass of the electron. This method was used by J. J. Thomson in his earliest identification of the electron (1897). For many years, the ratio e/m was known much more accurately than either e or m alone.*

---

* Thomson's first determination of e/m was quite crude. He found the ratio to lie between 1×10^{11} and 3×10^{11} C/kg. We now know the correct value to be 1.7588×10^{11} C/kg.

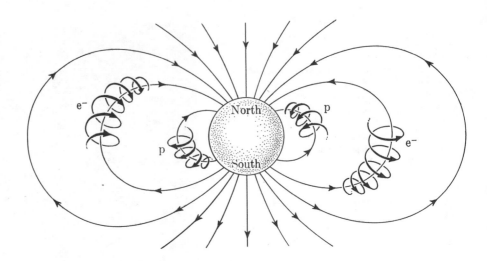

FIGURE 16.16   Trapping of charged particles in the Van Allen radiation belt.
Protons spiral one way, electrons the other, and both are reflected by the
magnetic mirrors near the poles. Helical paths are not to scale.

Before entering a region of nearly uniform magnetic field, the electron is
accelerated electrically through a known potential difference V, thereby
acquiring kinetic energy equal to eV:

$$\tfrac{1}{2}mv^2 = eV. \tag{16.31}$$

(This is valid for speeds well below the speed of light.)   Then it enters the
region of uniform **B**, moving perpendicular to the field lines.   From Equation
16.29, its radius of curvature is

$$r = \frac{mv}{eB}. \tag{16.32}$$

Equations 16.31 and 16.32 may be combined to eliminate the unknown speed v.
The result is a formula for e/m:

Charge-to-mass ratio
determined in CRT experiment

$$\frac{e}{m} = \frac{2V}{B^2r^2}. \tag{16.33}$$

On the right are experimentally measured quantities.   On the left is the ratio
of two fundamental constants.   With volts, teslas, and meters on the right side,
the left side is determined in coulomb/kilogram.

■ EXAMPLE 1:   In a lecture demonstration apparatus, electrons, after being
accelerated through a potential difference of 100 V, execute a semicircular path
of measured radius 4 cm.   In analyzing the experiment, is it important to take
the earth's field into account?   To answer the question, we can first find out
what total field must be acting on the electrons.   From Equation 16.33, this
field is

$$B = \frac{1}{r}\sqrt{\frac{2V}{e/m}}.$$

Numerically, it is

$$B = \frac{1}{0.04 \text{ m}} \sqrt{\frac{2 \times 100 \text{ V}}{1.759 \times 10^{11} \text{ C/kg}}}$$

$$= 8.43 \times 10^{-4} \text{ T} = 8.43 \text{ G}.$$

Since the earth's field of about 0.5 G is some 6 percent of this figure, it must be
included in the analysis.   ■

THE CYCLOTRON

Most modern accelerators make use of magnetic deflection to keep the particles
trapped within a fairly small domain of space while they are being accelerated.*
In the 33-GeV accelerator at Brookhaven, New York, for example, each proton
travels about 150,000 miles during its acceleration cycle, but because of magnetic
deflection it is held within a circle 840 ft in diameter while making this trip. The
first accelerator designed to hold particles in circular orbits while they were
gaining energy was the cyclotron, invented in 1931 by Ernest O. Lawrence and
M. Stanley Livingston.

In its original form, the cyclotron included two hollow metal containers
held between the pole faces of a large and powerful electromagnet (Figure
16.17). The metal containers can be thought of as the slightly separated halves
of a large pillbox sliced through the middle. Because of their D shape, the
containers are called the "dees" of the cyclotron. Each dee is electrically charged;
one positively and one negatively. In the gap between the dees there is therefore
an electric field, although there is very little electric field within each dee. The
lines of magnetic field are vertical and nearly uniform, passing through the dees
as well as through the gap. As the acceleration cycle proceeds, the magnetic
field remains steady and unchanging while the electric field is periodically reversed, pointing first from left to right, then from right to left, with several

Design of the cyclotron

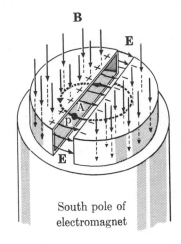

FIGURE 16.17   Early version of cyclotron.
The nearly uniform magnetic field points
vertically downward. (The upper pole face
of the electromagnet is not shown.) At the
instant shown, the proton at point A is being
electrically accelerated to the right, so that
its half-circle in the right dee will have a
slightly larger radius than its previous
half-circle in the left dee.

South pole of
electromagnet

---

* Linear accelerators are exceptions.

million reversals per second. Projectile particles—protons for example—are released near the center of the pair of dees and spiral outward in circles of gradually increasing radius until they are near the outer periphery of the dees. There they either may strike a target or be deflected through a thin window to form an energetic external beam. The dees themselves are enclosed within an evacuated chamber.

The operation of the cyclotron can best be understood by considering some intermediate time during the acceleration cycle. The magnetic field causes the proton to execute a circle with radius given by Equation 16.32. Twice in each revolution the proton crosses the gap between the dees. As it crosses from left to right, the left dee is positively charged and the right dee negatively charged, so the electric field in the gap points from left to right. The proton feels a momentary force in the direction of its motion. It gains energy and speed. During the time it executes its half circle in the right dee (with a slightly larger radius than in the preceding half circle), the potential difference of the dees is reversed. Therefore, at its next passage across the gap—this time from right to left—the proton again feels an electric accelerating force and gains another increment of energy, of speed, of momentum, and of radius of curvature.

One key to the success of the cyclotron is the stability of the particle orbits. The protons or other particles being accelerated must not drift off course and strike the inner walls of the dees. This stability is achieved by letting the magnetic field be very slightly weaker near the outer edge than at the center. It is left as a problem to show how the weakening of the field may be related to orbit stability.

A second key to the success of the cyclotron is the fact that the time required for a proton (for example) to execute each half circle within a dee is a constant, the same for low energy and small radius as for high energy and large radius. According to Equation 7.115, the angular frequency of a particle of charge e and mass m in a magnetic field B is

Cyclotron (angular) frequency

$$\omega_c = \left(\frac{e}{m}\right) B. \tag{16.34}$$

The subscript c indicates that this is the so-called cyclotron frequency. The actual frequency in revolutions per second is

$$v_c = \frac{\omega_c}{2\pi} = \frac{eB}{2\pi m}. \tag{16.35}$$

It is at this frequency that the potential on the dees must alternate.

■ EXAMPLE 2: The magnetic field strength in a 30-MeV proton cyclotron is 1 T. What is the required frequency of the oscillator controlling the potential of the dees? What is the physical dimension of the cyclotron? From Equation 16.35,

$$v_c = \frac{1.602 \times 10^{-19} \text{ C} \times 1 \text{ T}}{2\pi \times 1.673 \times 10^{-27} \text{ kg}}$$

$$= 1.52 \times 10^7 \text{ sec}^{-1} = 15.2 \text{ MHz},$$

a frequency in the short-wave radio band. The final speed of the proton is

$$v = \sqrt{\frac{2K}{m}} = \sqrt{\frac{2 \times 30 \times 10^6 \text{ eV} \times 1.602 \times 10^{-19} \text{ J/eV}}{1.673 \times 10^{-27} \text{ kg}}}$$

$$= 7.58 \times 10^7 \text{ m/sec,}$$

about one-fourth the speed of light.* The largest radius of curvature reached by the protons in this 30-MeV cyclotron can now be calculated. It is

$$r = \frac{mv}{eB} = \frac{(1.673 \times 10^{-27})(7.58 \times 10^7)}{(1.602 \times 10^{-19})(1)}$$

$$= 0.79 \text{ m.}$$

The diameter of the cyclotron is 1.58 m, or about 5 ft. This seems a moderate amount, but even this "low-energy" cyclotron requires many tons of iron for its magnet. ∎

One of the simple features of the cyclotron, the constant orbital frequency for all energies, is lost at particle speeds near the speed of light. Moreover, at energies beyond a few hundred MeV, the size and weight of the cyclotron magnets become prohibitively large. The modern successor to the cyclotron is called the synchrotron; it may be pictured roughly as a "hollow cyclotron." The general features of its operation are discussed in Section 3.6. For a proton synchroton, Equation 16.30 is written

At higher energy, synchrotrons replace cyclotrons

$$r = \frac{p}{eB}.$$

Since the radius on the left is constant, and since e is constant, the ratio p/B must remain constant. As the particle gains momentum, the magnetic field must be increased in exact proportion to the increasing momentum. In the National Accelerator, the magnetic field is increased from a small value to more than 1 T in a few seconds. The practical advantages of the synchrotron that make possible its extension to energies higher than any reached by cyclotrons are, first, that it requires a magnetic field only around its peripheral track—not in its hollow center—and, second, that its peak magnetic field does not need to be maintained continuously.

16.6   The magnetic field created by a moving charge

Based on Oersted's original discovery, we know that lines of magnetic field describe circles about a straight current-carrying wire (Figure 16.6). This behavior of the magnetic field created by moving charge—obviously very different from the radiating lines of electric field from a charge—can be discovered in a different way, by considering the cathode-ray tube referred to in Section 16.4. If a north pole held above the electron beam causes the beam to be deflected to the viewer's left (Figure 16.18), it is required by Newton's third law that the magnet itself experience an equal and opposite force to the viewer's right. To be more accurate, we should say that *if* Newton's third law is valid

---

* At a particle speed this close to the speed of light, the formula $K = \frac{1}{2}mv^2$ is no longer quite correct, but it is accurate enough for this example.

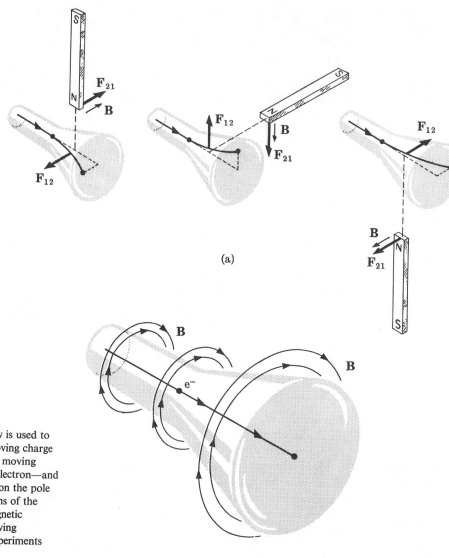

(a)

(b)

FIGURE 16.18   Newton's third law is used to relate the magnetic force on a moving charge to the magnetic field created by a moving charge. (a) The force F_{12} on an electron—and the equal and opposite force F_{21} on the pole of a magnet—for three orientations of the magnet. (b) Circular lines of magnetic field that must exist around a moving charge, in accordance with the experiments with a magnet.

for this new force, the equal reaction force to the right on the magnet is expected. Indeed, the measurement of this force verifies the applicability of Newton's third law. Since a stationary north pole experiences a force to the right, this means a magnetic field exists at that location pointing to the right: the moving beam of electrons has created a magnetic field. Above the beam, the field is to the viewer's right, to the right of the beam the field is directed downward, and so on. From the vantage point of the viewer in front of the tube face, the magnetic field describes clockwise circles about the electron beam [Figure 16.18(b)].

We conclude, then, that from the equal and opposite forces of magnet on moving electron and moving electron on magnet, we can derive the law of *field* created by a moving charge if we know the law of *force* acting on the moving charge. To express it a little more simply, Newton's third law requires that if a moving charged particle experiences a magnetic force, it must also create a magnetic field. Instead of actually deriving the law of field in this way, we shall state the law and work backwards, showing it to be consistent with Newton's third law.

A requirement of Newton's third law: If a particle experiences a magnetic force, it must create a magnetic field

The magnetic field created by a moving charge is given by

$$\mathbf{B} = \frac{\mu_0}{4\pi} q \frac{\mathbf{v} \times \mathbf{r}}{r^3} = \frac{\mu_0}{4\pi} q \frac{\mathbf{v} \times \mathbf{i}_r}{r^2}, \tag{16.36}$$

The field of a moving charge

where q is the charge, $\mathbf{v}$ is its velocity, $\mathbf{r}$ is the displacement vector from the location of the charge to the place where the field is being measured, and $\mathbf{i}_r$ is a unit vector parallel to $\mathbf{r}$. The constant μ_0 (the permeability constant) was introduced in Section 16.1. As shown in Figure 16.19(a), if a beam of negative particles moves to the right, the field $\mathbf{B}$ above the beam is directed into the page. On the pole of strength P the force produced by this field is

$$\mathbf{F}_{21} = P\mathbf{B} = \frac{\mu_0}{4\pi} Pq \frac{\mathbf{v} \times \mathbf{r}}{r^3}. \tag{16.37}$$

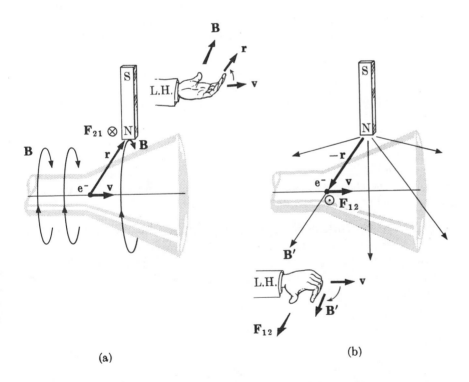

(a)   (b)

FIGURE 16.19   Interaction of moving charge and magnet. (a) The moving charge generates a field $\mathbf{B}$, which causes the pole of the magnet to experience force $\mathbf{F}_{21}$ (Equations 16.36 and 16.37). (b) The charge, in moving through the field $\mathbf{B}'$ of the pole, experiences a force $\mathbf{F}_{12}$ (Equation 16.38). The fact that $\mathbf{F}_{12} = -\mathbf{F}_{21}$ demonstrates the consistency of the equations for force and field. (A left hand is used in the illustrations since the charge is negative.)

The idealized pole produces a field $\mathbf{B}'$ which, back at the location of the moving charge, is

$$\mathbf{B}' = -\frac{\mu_0}{4\pi}\frac{P\mathbf{r}}{r^3}.$$

This is the same as Equation 16.6, except that the sign is reversed, since the displacement vector from the pole to the charge is $-\mathbf{r}$ [Figure 16.19(b)]. The electron, moving in this field, experiences a force

$$\mathbf{F}_{12} = q\mathbf{v} \times \mathbf{B}' = -\frac{\mu_0}{4\pi}qP\frac{\mathbf{v} \times \mathbf{r}}{r^3}. \tag{16.38}$$

The consistency of Equations 16.27 and 16.36 is demonstrated by the fact that $\mathbf{F}_{12} = -\mathbf{F}_{21}$.

It is instructive to compare Equation 16.36 with the electric-field equation,

$$\mathbf{E} = \frac{1}{4\pi\epsilon_0}\frac{q\mathbf{i}_r}{r^2}.$$

Laws of electric and magnetic fields compared

The particular constants $\mu_0/4\pi$ and $1/4\pi\epsilon_0$ are peculiarities of the system of units employed and are not themselves of fundamental importance (although they are vital in numerical work). The essence of the equations is in the other factors. Both fields are proportional to charge and both fall off in magnitude in proportion to $1/r^2$. The magnetic field generated by a charge is proportional to its speed; there is no such dependence of its electric field. The directional property of the magnetic field is more complicated than that of the electric field. The field $\mathbf{B}$ is directed perpendicular to the plane containing $\mathbf{v}$ and $\mathbf{r}$. Its magnitude is*

$$B = \frac{\mu_0}{4\pi}\frac{qv\sin\theta}{r^2}, \tag{16.39}$$

where θ is the angle between $\mathbf{v}$ and $\mathbf{r}$ [Figure 16.19(a)]. The field along the line of travel of the charge is zero. It takes on its maximum value directly to the side of the path, with $\mathbf{r}$ and $\mathbf{v}$ perpendicular.

■ EXAMPLE: A particle of charge q moves with constant speed v in a circle of radius a (Figure 16.20). What is the component of magnetic field created by the particle along the axis of the circle at a distance x from the center of the circle? As Figure 16.20 makes clear, $\mathbf{v}$ and $\mathbf{r}$ are perpendicular. Therefore, the magnitude of the field is given by

$$B = \frac{\mu_0}{4\pi}\frac{qv}{r^2}.$$

---

* Equations 16.36 and 16.39 are valid only for speeds much less than the speed of light. The formula for B valid at all speeds is

$$B = \frac{\mu_0}{4\pi}\frac{qv\sin\theta}{r^2}\frac{(1-(v^2/c^2))}{(1-(v^2\sin^2\theta/c^2))^{3/2}},$$

where θ has the same meaning as in Equation 16.39.

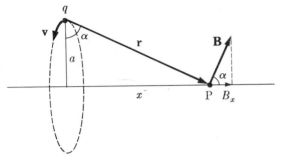

FIGURE 16.20   A particle of charge q moves uniformly in a circle. Its field at point P is inclined at angle α to the axis. (What is the assumed sign of q in this diagram?)

It makes an angle α with the axis, and

$$\cos \alpha = \frac{a}{r}.$$

The component of **B** along the axis is

$$B_x = B \cos \alpha = \frac{\mu_0}{4\pi} \frac{qva}{r^3}.$$

This is more usefully written as

$$B_x = \frac{\mu_0}{4\pi} \frac{qva}{(x^2 + a^2)^{3/2}}. \tag{16.40}$$

At the center of the circle, where $x = 0$, the field is directed along the axis and has magnitude

Axial field for a circling charge

$$B = \frac{\mu_0}{4\pi} \frac{qv}{a^2}. \tag{16.41}$$

Note that since the field direction elsewhere is rotating as the particle rotates, the component B_x is the same as the field averaged over time.   ∎

The reader wishing to consolidate his understanding of the laws of electromagnetism discussed so far should look ahead to the review in Section 16.11. No new fundamental laws or concepts are introduced in the remainder of this chapter, but it is important that the laws of moving charge be generalized to include electric current. In our technological world, current is the principal vehicle of moving charge.

16.7   The magnetic force on a current

Physically, a moving charged particle and a current in a wire are quite different: the current is electrically neutral; it involves a myriad of charged particles; and the average drift velocity of these particles along the wire is small compared with their random thermal velocity. Nevertheless, there is a simple mathematical correspondence between moving charge and current that can be derived by example. Consider the current in a straight wire (Figure 16.21). In a segment

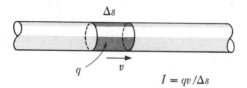

FIGURE 16.21 If a wire segment of length Δs contains charge q moving with drift velocity v, the current is $I = qv/\Delta s$.

of length Δs is contained a number of conduction electrons whose total charge is q and whose drift velocity is v. The time required for these electrons to flow past a point in the wire is $\Delta t = \Delta s/v$. The current is

$$I = \frac{q}{\Delta t} = \frac{qv}{\Delta s}.$$

This relation may be rewritten

$$qv = I\,\Delta s.$$

A generalization in vector form is

An important equivalence for current and moving charge

$$q\mathbf{v} \leftrightarrow I\,d\mathbf{s}. \tag{16.42}$$

The double arrow means "is equivalent to" or "may be replaced by." Any equation appropriate for moving charge may be transformed to an equation appropriate for current if $q\mathbf{v}$ is replaced by $I\,d\mathbf{s}$. The change from a finite quantity, $q\mathbf{v}$, to an infinitesimal quantity, $I\,d\mathbf{s}$, is necessary in order that the current at only one point be considered, to match the fact that the charge at one point is considered. The displacement vector $d\mathbf{s}$ is directed along the wire. If the direction of conventional current is the same as the direction of $d\mathbf{s}$, then I is positive; otherwise I is negative. It is a good practice to choose $d\mathbf{s}$ so that I is positive.

Transforming from Equation 16.27, we get, for the law of magnetic force on a current element,

The force on a current element

$$d\mathbf{F} = I'\,d\mathbf{s} \times \mathbf{B}. \tag{16.43}$$

This is a modern statement of a fundamental law discovered by Ampère not long after Oersted's discovery of the magnetic effect of a current. It provides an alternative *definition* of the concept of magnetic field. We may say that a magnetic field is that which is capable of exerting a force on a current, with properties determined by Equation 16.43. Measurement of the force on a known current determines the field.

It gives another definition of **B**

The form of this force law means that the force on a current-carrying wire is always transverse to the wire. It is also transverse to the lines of magnetic field. On a straight wire of length l in a uniform field $\mathbf{B}$, the magnitude of the force is

$$F = IlB \sin\theta, \tag{16.44}$$

where θ is the angle between the wire and the field (Figure 16.22). As shown in the figure, the direction of the force is determined by the right-hand rule of the vector product.

■ EXAMPLE: A wire, with a mass per unit length of 0.009 kg/m, is oriented east-west just above the equator (Figure 16.23). At its location, the earth's

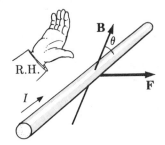

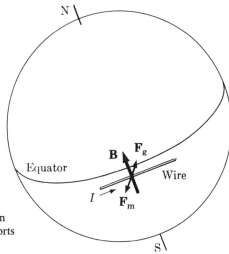

FIGURE 16.22   The magnetic force on a current-carrying wire is transverse to the field **B** and to the direction of the current.

FIGURE 16.23   The magnetic force $\mathbf{F}_m$ on an eastbound current above the equator supports the weight of the wire carrying the current.

magnetic field is horizontal, directed to the north, and has magnitude 3×10^{-5} T. What current must flow in the wire if the magnetic force is to support the weight of the wire? Application of the right-hand rule to Equation 16.43 shows that the current must flow from west to east. The magnetic force then acts vertically upward. Since $d\mathbf{s}$ is perpendicular to **B**, $dF_M = I\,ds\,B$, or

$$\frac{dF_M}{ds} = IB. \qquad (16.45)$$

This force per unit length must balance the gravitational force per unit length, which is

$$\frac{dF_g}{ds} = \frac{dm}{ds}\,g.$$

The required current is

$$I = \frac{(dm/ds)g}{B} = \frac{0.009 \text{ kg/m} \times 9.8 \text{ m/sec}^2}{3 \times 10^{-5} \text{ T}}$$

$$= 2,940 \text{ A.}$$

Although large by household standards, a current of this magnitude would not be uncommon in industrial applications. It is left as a problem to consider whether a wire of 0.009 kg/m could sustain such a current. ∎

CURRENT LOOP

The circulation of current in closed loops is of considerable importance in both the macroscopic and atomic domains. As a convenience for calculation, we shall consider a rectangular loop. Suppose it is oriented as shown in Figure 16.24, such that its sides 1 and 2, of length $2a$, are perpendicular to a uniform magnetic field $\mathbf{B}$; that its sides 3 and 4, of length $2b$, make an angle $\frac{1}{2}\pi - \varphi$ with the field; and that its axis (a line perpendicular to the plane of the loop) makes an angle φ with the field. When current I flows in the loop, the forces on the four sides cancel in pairs:

$$\mathbf{F}_1 = -\mathbf{F}_2,$$
$$\mathbf{F}_3 = -\mathbf{F}_4.$$

Therefore, the total force vanishes. However, the total torque is not zero. Picking point O in Figure 16.24(b) as a reference point (any other point would also be satisfactory), we find that forces $\mathbf{F}_3$ and $\mathbf{F}_4$ contribute nothing to the torque. Forces $\mathbf{F}_1$ and $\mathbf{F}_2$ contribute equal torques, directed upward from the page. The magnitude of each is $T_1 = F_1 b \sin \varphi$ so that the total torque is

$$T = 2F_1 b \sin \varphi. \tag{16.46}$$

From Equation 16.44, with $\sin \theta = 1$, the force F_1 is

$$F_1 = 2aIB.$$

Substitution of this expression for F_1 in Equation 16.46 gives

$$T = 4abIB \sin \varphi.$$

Since $4ab$ is equal to A, the area of the loop, this result may be expressed more simply by

$$T = IAB \sin \varphi. \tag{16.47}$$

Now A is actually the magnitude of the area vector $\mathbf{A}$, which is directed along the axis of the loop. If we let $\mathbf{A}$ point downward to the right in Figure 16.24(b), the torque on the loop may be written as

$$T = I\mathbf{A} \times \mathbf{B}. \tag{16.48}$$

This has the same form as Equation 16.14, which defines magnetic moment. Therefore, the magnetic moment of the loop is

The magnetic moment of a current loop

$$\boldsymbol{\mu} = I\mathbf{A}. \tag{16.49}$$

The loop acts like a magnet whose axis is along the axis of the loop. In the International System,

$$\text{unit of magnetic moment} = \text{A m}^2. \tag{16.50}$$

Equation 16.49 is actually much more general than our derivation might indicate. A loop of any shape with area $\mathbf{A}$ carrying current I has a magnetic moment equal to $I\mathbf{A}$. The direction of $\boldsymbol{\mu}$ can be determined by a right-hand rule (Figure 16.25). If the fingers of the right hand are curved in the direction of current flow around the loop, the right thumb indicates the direction of $\boldsymbol{\mu}$.

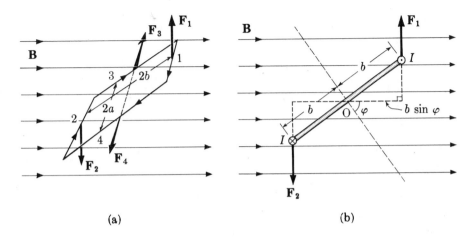

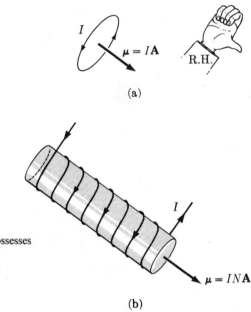

FIGURE 16.24   A rectangular loop in a magnetic field. (a) Perspective view.
(b) End view. Forces on the loop add to zero but produce a couple.

FIGURE 16.25   (a) A loop of current possesses
a magnetic moment. (b) The magnetic
moment of a coil of N turns is N times
greater.

This is also the direction of the north pole of the "equivalent magnet." For a   *It acts as a dipole*
solenoid of N identical loops, each of area A, the magnetic moment is

$$\mu = NIA. \tag{16.51}$$

★MAGNETIC MOMENT AND ANGULAR MOMENTUM

Consider a particle of charge q and mass m executing a circular orbit. It is
interesting to demonstrate that its magnetic moment is simply related to its
angular momentum. To be specific, let the particle rotate about the z axis, as

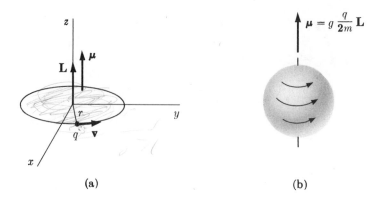

(a)   (b)

FIGURE 16.26   (a) A rotating charged particle generates a magnetic dipole moment proportional to its angular momentum: $\boldsymbol{\mu} = (q/2m)\mathbf{L}$.   (b) A similar relationship, with an added factor g, holds for any rotating charged structure.

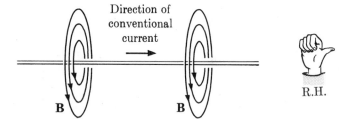

FIGURE 16.27   A right-hand rule is useful in establishing the direction of field lines about a current-carrying wire.

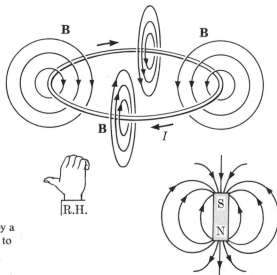

FIGURE 16.28   Magnetic field produced by a current loop. The field pattern is similar to that produced by a short magnet.

shown in Figure 16.26(a). To find the "current," imagine any fixed point on the orbit and ask how much charge passes that point after n revolutions of the particle. The charge is nq, the time is $2\pi rn/v$, and the effective current is

$$I = \frac{\text{charge}}{\text{time}} = \frac{qv}{2\pi r}.$$

From Equation 16.49, the magnetic moment is

$$\boldsymbol{\mu} = I\mathbf{A} = \frac{qv}{2\pi r}\,\pi r^2 \mathbf{k}$$

$$= \tfrac{1}{2}qvr\mathbf{k}. \tag{16.52}$$

The angular momentum of the particle is

$$\mathbf{L} = mvr\mathbf{k}. \tag{16.53}$$

The relationship between magnetic moment and angular momentum is, therefore,

$$\boldsymbol{\mu} = \frac{q}{2m}\,\mathbf{L}. \tag{16.54}$$

Magnetic moment of a circling charge

For any body of total charge q and total mass m rotating about a fixed axis, it is possible to write a similar relationship:

$$\mu_z = g\,\frac{q}{2m}\,L_z. \tag{16.55}$$

Definition of the g-factor

The dimensionless factor g, called the *gyromagnetic ratio*, or the "g-factor," is equal to 1 if the charge and mass of the body have the same spatial distribution; that is, if the charge-to-mass ratio is the same for all parts of the body.

16.8   Magnetic fields created by currents

Surrounding a straight current-carrying wire is a magnetic field whose lines describe circles with the wire as an axis (Figure 16.27). A right-hand rule is convenient for finding the field direction. If the right thumb indicates the current direction, the curved fingers of the right hand indicate the pattern of field lines. If the wire is bent into a loop in such a way that the current, seen from above, circulates clockwise (Figure 16.28), the magnetic field lines all dive into the center of the loop from above and point upward everywhere around the outer periphery of the loop. This is the simplest version of an electromagnet. The loop acts like a short magnet, with its north pole downward in this example, a conclusion we could also have reached from the earlier discussion of torque. A solenoid, like the one pictured in Figure 16.29, behaves like a number of current loops stacked one on top of the other. Its magnetic field is similar to that of a long bar magnet. The solenoid or coil is the basic design of all electromagnets.

The basic law governing the creation of magnetic fields by currents can be found as a transformation of Equation 16.36, using the equivalence of Formula 16.42. It is

$$d\mathbf{B} = \frac{\mu_0}{4\pi}\frac{I\,d\mathbf{s} \times \mathbf{r}}{r^3} = \frac{\mu_0}{4\pi}\frac{I\,d\mathbf{s} \times \mathbf{i}_r}{r^2}. \tag{16.56}$$

The field created by a current element

The notation and the geometry of the vectors are illustrated in Figure 16.30.

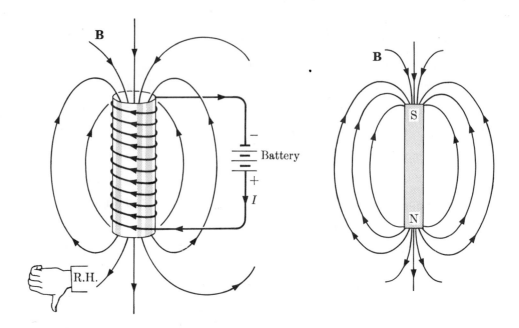

FIGURE 16.29   Magnetic field produced by a coil. The field pattern is similar to that produced by a long magnet. In the version of a right-hand rule shown here, the thumb indicates the direction of field lines emerging from the coil and also the direction of the magnetic moment.

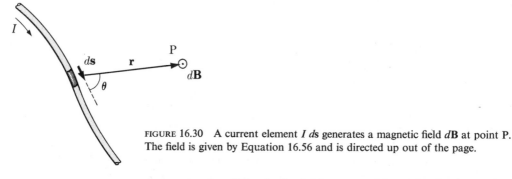

FIGURE 16.30   A current element $I\,d\mathbf{s}$ generates a magnetic field $d\mathbf{B}$ at point P. The field is given by Equation 16.56 and is directed up out of the page.

■ EXAMPLE 1:   What is the field generated by a circular loop of current on the axis of the loop? As shown in Figure 16.31, we call the radius of the loop a, the distance from the center of the loop to the point of observation x, and the current I. The reasoning is almost identical to that for a circling charged particle (see Figure 16.20). A current element $I\,d\mathbf{s}$ at the top of the loop creates the field $d\mathbf{B}$, whose component along the axis is dB_x. In the sum (or integral) of contributions from all parts of the circle, components of $d\mathbf{B}$ perpendicular to the axis cancel; only the components dB_x add to give a finite result. The total field $\mathbf{B}$ lies along the axis. Since $d\mathbf{s}$ and $\mathbf{r}$ are perpendicular, the magnitude of $d\mathbf{B}$ is, from Equation 16.56,

$$dB = \frac{\mu_0}{4\pi}\frac{I\,ds}{r^2}.$$

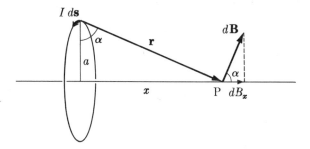

FIGURE 16.31   Each current element in a loop contributes an increment dB_x to the axial field at point P. The total field is $B = \int dB_x$. Components perpendicular to the axis cancel.

The component dB_x is

$$dB_x = dB \cos \alpha = \frac{\mu_0}{4\pi} \frac{Ia\ ds}{r^3}.$$

The integration is carried out around the loop for fixed x. Therefore every factor multiplying ds on the right is constant, and the integration becomes quite simple:

$$B_x = \frac{\mu_0}{4\pi} \frac{Ia}{r^3} \int_0^{2\pi a} ds = \frac{\mu_0}{2} \frac{Ia^2}{r^3}. \tag{16.57}$$

Expressed in terms of x, the answer is:

$$B = B_x = \frac{\mu_0}{2} \frac{Ia^2}{(x^2 + a^2)^{3/2}}. \tag{16.58}$$

Axial field of a current loop

We have noted also the fact that the magnitude of the total **B** is the same as B_x. Compare this expression for the field of a current loop with Equation 16.40 for the field of a circling charge. The two correspond exactly, with the equivalence

$$qv \leftrightarrow I \cdot 2\pi a. \tag{16.59}$$

∎

■ EXAMPLE 2, THE BIOT-SAVART LAW: Another important example is that of a long straight wire. We seek the field at point P a distance x from the wire (Figure 16.32). If the current I flows to the right, a current element $I\ d\mathbf{s}$ at distance s from the origin O contributes an increment of field $d\mathbf{B}$, which is directed into the page at P. Every other part of the wire contributes an increment of field in the same direction. The magnitudes dB may, therefore, be summed to find the total field. The magnitude of the contribution from the element $I\ d\mathbf{s}$ shown in Figure 16.32 is

$$dB = \frac{\mu_0}{4\pi} \frac{I\ ds}{r^2} \sin \theta = \frac{\mu_0}{4\pi} \frac{Ix\ ds}{r^3},$$

since $\sin \theta = \sin (\pi - \theta) = x/r$. Substitution of $\sqrt{x^2 + s^2}$ for r and transformation to an integral gives

$$B = \frac{\mu_0 Ix}{4\pi} \int_{-\infty}^{\infty} \frac{ds}{(x^2 + s^2)^{3/2}}. \tag{16.60}$$

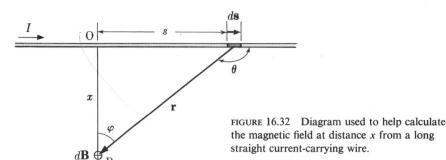

FIGURE 16.32   Diagram used to help calculate the magnetic field at distance x from a long straight current-carrying wire.

One may consult a table of integrals to obtain the answer. Alternatively, set $s = x \tan \varphi$ so that $ds = x \sec^2 \varphi \, d\varphi$ and $x^2 + s^2 = x^2 \sec^2 \varphi$. (Remember that x is a constant for the integration.) Then

$$B = \frac{\mu_0 I}{4\pi x} \int_{-\pi/2}^{\pi/2} \cos \varphi \, d\varphi.$$

The integral is equal to 2, and the final expression for the field at distance x from the wire is

Field of a straight wire

$$B = \frac{\mu_0 I}{2\pi x}. \tag{16.61}$$

This is sometimes called the Biot-Savart law. Although derived for an idealized infinite straight wire, it is important and useful, for it holds true close to any wire, whenever the distance x is less than the distance over which the wire curves appreciably. Note that the field falls off only inversely with the distance, not inversely with the square of the distance. ∎

∎ EXAMPLE 3:   (a) A circular loop of wire with a radius of 10 cm carries a current of 1,000 A. What is the magnetic field at its center? (b) At what distance from a long straight wire carrying the same current is the field the same as that at the center of the loop? In Equation 16.58, set $x = 0$ to get, for the field at the center of the loop,

$$B = \frac{\mu_0 I}{2a}. \tag{16.62}$$

Substitution of $I = 10^3$ A and $a = 0.1$ m gives

$$B = 6.28 \times 10^{-3} \text{ T} = 62.8 \text{ G}.$$

To find the equivalent distance from a straight wire, we could substitute this value of B, and $I = 10^3$ A, into Equation 16.61 and find

$$x = 0.0318 \text{ m} = 3.18 \text{ cm}.$$

A better way is to use the close algebraic similarity of Equations 16.61 and 16.62. If B and I are the same in these two equations, they imply that

$$x = \frac{a}{\pi}.$$

(Note, incidentally, that x has different meanings in Equations 16.58 and 16.61.) This example illustrates the fact that even rather large currents in single wires generate only modest magnetic fields.   ∎

AMPÈRE'S LAW

An integral theorem that is a consequence of Equation 16.56 is particularly useful in applications where some spatial symmetry prevails.   Usually called Ampère's law, it is written

$$\oint \mathbf{B} \cdot d\mathbf{s} = \mu_0 I. \qquad (16.63)$$

Ampère's law

The line integral on the left is extended around any closed curve. On the right, the current I is the net current passing through the area enclosed by the path of integration. In the situation shown in Figure 16.33, for instance, the net current through the area bounded by the curve C is $I_1 + I_2 - I_3$. As shown in the figure, a right-hand rule specifies the positive direction of current. If the right fingers follow the direction of integration around the closed curve, the right thumb indicates the direction of positive current.*   For the illustrated example, Ampère's law takes the form

The sign convention

$$\oint_C \mathbf{B} \cdot d\mathbf{s} = \mu_0 (I_1 + I_2 - I_3).$$

For an area pierced by no current, the line integral around the closed path is zero. It should be remarked that Equation 16.63 is valid only for steady currents not changing in time.

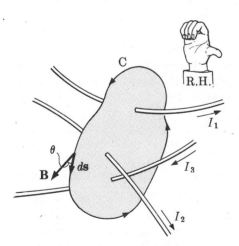

FIGURE 16.33   According to Ampère's law, the net current piercing an area (in this illustration, $I_1 + I_2 - I_3$) is proportional to the line integral, $\oint \mathbf{B} \cdot d\mathbf{s}$, around the closed curve C bounding the area. A right-hand rule relates the positive direction around the curve C and the positive direction of current through the area.

* This is also the direction assigned to the vector representing the enclosed area.

Certain similarities and differences between Ampère's law and Gauss's law are worth noticing. When sufficient symmetry of charge distribution prevails, Gauss's law,

$$\oint \mathbf{E} \cdot d\mathbf{S} = \frac{q}{\epsilon_0},$$

can usefully replace the law of field,

$$d\mathbf{E} = \frac{1}{4\pi\epsilon_0}\frac{dq\,\mathbf{i}_r}{r^2}.$$

Similarly, when currents are sufficiently symmetrical, Ampère's law, Equation 16.63, can usefully replace the law of field, Equation 16.56. In

Gauss's law,	Ampère's law,
an integral of	
E over a closed surface	**B** along a closed path
is proportional to the total	
charge contained in the enclosed volume.	current crossing the enclosed area.

We shall not demonstrate the equivalence of Equations 16.63 and 16.56—one an integral law, the other a differential law. Instead, we show by example how to make use of Ampère's law. Consider again a long straight wire, and choose for the path of integration a circle of radius x concentric with the wire (Figure 16.34). This is an example with cylindrical symmetry. Because of this symmetry, all angles φ measured around the wire must be equivalent. The field component B_φ directed around the wire cannot depend on φ. Since for the chosen path, $\mathbf{B} \cdot d\mathbf{s} = B_\varphi\,ds$, the integral around the closed curve C is

$$\oint_C \mathbf{B} \cdot d\mathbf{s} = B_\varphi \int ds = 2\pi x B_\varphi.$$

Ampère's law therefore reads

$$2\pi x B_\varphi = \mu_0 I, \tag{16.64}$$

which implies $B_\varphi = \mu_0 I/2\pi x$, the same result as given by Equation 16.61. Evidently the result is more simply obtained in this way.

It remains only to prove that the field has no longitudinal component B_z and no radial component B_ρ (see Figure 16.34). It is left as an exercise to prove, using Ampère's law and a different path of integration, that $B_z = 0$. We can give two arguments regarding B_ρ. First, if B_ρ were not zero, lines of magnetic field would begin or end at the wire. This is inconsistent with the requirement that magnetic field lines never begin or end (since there are no isolated poles). Second, fields created by a current should reverse direction when the current reverses direction. If an observer on one side of the wire associated positive B_ρ

with a current to the right and negative B_ρ with a current to the left, an observer

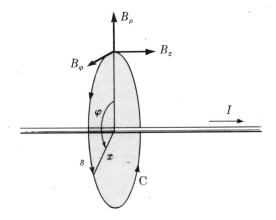

FIGURE 16.34 Ampère's law, applied to the circular path about a long straight wire, leads quickly to the Biot-Savart law for the field component B_φ. The other indicated components, B_ρ and B_z, in fact vanish.

on the other side of the wire would make the opposite association. Again symmetry enters. There is no reason why a law of field should depend on whether an observer is on one side of the wire or the other. Observers on both sides agree only if $B_\rho = 0$.

THE FIELD OF A SOLENOID

Magnetic fields for laboratory use or for practical purposes are most often produced by current-carrying coils or solenoids. Easiest to study theoretically is the idealized infinite solenoid (Figure 16.35). It consists of a wire carrying current I wound on a cylinder of radius a, with n turns of the wire per meter of length along the cylinder. We suppose n to be so large that the solenoid is well approximated as a sheet of current (nI A/m) on the surface of the cylinder. Because of the symmetry of this solenoid, the problem of finding the magnetic field it generates can be attacked with the help of Ampère's law. To show that the radial component B_ρ is zero is left as a problem. Here we consider the tangential component B_φ and the component parallel to the axis, B_z.

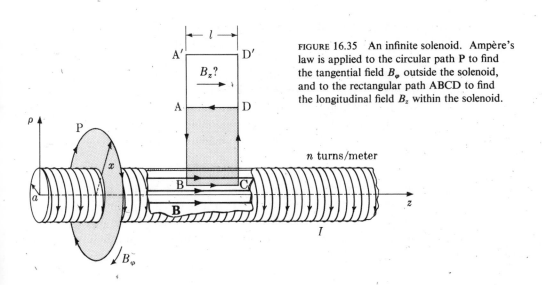

FIGURE 16.35 An infinite solenoid. Ampère's law is applied to the circular path P to find the tangential field B_φ outside the solenoid, and to the rectangular path ABCD to find the longitudinal field B_z within the solenoid.

n turns/meter

Consider first the circular path P, of radius x, shown in Figure 16.35. The same symmetry argument that was used for the straight wire implies that B_φ is the same at all points on this path. Therefore, since $\mathbf{B} \cdot d\mathbf{s} = B_\varphi\, ds$ along this path,

$$\oint_{\text{path P}} \mathbf{B} \cdot d\mathbf{s} = 2\pi x B_\varphi .$$

What current crosses the area enclosed by path P? Since a single wire spirals down the cylinder, it pierces the area once; the current, crossing from left to right in the figure, is I. Ampère's law gives $2\pi x B_\varphi = \mu_0 I$, or

The field outside a long solenoid: the same as the field of a straight wire

$$B_\varphi = \frac{\mu_0 I}{2\pi x} \qquad (x > a), \tag{16.65}$$

the same as if a straight wire ran along the axis (see Equation 16.64). Similar reasoning for a circular path about the axis *within* the cylinder, where no current pierces the area, leads to the result

$$B_\varphi = 0 \qquad (x < a). \tag{16.66}$$

To find the axial component B_z, we apply Ampère's law to the path ABCD in Figure 16.35. The line integral can be written

$$\oint \mathbf{B} \cdot d\mathbf{s} = \int_A^B B_\rho\, d\rho + \int_B^C B_z\, dz + \int_C^D B_\rho\, d\rho + \int_D^A B_z\, dz. \tag{16.67}$$

Even if we did not know that $B_\rho = 0$, we could conclude that the first and third integrals on the right must sum to zero. The radial field, if any, must be the same along AB as along CD (a symmetry argument) so that the integrals, tracing equivalent paths in opposite directions, must cancel. The fourth integral, from D to A, is also zero, as the following reasoning shows. For another path, A'BCD' (see the figure), the same current cuts the enclosed area. The path BC is unchanged. The integral along DA must therefore be the same as the integral along D'A':

$$\oint_D^A B_z\, dz = \int_{D'}^{A'} B_z\, dz.$$

This means that outside the cylinder, B_z is the same at all distances from the cylinder. If B_z were equal to a finite constant, the field would violate the requirement of Equation 16.23 that lines of magnetic field do not terminate. A finite number of lines would thread the solenoid from left to right, but an infinite number would be directed from right to left outside the solenoid. Energy difficulties would also result. The total stored energy in the magnetic field for a finite length of solenoid would be infinite. The axial field outside the cylinder must therefore be zero, the only constant that is physically acceptable:

$$B_z = 0 \qquad (\rho > a). \tag{16.68}$$

Among the four integrals on the right side of Equation 16.67, only the second is not zero. Its magnitude is $B_z l$. It must be equal to μ_0 times the current crossing the enclosed area. This current is nIl, the current in the wire times the number of turns in the distance l. Ampère's law for the path ABCD therefore reads

$$B_z l = \mu_0 n I l,$$

Accordingly, the axial field within the cylinder is

$$B_z = \mu_0 n I \qquad (\rho < a). \tag{16.69}$$

The field inside a long solenoid: axial and uniform

The infinite solenoid generates a *uniform field* within the cylinder, directed along its axis; and a *circling field*, equivalent to that of a straight wire, outside the cylinder.

■ EXAMPLE 4: A long thin solenoid, approximating an infinite solenoid, carries 10 A in a coil with 5,000 turns/meter. If its radius is 4 cm, what magnetic field does it generate just inside and just outside the cylinder? The axial field is the same everywhere inside the cylinder, and is given by Equation 16.69:

$$B_z = \mu_0 n I = (4\pi \times 10^{-7})(5 \times 10^3)(10)$$
$$= 0.0628 \text{ T} = 628 \text{ G}.$$

The field just outside the cylinder is circular. Its magnitude is found by setting $x = a = 0.04$ m in Equation 16.65. This gives

$$B_\varphi = \frac{(4\pi \times 10^{-7})(10)}{(2\pi)(0.04)}$$
$$= 0.5 \times 10^{-4} \text{ T} = 0.5 \text{ G}.$$

From inside to outside the coil, the magnitude of B decreases by a factor of more than a thousand. It is a common approximation to ignore the component B_φ.   ■

For a typical solenoid, $B_{\text{outside}} \ll B_{\text{inside}}$

The field of an actual solenoid, whose length is eight times its radius, is depicted in Figure 16.36. The field lines indicate a strong, nearly uniform field near the center of the solenoid and a much weaker field outside the solenoid. The graph in Figure 16.36(b) presents B_z vs z along the axis, with the origin at the midpoint of the coil. The field at the center is 97 percent of $\mu_0 n I$.

■ EXAMPLE 5: A finite solenoid with N turns is wrapped into a torus (Figure 16.37). What field does it generate? To apply Ampère's law, we choose a circular path of radius r, as shown in the figure. If $r_1 < r < r_2$, where r_1 and r_2 are the inner and outer radii of the torus, the enclosed area is pierced by N wires, all carrying current I in the same direction. Ampère's law takes the form

$$\oint \mathbf{B} \cdot d\mathbf{s} = \mu_0 N I.$$

The integral on the left is $2\pi r B_\varphi$. The field circling within the torus is, therefore,

$$B_\varphi = \frac{\mu_0}{2\pi} \frac{N I}{r} \qquad (r_1 < r < r_2). \tag{16.70}$$

The field inside a torus: $B \sim 1/r$

Note the dependence on r; the field within the torus is nonuniform.

If the radius r of the path of integration is chosen to be either less than r_1 or greater than r_2, the current crossing the enclosed area is zero. The component B_φ is, therefore, zero everywhere outside the torus:

$$B_\varphi = 0 \qquad (r < r_1 \quad \text{or} \quad r > r_2). \tag{16.71}$$

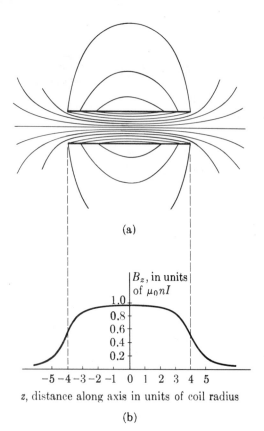

(a)

(b)

z, distance along axis in units of coil radius

FIGURE 16.36   Field of a solenoid whose length is eight times its radius. (a) Pattern of field lines. (b) Graph of B_z vs z along the axis of the solenoid. [Diagrams from Berkeley Physics Course, Volume 2, *Electricity and Magnetism*, by Edward M. Purcell (New York: McGraw-Hill Book Co., 1964); with permission of Education Development Center, Inc.]

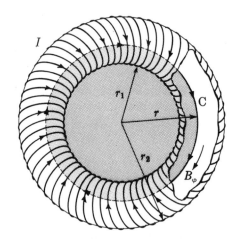

FIGURE 16.37   A toroidal solenoid. Ampère's law is applied to the circular path C to find the field within the torus. Similar paths with $r < r_1$ and $r > r_2$ are used to deduce that $B_\varphi = 0$ outside the solenoid.

Outside the torus, would you expect to find nonzero components B_ρ (radial) or B_z (perpendicular to the page in Figure 16.37)?   ∎

16.9   Definition of the ampere

The force between two current-carrying wires is "purely" magnetic, although no magnets are involved. This force may be used to define the ampere, in the same way that the force between poles is used to define pole strength. Figure 16.38 shows two parallel wires conducting current in the same direction. The current I_1 in wire 1 creates magnetic field $\mathbf{B}_1$. At the location of wire 2, a distance d away, the field $\mathbf{B}_1$ is directed vertically downward; its magnitude is given by the Biot-Savart law, Equation 16.61,

$$B_1 = \frac{\mu_0 I_1}{2\pi d} . \tag{16.72}$$

The current I_2, in this field, experiences a force per unit length whose magnitude is (Equation 16.43)

$$\frac{dF_2}{ds} = I_2 B_1 \qquad (16.73)$$

and whose direction is toward the other wire. Substituting the right side of Equation 16.72 for B_1 in Equation 16.73 gives

$$\frac{dF_2}{ds} = \frac{\mu_0}{2\pi} \frac{I_1 I_2}{d} . \qquad (16.74)$$

Force between parallel conductors

Similar reasoning shows that wire 1 is attracted to wire 2 with equal force per unit length. (The interchange of subscripts 1 and 2 leaves the expression for the force unchanged.) For oppositely directed currents, the force is repulsive.

Equation 16.74 states a fundamental law of force between currents. It affords a definition in principle of the unit of current. Recall that μ_0 is arbitrarily assigned the numerical value $4\pi \times 10^{-7}$ N/A^2. Therefore, an experimental (or operational) definition of the ampere may be given in the following way (we quote the official definition of the International Committee on Weights and Measures): "The ampere is that constant current which, if maintained in two straight parallel conductors of infinite length, of negligible circular cross section, and placed 1 meter apart in vacuum, would produce between these conductors a force equal to 2×10^{-7} newton per meter of length."

The ampere defined

With the definition of the ampere in hand, the unit of magnetic field may be defined—for example, with the help of Equation 16.43. The units of current and time together determine the unit of charge, from which the unit of electric field, in turn, is defined. The meter, kilogram, second, and ampere suffice to define any electrical unit.

In practice, the ampere is defined not with long straight parallel wires but with wires wound in coils of precisely known size and shape. The principle, however, is the same. For some other geometrical arrangement of wires, Equation 16.74 would be replaced by

$$\frac{dF}{ds} = \mu_0 \times (\text{known geometrical factor}) \times I_1 I_2 . \qquad (16.75)$$

FIGURE 16.38   Parallel currents attract, with a force per unit length given by Equation 16.74.

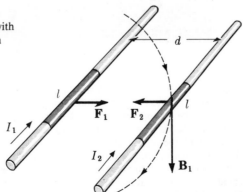

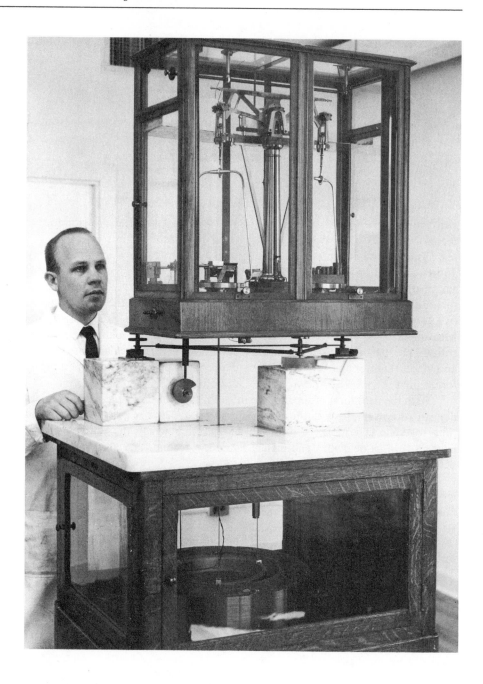

FIGURE 16.39   The National Bureau of Standards current balance. The same current I flows through a fixed outer coil and a movable inner coil (near the bottom of the photograph). The balance above is used to measure the force on the inner coil. Through a formula, $F = \mu_0 \times$ (a known geometrical factor) $\times I^2$, the current in amperes is related to the force in newtons. This difficult standardization is carried out only rarely. In practice, certain chemical cells and resistors maintained by the Bureau of Standards provide secondary standards for electrical measurement. (Photograph courtesy of the U.S. National Bureau of Standards.)

The force per unit length of wire remains equal to known factors times the product of two currents. It is, of course, easy to arrange the *same* current to pass through two coils so that the final relationship has the form $F \sim I^2$. Figure 16.39 shows a "current balance" at the National Bureau of Standards. The force on a current-carrying coil is transmitted to one pan of a sensitive balance. The balance is used to measure the force and thereby determine the current.

An equation such as Equation 16.74 may be derived from other equations, or it may be regarded as a primary statement of experimental fact. For electromagnetism, as for any other theory, all we ask of the theory is that it provide an economical and satisfying description of phenomena and the power to predict new phenomena. Equations, like physical concepts, can be viewed in different ways. Which equations are called primary or fundamental and which are called secondary or derived are matters of taste and custom, not of strict logic.

★16.10   Magnetism in matter

André Marie Ampère was led by his studies of the magnetic effects of currents to suggest that *all* magnetism, including the magnetism of natural magnets, might be the result of currents. He envisioned circulating currents within a bar magnet to account for the fact that its field resembled that of a solenoid (Figure 16.29). Efforts to detect such currents failed, but in the absence of poles that could be isolated there was no better theory of magnetism. Scientists had to assume that microscopic current loops within matter acted to produce the field of a permanent magnet.

Nearly a century elapsed before Ampère's hypothesis could be verified. According to modern atomic theory, electrons within every atom whirl in orbits of 10^{-10} m or less. In addition, every electron spins about its own axis, a further and even smaller-scale manifestation of moving charge. Because of these rotational motions of charge within every atom, no material is free of some magnetic properties. However, for most materials the individual current loops are oriented in all directions at random, and the magnetic fields they create cancel each other out, leaving no large-scale magnetic effect.

Most materials fall into one of the following three magnetic classes:

1. *Diamagnetic materials.* In these materials (water and table salt are examples), the magnetic effects of orbital and spin motion cancel separately within every molecule or ion. Small dipole moments can be *induced* in these materials by external fields. The induced dipoles slightly weaken the applied field. A diamagnetic material is weakly repelled by an ordinary magnet.

Three kinds of materials

2. *Paramagnetic materials.* In these materials (oxygen and aluminum are examples), each molecule or ion possesses a permanent magnetic dipole moment. Normally these are randomly oriented. In an applied field, the magnetic dipoles are partially aligned and slightly strengthen the applied field. A paramagnetic material is weakly attracted to an ordinary magnet.

3. *Ferromagnetic materials.* In these materials (iron and nickel are examples), the nature of the interaction between adjacent atoms is such that electron spins are spontaneously aligned for many atoms, which form a domain. Each domain is a tiny but powerful permanent magnet. Normally, the domains are randomly oriented. In an applied field, the domains are partially aligned

and greatly strengthen the applied field. A ferromagnetic material is strongly attracted to an ordinary magnet.

The discussion that follows will apply to paramagnetic and ferromagnetic materials (and, with only minor changes in wording, to diamagnetic materials). There is one complexity of ferromagnetism that we shall overlook. A sample of ferromagnetic material can be permanently altered by its magnetic history. If an applied field is removed, for instance, the sample may retain some permanent magnetism and not revert to its previous state.*

From atomic magnetism comes the induced field

Consider a thin cylinder of magnetic material placed in a uniform magnetic field $\mathbf{B}_0$ (Figure 16.40). The partial alignment of dipoles or domains within the material enhances the field so that the net field within the material is

$$\mathbf{B}_{net} = \mathbf{B}_0 + \mathbf{B}_{induced} . \qquad (16.76)$$

A fictitious surface current reproduces $\mathbf{B}_{induced}$

The quantities $\mathbf{B}_{net}$ and $\mathbf{B}_{induced}$ are to be interpreted as spatial averages over regions containing many dipoles or domains. The induced field can be accounted for by a fictitious surface current, $\mathscr{I}_{bound}$ (A/m), much in the manner originally visualized by Ampère. The *actual* process of magnetic alignment within the material can be simulated in its effect by the *artificial* device of the bound surface current. The induced field and the fictitious current are related by

$$B_{induced} = \mu_0 \mathscr{I}_{bound} \qquad (16.77)$$

if the sample is a long thin rod. (This result follows from Equation 16.69 for an infinite solenoid.)

A parameter of interest is the factor by which the magnetic material alters the field. This parameter is the *permeability*, defined by

Definition of permeability

$$\kappa_m = \frac{B_{net}}{B_0} .\dagger \qquad (16.78)$$

For a typical paramagnetic material, κ_m is a constant only slightly greater than 1. For a diamagnetic material, it is slightly less than 1. For such substances, it is usual to define the *magnetic susceptibility* χ_m by

$$\chi_m = \kappa_m - 1.\ddagger \qquad (16.79)$$

For a ferromagnetic material, the permeability κ_m is much greater than 1; it is approximately constant for weak fields B_0 and may increase somewhat as B_0 is increased, but it always decreases markedly as B_0 becomes large. Some permeabilities and susceptibilities appropriate for weak fields are listed in Table 16.1.

---

* See Joseph J. Becker, "Permanent Magnets," *Scientific American*, December, 1970.

† This quantity is evidently dimensionless. Sometimes a dimensional quantity μ, defined by $\mu = \kappa_m \mu_0$, is also called permeability. To confuse matters further, the notation μ is often used instead of κ_m to denote the dimensionless permeability.

‡ Other definitions of susceptibility are also in use. Some handbooks give the molar susceptibility χ_A in cgs units. The susceptibility used here is related to χ_A by $\chi_m = (4\pi\rho/M.W.)\chi_A$, where ρ is the density of the material in gm/cm³ and $M.W.$ is its molecular weight.

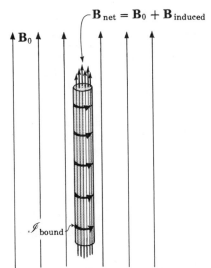

$$\mathbf{B}_{net} = \mathbf{B}_0 + \mathbf{B}_{induced}$$

FIGURE 16.40   The field in a thin rod of ferromagnetic material is enhanced by the partial alignment of magnetic domains within the material. The field from this source, $\mathbf{B}_{induced}$, can also be attributed to a fictitious surface current, $\mathscr{I}_{bound}$.

TABLE 16.1   SELECTED PERMEABILITIES κ_m AND SUSCEPTIBILITIES χ_m

Values apply to materials at standard conditions of temperature and pressure in weak magnetic fields.

Substance	Permeability, $\kappa_m = 1 + \chi_m$
DIAMAGNETIC	
Copper (Cu)	$1 - 9.7 \times 10^{-6}$
Gold (Au)	$1 - 34.5 \times 10^{-6}$
Sodium chloride (NaCl)	$1 - 14.1 \times 10^{-6}$
Water (H$_2$O)	$1 - 9.1 \times 10^{-6}$
PARAMAGNETIC	
Aluminum (Al)	$1 + 20.7 \times 10^{-6}$
Magnesium (Mg)	$1 + 11.8 \times 10^{-6}$
Oxygen (O$_2$)	$1 + 1.94 \times 10^{-6}$
Sodium (Na)	$1 + 8.5 \times 10^{-6}$
FERROMAGNETIC	
2–81 Permalloy* (81% Ni, 17% Fe, 2% Mo)	125
Iron (> 99.9% Fe)	200–5,000†
4–79 Permalloy* (79% Ni, 16.7% Fe, 4% Mo, 0.3% Mn)	20,000
Supermalloy* (79% Ni, 15.7% Fe, 5% Mo, 0.3% Mn)	100,000

* Special alloys are defined not only by their composition, but also by specific recipes for their fabrication.
† The permeability of iron (and other materials) varies widely, depending on the kinds of impurities and the method of fabrication.

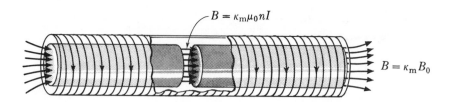

FIGURE 16.41   Within a gap in an iron core or near its end, the magnetic field is greater by a factor of κ_m (the permeability) than the field of the same solenoid without an iron core.

IRON-CORE MAGNET

An iron core enhances the field

If an iron rod (or rod of other ferromagnetic material) is inserted in a solenoid, its effect is to increase the field markedly. If we imagine a small gap in the rod deep inside the solenoid (Figure 16.41), the field **B** measured there would have magnitude

$$B = \kappa_m \mu_0 n I, \tag{16.80}$$

greater by a factor κ_m than the field without the iron present. Notice that this enhancement, although *caused* by the iron, is *measured* in air. A typical laboratory magnet is an air-gap magnet, with lines of magnetic field crossing the region where experiments are to be done from one iron pole face to another. For the solenoid shown in Figure 16.41, the factor κ_m is also relevant at the end of the solenoid. In the immediate vicinity of the end of the rod,

$$B = \kappa_m B_0,$$

where B_0 is the field that would exist at that point if no ferromagnetic material were present.

Although a single factor κ_m suffices to describe simple macroscopic properties of ferromagnets, the underlying atomic theory is subtle and complex. Probably the most remarkable fact about ferromagnetism is that it arises from the spin motion of electrons. Not even the vision of Ampère could have foreseen this. For those few materials whose energy is lowered when the axes of electron spin array themselves in parallel, there occurs a natural tendency for self-reinforcement of the atomic magnetism. Spinning elementary particles obeying the laws of quantum mechanics turn out to account for the properties of lodestones discovered by the ancients.

16.11   Summary of electromagnetic laws

Three new concepts:
q, **E**, **B**

The theory of electromagnetism rests upon some "old" concepts drawn from mechanics—length, time, force, energy. To these have been added three new "pure" electromagnetic concepts—charge, electric field, and magnetic field. A fourth—magnetic pole strength—is waiting in the wings in case it is needed. Tying these new concepts together and linking them with mechanical quantities are the set of laws that have been introduced in this and the previous chapter. A convenient way to catalogue the laws of electromagnetism is in terms of the q-**E**-**B** triangle in Figure 16.42. Each of the three electromagnetic quantities—charge q, electric field **E**, and magnetic field **B**—is capable of influencing the

other two. Associated with each of the six arrows in Figure 16.42 is a fundamental law of electromagnetism. The arrow from q to **B** designates the influence
of charge on magnetic field, the arrow from **E** to q designates the influence
of electric field on charge, and so on. Each law can be given a qualitative and a
quantitative statement.

1. $q \rightarrow \mathbf{E}$

   In words: Charge creates electric field.

   In symbols:

   $$\mathbf{E} = \frac{1}{4\pi\epsilon_0} \frac{q\mathbf{i}_r}{r^2} . \qquad (15.20)^*$$

Of equivalent physical content is the integral theorem called Gauss's law,

$$\oint \mathbf{E} \cdot d\mathbf{S} = \frac{q}{\epsilon_0} . \qquad (15.36)$$

2. $\mathbf{E} \rightarrow q'$

   In words: An electric field exerts a force on a charge.

   In symbols:

   $$\mathbf{F} = q'\mathbf{E}. \qquad (15.18)$$

3. $q \rightarrow \mathbf{B}$

   In words: Moving charge or current creates a magnetic field.

   In symbols:

   $$\mathbf{B} = \frac{\mu_0}{4\pi} \frac{q\mathbf{v} \times \mathbf{i}_r}{r^2} , \qquad (16.36)$$

   $$d\mathbf{B} = \frac{\mu_0}{4\pi} \frac{I\, d\mathbf{s} \times \mathbf{i}_r}{r^2} . \qquad (16.56)$$

The integral theorem linking field to current is Ampère's law:

$$\oint \mathbf{B} \cdot d\mathbf{s} = \mu_0 I. \qquad (16.63)$$

4. $\mathbf{B} \rightarrow q'$

   In words: A magnetic field exerts a force on a moving charge or a current.

   In symbols:

   $$\mathbf{F} = q'\mathbf{v} \times \mathbf{B}, \qquad (16.27)$$

   $$d\mathbf{F} = I'\, d\mathbf{s} \times \mathbf{B}. \qquad (16.43)$$

5. $\mathbf{B} \rightarrow \mathbf{E}$

   In words: A changing magnetic field creates an electric field.

6. $\mathbf{E} \rightarrow \mathbf{B}$

   In words: A changing electric field creates a magnetic field.

   Quantitative statements for laws 5 and 6 are introduced in the next chapter.

   A pair of laws outside of our q-**E**-**B** triangle that require explicit statement
are concerned with the intrinsic properties of charge and pole strength.

---

* Equations in this section are labeled with their earlier numbers.

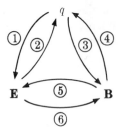

FIGURE 16.42   The *q*-**E**-**B** triangle, a schematic reminder of fundamental laws connecting the concepts of charge, electric field, and magnetic field.

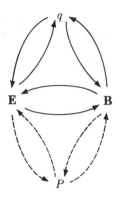

FIGURE 16.43   There would be more connecting links if a fourth concept, pole strength, were to become reality.

7. Charge Conservation

The total charge in an isolated system remains constant. An alternative statement: In an isolated event, the total charge after the event is the same as the total charge before the event.

8. Pole-Strength Conservation

The total pole strength in any system is constant and is equal to zero. An implication of this law is the magnetic equivalent of Gauss's law,

$$\oint \mathbf{B} \cdot d\mathbf{S} = 0. \tag{16.23}$$

If magnetic poles were to become reality, not fiction, the *q*-**E**-**B** triangle would need to become a diamond with four more connecting links (Figure 16.43). The magnetic field created by a pole is

$$\mathbf{B} = \frac{\mu_0}{4\pi} \frac{P\mathbf{i}_r}{r^2}. \tag{16.6}$$

The magnetic force on a pole is

$$\mathbf{F} = P'\mathbf{B}. \tag{16.7}$$

A moving pole generates an electric field,

$$\mathbf{E} = -\frac{\mu_0}{4\pi} \frac{P\mathbf{v} \times \mathbf{i}_r}{r^2}. \tag{16.81}$$

New laws if poles exist   Finally, a pole moving in an electric field experiences an electric force,

$$\mathbf{F} = -\mu_0 \epsilon_0 P'\mathbf{v} \times \mathbf{E}. \tag{16.82}$$

The similarity of these last two equations to Equations 16.36 and 16.27 is clear. A magnetic current may also be defined, but we shall not pursue that idea here.

The first complete summary of the laws of electromagnetism was given in 1862 by Maxwell. Later, in the hands of Oliver Heaviside and Heinrich Hertz, Maxwell's theory was brought into the elegant and concise mathematical form that we still use today. The Heaviside-Hertz equations,* just four in number, contain electric and magnetic fields and charge and, except for the variables of space and time, nothing else. They are summarized in Section 17.5.

From three new concepts and a few fundamental laws has flowed a technology so widespread and so intimately bound up with modern life that we can scarcely visualize civilized society without pervasive electromagnetism, even though such society existed only a century ago. In the next chapter we shall develop aspects of the theory concerned with fields that change in time. These phenomena of change have explained light, deepened our understanding of the unity of electromagnetism, and have provided engineering dividends as well.

---

* Physicists usually call these "Maxwell's equations," more out of honor to the great achievements of Maxwell than out of historical accuracy. In what follows, we shall adhere to this now well-established tradition.

Summary of ideas and definitions

(Laws and equations summarized in Section 16.11 are not repeated here.)

Magnetism results from charge in motion. It could also result from free magnetic poles, but such entities have not been found in nature.

Magnetic poles are convenient fictions. The end of a long magnet behaves approximately as a pole.

The north-seeking end of a compass is a north pole with positive pole strength; the other end is a south pole with negative pole strength.

Poles obey a Coulomb-like law of attraction and repulsion (Equation 16.2).

The permeability constant that appears in magnetic laws is chosen arbitrarily to have a precise numerical value: $\mu_0 = 4\pi \times 10^{-7}$ N/A^2.

Magnetic field is an axial vector quantity measured in teslas, or weber/m^2. It may be defined by (1) the force on a pole (Equation 16.7), (2) the force on a moving charge (Equation 16.27), (3) the force on a current (Equation 16.43), [or (4) its effect in inducing an emf (Equation 17.1)].

Magnetic and electric fields obey a law of superposition.

The energy density stored by the magnetic field is

$$u = \frac{1}{2\mu_0} B^2. \tag{16.24}$$

Magnetic lines of field would begin and end on poles. In the absence of poles, the field lines never terminate.

Poles P and $-P$ separated by displacement $\mathbf{l}$ have a magnetic (dipole) moment $\mu = P\mathbf{l}$; a current I in a loop of area $\mathbf{A}$ has a magnetic moment $\mu = I\mathbf{A}$ (Equations 16.11 and 16.49).

The torque on a magnetic moment is $\mathbf{T} = \mu \times \mathbf{B}$; its potential energy is $U = -\mu \cdot \mathbf{B}$ (Equations 16.14 and 16.16).

The magnetic moment and the angular momentum of a circling charge are related by $\mu = (q/2m)\mathbf{L}$ (Equation 16.54).

Key discoveries in the period 1820–1860, especially by Oersted, Ampère, Faraday, and Maxwell, welded electricity and magnetism together and led to the electromagnetic theory of light.

If a moving charge creates a magnetic field, it must also, according to Newton's third law, experience a force in a magnetic field.

Magnetic deflection holds particles in the Van Allen radiation belt and in cyclotrons and synchrotrons, bends particle tracks in bubble chambers, guides electrons in television tubes, and can be used to measure the charge-to-mass ratio of particles.

The equivalence between moving charge and current is expressed by

$$q\mathbf{v} \leftrightarrow I\,d\mathbf{s}. \tag{16.42}$$

The magnetic field on the axis of a current loop is given by Equation 16.58.

The magnetic field at distance x from a straight current-carrying wire is

$$B = \frac{\mu_0 I}{2\pi x} \qquad \text{(Biot-Savart law).} \qquad (16.61)$$

The same law applies outside an infinite solenoid.

The magnetic field within an infinite solenoid is

$$B = \mu_0 n I. \qquad (16.69)$$

Parallel currents attract; antiparallel currents repel.

The force between current-carrying coils is used to define the ampere.

Diamagnetic materials weakly diminish an applied magnetic field; paramagnetic materials weakly enhance an applied field; ferromagnetic materials strongly enhance an applied field.

The strength of an iron-core magnet is greater than the strength of an air-core magnet of the same design by a factor κ_m, the permeability of the iron.

QUESTIONS

Section 16.1   Q16.1   A positively charged particle is placed midway between the north pole of one stationary magnet and the south pole of another stationary magnet. In which direction will it move?

Q16.2   Is the force exerted by one stationary magnetic pole on another stationary pole a central force? Is it a conservative force?

Section 16.2   Q16.3   Inside a certain laboratory room there is said to be a magnetic field but no electric field. What experiments using magnets and/or charged particles might be performed to check the correctness of the assertion?

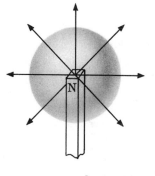

Q16.4   A hypothetical magnetic monopole in the cosmic radiation is slowed to thermal speed high in the atmosphere. Discuss its subsequent motion.

Q16.5   The accompanying figure shows a Gaussian surface enclosing one end of a long magnet. How can this figure be reconciled with Equation 16.23, which requires that no net magnetic flux cross a closed surface?

Q16.6   An electrically charged magnet is acted upon simultaneously by electric, magnetic, and gravitational fields. Suggest ways to distinguish the three effects.

Section 16.3   Q16.7   The magnet shown in Figure 16.9 is reversed, so that its south pole is nearer the coil, and then the magnet is drawn upward away from the coil. In what direction is the induced current as the magnet is being drawn away?

Q16.8   The switch in Figure 16.10 is (a) closed, then (b) left closed for a time, and then (c) opened. Describe the action of the meter attached to the lower coil.

Q16.9   Describe one experiment that supports the hypothesis that electric current is equivalent to charge in motion. Is this an experiment that could have been carried out in the first half of the nineteenth century (when batteries were available but controlled beams of charged particles were not available)?

Q16.10 (1) A particle of known charge is moving with known velocity through a   Section 16.4
        region in which there is a magnetic field. Does a single force measurement
        suffice to determine the magnetic field? Explain. (2) If the same particle
        is in a region where there is an electric field, does a single force measurement
        suffice to determine the electric field? In each case, assume that only one
        field is nonzero.

Q16.11 (1) Sketch the lines of magnetic field surrounding a hypothetical isolated
        magnetic pole. (2) Discuss the motion of a charged particle that starts moving
        directly toward a fixed pole. (3) Are there any initial conditions that would
        enable a charged particle to execute a circular orbit in the field of a fixed
        pole? Justify your answer.

Q16.12 As shown in the figure, an airplane flies northward with its wings perpen-
        dicular to the downward-sloping lines of the earth's magnetic field. (1) What
        is the direction of the magnetic force on an electron in the metal wing?
        (2) What is the direction of the induced current (conventional current)?
        (3) Why does this induced current flow only for a limited time and then stop?

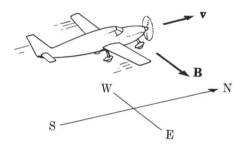

Q16.13 Is force a polar vector quantity or an axial vector quantity? Show that your
        answer is consistent with Equations 15.18 and 16.27.

Q16.14 Consider an imaginary sphere of fixed radius R centered on a moving charged   Section 16.6
        particle. (1) At what point(s) on the sphere is the magnetic field most intense?
        (2) At what point(s), if any, is the magnetic field zero? (3) Answer the same
        two questions for the electric field if the speed of the particle is small in
        comparison with the speed of light.

Q16.15 Is there any location at which the magnetic field created by a moving charged
        particle is parallel to the velocity of the particle?

Q16.16 As shown in the figure, a positively charged particle moves upward along the   Section 16.7
        z axis and passes through the center of a circular loop of current-carrying
        wire that lies in the xy plane. Discuss the forces acting on the particle and
        on the loop.

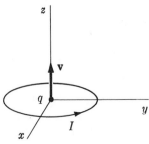

Q16.17 A switch is closed, causing current to flow upward, as shown in the figure, through a thin flexible wire parallel to a strong bar magnet. (1) What shape does the wire assume as a result of the magnetic forces acting on it? (2) At the first instant the current flows, before the wire has had time to deform, is there a net force acting on the magnet? If so, what is its direction? (3) At this same instant, what is the direction of the total torque acting on the magnet?

Q16.18 (1) If the current in the loop in Figure 16.24 is a steady current of fixed magnitude, and if the loop is free to swing about an axis that passes through its center and is parallel to its sides 1 and 2, how will the loop move? (2) Suggest a way to use magnetic forces to keep the loop rotating in one direction (this is the essential idea of a motor).

Section 16.8

Q16.19 (1) If a circular current loop is free to turn, how will it align itself in an external magnetic field? With this alignment, is the field produced by the loop at the center of the loop parallel, antiparallel, or perpendicular to the external field? (2) If the external field is nonuniform, there will be a net force on the loop after it is aligned. Does this force tend to move the loop toward a region of stronger or weaker field?

Q16.20 (1) At a large distance r from a "black box," the magnetic field strength varies in proportion to $1/r^3$. (a) What distribution of current in the box might account for this field? (b) What arrangement of poles in the box might account for the field? (2) Answer the same pair of questions if the field strength varies in proportion to $1/r^2$.

Q16.21 Is the magnetic field between a pair of parallel wires carrying equal current stronger or weaker than the field at the same place would be if only one of the wires were carrying current? Answer for (a) currents in the same direction and (b) currents in the opposite direction. State briefly the reason for each answer.

Q16.22 Explain carefully why the component B_φ in Figure 16.34 does not depend on φ. What physical properties of the current-carrying wire are needed to sustain this symmetry argument?

Q16.23 Give a simple physical argument that explains why the tangential field B_φ outside the solenoid in Figure 16.35 is the same as the field of a straight wire running along the axis of the solenoid. How would the result differ if the current in the solenoid followed coaxial circles on the surface of the cylinder instead of spiraling down the cylinder?

Q16.24 Discuss the magnetic field outside the torus in Figure 16.37. What components of the field, if any, are not zero?

Section 16.9

Q16.25 Explain carefully why the current exerted on one coil carrying current I_1 by another coil carrying current I_2 is always proportional to I_1I_2 (Equation 16.75), regardless of the shapes, separation, or orientations of the coils.

Section 16.10

Q16.26 Would you expect a monatomic gas such as helium or neon to be diamagnetic, paramagnetic, or ferromagnetic? Give a reason for your answer.

Q16.27 Suggest a reason why the permeability of iron decreases markedly as the applied field B_0 is increased to very large values (more than a few teslas).

Q16.28 What is a common use of iron that depends on its being ferromagnetic? What is a common use that does not depend on its being ferromagnetic?

E16.1 The pole strengths at points A and B in Figure 16.1 are $P_A = P_B = 40$ michells; these poles are separated by 0.01 m. (1) What are the magnitudes of the forces $\mathbf{F}_{AB}$ and $\mathbf{F}_{BA}$? (2) If you were holding the magnets in your hands, would these forces be (a) imperceptible, (b) noticeable but manageable, or (c) more than you could resist?

E16.2 Two identical bar magnets are arranged as shown in the figure. Each magnet acts approximately as a pair of poles whose strengths are $P_1 = +30$ michells and $P_2 = -30$ michells. The length of each magnet (between its poles) is 0.06 m and the distance between the magnets is 0.08 m. (1) Do the magnets repel or attract one another? (2) Find the *total* force acting on the magnet on the right. (3) If the magnet on the left is inverted so that the positions of its poles are interchanged, how does the total force on the other magnet change?

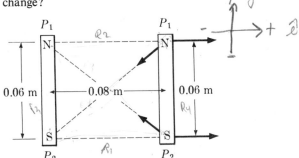

E16.3 Two equal magnetic poles, each of strength 1 magnetostatic unit (msu), when placed 1 cm (0.01 m) apart exert on each other a force of 1 dyne (10^{-5} N). Show that the conversion factor relating the Gaussian and SI units of pole strength is 10 msu/michell.

E16.4 At a distance of 1 cm from the pole of a long thin magnet, the magnetic field is measured to be 0.02 T (200 G). (1) What is the pole strength of this pole of the magnet? (2) If two such poles were placed 1 cm apart, what force would one pole exert on the other?

E16.5 Using SI units, show that each of the following quantities is expressed in m/sec: (1) P/q (pole strength/charge), (2) E/B (electric field/magnetic field), and (3) $1/\sqrt{\mu_0\epsilon_0}$.

E16.6 According to quantum theory, the pole strength of an isolated magnetic pole (if such were to exist) must be an integral multiple of a unit P_0 given by

$$P_0 = \frac{1}{2}\frac{4\pi}{\mu_0}\frac{\hbar}{e},$$

where e is the quantum unit of charge. (1) Evaluate P_0 in michells (see Equation 16.4). (2) What is the magnetic field generated by a particle of pole strength P_0 at a distance of 1 Å from the particle? Is this field "large" or "small"?

E16.7 A compass needle, pivoted at its center, is oriented perpendicular to the direction of the earth's magnetic field. It experiences a torque of

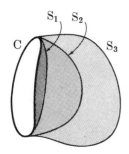

3×10^{-5} N m. If the compass needle can be approximated as a pair of poles of strength $P_1 = 25$ michells and $P_2 = -25$ michells separated by 0.03 m, what is the magnitude of the earth's magnetic field **B** at this location?

E16.8 Surfaces S_1, S_2, and S_3 in the figure are bounded by the same closed curve C. (1) Show that the magnetic flux through every surface bounded by C is the same. (HINT: Consider the total flux through the closed surface formed by any two surfaces bounded by C.) (2) Show by a physical example and a sketch that the same theorem is not true of electric field.

E16.9 (1) What is the stored energy density (J/m³) in the gap of a strong laboratory magnet where the magnetic field is $B = 10$ T (10^5 G)? (2) What magnitude of electric field would be required in order to have the same density of stored electric energy? Are such electric fields common in the laboratory? Why or why not?

E16.10 The electromagnetic radiation within a laser possesses an energy density of 10^4 J/m³, divided equally between electric and magnetic fields. (1) Find the rms values of the electric and magnetic fields in the laser. (2) At what distance from a proton is the energy density in the electric field the same as in this laser?

Section 16.3 **E16.11** Although not indicated in the drawing, a force also acts on the south pole of the magnet in Figure 16.7. (1) Does a net force act on the magnet? If so, what is the direction of the net force? (2) Does a torque act on the magnet about its center of mass? If so, what is the direction of the torque vector?

Section 16.4 **E16.12** If you hold in your hand a rod with a net charge of 3.3×10^{-7} C and swing it briskly at a speed of 10 m/sec across the lines of magnetic field of a powerful magnet whose field is 3 T, what force acts on the rod? Would this force be perceptible? Compare it with some more familiar force.

E16.13 An electron in a TV tube moves with a speed $v = 2 \times 10^7$ m/sec through a magnetic field $B = 0.08$ T. (1) What are the greatest and least magnitudes of force that the electron might feel? (2) If the acceleration of the electron is $a = 1.01 \times 10^{17}$ m/sec², what angle does its track make with the magnetic field?

E16.14 A proton moving from west to east near the equator in the earth's magnetic field of 0.3 G (3×10^{-5} T) experiences an upward magnetic force. With what speed must it move in order that this force balance the force of gravity acting downward on the proton?

E16.15 The combined electric and magnetic force on a particle,

$$\mathbf{F} = q\mathbf{E} + q\mathbf{v} \times \mathbf{B},$$

is called the *Lorentz force*. (1) Show that if the Lorentz force on a particle is zero in a region where **E** and **B** are not zero, (a) **E** must be perpendicular to **B** and (b) B and E must satisfy the inequality $B \geq E/v$. (2) If a proton moves with a speed of 10^7 m/sec directly across the lines of a magnetic field of magnitude 10^{-2} T, what magnitude of electric field is required in order that the proton be undeflected? Would it be relatively easy to produce such an electric field?

E16.16 Prove that measurements of the acceleration of a charged particle in an arbitrary combination of electric and magnetic fields can reveal only the charge-to-mass ratio of the particle, never its charge or mass separately.

E16.17   The position of a particle of mass m and charge q is given as a function of time by $\mathbf{r} = a \sin \omega t\ \mathbf{i}$. (1) Describe the motion in words. (2) What *total* force acts on the particle? (3) If the particle moves in a region of constant magnetic field $\mathbf{B} = B\mathbf{k}$, what *magnetic* force acts on the particle? (4) Give a vector expression—a function of time—for the *nonmagnetic* force acting on the particle.

E16.18   Consider a low-energy electron moving in a circle above the earth's atmosphere at a speed of 2×10^6 m/sec in a magnetic field of 10^{-5} T. (1) What force acts on the electron? (2) What is the radius of its circular path? (3) An electron in a hydrogen atom moves with about the same speed. Its motion can be approximately described as circular with a radius of 5×10^{-11} m. What is the factor of difference between the force on the electron in the hydrogen atom and the force on the electron of equal speed in the Van Allen belt?

Section 16.5

E16.19   An electron follows a helical path in a uniform magnetic field of 0.1 T directed along the z axis. At $t = 0$, the velocity of the electron in m/sec is $\mathbf{v} = 8 \times 10^6\mathbf{i} + 6 \times 10^6\mathbf{k}$. (1) How much time elapses until the electron completes 10 turns? (2) What is the displacement vector of the electron in this time?

E16.20   A proton in a bubble chamber in which the magnetic field is $B = 1$ T leaves a track whose radius of curvature is 10 m. (1) What is $p_\perp$, the component of the proton's momentum perpendicular to $\mathbf{B}$? (2) Is the nonrelativistic formula $p_\perp = mv_\perp$ valid in this case?

E16.21   If an electron in a cathode-ray tube is accelerated by a potential $V = 2{,}000$ V and then deflected by a magnetic field $B = 0.1$ T, what is the radius of curvature of its trajectory in the magnetic field?

E16.22   The relativistic formula for the momentum of a particle of mass m and velocity $\mathbf{v}$ is

$$\mathbf{p} = \frac{m\mathbf{v}}{\sqrt{1 - (v^2/c^2)}}\ ,$$

where c is the speed of light. (1) Taking advantage of Equation 16.30, show that Equation 16.34 for the cyclotron frequency of a particle executing circular motion in a magnetic field must be replaced at high speed by

$$\omega_c = \frac{eB}{m}\sqrt{1 - \frac{v^2}{c^2}}\ .$$

(2) The final speed of a proton in a 30-MeV cyclotron is $0.25c$. By what percentage must the frequency of the oscillating potential on the cyclotron decrease as the protons accelerate from low speed to their final speed?

E16.23   The properties of a 30-MeV proton cyclotron are specified in Example 2 in Section 16.5. Suppose physicists decide to use this same cyclotron to accelerate deuterons. The charge of a deuteron is the same as the charge of a proton; its mass is twice the proton mass. (1) What is the frequency (in revolutions/sec, or Hz) of the deuterons in the cyclotron? (2) What is the maximum kinetic energy achieved by the deuterons? *Optional:* For any nucleus of charge $q = Ze$ and mass $M = Am_p$ used as a projectile in this cyclotron, develop formulas for the frequency and the maximum energy as functions of Z and A.

E16.24 A pellet carrying a net charge of 2×10^{-8} C flies past the center of a clock face headed toward the 3-o'clock position at a speed of 30 m/sec. The radius of the clock face is 5 cm. At this instant, find the magnitude and direction of the magnetic field created by the moving pellet at (a) the 9-o'clock position, (b) the 12-o'clock position, and (c) the 1-o'clock position.

E16.25 In a loop of wire of radius 0.1 m, 10^{22} electrons are circulating. If the magnetic field at the center of the loop is measured to be 10^{-2} T, what is the average speed of the electrons around the loop?

E16.26 The particle of charge q shown in the figure moves with constant speed v along the x axis and passes the origin at $t = 0$; its position is given by $x = vt$. Show that the magnetic field created by the moving particle at point P $(x = 0, y = a)$ has a fixed direction and a magnitude given by

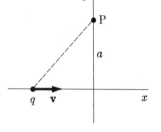

$$B = \frac{\mu_0}{4\pi} \frac{qva}{(a^2 + v^2 t^2)^{3/2}} .$$

Sketch a graph of B vs t.

E16.27 Let u_M and u_E designate the energy densities in the magnetic field and in the electric field respectively at the point P at $t = 0$, the moment when the particle described in the preceding exercise passes the origin. (1) Obtain expressions for u_M and u_E. (2) Show that the ratio of these energy densities is

$$\frac{u_M}{u_E} = \epsilon_0 \mu_0 v^2.$$

(3) Verify that $(\epsilon_0 \mu_0)^{-1} = 9 \times 10^{16}$ m²/sec². What does this imply about the magnitude of u_M/u_E?

E16.28 In a magnetic field of 0.02 T (200 G), an electron executes a circular path whose radius is 3 mm. (1) What is the momentum of the electron? (2) What is its speed? Is the formula $p = mv$ approximately valid? (3) What is the magnitude of the magnetic field created by the electron at the center of its circular path? Compare this field in magnitude and direction with the original field of 0.02 T that caused the deflection.

E16.29 (1) If the motion of an electron in an atom is approximated as motion in a circle of radius 10^{-10} m at a speed of 2×10^6 m/sec, what magnetic field does the electron create at the center of the atom? (2) The magnetic moment of a proton is $\mu = 1.41 \times 10^{-26}$ A m². What energy in eV is required to turn the proton's magnetic moment from parallel to antiparallel alignment with the field created by the circling electron?

E16.30 As a function of time t, the position of particle 1, whose charge is q_1, is given by $x_1 = v_1 t$, $y_1 = d$, $z_1 = 0$; and the position of particle 2, whose charge is q_2, is given by $x_2 = y_2 = 0$, $z_2 = v_2 t$. Find the total force (electric plus magnetic) acting on each particle at $t = 0$. (Assume the speeds v_1 and v_2 to be much less than the speed of light.)

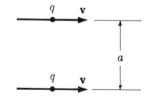

E16.31 As shown in the figure, two particles of equal charge q move side by side with equal speed v along parallel tracks separated by a distance a. Find the electric and magnetic forces acting on the upper particle (a) in the laboratory frame of reference and (b) in a frame moving with the particles. In which frame is the vector sum of the electric and magnetic forces greater? (In this exercise, use the nonrelativistic formulas for forces and fields. The "paradoxical" result that the total force depends on the frame of reference is resolved by the theory of relativity.)

E16.32 (1) An electron executes a circular orbit of radius 5×10^{-11} m at a speed of 3×10^6 m/sec. What is the electron "current" in amperes? (2) In a circular loop of wire of radius 1 cm, 10^{21} electrons circulate at an average speed of 1 cm/sec. What is the current in the wire?

Section 16.7

E16.33 What is the magnetic moment of the orbiting electron described in the preceding exercise? How does this calculated orbital magnetic moment compare with the spin magnetic moment of the electron, which is

$$\mu_s = \frac{e\hbar}{2m},$$

where e is the quantum unit of charge and m is the electron's mass?

E16.34 (1) If 10^{12} protons/sec emerge from a cyclotron and each proton has a kinetic energy of 10 MeV, what is the current of the proton beam? (2) What is the power of the beam in watts? Would it be uncomfortable to stand in the way of the beam?

E16.35 The D-shaped loop of wire shown in the figure consists of a semicircle of radius a and a straight section of length $2a$. The plane of the loop is perpendicular to the direction of a uniform magnetic field **B**, and the current in the loop is I. Prove that the total force acting on the loop is zero.

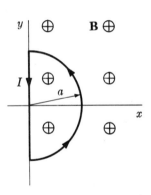

E16.36 (1) What is the magnetic moment of the loop described in the preceding exercise? (2) Does any torque act on the loop when it is oriented as shown in the figure? For what orientation of the loop relative to **B** is the torque maximum?

E16.37 A solenoid consists of 500 turns of wire on a cylinder of cross-sectional area $A = 10^{-4}$ m^2 and length $l = 0.1$ m. If the wire conducts a current of 2 A, what is the effective pole strength of this electromagnet? (HINT: Use the concept of magnetic moment.)

E16.38 Let x be the distance from the center of a circular current loop, measured along the axis of the loop. (1) Show that for large x the magnetic field on the axis may be written

Section 16.8

$$\mathbf{B} \cong \frac{\mu_0}{2\pi} \frac{\mu}{x^3}.$$

What is the meaning of μ? (2) What is the percentage error in B calculated from this formula if $x = 10a$, where a is the radius of the loop?

E16.39 (1) The figure shows a finite segment of wire carrying current I. Show that the contribution of this segment to the magnetic field at point P can be written

$$B_1 = \frac{\mu_0 I}{4\pi x} (\sin \alpha + \sin \beta),$$

where the distance x and the angles α and β are defined in the figure. (2) Verify the consistency of this result with the Biot-Savart law (Equation 16.61) if the length of the wire segment approaches infinity. (3) What is the magnetic field at the center of a square loop of side l carrying current I?

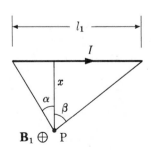

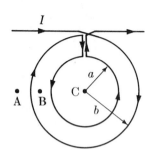

E16.40   A current-carrying wire is bent into the shape shown in the figure. Its straight sections extend a great distance to the left and right. (1) Show that if the magnetic field at point C is zero, the radii a and b must be related by

$$\frac{a}{b} = \frac{\pi}{\pi + 1}.$$

(2) What are the directions of the magnetic fields at points A and B?

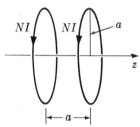

E16.41   The figure shows an arrangement known as a Helmholtz coil: It consists of two coaxial coils, each of radius a, separated by the distance a. Each coil has N turns of wire carrying the same current I. Show that the magnetic field at the midpoint between the coils is

$$B_z = \frac{8}{5\sqrt{5}} \frac{\mu_0 N I}{a}.$$

E16.42   A circular loop 10 cm in diameter carries a current of 50 A. Two protons start from the center of the loop, both with a speed of 10^2 m/sec. (1) The velocity of the first proton is directed initially along the axis of the loop. (2) The velocity of the second proton is directed initially toward the periphery of the loop. Describe the motion of both in words.

E16.43   Use Ampère's law and the contour C shown in the figure to prove that B_z, the component of magnetic field parallel to an infinite straight current-carrying wire, is zero. (You may assume that the field diminishes in magnitude as the distance from the wire increases.)

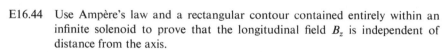

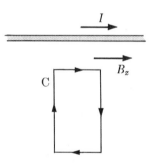

E16.44   Use Ampère's law and a rectangular contour contained entirely within an infinite solenoid to prove that the longitudinal field B_z is independent of distance from the axis.

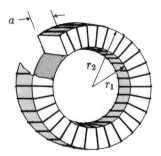

E16.45   The figure shows a toroidal solenoid whose cross section is a rectangle; the inner and outer radii of the toroid are r_1 and r_2, respectively, and its width is a. (1) Show that the magnitude of the magnetic field within the solenoid is given by Equation 16.70. (2) What is the total magnetic flux Φ_B threading the solenoid?

E16.46   For the solenoid described in Example 4 in Section 16.8, find (a) the energy density (J/m³) within the solenoid and (b) the approximate total energy stored in the field within the solenoid if its length is 40 cm.

E16.47   As shown in the figure, thin coaxial cylinders of radius a and b carry equal currents in opposite directions. The current densities are independent of φ. Using Ampère's law, find the tangential magnetic field B_φ (1) for $a < r < b$ and (2) for $r > b$.

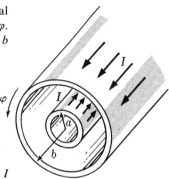

E16.48   A small loop of radius a and a large loop of radius b carry equal currents I and are centered at the same point (see the figure). Give an expression for the magnitude of the torque acting on the smaller loop as a function of the angle θ between the axes of the two loops.

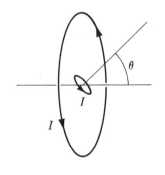

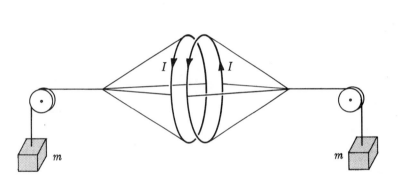

E16.49   The arrangement shown in the figure is in mechanical equilibrium. The radius of the loops is 10 cm and their separation is 1 cm; the current in each loop is $I = 1{,}000$ A. (1) What is the approximate magnitude of the mass m? (2) Is the system in stable equilibrium? Why or why not?

Section 16.9

E16.50   Verify the dimensional consistency of Equation 16.77, $B_{\text{induced}} = \mu_0 \mathscr{I}$.

Section 16.10

E16.51   As shown in Figure 16.40, a rod of ferromagnetic material is aligned in a magnetic field. The field at a considerable distance from the rod is $B_0 = 0.005$ T. The field near one end of the rod is $B_{\text{net}} = 0.5$ T. (1) What is the permeability of the material? (2) What is the magnitude of the fictitious surface current $\mathscr{I}_{\text{bound}}$ in A/m? Does this surface current seem "large" or "small"?

E16.52   A long thin solenoid carries a current of 5 A in a coil with 10^4 turns/m. Initially, the solenoid is filled with air, whose permeability may be taken to be exactly 1. Then solid cylinders are placed inside the solenoid in the manner shown in Figure 16.41, leaving an air gap in the center. (1) What is the initial magnitude of the magnetic field within the solenoid? (2) Find the *change* of magnetic field in the center of the solenoid if the material that is inserted is (a) copper, (b) aluminum, or (c) 2-81 permalloy. (For necessary data, see Table 16.1.)

PROBLEMS

Field of a dipole   **P16.1**   A pole of strength P is located at $x = a$, $y = 0$, and a pole of strength $-P$ is located at $x = -a$, $y = 0$. Show that the magnetic field on the y axis is given by

$$\mathbf{B} = -\frac{\mu_0}{4\pi}\frac{\boldsymbol{\mu}}{(y^2 + a^2)^{3/2}},$$

where $\boldsymbol{\mu}$ is the dipole moment of the pair of poles. What is an approximate expression for $\mathbf{B}$ on the y axis if $y \gg a$?

For **B**, *constant direction*   **P16.2**   An experimenter wishes to produce a magnetic field whose direction at all
requires constant magnitude   points in a certain region is parallel to a given axis and whose magnitude varies with distance along this axis. Prove that in the absence of free poles he cannot do so.

Magnetic mirror   **P16.3**   An electron spirals along lines of magnetic field that converge as the field becomes stronger (see the figure). Explain carefully why the electron is caused to move in a curve of smaller radius and why the component of the electron's velocity along the field direction decreases until the electron may be "reflected" and drift back toward the region of weaker field.

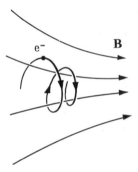

Velocity filter   **P16.4**   Design a "velocity filter," a device that uses electric and magnetic fields and selects particles of a specified velocity. If particles of various nonzero charges and various velocities enter one end of the device, only those particles having a certain narrow range of velocity (but any charge) should leave the other end of the device.

Electric generator   **P16.5**   A simple form of an electric generator is shown in the diagram: a wire slides upward with speed v along stationary wires that are separated by distance l and are joined at the top; a uniform magnetic field $\mathbf{B}$ points into the page. (1) Give the magnitude and direction of the magnetic force acting on an electron in the moving wire. (2) Explain why current circulates around the loop as long as the wire segment is moving. (3) Carefully discuss this phenomenon of current generation from the viewpoint of an observer moving upward at speed v; for this observer the wire segment is stationary. In this frame of reference is there an electric field in the wire segment? If so, what are its magnitude and its direction?

Motion in crossed **E** *and* **B**   **P16.6**   Between the parallel plates shown in the figure are a uniform electric field
fields   directed to the right ($\mathbf{E} = E\mathbf{i}$) and a uniform magnetic field directed into the

page ($\mathbf{B} = -B\mathbf{k}$). Ions of mass m and positive charge q enter the space between the plates with an initial velocity $\mathbf{v}_0$ such that the ions pass close to the right-hand plate without striking it. Show that the radius of curvature of the ions' path at point P is given by

$$r = \frac{v_0^2 + 2\beta Ed}{\beta B \sqrt{v_0^2 + 2\beta Ed} - \beta E},$$

where $\beta = q/m$, the charge-to-mass ratio of the ions.

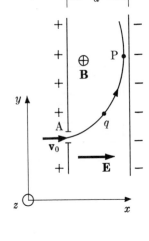

P16.7 (1) Show that the differential equations of motion of the ions described in the preceding problem are

$$\frac{d^2x}{dt^2} = \omega \bar{v} - \omega \frac{dy}{dt},$$

$$\frac{d^2y}{dt^2} = \omega \frac{dx}{dt},$$

where $\omega = qB/m$ and $\bar{v} = E/B$. (2) What is the dimension of ω? What is its physical significance? (3) What is the dimension of $\bar{v}$? What is its physical significance? (4) In the figure for the preceding problem, move the origin of the coordinate system to point A. Show that if an ion is released from rest at this point at $t = 0$, its subsequent motion is described by

$$x = \frac{\bar{v}}{\omega}(1 - \cos \omega t),$$

$$y = \bar{v}t - \frac{\bar{v}}{\omega} \sin \omega t.$$

(These equations define a curve called a *cycloid*.) (5) For this special case ($v_0 = 0$), find y_P if the maximum value of x is $x_P = d$.

P16.8 In a cyclotron the magnetic field (into the page in this diagram) weakens slightly in going from the center to the edge of the pole face. The circle through A and B is a "proper" trajectory for a proton partway through its acceleration phase. If the field were exactly constant, a displaced circle through A' and B' would also be possible. Show that the gradual weakening of the field from center to edge tends to "stabilize" the orbits. Consider first a proton that is accidentally at A' instead of A (but with the same velocity), then a proton that is accidentally at B' instead of B. Stability means that these displaced protons should tend to return to the "proper" trajectory.

Stability of cyclotron orbits

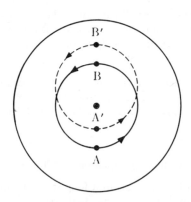

Focusing action of magnetic field

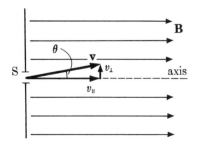

P16.9 Electrons emerging from slit S into a region of uniform magnetic field **B** have velocities that have a fixed magnitude v but make various angles θ with the field direction (see the figure). If the angles are small ($\theta \ll 1$ radian), show that the electrons all cross the axis again at approximately the same distance L from the slit, with L given by

$$L = \frac{2\pi m v}{eB}.$$

Wire conducting a large current

P16.10 According to the example in Section 16.7, a wire with a mass per unit length of 0.009 kg/m must conduct a current of 2,940 A in order to support its own weight in the earth's magnetic field near the equator. (1) In order to assess the reasonableness of this arrangement, assume that the wire is made of copper and evaluate the following quantities: (a) the diameter of the wire, (b) its resistance per unit length, (c) the change of potential per unit length along the wire, and (d) the power dissipated as heat per unit length of wire. (2) If no heat were carried away, how long would it take for the temperature of the wire to rise 10^3 K? (Relevant data for copper [near room temperature]: density, 8.96×10^3 kg/m^3; conductivity, $\sigma = 6 \times 10^7$ (Ω m)$^{-1}$; specific heat, C $= 0.092$ kcal/kg K.)

P16.11 Assume that the wire described in the example of Section 16.7 and in the preceding problem is a superconductor whose density is 6×10^3 kg/m^3. (1) Find the magnetic field created by the current just outside the surface of the wire. (2) A sufficiently intense magnetic field next to a superconductor can cause the material to lose its superconducting properties. Find out more about this subject in an outside reference and decide whether the wire in this example would probably remain superconducting when its current is nearly 3,000 A.

Magnetic moment of a rotating charged body

P16.12 Prove the statement made after Equation 16.55, that the magnetic moment μ_z and the angular momentum L_z of a body rotating about a fixed axis are related by

$$\mu_z = \frac{q}{2m} L_z$$

if the charge-to-mass ratio is the same for all parts of the body; here q is the total charge of the body and m is its total mass. (SUGGESTION: Consider the contribution of an infinitesimal part of the body to the magnetic moment, and sum [integrate] to get the total magnetic moment.)

P16.13 A solid metal sphere of uniform density rotates with angular speed ω about an axis through its center. A total charge q is spread uniformly over the *surface* of the sphere, whose radius is R. Prove that the magnetic moment of the sphere is

$$\mu_z = \tfrac{1}{3}qR^2\omega$$

and that its gyromagnetic ratio (defined by Equation 16.55) is $g = \tfrac{5}{3}$.

Newton's third law and the Biot-Savart law

P16.14 Find the magnetic field created by a current in a long straight wire in the following somewhat unorthodox way. Assume that a magnetic pole is located at a distance x from the wire (see the figure). Calculate the forces on the wire produced by the action of the pole's inverse-square magnetic field. Assume the validity of Newton's third law, according to which the pole experiences an equal and opposite force. From the force on the pole deduce the field that the current in the wire must be creating at the location of the pole.

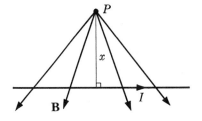

P16.15 As shown in the figure, a long wire along the z axis carries current I_1, and a thin rod of length $2b$ in the xy plane at $x = a$ carries current I_2 (imagine, for instance, that charged spheres at $y = -b$ and $y = b$ are being neutralized). (1) Show that the total force on the rod is zero. (2) What is the direction of the torque on the rod? (3) Use *order-of-magnitude reasoning* to show that the magnitude of the torque on the rod is given approximately by

Force and torque on a wire perpendicular to another wire

$$T \approx \frac{\mu_0}{\pi} I_1 I_2 b \qquad \text{if} \qquad b \gg a.$$

Optional: Show that the exact expression for the magnitude of the torque is

$$T = \frac{\mu_0 I_1 I_2}{\pi} \left(b - a \text{ arc tan} \frac{b}{a} \right).$$

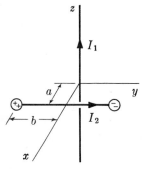

P16.16 Current I flows in a wire bent into a square of side l. (1) Find the magnetic field at any point on the axis of this current loop. (2) Show that for large distance x from the loop, the magnetic field is given approximately by

Field of a square current loop

$$\mathbf{B} = \frac{\mu_0}{2\pi} \frac{\mu}{x^3}.$$

P16.17 (1) Find the magnetic field at the point P shown in the figure; this point lies in the same plane as a square current loop of side l. (2) Give approximate formulas for the magnitude of $\mathbf{B}$ that are valid for (a) $x \to \frac{1}{2}l$ and (b) $x \to \infty$.

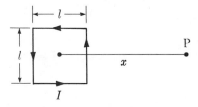

P16.18 Prove that the radial component of magnetic field is zero both inside and outside an infinite solenoid.

For an infinite solenoid, $B_\rho = 0$

P16.19 Obtain the magnetic field on the axis of an infinite solenoid by treating the solenoid as a set of equally spaced coaxial circular current loops. Let the number of loops per meter be n and let the current in each be I. (HINT: The current per unit distance along the solenoid is In and the current in distance dx is $In \, dx$.)

Solenoid as a set of circular loops

P16.20 This is a continuation of the preceding problem. Consider a finite solenoid of length $2L$ and radius r made up of N circular loops carrying current I (the number of loops per unit distance along the solenoid is $n = N/2L$). (1) Find the magnetic field on the axis (a) at the midpoint of the solenoid and (b) at one end of the solenoid. (2) For $L = 4a$ (the condition of Figure 16.36), evaluate $B/(\mu_0 nI)$ numerically at these two points.

Helmholtz coil   **P16.21** Two coaxial circular loops of radius a carry the same current I and are separated by the distance l. (1) Give an expression for B_z, the magnetic field on the axis between the coils at a distance z from the center of one coil and a distance $l - z$ from the center of the other coil. (2) Show that $dB_z/dz = 0$ at $z = \frac{1}{2}l$ for any l. (3) Show that $d^2B_z/dz^2 = 0$ at $z = \frac{1}{2}l$ for $l = a$. (The condition $l = a$ defines the Helmholtz coil [see Exercise 16.41]. The vanishing of both derivatives means that the field is almost uniform near the center of a Helmholtz coil.)

Effective pole strength of   **P16.22** A long straight solenoid of radius r has n turns/meter and carries current I.
solonoid   (1) What is the magnetic flux leaving one end of the solenoid? (2) Show that the effective pole strength of the solenoid is $P = \pi r^2 nI$.

Magnetic field within a   **P16.23** Within a cylindrical wire of radius a is a uniform current density $J = I/\pi a^2$
current-carrying wire   (I is the total current in the wire). Find the magnetic field within the wire.

Field of a plane current sheet   **P16.24** Find the magnetic field produced by an infinite plane sheet of current (see the figure). Let the current be in the x direction and let $\mathscr{I}$ be the current per unit distance y. Consider all three components of **B**.

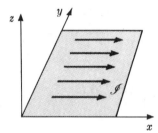

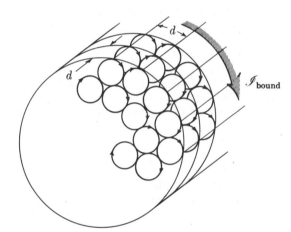

Model of bound surface   **P16.25** The figure shows a model of a ferromagnetic material. Each atom is treated
current   as a tiny current loop generated by an electron of charge (magnitude) e orbiting at speed v in a circle of diameter d. The spacing between atoms is also d. All of the currents within the material cancel, but those on the surface contribute to a net surface current $\mathscr{I}_{\text{bound}}$. (1) Show that if all of the loops are aligned, the surface current is given approximately by

$$\mathscr{I}_{\text{bound}} \cong \frac{ev}{\pi d^2}.$$

(2) Evaluate $\mathscr{I}_{\text{bound}}$ numerically for $v = 2 \times 10^6$ m/sec and $d = 2 \times 10^{-10}$ m and show that it produces an induced magnetic field $B_{\text{induced}} \cong 3$ T. (This calculation gives the correct order of magnitude of the maximum induced field in a ferromagnet. A careful treatment of the model illustrated here leads to the formula $\mathscr{I}_{\text{bound}} = 2ev/\pi^2 d^2$. Recall that it is actually the *spin* motion of electrons, not the *orbital* motion, that accounts for ferromagnetism.) *Optional:* Using the numerical magnitudes of v and d suggested above, find the magnetic moment of a single current loop in this model and compare it with the Bohr magneton given in Appendix 3.

17 Changing Fields

More often than not in scientific history, the full latent power of a new discovery required considerable time to be appreciated. Indeed, the more fundamental the discovery, the greater is the realm of nature it encompasses; and, therefore, the less likely is it that its full ramifications are quickly grasped, even though its importance may be sensed at once. Over a period of two centuries, for example, Newton's laws of motion, besides spawning countless developments in mathematics, came to encompass an ever larger part of nature, in particular being extended into the molecular domain to account for heat and temperature. In the development of electromagnetism, too, a number of key discoveries have had to percolate through the minds of many men, being correlated and examined in new ways before their full content could be assimilated and electromagnetic theory brought to final form. The evolution of electromagnetism as a quantitative theory—discounting its twentieth-century confrontation with the quantum theory, a confrontation still in a state of uneasy and uncertain harmony—can be said to have begun about 1785 with Coulomb's law of electrical force and to have ended about 1905 with Einstein's theory of relativity. Its most active period of development, when the links between electricity and magnetism were discovered and welded into a concise mathematical form, extends from Oersted's discovery of the magnetic force produced by an electric current in 1820 to Heaviside's formulation of the electromagnetic laws in 1885.

Gradual consolidation of electromagnetism in the nineteenth century

Central figures in this active period in the history of electromagnetism were Michael Faraday and James Clerk Maxwell. As already noted, Faraday discovered the phenomenon of electromagnetic induction and introduced the idea of lines of force, the latter leading to the fruitful concept of field. It was also Faraday who arrived at the view that the atomic basis of matter is essentially electrical in nature and that a specific amount of electricity is associated with

1 mole of a substance.* To Maxwell we owe the prediction of electromagnetic radiation and also the first general mathematical formulation of electromagnetic theory. In this chapter we shall be concerned with the key discoveries illustrated in Figures 16.9–16.11 and with their implications for a.c. circuits and electromagnetic radiation. The great significance of these laws of induction is that they express connections between fields alone, with no reference to charge (or to poles). Accordingly, they govern the interaction of fields even in space far removed from matter.

Laws of induction link fields without charge

17.1   Electromagnetic induction

Although the laws of induction stand properly as separate significant statements about electric and magnetic fields, both have interesting and close connections with the laws of moving charge considered in the previous chapter. One way to lay bare such a connection is to focus attention on relative motion. In the induction experiment of Figure 16.9, a bar magnet is moved toward a stationary coil. Consider what happens if, instead, a coil is moved toward a stationary magnet (Figure 17.1). Because of the bulk motion of the coil, electrons in the wire are moving through a magnetic field. Accordingly, they experience a force. The particular electron designated in Figure 17.1, for instance, is moving vertically upward at a point where the magnetic field lines are directed to the east. The force, equal to $-e\mathbf{v} \times \mathbf{B}$, acts to the south, along the wire. Every other electron experiences a force parallel to the wire, and a current is caused

Different frames of reference reveal links between different laws

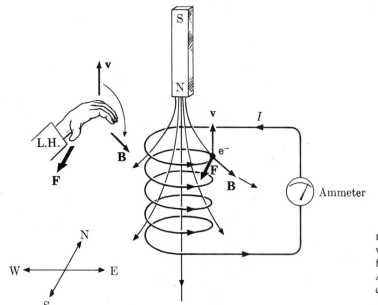

FIGURE 17.1   Faraday induction experiment with stationary magnet and moving coil. The force on a particular electron is indicated. Arrows on the wire designate the direction of conventional current.

---

* For a substance whose atoms gain or lose a single electron in chemical combination, the molar amount of electricity is the charge carried by 6.02×10^{23} electrons. This amount of charge, now known as the faraday, is approximately 96,500 C.

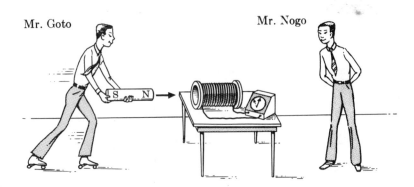

Mr. Goto   Mr. Nogo

FIGURE 17.2   Induction experiment in which one observer sees a stationary coil and a moving magnet, the other observer sees a stationary magnet and a moving coil.

to flow. Seen from above, the electrons move clockwise, and the direction of conventional current flow is counterclockwise. If the direction of motion of the coil were reversed, or if the direction of the magnetic field were reversed, the direction of current flow would also be reversed.

It is natural to assume that only relative motion of the magnet and the coil should matter. If we do make this assumption, we can predict the result of the Faraday experiment: A moving magnet should induce a current in a stationary coil. This is indeed what happens. To see why a law of relativity "ought" to hold true for the coil and the magnet, imagine the Faraday experiment carried out in the following unorthodox manner by a pair of Japanese experimenters, Mr. Goto and Mr. Nogo (Figure 17.2). Mr. Nogo stands motionless, at rest with respect to a coil of wire connected to a meter. Mr. Goto, holding a magnet, skates toward the coil. As Goto's magnet approaches the coil, a current is induced. From Nogo's point of view, a moving magnet has generated a current in a stationary wire. From Goto's point of view, a stationary magnet has generated a current in a moving wire. Since both see the same current recorded by the same meter, they must agree that a current was generated. Hence both of their ways of stating the law of induction must be correct.

The "logic" of this interpretation of the hypothetical experiment rests on a fundamental assumption, the assumption that absolute motion is meaningless. According to this assumption, Mr. Goto's frame of reference is as acceptable as Mr. Nogo's frame of reference for the description of physical events. A law of nature valid in one frame is valid in the other frame. This far-reaching assumption about the invariance of physical laws is a foundation stone of the theory of relativity.

A hint about relativity

We shall now give a quantitative statement of the law of electromagnetic induction and then, with the help of an idealized version of the experiment just described, demonstrate its consistency with laws of force and field introduced earlier. In integral form, the law reads

$$\oint \mathbf{E} \cdot d\mathbf{s} = -\frac{d\Phi_B}{dt},$$
(17.1)

The law of electromagnetic induction

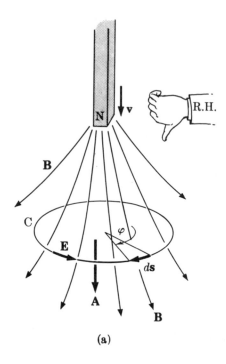

FIGURE 17.3   Seen from above, the positive direction around a curve C is chosen to be clockwise, with the area vector of the enclosed area directed downward. For the illustrated motion of a magnet, the flux is positive and growing, so the emf, from Equation 17.1, is negative. This means that the induced electric field is directed opposite to ds, in this case counterclockwise.

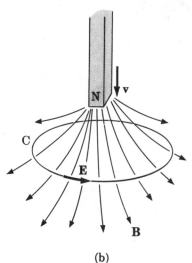

(a)   (b)

where Φ_B, the magnetic flux, is defined by

$$\Phi_B = \int \mathbf{B} \cdot d\mathbf{S}. \qquad (17.2)$$

Figure 17.3 illustrates the meaning of this law and also gives the necessary sign conventions. Some closed curve C is selected, which could be an actual loop of wire, or could be a path in space. The line integral of **E** on the left side of Equation 17.1 is carried out around the curve C, and the flux of **B** (Equation 17.2) is calculated over the area enclosed by this curve. A right-hand rule

Sign conventions   relates the positive directions of path length and area. In the figure, for instance, the area vector is chosen to point downward. With the right thumb indicating this direction, the curved fingers of the right hand give the direction of ds around the curve. Figure 17.3(a) shows an earlier time and Figure 17.3(b) a later time as the north pole of a magnet moves downward toward the loop defined by C. Since the lines of **B** are directed downward, the flux is positive:

$$\Phi_B > 0.$$

The magnitude of this flux is growing, so its time derivative is also positive:

$$\frac{d\Phi_B}{dt} > 0.$$

Equation 17.1 then implies that the line integral of **E** is negative:

$$\oint \mathbf{E} \cdot d\mathbf{s} < 0.$$

This means that the induced electric field **E** is directed opposite to *d***s**, as shown in the figure. If the magnet were moving upward, Φ_B would be positive but decreasing; in that case $d\Phi_B/dt$ would be negative, and **E** would be in the same direction as *d***s**.

On the right side of Equation 17.1 is a quantity related to changing magnetic field. On the left side appears electric field. This equation gives expression to the law of induction previously stated qualitatively: A changing magnetic field creates an electric field (the **B** → **E** line in the *q*-**E**-**B** triangle of Figure 16.42). We see now that it could better be stated: A changing magnetic flux creates an electromotive force. Recall the definition of emf (Equation 15.49). For a closed loop it is

Revised wording for the **B** → **E** *link*

$$\mathscr{V} = \oint \mathbf{E} \cdot d\mathbf{s}. \tag{17.3}$$

For a *static* electric field, this quantity is zero because **E** is then a conservative field. This conclusion is confirmed by Equation 17.1. If magnetic flux does not change, there is no induced emf. With changing conditions, on the other hand, the electric field is not conservative, and a net emf may be generated around a closed path. The law of electromagnetic induction may also be written

A changing **E** *is not conservative*

$$\mathscr{V} = -\frac{d\Phi_B}{dt}. \tag{17.4}$$

Changing flux produces emf

A final remark about Equation 17.1: Notice the absence of charge or current in the equation. This is a law of fields alone.*

■ EXAMPLE 1: In Figure 17.3(a) the flux through the loop of 4-cm diameter is 0.005 Wb. Half a second later, Figure 17.3(b), the flux is 0.007 Wb. If the loop is a wire with a resistance of 0.2 Ω, what is the magnitude of the induced current? The average rate of change of flux is

$$\frac{d\Phi_B}{dt} = \frac{(0.007 - 0.005) \text{ Wb}}{0.5 \text{ sec}} = 0.004 \ \frac{\text{Wb}}{\text{sec}}.$$

The cylindrical symmetry of the situation implies that the field **E** has constant magnitude around the loop; therefore

$$\oint \mathbf{E} \cdot d\mathbf{s} = 2\pi r E_\varphi,$$

where E_φ is the component of **E** in the direction of *d***s**. (Actually, in this example, $E = -E_\varphi$; the induced field is directed along the wire.) Application of Equation 17.1 gives the electric field induced in the wire. It is

$$E_\varphi = -\frac{d\Phi_B/dt}{2\pi r} = -\frac{0.004 \text{ Wb/sec}}{\pi \times 0.04 \text{ m}} = -0.0318 \text{ V/m}.$$

The emf around the loop is

$$\mathscr{V} = -0.004 \text{ Wb/sec} = -0.004 \text{ V}.$$

---

* Equation 17.1, or its equivalent, Equation 17.4, is often called *Faraday's law of induction*. Actually, the version of the law presented here was formulated long after Faraday's pioneer work on the subject.

Application of Ohm's law then gives

$$I = \frac{\mathscr{V}}{R} = \frac{-0.004 \text{ V}}{0.2 \text{ }\Omega} = -0.02 \text{ A}. \tag{17.5}$$

The negative sign simply means that the direction of the current is opposite to the chosen direction of $d\mathbf{s}$. Generally, in circuits, emf's may be regarded as equivalent to sources of potential. In this example, the source is distributed around the loop rather than being localized like a battery or generator. Recall that the most basic form of Ohm's law (Equation 15.84) is expressed in terms of field, not potential. This justifies the use of emf in Equation 17.5. (Note, incidentally, that the dimension of the coil was not necessary to the calculation of current. We used it only for the subsidiary calculation of the electric field.)   ■

★CONSISTENCY OF THE LAW OF ELECTROMAGNETIC INDUCTION WITH OTHER LAWS OF ELECTROMAGNETISM

An idealized version of the Nogo-Goto experiment (Figure 17.2) can show that the law of electromagnetic induction, Equation 17.1 or 17.4, conforms to other laws of field and force introduced in Chapter 16. Imagine a solenoid so long that one end of it acts like a magnetic pole of strength P, creating a magnetic field

$$\mathbf{B} = \frac{\mu_0}{4\pi} \frac{P}{r^2} \mathbf{i}_r , \tag{17.6}$$

where r is measured from the pole. The solenoid moves parallel to its axis with velocity $\mathbf{v}$ toward a circular loop of wire of radius R (Figure 17.4). For mathematical convenience we suppose that the distance x of the loop from the

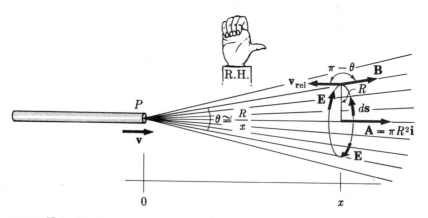

FIGURE 17.4   The inverse-square magnetic field of an idealized pole links a distant loop of radius R. In a frame of reference in which the loop is at rest and the magnet moves, the law of electromagnetic induction applies: The increasing magnetic flux generates an electric field. In a frame in which the magnet is at rest and the loop moves, a law of moving charge applies: A charge in the loop experiences a force $\mathbf{F} = q\mathbf{v}_{rel} \times \mathbf{B}$.

pole is much greater than the radius R. We let the area vector of the loop be directed to the right along the x axis,

$$\mathbf{A} = \pi R^2 \mathbf{i}, \tag{17.7}$$

so that looking from the pole toward the loop, $d\mathbf{s}$ is directed clockwise around the loop.

In a frame of reference in which the solenoid is at rest and the loop moves, any charge q in the wire is moving through a magnetic field and therefore experiences a force

$$\mathbf{F} = q\mathbf{v}_{\text{rel}} \times \mathbf{B}, \tag{17.8}$$

A magnetic force in one frame of reference

where $\mathbf{v}_{\text{rel}} = -\mathbf{v}$. In the laboratory frame of reference, where this force acts on a *stationary* charge, there is, by *definition*, an electric field at the location of the charge. It is

$$\mathbf{E} = \frac{\mathbf{F}}{q} = \mathbf{v}_{\text{rel}} \times \mathbf{B}. \tag{17.9}$$

An electric force in another frame

As indicated in Figure 17.4, this field acts along the wire, opposite in direction to $d\mathbf{s}$. It has magnitude

$$E = vB \sin (\pi - \theta) = vB \sin \theta.$$

Since the angle θ (defined in Figure 17.4) is small, we have, approximately,

$$E \cong vB\theta \cong \frac{vBR}{x}. \tag{17.10}$$

The line integral of $\mathbf{E}$ is

$$\oint \mathbf{E} \cdot d\mathbf{s} = -E \cdot 2\pi R.$$

Substitution from Equations 17.10 and 17.6, with the further approximation $r \cong x$, gives

$$\oint \mathbf{E} \cdot d\mathbf{s} = -\frac{1}{2} \mu_0 P \frac{R^2}{x^3} v. \tag{17.11}$$

Relative motion produces an emf

Now we turn our attention to the rate of change of magnetic flux. In evaluating $\mathbf{v}_{\text{rel}} \times \mathbf{B}$, it was essential to take into account the small angle θ between $\mathbf{B}$ and the x axis, for otherwise the vector product would have been calculated to be zero. In finding the flux of $\mathbf{B}$, however, this small angle may be neglected, and $\mathbf{B}$ may be approximated as a constant vector over the area of the loop*:

$$\mathbf{B} \cong \frac{\mu_0}{4\pi} \frac{P}{x^2} \mathbf{i}. \tag{17.12}$$

---

* Consider, for example, the magnetic field $\mathbf{B}$ at distance R from the axis. Needed for the flux calculation is $B_x = B \cos \theta \cong B(1 - \frac{1}{2}\theta^2)$. The component B_x differs from B only by a term of *second* order in the small angle θ. This term may be ignored. Appearing in the calculation of the vector product, on the other hand, is $\sin \theta \cong \theta$, a quantity of *first* order in θ, which cannot be ignored.

With this approximation, the flux of **B** is simple:

$$\Phi_B = \int \mathbf{B} \cdot d\mathbf{S} = \mathbf{B} \cdot \int d\mathbf{S} = \mathbf{B} \cdot \mathbf{A}.$$

Substitution from Equations 17.7 and 17.12 gives

$$\Phi_B = \frac{1}{4} \mu_0 P \frac{R^2}{x^2}.$$

The time rate of change of this flux is $d\Phi_B/dt = (d\Phi_B/dx)(dx/dt)$. Since $dx/dt = -v$, this differentiation gives

Relative motion causes the flux to change

$$\frac{d\Phi_B}{dt} = \frac{1}{2} \mu_0 P \frac{R^2}{x^3} v. \qquad (17.13)$$

Comparison of Equations 17.11 and 17.13 shows that $\oint \mathbf{E} \cdot d\mathbf{s} = -d\Phi_B/dt$, the same as Equation 17.1. For the special case considered, this constitutes a derivation of the law of electromagnetic induction from previously established laws: the magnetic field of a point pole (Equation 17.6), the magnetic force on a moving charge (Equation 17.8), and the definition of electric field (Equation 17.9). We have also assumed the validity of the laws of electromagnetism in a moving frame of reference.

THE ROLE OF MAGNETIC FLUX

Flux can change without physical motion

It is an immediate implication of Equation 17.1 that the phenomenon of induction does not require physical motion. If magnetic flux changes, by whatever means, an emf is induced. Faraday was aware of this fact in his earliest research on electromagnetic induction. He carried out experiments such as the one depicted in Figure 16.10, in which a changing current in one circuit induces a current in another circuit.

■ EXAMPLE 2: Inside a solenoid is a steady field, $B_0 = 0.05$ T. When a switch is opened [see Figure 17.5(a)], the field decreases exponentially to zero:

$$B = B_0 e^{-t/\tau},$$

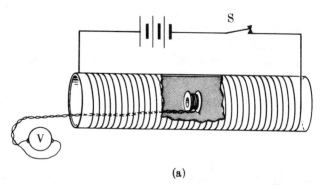

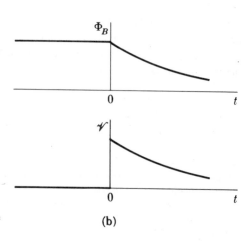

(a)

(b)

FIGURE 17.5   (a) A ten-turn coil within a solenoid. (b) When the switch S is opened, the flux linking the coil (Φ_B) starts to fall exponentially to zero. The induced emf in the coil ($\mathscr{V}$) jumps to a maximum value and then decreases exponentially.

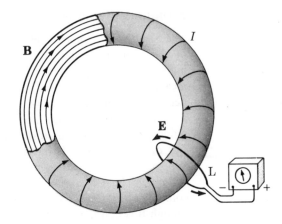

FIGURE 17.6 Induction of an electric field in a region where the magnetic field is zero. The direction of induced field E in the loop L is shown for decreasing magnetic flux.

where $\tau = 0.01$ sec. What is the maximum emf induced in a coil of 10 turns and area 6 cm² that is inside the solenoid and coaxial with it? Let us work only with magnitudes. The flux is

$$\Phi_B = BA = B_0 A e^{-t/\tau}.$$

Its time rate of change is

$$\frac{d\Phi_B}{dt} = -\frac{B_0 A}{\tau} e^{-t/\tau}.$$

From Equation 17.1, for one turn of the coil,

$$\oint \mathbf{E} \cdot d\mathbf{s} = \frac{B_0 A}{\tau} e^{-t/\tau}.$$

The magnitude of the total emf induced in N turns is

$$\mathcal{V} = \frac{N B_0 A}{\tau} e^{-t/\tau}.$$

This has its maximum value at $t = 0$. Setting $N = 10$, $B_0 = 0.05$ T, $A = 6 \times 10^{-4}$ m², and $\tau = 0.01$ sec in this formula gives

$$\mathcal{V}_{max} = 0.03 \text{ V}.$$

Thereafter, $\mathcal{V}$ also decreases exponentially [Figure 17.5(b)]. ■

An even more remarkable implication of Equation 17.1 is the fact that an electric field can be generated at a place where the magnetic field is equal to zero. A device for achieving this kind of induction is shown in Figure 17.6. In a superconducting torus there is a current I, circulating as shown. The magnetic field that it produces is contained entirely within the torus. A loop of wire L, encircling the torus, is in a region of zero magnetic field, even though a magnetic flux threads through the loop. If the current decreases (the torus could, for example, be warmed until it is no longer superconducting, at which point the current would fall to zero), the flux through the loop decreases, inevitably establishing an emf in the loop. This interesting consequence of the law of electromagnetic induction could scarcely have been predicted directly from the previous laws of force and field. Even physicists familiar with this phenomenon find it fascinating that flux can "reach out" and influence field-free space.

Changing **B** *in one place can produce* **E** *in another place*

DEFINITION OF THE WEBER AND THE TESLA

The weber defined by induced emf

The SI units of magnetic field and flux are established with the help of the law of electromagnetic induction, Equation 17.1. One reason for this is that a high-precision measurement of emf is much easier than a high-precision measurement of force. The International Committee on Weights and Measures defines the weber as follows: "The weber is the magnetic flux which, linking a circuit of one turn, produces in it an electromotive force of 1 volt as it is reduced to zero at a uniform rate in 1 second." In other words, if the left side of Equation 17.1 is measured to be 1 V, the right side is defined to be 1 Wb/sec. The tesla is then defined as 1 Wb/m². To measure the magnitude of a *static* field **B**, it is common practice to measure the emf induced in a rotating coil. The rotation of the coil causes the flux through the coil to change, even though **B** is constant.

17.2   Applications of electromagnetic induction

THE GENERATOR

Principle of the generator: A coil rotates in a magnetic field

A principal application of electromagnetic induction in our technological world is the generation of electric current. An actual generator is a complicated piece of machinery. Nevertheless, the principle of its operation can be demonstrated in a simple way. Consider a coil of area **A** rotating at constant angular speed ω in a uniform magnetic field **B**, as shown in Figure 17.7. The angle between **A** and **B** is

$$\theta = \omega t$$

(if the zero of time is chosen to be a time when $\theta = 0$). Since both **A** and **B** are vectors of constant magnitude, the magnetic flux through the area of the coil* is

$$\Phi_B = \mathbf{B} \cdot \int d\mathbf{S} = \mathbf{B} \cdot \mathbf{A}$$

$$= BA \cos \omega t. \tag{17.14}$$

Its time rate of change is

$$\frac{d\Phi_B}{dt} = -\omega BA \sin \omega t.$$

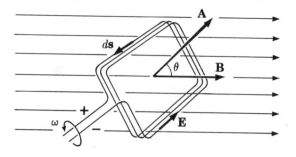

FIGURE 17.7   Principle of the generator. A coil rotates in a magnetic field. The signs indicate the polarity at the moment shown, when the flux is decreasing and **E** is parallel to *d***s**.

---

* The flux through a given area is often called the flux "linking" the area. See the official definition of the weber, for example.

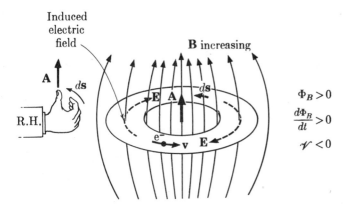

FIGURE 17.8   Principle of the betatron. The magnetic field serves a dual
purpose. (1) It deflects the electrons in a circular path. (2) By changing, it
creates an electric field that accelerates the electrons to higher speed.

The law of electromagnetic induction therefore implies

$$\mathscr{V} = \oint \mathbf{E} \cdot d\mathbf{s} = \omega B A \sin \omega t. \qquad (17.15)$$ *Induced emf is sinusoidal*

This is the generated emf for a single turn of wire. For N turns, the total emf
would be $\mathscr{V}_{total} = N\mathscr{V}$. The output of a generator is a sinusoidal emf whose
amplitude is proportional to ω, B, A, and N. In the United States, ω is a fixed
constant—$2\pi \times 60$ radian/sec—so that the output emf for a particular generator
is determined by the choice of field B, coil area A, and number of turns N. It is
worth emphasizing again that the design of the generator determines emf, not
current. The current that it supplies is determined by the external circuit to
which the generator is connected, and may vary over a wide range.

★THE BETATRON

Another device that quite directly illustrates the law of electromagnetic induction
is the betatron, a special kind of particle accelerator. It provides an interesting
example of the direct utilization of a law of interacting fields in a vacuum
instead of a wire. In the cyclotron and synchrotron, a magnetic field is employed
for particle deflection, and a separate electric field is used for increasing the speed
of the particles. In the betatron, a single magnetic field is harnessed for both   *The magnetic field does*
purposes. Electrons (beta particles) move within an evacuated toroid (Figure   *double duty*
17.8). A magnetic field passes through the toroid as well as through its hollow
center. The electrons, deflected by the magnetic field, make their way around the
toroid in a circular path. Acceleration of the electrons to higher speed is
accomplished simply by increasing the strength of the magnetic field. As the
magnetic field changes from weaker to stronger, it creates an electric field within
the toroid (as well as elsewhere). This electric field pushes the electrons to
higher speed. The remarkable fact is that with a suitable choice of the magnetic
field in the center relative to that in the toroid, the increasing deflecting power of
the magnetic field can be made to keep perfect pace with the increasing energy

of the electrons, so that electrons will continue to move in a circle of constant radius.

To explore the betatron action mathematically, we consider any moment during the acceleration cycle when a total magnetic flux Φ_B threads the electron orbit and when the value of the magnetic field at the location of the electron track is B_r. At that moment the electron has momentum p. Its radius of curvature is, according to Equation 16.30,

$$r = \frac{p}{eB_r}. \tag{17.16}$$

Since r is to be a constant and since the charge e is a constant, the ratio p/B_r must be constant. The momentum must grow in direct proportion to the field. We may rewrite Equation 17.16 in the form

$$p = reB_r$$

and differentiate it with respect to time, obtaining

$$\frac{dp}{dt} = re\frac{dB_r}{dt}. \tag{17.17}$$

On the left is the rate of change of the *magnitude* of the electron's momentum, not the same as the vector quantity $d\mathbf{p}/dt$. As it whirls around the toroid, the electron is responding to two forces: a magnetic force, which acts as a centripetal force, changing the direction of $\mathbf{p}$ but not changing its magnitude; and an electric force, which pushes the electron in its direction of motion (Figure 17.8). Only the electric force is responsible for the change in the magnitude of $\mathbf{p}$. Therefore, according to Newton's second law,

$$\frac{dp}{dt} = F_E = eE. \tag{17.18}$$

(Note that a negative sign is not needed. Although $\mathbf{F}_E = -e\mathbf{E}$, the magnitude equation is $F_E = eE$.) Equations 17.17 and 17.18 express dp/dt in two different ways. From these equations we obtain a relationship between E and B_r,

Condition for constant orbital radius as B_r and p grow

$$E = r\frac{dB_r}{dt}. \tag{17.19}$$

It should be mentioned at this point that electrons in a betatron are highly relativistic, moving near the speed of light. We have mentioned before that Equation 17.16 remains valid in this limit. Now we add the fact that Equation 17.18, derived from classical mechanics, is also valid in relativity theory. Until studying relativistic electrodynamics in a more advanced course, the student must accept these facts without proof. Many equations of classical mechanics do *not* remain valid for speeds near the speed of light. However, most of the equations of electromagnetism presented in these chapters do remain valid.

So far, we have not invoked the law of electromagnetic induction. It provides another relationship between E and B. The emf around the loop of the electron orbit is

$$\mathscr{V}_{\text{loop}} = \oint \mathbf{E} \cdot d\mathbf{s} = -2\pi r E. \tag{17.20}$$

Since $\mathbf{E}$ is antiparallel to $d\mathbf{s}$ and of constant magnitude around the loop, the integral may be performed readily. The flux Φ_B we may write in the form

$$\Phi_B = B_{av}A = \pi r^2 B_{av}. \tag{17.21}$$

The meaning of B_{av} is the average value of the vertical component of $\mathbf{B}$ over the area A of the loop. Technically, its definition is

$$B_{av} = \frac{1}{A} \int \mathbf{B} \cdot d\mathbf{S}. \tag{17.22}$$

Again taking into account the fact that r is constant, we can differentiate Equation 17.21 with respect to time to obtain

$$\frac{d\Phi_B}{dt} = \pi r^2 \frac{dB_{av}}{dt}. \tag{17.23}$$

Substituting from Equations 17.20 and 17.23 in Equation 17.1 gives

$$-2\pi rE = -\pi r^2 \frac{dB_{av}}{dt},$$

from which we conclude

$$E = \frac{1}{2} r \frac{dB_{av}}{dt}. \tag{17.24}$$

Electric field induced by changing flux

To review the reasoning: Equation 17.19 follows from mechanics, considering the forces acting on the electrons. Equation 17.24 follows from the law of electromagnetic induction, linking fields without reference to charge. Both equations express the tangential electric field E in terms of the time derivative of a magnetic field. Equating the two expressions for E, we get

$$\frac{dB_r}{dt} = \frac{1}{2} \frac{dB_{av}}{dt}. \tag{17.25}$$

The general relationship between B_r and B_{av} that satisfies this differential equation is

$$B_r = \tfrac{1}{2}B_{av} + C,$$

where C is a constant. It is a reasonable assumption that all parts of the field grow together, with no changes in the relative strength of different parts. If this is true, B_r is directly proportional to B_{av} and $C = 0$. Then

$$B_r = \tfrac{1}{2}B_{av}. \tag{17.26}$$

Final condition on field

Thus the betatron will perform as expected if the average magnetic field inside the electron orbital circle is twice the value of the field at the orbit. It is easy to design an electromagnet whose field has this property.

■ EXAMPLE: The electrons in a betatron constitute a circular current loop that itself generates a magnetic field. If 10^{10} electrons circulate at radius $r = 0.5$ m in a peak field $B_r = 0.4$ T, how does the field generated by the electrons compare in magnitude and direction with the external field applied to the electrons? To find the direction, refer to Figure 17.8. Seen from above, the electrons fly counterclockwise, which is equivalent to a clockwise conventional current. This current produces a downward-pointing field in the central region, *opposite* to the direction of the applied field. The magnitude of the current is, from Formula 16.59,

$$I = \frac{qv}{2\pi r} = \frac{Nec}{2\pi r}.$$

After the second equal sign, we have set $q = Ne$ and $v = c$.* Setting $N = 10^{10}$, $e = 1.6 \times 10^{-19}$ C, $c = 3 \times 10^8$ m/sec, and $r = 0.5$ m yields

$$I = 0.153 \text{ A}.$$

Equation 16.58 then gives, for the field produced by this current at the center of the betatron,

$$B = \frac{\mu_0 I}{2r} = 1.9 \times 10^{-7} \text{ T}.$$

Electron-generated field opposes applied field, but is much weaker

The external field at this point is somewhat more than twice the peripheral field, or about 1 T, enormously greater than the electron-generated field. Even close to the electron beam, the difference is large. If we suppose that the electron beam is spread over a few centimeters, we can use the Biot-Savart law (Equation 16.61) to find the electron-generated field close to the electron beam. For $x = 5$ cm $= 0.05$ m, Equation 16.61 gives

$$B = 6.1 \times 10^{-7} \text{ T},$$

much less than B_r. We conclude that the circulating electrons do not significantly perturb the externally applied field.   ∎

17.3   Magnetoelectric induction

Because of the symmetry between electricity and magnetism that has been repeatedly emphasized in these pages, it should not be surprising that a law of magnetoelectric induction exists, exactly matching the law of electromagnetic induction. The discovery by Maxwell illustrated in Figure 16.11 was expressed qualitatively in these words: A changing electric field creates a magnetic field (the $\mathbf{E} \rightarrow \mathbf{B}$ line in Figure 16.42). A wording more closely fitting the quantitative law is: A changing electric flux creates a magnetomotive force. The law in integral form, valid in a region free of electric currents, is written

Induction of a magnetic field by a changing electric flux

$$\oint \mathbf{B} \cdot d\mathbf{s} = \mu_0 \epsilon_0 \frac{d\Phi_E}{dt}. \tag{17.27}$$

The line integral on the left is sometimes called the magnetomotive force.

---

* You may test the assumption that the electrons are moving at nearly the speed of light as follows. From the equation, $p = reB_r$, calculate the momentum of an electron. *Try* the nonrelativistic formula, $p = mv$. If it yields a speed v that is substantially less than c, this is the correct speed, and the electron is nonrelativistic. If it yields a speed v that is much greater than c, this shows that the electron is in fact relativistic and is actually moving at a speed close to, but slightly less than, c, which is the maximum possible speed of a particle.

Physically, it is the energy per unit pole strength that would be given to a magnetic pole that circled once around the loop chosen for integration. On the right, the electric flux is defined by

$$\Phi_E = \int \mathbf{E} \cdot d\mathbf{S}, \qquad (17.28)$$

with the integral extending over the area enclosed by the loop. Equation 17.27 (with 17.28) bears an obvious resemblance to Equation 17.1 (with 17.2). The appearance in Equation 17.27 of the constants μ_0 and ϵ_0, which are absent in Equation 17.1, is a peculiarity of SI units and is without physical significance. On the other hand, the fact that the signs on the right sides of these two equations are opposite is important and would be true in any system of units.

For steady currents, we previously wrote Ampère's law (Equation 16.63) as

$$\oint \mathbf{B} \cdot d\mathbf{s} = \mu_0 I,$$

where I is the net current piercing the area bounded by the integration loop. For steady currents, then, the magnetomotive force around a closed loop is proportional to the current threading the loop. For changing fields and no current, it is proportional to the rate of change of electric flux through the loop. More generally, the magnetomotive force is determined by the sum of these two contributing effects. The accurate law, valid for all situations, is

$$\oint \mathbf{B} \cdot d\mathbf{s} = \mu_0 I + \mu_0 \epsilon_0 \frac{d\Phi_E}{dt}. \qquad (17.29)$$

Ampère's law and magnetoelectric induction combined

The right side of this equation may be written

$$\mu_0 \left[I + \epsilon_0 \frac{d\Phi_E}{dt} \right].$$

It is the term $\epsilon_0 \, d\Phi_E/dt$ that Maxwell christened "displacement current." He thought of this quantity as a kind of current, because its effect duplicates the effect of the true current. To see this clearly, refer again to Figure 16.11. So far as its role in producing magnetic field is concerned, the increasing electric flux in the space between the plates behaves exactly like the current in the wires outside the plates.

The concept of displacement current

Historically, magnetoelectric induction—the creation of a magnetic field by a changing electric flux—was the last interlocking piece to be put into place, completing the basic structure of electromagnetic theory. It was vitally important because it led to an understanding of electromagnetic radiation.

Our final form of the law of magnetoelectric induction, Equation 17.29, does not exactly match Equation 17.1. The asymmetry is a manifestation of the existence of charge and not poles. If poles existed, another term would have to be added to Equation 17.1, a magnetic current term analogous to the electric current term in Equation 17.29 (this term is displayed in Equation 17.40).

■ EXAMPLE 1:   A capacitor with parallel circular plates of radius R and area A is being charged by a current I so that its charge is growing at the rate $dq/dt = I$ (Figure 17.9). What magnetic field exists at a point P above the capacitor? To apply Equation 17.29, choose a circular path C_1 that passes through the point P

[Figure 17.9(a)]. The approximately uniform electric field between the plates has magnitude

$$E = \frac{\sigma}{\epsilon_0},$$

where σ is the charge per unit area on one plate (this repeats Equation 15.44). The total electric flux passing through the plane area A_1 defined by C_1 is the same as that through the smaller area A [see Figure 17.9(a)],

$$\Phi_E = EA = \frac{q}{\epsilon_0}. \tag{17.30}$$

(We use the fact that $\sigma = q/A$. Note that Equation 17.30 also follows from Gauss's law.) The rate of change of electric flux is

$$\frac{d\Phi_E}{dt} = \frac{1}{\epsilon_0}\frac{dq}{dt} = \frac{1}{\epsilon_0}I.$$

Since no true current I pierces the area A_1, the first term on the right side of Equation 17.29 is zero. The second term is

$$\mu_0\epsilon_0 \frac{d\Phi_E}{dt} = \mu_0 I,$$

and the law reads

$$\oint \mathbf{B} \cdot d\mathbf{s} = \mu_0 I. \tag{17.31}$$

As suggested approximately by Figure 16.11, the magnetic field surrounding the capacitor is exactly the same as if the current flowed through it. At distance r from the center of the capacitor, the field is directed tangentially and its magnitude is given by the Biot-Savart law (Equation 16.61),

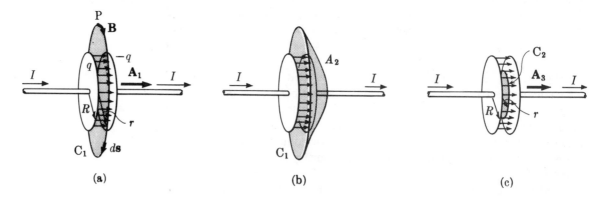

(a)   (b)   (c)

FIGURE 17.9   Magnetoelectric induction. The magnetomotive force, $\oint \mathbf{B} \cdot d\mathbf{s}$, around a path C_1 is determined by (a) the rate of change of electric flux across the enclosed area A_1 (if no actual current cuts the area); or (b) the current cutting the area A_2 (if no electric flux links this area); or, more generally, by both current and changing electric flux. (c) A path C_2 enclosing area A_3 is used to find the magnetic field between the capacitor plates.

$$B = \frac{\mu_0 I}{2\pi r} \quad (r \geq R). \tag{17.32}$$

*B field created by changing
E field of capacitor*

Now we may argue that the result given by Equation 17.31 is a necessity. The area defined by the circle C_1 need not be a plane. We can imagine another area A_2 that is stretched to go around the capacitor, not through it [Figure 17.9(b)]. Then *no* electric flux cuts through the surface, but a current I does cut it. Merely by changing a fictitious mathematical surface, with no physical change at all, we have caused one term on the right side of Equation 17.29 to vanish and the other term to appear. Therefore $\mu_0 I$ must be the correct magnitude of the right side of the equation, regardless of the shape of the surface.

■ EXAMPLE 2:   What is the magnetic field within the capacitor of Figure 17.9 as it is being charged? This time we may choose a circle C_2 of radius r less than R and let it define a plane area A_3 parallel to the plates [Figure 17.9(c)]. The electric flux linking this area is

$$\Phi_E = EA_3 = \frac{qA_3}{\epsilon_0 A} = \frac{qr^2}{\epsilon_0 R^2}.$$

Its time rate of change is (since only q is variable)

$$\frac{d\Phi_E}{dt} = \frac{1}{\epsilon_0} \frac{r^2}{R^2} I.$$

Since no true current cuts the area A_3, the first term on the right side of Equation 17.29 is zero. The second term is

$$\mu_0\epsilon_0 \frac{d\Phi_E}{dt} = \mu_0 \frac{r^2}{R^2} I. \tag{17.33}$$

The symmetry of the situation tells us that B_φ, the tangential component of **B**, is constant around the path C_2. Therefore, the line integral on the left side of Equation 17.29 is

$$\oint \mathbf{B} \cdot d\mathbf{s} = B_\varphi \cdot 2\pi r. \tag{17.34}$$

Substituting from Equations 17.33 and 17.34 in Equation 17.29 gives

$$B = \frac{\mu_0 I r}{2\pi R^2} \quad (r \leq R). \tag{17.35}$$

*Magnetic field within
capacitor*

(We have dropped the subscript φ because **B** is in the φ direction: $B_\varphi = B$.) Within the capacitor, B is proportional to r. Outside (Equation 17.32), it is proportional to $1/r$.   ■

CONSISTENCY OF THE LAW OF MAGNETOELECTRIC INDUCTION
WITH OTHER LAWS OF ELECTROMAGNETISM

As we have already learned, a moving charge creates a magnetic field. A stationary charge does not. These facts can be interpreted in terms of fields alone. When a charge moves, electric flux changes, and this generates a magnetic field. Consider, for example, a charge q moving in a straight line with constant speed v

*Laws of moving charge and
changing field are closely
related*

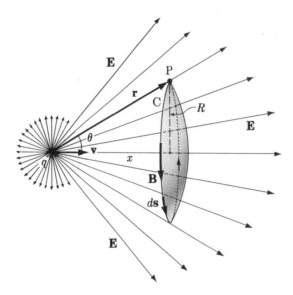

FIGURE 17.10   Two ways to look at the same phenomenon. (1) A law of moving charge: Because q is moving, a magnetic field **B** is created at point P.   (2) The law of magnetoelectric induction: Because the electric flux through the area enclosed by curve C is changing, a magnetomotive force, $\oint$ **B** · ds, is generated around the curve C.

(Figure 17.10). What magnetic field does it produce at a point P whose displacement from the charge is **r**? One answer is provided directly by Equation 16.36. The field is perpendicular to both **v** and **r** and has magnitude

$$B = \frac{\mu_0}{4\pi} \frac{qv \sin \theta}{r^2}, \tag{17.36}$$

where θ is the angle between **v** and **r** (Figure 17.10). It is not hard to prove that the same answer is provided by Equation 17.27. Here we outline the approach and leave the details as a problem. Through the point P we construct a circle of radius R whose center is at distance x from the charge and whose axis is parallel to **v**. The construction is similar to that in Figure 17.4, except that we do not make the approximation $R \ll x$. According to Gauss's law, the *total* flux emanating from the charge q is q/ϵ_0. The fraction of this flux linking the circle C is the fraction of the area of a sphere of radius r that is defined by the circle C. This fraction is $\frac{1}{2}(1 - \cos \theta)$. The flux of interest, therefore, is

$$\Phi_E = \frac{q}{2\epsilon_0} (1 - \cos \theta). \tag{17.37}$$

This flux Φ_E is changing because the angle θ is changing. One may therefore differentiate Equation 17.37 with respect to time and use this derivative in Equation 17.27. Symmetry considerations show that the left side of Equation 17.27 is $2\pi RB$. From these manipulations, the result expressed by Equation 17.36 is derived in a different way. Obviously, the displacement current, as represented by the right side of Equation 17.27, is an essential concept without which the laws of electromagnetism would be inconsistent.

17.4   Lenz's law

An interesting general statement about electromagnetic phenomena is Lenz's law, not itself really an independent law but a useful way to formulate the implications of energy conservation in electromagnetism. It is this: If a change 1 produces an effect 2, the effect 2 will create a reaction 3 opposing the original change 1. Lenz's law is sometimes loosely expressed by the phrase, "Nature fights back." Imagine, for example, the north pole of a magnet moving downward past a horizontal wire (Figure 17.11). The motion of the magnet causes a current to be induced in the wire. The induced current in turn produces a magnetic field (B_2), and this field exerts a force on the magnet, opposing its motion. You may verify, by using separate laws of force and field, that indeed the reaction field opposes the motion of the magnet. (To find the direction of the induced current, for instance, consider the force on an electron in the wire moving upward relative to the magnet.) The implication of Lenz's law in this example is that an external force must be applied to the magnet to keep it moving. Work must be done. This is necessary for energy conservation, since the induced current can itself expend energy or do work. If no work were required to induce the current, there would be energy output with no energy input. It is exactly this principle that applies to the generator. In Figure 17.7, a coil is shown rotating in a magnetic field. The induced current causes the coil to have a dipole moment. The field exerts a torque on this dipole moment, opposing its rotation. When you switch on a light, you draw more current from a generator. This extra current increases the dipole moment of a coil in a generator and increases the torque opposing its motion. To maintain the constant angular velocity of the generator, a steam turbine or other outside source of mechanical energy must increase the work it does on the generator. Through this chain, involving fundamental laws of electric and magnetic fields, the energy of combustion or nuclear fission in a distant power plant is supplied to the light.

Statement of Lenz's law

It is an implication of energy conservation

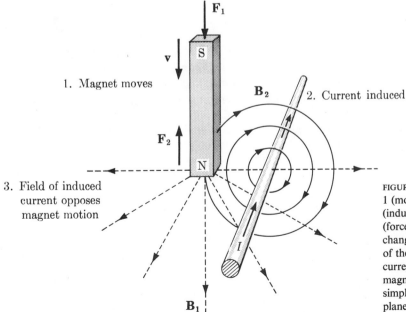

1. Magnet moves

2. Current induced

3. Field of induced current opposes magnet motion

FIGURE 17.11   Lenz's law at work. A change 1 (moving magnet) produces an effect 2 (induced current), which produces a reaction 3 (force F_2 on magnet) opposing the original change. In the figure, B_1 designates the field of the magnet and B_2 the field of the induced current. A force F_1 is required to keep the magnet moving. (To keep the diagram simple, field lines are shown in only one plane.)

*It helps determine the
direction of an induced field*

The betatron also affords an interesting application of Lenz's law. How could we conclude, without careful attention to signs in Equation 17.1, that the changing magnetic field in the betatron tends to speed up the electrons and not to slow them down? Let the magnetic field be directed upward, as in Figure 17.8. An electron moving in this field will be deflected to its own left. It therefore executes a counterclockwise loop, as seen from above. The magnetic field created by the electrons is directed downward at the center of the toroid. (This field, not shown in Figure 17.8, is, as calculated earlier, far weaker than the original upward-pointing field.) Now we apply Lenz's law. If the upward-pointing magnetic field is increased, the electrons must be influenced in such a way as to oppose the increase. They must, therefore, be accelerated to higher speed in order for their downward-pointing magnetic field to grow, which tends to counteract the increase of the applied field.

Other examples of Lenz's law will be left to the end of the chapter. Note that Lenz's law must be carefully distinguished from Newton's third law of equal and opposite forces. If a magnet is at rest with respect to a current-carrying wire, the wire will experience a force, and the magnet will experience an equal and opposite force. This is *not* an application of Lenz's law because no exchange of energy is involved. If the magnet were moved, energy would become relevant and Lenz's law could be invoked to help determine whether the current flow would be increased or decreased by the motion.

17.5   Maxwell's equations

Our purpose in this section is to gather together and display the four fundamental equations known as Maxwell's equations. These equations have already been developed in this chapter and the preceding two, so no new laws or new ideas are involved. It is nevertheless worthwhile for the student to examine them all together, partly for review and consolidation of knowledge, partly to gain additional insight into the *simplicity* and the *symmetry* of the whole structure of electromagnetism.

Below we enumerate the laws, mathematically and verbally, and mention a significant physical consequence of each. Terms covered by a shaded rectangle are those that would be present if free magnetic poles exist but are zero in the absence of such entities. Phrases in brackets go with the shaded terms and would be relevant only if isolated poles existed. Equation numbers on the left cite the earlier appearance of the equations.

1. GAUSS'S LAW

(15.36)
$$\oint \mathbf{E} \cdot d\mathbf{S} = \frac{q}{\epsilon_0} .$$
(17.38)

In words: The net electric flux emerging from a closed surface ($\Phi_E{}^c \equiv \oint \mathbf{E} \cdot d\mathbf{S}$) is proportional to the total charge contained within the surface. A physical consequence: The electric field associated with a stationary point charge is a central inverse-square field. This in turn is related to Coulomb's law of electric force.

2. THE SOLENOIDAL CHARACTER OF THE MAGNETIC FIELD [OR GAUSS'S LAW FOR POLES]

no such thing as P

(16.22, 16.23)
$$\oint \mathbf{B} \cdot d\mathbf{S} = \mu_0 P. = 0 \qquad (17.39)$$

In words: The net magnetic flux emerging from a closed surface ($\Phi_B^c \equiv \oint \mathbf{B} \cdot d\mathbf{S}$) is zero [or is proportional to the total pole strength contained within the surface]. A physical consequence: Lines of magnetic field never begin or end. [Lines would end on poles, which would create inverse-square central fields and would attract or repel according to a Coulomb-like law of force.]

3. THE LAW OF ELECTROMAGNETIC INDUCTION [AND AMPÈRE'S LAW FOR MAGNETIC CURRENT]

(17.1)
$$\oint \mathbf{E} \cdot d\mathbf{s} = -\mu_0 I_M - \frac{d\Phi_B}{dt}. \qquad (17.40)$$

In words: The emf around a closed path ($\oint \mathbf{E} \cdot d\mathbf{s}$) is determined by the rate of change of magnetic flux through an area bounded by the path [and would also be determined by the net magnetic current I_M ($I_M = dP/dt$, pole strength per unit time) piercing the area]. A physical consequence: A moving magnet or a changing magnetic flux can induce a current in a coil. [A magnetic current would be encircled by lines of electric field.]

4. THE LAW OF MAGNETOELECTRIC INDUCTION AND AMPÈRE'S LAW

(17.29)
$$\oint \mathbf{B} \cdot d\mathbf{s} = \mu_0 I + \mu_0 \epsilon_0 \frac{d\Phi_E}{dt}. \qquad (17.41)$$

In words: The magnetomotive force around a closed path ($\oint \mathbf{B} \cdot d\mathbf{s}$) is determined by the rate of change of electric flux through an area bounded by the path and by the net current I piercing the area. A physical consequence: A moving charge or a current creates a magnetic field.

The beautiful symmetry of these equations is evident (overlook the inessential asymmetry produced by the unit-dependent constants ϵ_0 and μ_0). They are obviously better balanced with the magnetic pole and current terms present than with these terms absent. This is one reason that physicists continue to show an interest in the possible existence of isolated poles. However, it appears so far that nature has chosen to be economical of concepts rather than perfectly balanced between electricity and magnetism. Also worth reflecting on is the enormous *power* locked in these few relatively simple equations. Topics discussed so far in these chapters have provided some indication of the vast range of application of Maxwell's equations. One need only ponder the pervasive impact of modern technology and communications to sense the role played by Maxwell's equations in the past hundred years.

One more law deserves explicit mention in this review and summary. It is the so-called Lorentz force law—actually two laws in one—giving the electric and magnetic force acting on a charged particle.

Magnetic pole terms would give perfect balance to electricity and magnetism

Maxwell's equations underlie much of modern technology

5. LORENTZ FORCE LAW

Force on a charged particle   (15.18, 16.27) $$\mathbf{F} = q'\mathbf{E} + q'\mathbf{v} \times \mathbf{B}.$$ (17.42)

Maxwell's equations relate fields to charge and current. This law relates fields to force. The reason the Lorentz force law is not elevated to the same status as the other four laws is that it may be taken to *define* the fields. Recall that electric field $\mathbf{E}$ is defined as force per unit charge when $\mathbf{v} = 0$. This definition uses the first term in Equation 17.42. Similarly, the second term in the equation defines magnetic field. Although fields are defined in terms of force, their significance goes much further. To give one example, fields are repositories of stored energy (Equation 16.25). [Finally, we mention the analogous force law that would apply to magnetic poles if they exist.]

Force on a magnetic pole   (16.7, 16.82) $$\mathbf{F}_\mathbf{M} = P'\mathbf{B} - \mu_0\epsilon_0 P'\mathbf{v} \times \mathbf{E}.$$ (17.43)

★MAXWELL'S DIFFERENTIAL EQUATIONS

Equations 17.38–17.41 give Maxwell's equations in *integral* form. They may also be expressed in *differential* form, as shown in Table 17.1. It is beyond the scope of this text to use or even to discuss the exact meaning of these differential equations. They are presented here for auxiliary information and to some extent for their esthetic value. The student is *not* expected to study or understand them at this stage of his career. We make only these few remarks about the differential form of Maxwell's equations. A term-by-term correspondence to the integral form of the equations is evident. The equations relate derivatives of $\mathbf{E}$ and $\mathbf{B}$—both time and space derivatives—to charge density and current density. They are *local* equations. The fields in the neighborhood of a point—both the spatial and temporal neighborhood—are related to the charge and current at that point. Thus the idea of action at a distance is completely missing from

TABLE 17.1   MAXWELL'S EQUATIONS IN DIFFERENTIAL FORM

EQUATIONS

The equations correspond, in order, to Equations 17.38–17.41 in the text. The *divergence* operator ($\nabla \cdot$) and the *curl* operator ($\nabla \times$) are defined in Appendix 6.

1. $\nabla \cdot \mathbf{E} = \dfrac{\rho}{\epsilon_0}$

2. $\nabla \cdot \mathbf{B} = \cancel{\mu_0\rho_\mathbf{M}} = 0$

3. $\nabla \times \mathbf{E} = \cancel{-\mu_0\mathbf{J}_\mathbf{M}} - \dfrac{\partial \mathbf{B}}{\partial t}$

4. $\nabla \times \mathbf{B} = \mu_0\mathbf{J} + \mu_0\epsilon_0 \dfrac{\partial \mathbf{E}}{\partial t}$

DEFINITIONS

  ρ = charge density (C/m³)
  $\rho_\mathbf{M}$ = magnetic pole density (michell/m³)*
  $\mathbf{J}$ = electric current density (C/m² sec)
  $\mathbf{J}_\mathbf{M}$ = magnetic current density (michell/m² sec)

* The michell is defined by Equations 16.2–16.4.

these equations. Nevertheless, it is in the nature of a differential equation that
although the equation itself spans only an infinitesimal neighborhood, the
solution to the equation spans a finite, or possibly even an infinite, range of
space and time.

Maxwell's differential equations are local laws with global solutions

> action of finding a

17.6   Inductance

An action as simple as switching a current on or off brings into play the law of
electromagnetic induction. Imagine a wire bent into a circle in which a steady
direct current is flowing (Figure 17.12). Around the wire are lines of magnetic
field created by the current. What happens when the source of the current is
suddenly disconnected, for example by throwing a switch in the circuit to the
"off" position? One might suppose that the current simply stops with equal
suddenness. It does not. Although the current must, of course, stop eventually,
the laws of electromagnetism prevent this from happening instantly. As the
current begins to diminish in strength, the flux through the loop also diminishes.
This changing magnetic flux creates in the wire an electric field. By Lenz's law,
we know that this electric field must act in a direction to keep the current
flowing, for this will be the direction opposing the change. On the other hand,
we know that the current cannot continue unabated because there would then

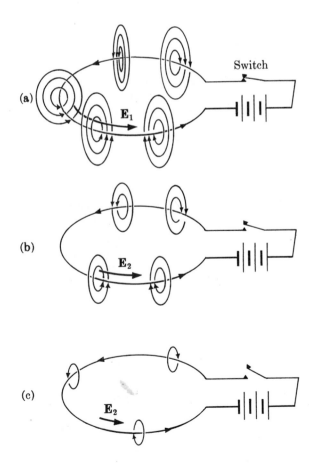

FIGURE 17.12   Self-induction. As a switch is
opened, the diminishing magnetic field
associated with the diminishing current
induces an electric field in the wire that
prevents the current from stopping suddenly.
In diagram (a), E_1 designates the field in the
wire produced by the battery. In diagrams
(b) and (c), at later times, E_2 designates the
self-induced electric field. The time scale is
much less than one second.

be no changing magnetic field to create an electric field to keep the current flowing. The current decreases, but gradually, not suddenly. Similar arguments show that when a circuit is switched on, the current must rise gradually to its final value. In a practical case, the actual time required for the current to fade away or to build up is too short to measure without sensitive apparatus. When a light is switched on, for instance, we are unaware of the time lag between throwing the switch and seeing the light since the lag amounts to a very small fraction of a second.

Self-induction and mutual induction

This effect tending to oppose any change in the magnitude of a steady current is called *self-induction*. A changing magnetic field acts back on the circuit creating it. In the closely related phenomenon of *mutual induction*, a changing magnetic field created by one circuit induces an emf in another circuit.

It is possible to define for a wire or a circuit a quantity called *inductance*. Just as resistance is the measure of opposition to flow of current, inductance is the measure of opposition to a *change* in the flow of current. If current is changing at a certain rate in a circuit, an electric field and an emf are generated in the circuit to oppose the change. The emf is proportional to the rate of change of magnetic flux (Equation 17.1), which in turn is proportional to the rate of change of current. In symbols,

$$\mathscr{V} \doteq -\frac{d\Phi_B}{dt},$$

$$\Phi_B \sim I, \qquad \frac{d\Phi_B}{dt} \sim \frac{dI}{dt}.$$

Eliminating the intermediary of the magnetic flux, we conclude that the ratio of emf to the time rate of change of current is a constant for any particular circuit or circuit element. It is this ratio that is defined to be the inductance of the circuit*:

Definition of inductance

$$L = -\frac{\mathscr{V}}{dI/dt}. \tag{17.44}$$

The negative sign is necessary in order that the inductance, indicated by L, be a positive quantity. An increasing current generates a negative emf opposing the increase; a decreasing current generates a positive emf promoting persistence of the current. The SI unit of inductance is called the henry (H). Equation 17.44 shows it to be equal to 1 V sec/A or 1 Ω sec:

The henry

$$\text{unit of inductance} = \text{henry (H)} = \text{V sec/A} = \Omega \text{ sec.} \tag{17.45}$$

We note in passing that the henry is also equal to 1 N m/A². Sometimes the permeability constant μ_0, is expressed as

$$\mu_0 = 4\pi \times 10^{-7} \text{ H/m}, \tag{17.46}$$

which is equivalent to Equation 16.3.

---

* Mutual inductance is defined by $L_{21} = |\mathscr{V}_2/(dI_1/dt)|$, the ratio of induced emf in circuit 2 to rate of change of current in circuit 1. Strictly speaking, the quantity L defined by Equation 17.44 for a single circuit should be called self-inductance. More commonly it is called simply inductance.

FIGURE 17.13   The inductor. (a) Schematic representation of an inductor used in circuit diagrams. (b) Typical physical arrangement of actual inductor. Bending the coil into a toroid minimizes the magnetic disturbance of other nearby circuit elements.

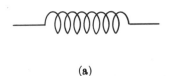

(a)   (b)

THE INDUCTOR

Just as a circuit element designed to add resistance to a circuit is called a resistor, a circuit element designed to add inductance is called an inductor. An ordinary straight wire has some inductance, but far more inductance can be achieved by winding a wire into a coil (Figure 17.13). Then the changing magnetic flux created by one part of the wire has a chance to influence many other parts of the wire. In some circuits it is desired to minimize the so-called transient effects that arise from the time lag in current changes. Then the circuit must be designed with as little inductance as possible. At least equally often, however, the inertial effect of an inductor serves some beneficial purpose in a circuit. Probably the most important role of inductance is in a circuit designed to produce electric oscillations, the subject of the next section.

A coil enhances inductance

Inductance depends only on the geometry of a wire or circuit. For one particular geometrical arrangement, the cylindrical solenoid, inductance is rather easily calculable. A uniformly wound solenoid of length much greater than its diameter generates in its interior a nearly uniform field whose magnitude is, from Equation 16.69,

$$B = \mu_0 \frac{NI}{l}.$$

Here N is the number of turns of wire and l is the length of the solenoid. The flux threading each turn of the wire is then

$$\Phi_B = BA = \mu_0 \frac{NA}{l} I, \tag{17.47}$$

where A is the cross-sectional area of the solenoid. Needed in the law of electromagnetic induction is the rate of change of Φ_B, which is

$$\frac{d\Phi_B}{dt} = \mu_0 \frac{NA}{l} \frac{dI}{dt}.$$

According to Equation 17.1, this is equal to $-\oint \mathbf{E} \cdot d\mathbf{s}$, or $-\mathcal{V}_{\text{loop}}$, for one turn of the wire. The total induced emf is, therefore,

$$\mathcal{V} = N\mathcal{V}_{\text{loop}} = -\mu_0 \frac{N^2 A}{l} \frac{dI}{dt}. \tag{17.48}$$

Finally, from the definition of inductance given by Equation 17.44, we have, for the idealized solenoid,

$$L = \mu_0 \frac{N^2 A}{l}. \tag{17.49}$$

Inductance of a long solenoid

■ EXAMPLE: A coil has 1,000 turns, length 40 cm, and cross-sectional area 10 cm². What is its inductance? What would be its inductance if an iron core of permeability $\kappa_m = 3,000$ were inserted in the coil? From Equation 17.49,

$$L = 4\pi \times 10^{-7} \frac{H}{m} \times \frac{10^6 \times 10^{-3} \ m^2}{0.4 \ m}$$

$$= 3.14 \times 10^{-3} \ H = 3.14 \ \text{millihenry (mH)}.$$

According to Equation 16.78, the effect of an iron core is to increase the field by a factor κ_m. In each of Equations 17.47 through 17.49, this factor should be included on the right side of the equation. The inductance with the iron core is, therefore,

An iron core increases inductance

$$L' = \kappa_m L = 9.42 \ H.$$

These are typical figures for fairly large sized air-core and iron-core inductors. An iron-core inductor in the millihenry range would have much smaller physical dimensions.

■

THE *LR* CIRCUIT

For the analysis of circuits, Equation 17.44 is usefully rewritten

$$\mathcal{V} = -L \frac{dI}{dt}. \tag{17.50}$$

This gives the emf generated across any inductor by a changing current in the inductor. Consider, for example, the so-called *LR* circuit diagrammed in Figure 17.14(a). An inductor and resistor in series are connected to a square wave generator, which, at a fixed frequency of repetition, alters the potential applied across the combination from zero to V_1, back to zero, to V_1, and so on. The circuit is equivalent to the circuit diagrammed in Figure 17.14(b), in which a switch S can be thrown almost instantaneously from position A to position B

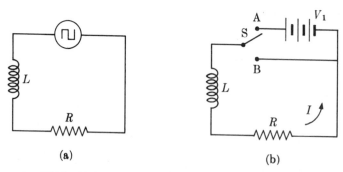

(a)   (b)

FIGURE 17.14   (a) An *LR* combination connected to a square-wave generator. (b) An equivalent circuit in which the *LR* combination is alternately connected to a battery and short circuited. For either circuit, an oscilloscope connected across the resistor would display the potential across the resistor, which is proportional to the current in the circuit.

or from B back to A. We analyze the behavior of the circuit in terms of the second diagram.

Suppose, first, that the switch has been in position A for some time, so that there is a steady current in the circuit,

$$I_1 = \frac{V_1}{R}. \tag{17.51}$$

The idealized inductor has no resistance, so that, for steady current, there is zero potential difference between its ends. (For steady current, the only function of the inductor is to store energy in its magnetic field.) Then, suddenly, at a time we may call $t = 0$, the switch is thrown to position B. The current starts to decrease, generating across the inductor an emf, as given by Equation 17.50. In effect, the emf of the inductor replaces the potential of the battery as the source of the current through the resistor. Experiencing this emf, the resistor conducts current I given by

$$I = \frac{\mathscr{V}}{R}. \tag{17.52}$$

Eliminating $\mathscr{V}$ between Equations 17.50 and 17.52, we get $-L(dI/dt) = IR$, or

$$\frac{dI}{dt} = -\frac{R}{L}I, \tag{17.53}$$

Equation governing LR circuit

which is a differential equation for the current I. Its solution is a function $I(t)$ with the property that the derivative of the function is proportional to the negative of the function. The only function with this property is the decreasing exponential. The solution may be written

$$I = I_1 e^{-Rt/L} = I_1 e^{-t/\tau}. \tag{17.54}$$

Its exponential solution

The quantity τ, given by

$$\tau = \frac{L}{R}, \tag{17.55}$$

is called the time constant of the circuit.* It is the time required for the current to decay to $1/e$ of its initial value (Figure 17.15). (Notice the interesting similarity of behavior of the LR and RC circuits—see Figures 15.40 and 15.41, and Equations 15.123 to 15.125.) As differentiation demonstrates, Equation 17.54 is a solution of Equation 17.53 for any value of the constant I_1. However, in this example we must choose $I_1 = V_1/R$. This is the value of the current the moment before the switch is thrown. Since current cannot change instantaneously, it must also be the value of the current the moment after the switch is thrown.

Suppose that at some later time T the current in the circuit has fallen to zero or very near zero and that the switch S is thrown back to position A. The

---

* Since an actual inductor has some resistance, the quantity R in Equation 17.55 should be the total resistance of the inductor and the resistor.

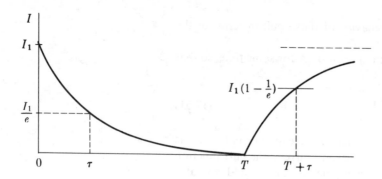

FIGURE 17.15   Current in an *LR* circuit. The switch in Figure 17.14(b) is thrown to position B at $t = 0$ and to position A at $t = T$.

emf applied to the resistor is now $V_1 + \mathcal{V}$ so that the equation governing the circuit is

$$V_1 - L\frac{dI}{dt} = IR. \tag{17.56}$$

As the current grows, the first term on the left side is positive, and the second term is negative. The "back-emf" of the inductor partially offsets the potential supplied by the battery. The net emf applied to the resistor is less than it would be without the inductor. When the current finally builds to its maximum steady value, I_1, the rate of change of current approaches zero, the emf of the inductor approaches zero, and the simple Ohm's law behavior, given by $V_1 = I_1R$, is restored. Equation 17.56 may be re-expressed,

$$L\frac{dI}{dt} + RI - V_1 = 0. \tag{17.57}$$

Although slightly more complicated than Equation 17.53, this differential equation still has a solution expressed in terms of the exponential function. The solution with the appropriate initial condition at $t = T$ is

Solution for rising current

$$I = I_1(1 - e^{-(t-T)/\tau}), \tag{17.58}$$

where $I_1 = V_1/R$ and $\tau = L/R$ (Equations 17.51 and 17.55). The reader may verify that Equation 17.58 is a solution of Equation 17.57 and that it has the proper initial value, $I(T) = 0$. Graphs of Equations 17.54 and 17.58 appear in Figure 17.15.

A typical small inductor has an inductance of about 10^{-2} H and a resistance of a few ohms. Placed in series with a resistor with $R = 100\ \Omega$, its time constant is about 10^{-4} sec. Such a time constant is easy to measure with an oscilloscope but is below the threshold of detectability without instruments. In everyday circuits with lights and small motors, we are dealing with time constants in the millisecond range, so we do not notice the time lags produced by inductance.

17.7   Oscillation: the *LC* circuit

One function of capacitors is to serve as static storage depots for charge and electrical energy. Probably even more important is their role in a.c. circuits. Whenever a capacitor is being charged or discharged, current is effectively flowing "through" it (see Figure 17.9). The current is simply the rate of change of charge on the capacitor:

$$I = \frac{dq}{dt} .$$
(17.59)

Since the charge is expressed in terms of the potential across the capacitor and its capacitance by

$$q = CV,$$

the current can be written

$$I = C \frac{dV}{dt} .$$
(17.60)

Current and potential for a capacitor

A simple but important circuit that is at the heart of most oscillators is the *LC* circuit. In simplest form, it consists of a capacitor and an inductor connected together [Figure 17.16(a)]. We idealize the circuit by ignoring its resistance. When current changes in the circuit, an emf is induced across the inductor so that the inductor may be considered to be a source of potential, much like a battery. Its emf can be equated to the potential across the capacitor. In order to bring Equation 17.50 together with Equation 17.60, we must differentiate it:

$$\frac{d\mathscr{V}}{dt} = -L \frac{d^2I}{dt^2} .$$
(17.61)

Current and potential for an inductor

The equality $\mathscr{V} = V$ means that the two time derivatives are also equal. From Equations 17.60 and 17.61,

$$\frac{I}{C} = -L \frac{d^2I}{dt^2} .$$

This equation may be rewritten in the form

$$\frac{d^2I}{dt^2} = -\frac{1}{LC} I.$$
(17.62)

Equation governing LC circuit

It is a differential equation that asks the question: What function $I(t)$ has a second derivative proportional to the negative of itself? The functions with this property are the sine and cosine functions. The general solution of Equation 17.62 includes both functions. However, we may select a particular solution and write

$$I = I_0 \sin \left(\frac{t}{\sqrt{LC}} \right) = I_0 \sin \omega t,$$
(17.63)

Its sinusoidal solution

where, for notational convenience, we introduce the definition,

$$\omega = \frac{1}{\sqrt{LC}} .$$
(17.64)

This important result states that the current in the idealized *LC* circuit oscillates indefinitely at a frequency determined by the product *LC*. The quantity ω is

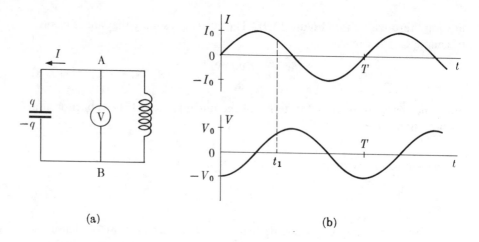

(a)   (b)

FIGURE 17.16   The *LC* circuit. (a) Idealized version of the circuit. Oscillation proceeds indefinitely if $R = 0$. (b) Graphs of *I* vs *t* and *V* vs *t*. At the time t_1, corresponding to the situation shown in the circuit diagram, the current, $I = dq/dt$, is positive and decreasing, and the potential, $V = V_A - V_B$, is positive and increasing.

the angular frequency. The true frequency is $v = \omega/2\pi$, or

The characteristic frequency

$$v = \frac{1}{2\pi\sqrt{LC}}.$$ (17.65)

The inverse of the frequency is the period, T:

$$T = 2\pi\sqrt{LC}.$$ (17.66)

With *L* in henrys and *C* in farads, *T* is in seconds and *v* in sec^{-1}, or Hz.

To find the emf across the inductor, we may differentiate Equation 17.63 and substitute the resulting expression for dI/dt in Equation 17.50. This emf in turn is equal to *V*, the potential across the capacitor, which is, therefore,

$$V = -LI_0\omega \cos \omega t.$$

This may be written

$$V = -V_0 \cos \omega t,$$ (17.67)

Potential and current differ
in phase

where $V_0 = LI_0\omega$. Graphs of *I* vs *t* and *V* vs *t* are shown in Figure 17.16(b). Both *I* and *V* oscillate sinusoidally but with a phase difference of $\pi/2$. It is characteristic of all circuits containing capacitors and/or inductors to have a phase difference between current and potential. Only in a circuit containing resistors alone is *V* directly proportional to *I*.

The quantity V_0 in Equation 17.67 is equal to $LI_0\omega$. Since $\omega = 1/\sqrt{LC}$, we have, for the relation between peak potential V_0 and peak current I_0,

$$V_0 = I_0 \sqrt{\frac{L}{C}}.$$ (17.68)

The behavior of the oscillator can be understood in qualitative terms.

Suppose that at a particular instant the capacitor is charged and that no current flows. Current will then begin to flow as the capacitor discharges through the inductor. Because of the inductance, the current will build up gradually. At some later time, the capacitor will be fully discharged. By this time, however, the current will have built up and the inductor will not let it stop at once. The continuation of the current builds up opposite charge on the capacitor until, finally, the current ceases with the capacitor oppositely charged. It then starts to discharge in the opposite direction, and the cycle continues. In terms of energy, we can describe the oscillation as a continual transformation of magnetic field energy in the inductor to electric field energy in the capacitor and back again.

■ EXAMPLE: What is the energy of an oscillating LC circuit? We may consider an instant of time, say $t = 0$, when $I = 0$. At that instant, the only energy in the circuit is the energy stored in the capacitor. It is

Energy of an LC circuit

$$U = \tfrac{1}{2}CV_0{}^2. \tag{17.69}$$

Because of energy conservation, this must be the energy of the circuit at all other times as well. If $V_0{}^2$ in Equation 17.69 is replaced by $I_0{}^2 L/C$ (from Equation 17.68), another interesting expression for the energy results:

$$U = \tfrac{1}{2}LI_0{}^2. \tag{17.70}$$

This equation has an important and more general interpretation: It must be the energy stored by the inductor (because of the inductor's magnetic field) at an instant when $q = 0$ and the energy of the capacitor is zero. Such a time is $t = \tfrac{1}{4}T = \pi/2\omega$, when $I = I_0$ and $V = 0$. It follows that the stored energy of an inductor at any time is

$$U = \tfrac{1}{2}LI^2. \tag{17.71}$$

Energy stored by an inductor

In general, for any time t, part of the energy of the circuit is stored by the capacitor, part by the inductor. The total energy is

$$U = \tfrac{1}{2}CV^2 + \tfrac{1}{2}LI^2$$
$$= \tfrac{1}{2}CV_0{}^2 \cos^2 \omega t + \tfrac{1}{2}LI_0{}^2 \sin^2 \omega t.$$

Since $\tfrac{1}{2}CV_0{}^2 = \tfrac{1}{2}LI_0{}^2$, this can be written

$$U = \tfrac{1}{2}CV_0{}^2(\cos^2 \omega t + \sin^2 \omega t) = \tfrac{1}{2}CV_0{}^2,$$

verifying that Equation 17.69 gives the energy at all times. ■

In Equation 17.63, I_0 is an arbitrary constant equal to the maximum current in each cycle of oscillation. For the idealized LC circuit of Figure 17.16(a), free of energy loss, any magnitude of oscillating current can be sustained indefinitely. In practice this is, of course, unrealistic. Some resistance in the circuit will drain electromagnetic energy from the circuit during each oscillation, until the current ceases. The idealized circuit is analogous to a frictionless pendulum. Resistance in the circuit acts like friction on the pendulum. To keep the electrical oscillation going, the circuit must be gently "tapped" each cycle to supply the lost energy. This "tapping" can be done by mutual induction from a neighboring circuit or by other methods. If the resistance in the circuit is not

The LC circuit and the
harmonic oscillator: a close
analogy

too great, it has very little effect on the frequency of oscillation, and Equations 17.65 and 17.66 remain good approximations.

The analogy of the electrical oscillator to a swinging pendulum is more than superficial. The equations describing the electrical and mechanical oscillators are mathematically identical. If Equation 17.62 is rewritten

$$L\frac{d^2I}{dt^2} = -\frac{1}{C}I, \qquad (17.72)$$

it bears an obvious kinship to Equation 7.22 for a mechanical oscillator, which can be written

$$m\frac{d^2x}{dt^2} = -kx.$$

The inductance of the circuit plays the same role as the mass of a pendulum (the inertial property). The inverse of the capacitance acts like the force constant k. (For a pendulum of length l, $k = mg/l$.) Also, compare Equations 17.66 and 7.33.

As a practical point of similarity between a pendulum and an oscillator circuit, both are used to keep time. This does not mean that all oscillators drive clocks (although some do). Rather, the oscillator provides a very rapid regularly repeating signal of known frequency that can be used for a number of applications. Chief among them is to generate radio waves of specific frequency. Every radio transmitter contains one or more oscillator circuits, and so does every radio receiver. In the receiver a weak signal from the antenna "taps" at an *LC* circuit within the radio to set it into electrical oscillation (see Figure 17.25). To choose an interesting but less common example, electrical oscillators are used to create the sounds of "electronic music." Some piano tuners have also found it expedient to replace tuning forks with electrical oscillators. Practical oscillators utilizing *LC* circuits can easily provide not only the audible range of frequencies but also a much broader range, from about 1 Hz to about 10^9 Hz.

17.8   The wave nature of light

For centuries, light was a subject of scientific study independent of electricity and magnetism. Finally, in the 1860s, the long strand of optical exploration was woven into the recently united strands of electricity and magnetism, yielding the unified theory of electromagnetism. In the next section, we shall return to this pinnacle of achievement, after summarizing in this section some background facts about the nature of light.

Early knowledge of light

By 1700, several important facts about light were known. White light was known to consist of a mixture of colors. Light was known to deflect upon passing from one medium to another (refraction), the amount of deflection depending on the color. The speed of light in empty space was known to be the same for all colors (otherwise a moon of Jupiter would appear one color when it began to appear from behind Jupiter, later other colors, or white), and the magnitude of this speed was known in rough approximation. Light was known to travel in straight lines in a uniform medium and to experience a slight deflection in passing an obstacle. It was known to carry energy. And a peculiar phenomenon called double refraction was known: Upon entering some crystals, light undergoes not one deflection but two at once, splitting into two separate beams.

In spite of this and other knowledge accumulated during the eighteenth century, the nature of light remained a mystery for another hundred years. The fundamental question to be decided was: Does light consist of particles or is it a wave phenomenon? When the wave theory triumphed early in the nineteenth century, the defeated adherents of the particle theory could scarcely have imagined that after another hundred years light would turn out to consist of particles after all, leading to the modern resolution of the argument: Light is both wave and particle.

Waves vs particles

Given the facts that light travels at a fixed speed in straight lines through empty space carrying energy from one place to another, a quite natural first guess is that light must consist of a stream of particles. This is the view commonly believed to have been championed by Newton, although, in fact, Newton recognized that the evidence about the nature of light was inadequate to decide one way or the other. The idea of light particles raised two problems in particular. (1) Why does an object giving off light apparently lose no weight and an object absorbing light gain no weight? No one had yet imagined massless particles. (2) Why is the speed of light invariable? One might suppose that the particles of different colors of light should travel at different speeds or that a more intense source of light should give off faster particles of light.

Particles, pro and con

The wave theory, whose early champion was Newton's contemporary Christiaan Huygens, accounted nicely for these two difficulties. A wave can transmit energy without conducting mass from one place to another, and it is a feature of some waves to have a fixed speed, independent of their strength and wavelength. The speed of sound in air, for instance, is almost independent of intensity and pitch. Both wave and particle theories can give an account of refraction but with an important difference. The wave theory requires that light move more slowly in the denser medium, the particle theory that it move more quickly in the denser medium. When, in the mid-nineteenth century, experiment finally decided in favor of the slower speed, the wave theory was already rather firmly established.

Arguments for waves

One difficulty with the wave idea seemed to be that it required an all-pervasive substance filling space that could transmit the light vibrations. The ether invented for this purpose had to be a very ethereal substance indeed, for unlike water and air, it had to be totally transparent and frictionless, offering no impediment to the passage of material objects through it. (Otherwise, the earth would dissipate energy and would spiral into the sun.) In spite of these unlikely properties, the ether was acceptable to most scientists.

The remarkable ether

TRIUMPH OF THE WAVE THEORY

Quite independent of arguments and speculation about the ether, a series of experiments in the first two decades of the nineteenth century so strongly supported the wave idea that there could no longer be any doubt that light is a wave motion. The conclusive evidence came through the phenomena of diffraction and interference. A wave passing an obstacle does not leave a precise sharp shadow but is deflected a little into the dark region, giving the shadow a slightly fuzzy edge. This is *diffraction.* Two waves of the same frequency arriving at the same point may strengthen each other if they are crest to crest and trough to trough, or they may cancel each other out if the crest of one coincides with the trough of the other. This is *interference.* A little thought will show that each of these phenomena would be rather difficult to explain in terms of light particles. The wave theory, of course, did more than give a qualitative explanation of the existence of these phenomena. It provided a quantitative theory of diffraction and interference that accorded perfectly with the experimental facts. The exact way in which the light intensity varies smoothly through the region of the fuzzy shadow edge, for example, is predicted, as is the pattern of interference resulting from two slit sources of light. These and other characteristic wave phenomena are discussed in the next chapter.

It is important to note at this point that the interference and diffraction experiments which established the wave nature of light are as valid today as when they were first performed. In spite of our deeper knowledge which leads us now to say that light does, after all, consist of particles—photons—the old experiments cannot be rejected. Fortunately, the theory of quantum mechanics has come along to explain how photons can exhibit both wave and particle properties and how all other particles can do so too.

The same phenomena that proved the existence of light waves provided a tool for measuring wavelength, and it was soon learned that different colors are distinguished by different wavelengths. Visible light spans about one octave* of wavelength, from shortwave violet, 3.5×10^{-7} m (3,500 Å), to long-wave red, 7×10^{-7} m (7,000 Å). Although small, these wavelengths are still several thousand times larger than the diameter of an atom, which is about 2×10^{-10} m (2 Å).

For any propagating wave of definite wavelength and frequency, a very simple equation holds true:

$$\lambda v = v, \tag{17.73}$$

where λ is the wavelength, v is the frequency, and v is the speed of the wave.† Since λ is the length of one full cycle of the wave and since v is the number of cycles per unit time passing a fixed point, the product λv must be the speed of the wave. This is most easily seen, perhaps, by writing $\lambda = vT$, where T is the period of the wave ($T = 1/v$). Then the equation is equivalent to the simple kinematic equation of constant-speed motion, $s = vt$. For light, whose speed in vacuum is

$$c = 3.00 \times 10^8 \text{ m/sec}, \tag{17.74}$$

---

* An octave represents a factor-of-two change in wavelength or frequency. For example, if middle C is tuned to 262 Hz, the C one octave higher is 524 Hz, and the next C (high C) is 1,048 Hz.

† The product of wavelength and frequency is called the *phase velocity* of the wave. Also important is the *group velocity*, the speed at which energy in a wave pulse or wave train is propagated. Group velocity is given by $v_g = -\lambda^2 \, dv/d\lambda$. For electromagnetic waves in a vacuum and other waves for which the product λv is constant, group velocity and phase velocity are equal.

the wavelength-frequency relation is written

$$\lambda v = c. \tag{17.75}$$

A simple equation governing light waves

For example, green light, with $\lambda \cong 5 \times 10^{-7}$ m, has a frequency $v \, (= c/\lambda)$ of about 6×10^{14} Hz.

TRANSVERSALITY

By 1820, light was known to consist of waves; the phenomena of interference had been explained mathematically; the wavelength of light had been measured, at least approximately; the existence of waves shorter and longer than light (ultraviolet and infrared) had been established; and an important new idea, the transversality of light, had found acceptance. Thomas Young in England, who was the first to propose a wave explanation for interference (1801), was also responsible for the suggestion (1817) that the vibrating motion in light waves might be transverse to the direction of propagation of the wave. A garden hose that is stretched out on a lawn and then snapped up and down at one end provides an example of a transverse vibration. The motion of any part of the hose is approximately vertical, transverse to the motion of the wave, which is horizontal. By contrast, sound waves or shock waves that pass through a medium are longitudinal—the material vibrates in the direction in which the wave is proceeding.* A man struck by a shock wave from an explosion is first pushed away from the explosion, then sucked back toward it; thus he is caused to vibrate along the direction of the wave motion. From the time of Christiaan Huygens's pioneer work on waves in the seventeenth century, it had been assumed that light, if a wave, was a longitudinal wave. Nevertheless, Young's contrary suggestion was not long in finding acceptance. Two important puzzles were ripe for solution, and the hypothesis of transversality of light waves nicely accounted for both.

The first of these puzzles was the phenomenon of double refraction, which had gone unexplained since its discovery by Erasmus Bartholinus in 1669. It was necessary only to assume that the speed of light in the crystal depends on the orientation of the direction of vibration. Light vibrating in one direction will then be refracted differently from light vibrating in another direction. For a longitudinal wave there is only one possible direction for the vibration; hence there is no basis for explaining double refraction. It would seem that a transverse wave should have infinitely many different possible directions of vibration (Figure 17.17). Indeed it does. However, it has only two *independent* directions, perpendicular to each other (and to the direction of propagation). Any intermediate direction of vibration can be resolved into the two independent directions, just as any vector in a plane can be resolved into two components. For this reason, crystals are at most doubly-refracting, not triply- or multi-refracting (Figure 17.18).

Double refraction supports the transversality of light waves

---

* Sound waves in a gas are strictly longitudinal. A solid can support transverse sound waves as well as the more common longitudinal waves. A surface wave on water is an example of a combined transverse and longitudinal vibration.

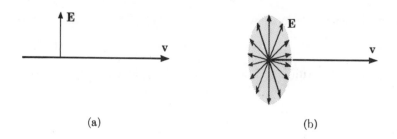

(a)   (b)

FIGURE 17.17   (a) Polarized wave, represented schematically by single electric field vector perpendicular to the direction of propagation. (b) Unpolarized wave, actually a mixture of many different polarized waves, represented by **E** vectors in all possible transverse directions. Every component of the unpolarized wave can be resolved into just two independent polarization directions.

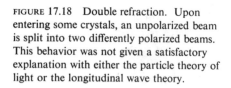

FIGURE 17.18   Double refraction. Upon entering some crystals, an unpolarized beam is split into two differently polarized beams. This behavior was not given a satisfactory explanation with either the particle theory of light or the longitudinal wave theory.

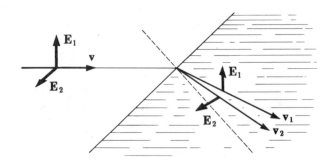

Polarization phenomenon:
another support for
transversality

Apart from double refraction, light was known to have a dual character in general. In 1808 Etienne Malus discovered that light could be polarized by reflection from glass and many other substances. Eight years later Dominique Arago and Augustin Fresnel learned to their surprise that light beams with different polarization could not be made to cancel each other through interference. This was the second important puzzle that was quickly clarified by Young's suggestion of transverse vibration. No matter how arranged, two beams not vibrating in parallel cannot interfere with one another.

Even after these advances, there remained deep mysteries of light that required another century to plumb. Why does light travel at the speed it does, and why is its speed independent of its wavelength? What exactly is the nature of the vibrating medium? What is the mechanism of emission and absorption of light? Why is light polarized by reflection and refraction? What is the connection between light and thermal radiation? What is the connection between light and electricity and magnetism? By 1820 not all of these questions had even been asked, much less answered. Eventually, all of them proved important, and all found answers.

17.9   The electromagnetic theory of light

According to the two basic induction laws (Equations 17.1 and 17.27), electric and magnetic fields can interact in space free of matter. With these laws in hand,

Maxwell went on to predict the existence of electromagnetic waves—combinations of electric and magnetic fields that, through continually oscillating change, reinforce each other and propagate through space. From the laws of electromagnetism can be derived a wave equation satisfied by the electric field and an identical wave equation satisfied by the magnetic field. In addition, the laws imply definite relationships between the two fields in the wave. Among other aspects of the waves, Maxwell could predict these: (1) The electromagnetic wave is transverse. The electric and magnetic fields are perpendicular to each other and to the direction of propagation (Figure 16.12). (2) The electric and magnetic fields in the wave are in a perfect state of balance, each field carrying half the energy. With SI units, this means (from Equation 16.25)

Essential features of electromagnetic waves

$$\frac{1}{2}\,\epsilon_0 \overline{E^2} = \frac{1}{2\mu_0}\,\overline{B^2}. \tag{17.76}$$

Here $\overline{E^2}$ and $\overline{B^2}$ indicate mean-square values of the varying fields. (3) The speed of the waves is a constant given by

$$c = \frac{1}{\sqrt{\mu_0 \epsilon_0}}. \tag{17.77}$$

Since the constant $1/\sqrt{\mu_0 \epsilon_0}$, determined from measurements in electric circuits, was already known to be equal to the speed of light, it was a short step for Maxwell to proceed to the suggestion that light was such an electromagnetic wave. "We can scarcely avoid the inference," he wrote, "that light consists in the transverse undulations of the same medium which is the cause of electric and magnetic phenomena." Thus were the science of optics and the science of electromagnetism united.

The union of light and electromagnetism

★THE WAVE EQUATION

In empty space, the third and fourth of Maxwell's equations, Equations 17.40 and 17.41, take the form

$$\oint \mathbf{E} \cdot d\mathbf{s} = -\frac{d\Phi_B}{dt}, \tag{17.78}$$

$$\oint \mathbf{B} \cdot d\mathbf{s} = \mu_0 \epsilon_0 \frac{d\Phi_E}{dt}. \tag{17.79}$$

The laws of induction in empty space

From these we wish to find separate equations for **E** and **B**. To simplify the mathematics we shall specialize to an **E** field that is in the x direction and a **B** field in the y direction,

$$\mathbf{E} = E(x, y, z, t)\mathbf{i}, \tag{17.80}$$

$$\mathbf{B} = B(x, y, z, t)\mathbf{j}. \tag{17.81}$$

Special assumptions

The arguments show that E and B depend on the spatial coordinates and the time. First let us apply Equation 17.78 to the infinitesimal path C_1 shown in Figure 17.19. The line integral on the left side is, approximately,

$$\oint \mathbf{E} \cdot d\mathbf{s} \cong E(x, y, z + \Delta z, t)\,\Delta x - E(x, y, z, t)\,\Delta x. \tag{17.82}$$

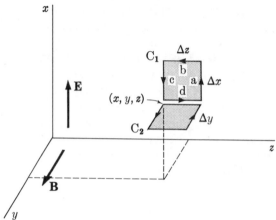

FIGURE 17.19   The law of electromagnetic induction, applied to the path C_1, leads to Equation 17.85, relating the space rate of change of E to the time rate of change of B. The law of magnetoelectric induction, applied to the path C_2, leads to Equation 17.86, relating the space rate of change of B to the time rate of change of E. These particular contours are appropriate for the postulated condition that **E** is in the x direction and **B** is in the y direction.

The first of these two terms is contributed by side a, along which **E** is parallel to d**s**, the second by side c, along which **E** is antiparallel to d**s**. Sides b and d, where **E** is perpendicular to d**s**, contribute nothing. The right side of Equation 17.82 may be written

$$\frac{E(x, y, z + \Delta z, t) - E(x, y, z, t)}{\Delta z} \, \Delta x \, \Delta z.$$

The quotient is approximately the partial derivative of E with respect to z (it is exactly so in the limit $\Delta z \to 0$). Therefore, Equation 17.82 becomes

$$\oint \mathbf{E} \cdot d\mathbf{s} \cong \frac{\partial E}{\partial z} \Delta x \, \Delta z. \tag{17.83}$$

This usefully re-expresses the left side of Equation 17.78. On the right side we need the flux of **B** through the area bounded by C_1. It is

$$\Phi_B = \mathbf{B} \cdot \Delta\mathbf{A} = B \, \Delta x \, \Delta z.$$

Its time derivative is

$$\frac{d\Phi_B}{dt} = \frac{\partial B}{\partial t} \Delta x \, \Delta z. \tag{17.84}$$

Substituting from Equations 17.83 and 17.84 in Equation 17.78 gives

Electromagnetic induction in differential form

$$\frac{\partial E}{\partial z} = -\frac{\partial B}{\partial t}. \tag{17.85}$$

This is the law of electromagnetic induction in differential form for our special choice of field directions; it would also have followed directly from Equation 3 in Table 17.1.

Next we may apply the law of magnetoelectric induction, Equation 17.79, to the path C_2 shown in Figure 17.19. The reasoning is quite similar to that given above for path C_1, and we leave the details to the reader. The result is

$$-\frac{\partial B}{\partial z} = \mu_0\epsilon_0 \frac{\partial E}{\partial t}. \tag{17.86}$$

Magnetoelectric induction in differential form

This differential equation would also follow directly from Equation 4 in Table 17.1.

To obtain an equation for E alone, we may differentiate Equation 17.85 with respect to z to obtain

$$\frac{\partial^2 E}{\partial z^2} = -\frac{\partial^2 B}{\partial z\,\partial t},$$

and differentiate Equation 17.86 with respect to t to obtain

$$-\frac{\partial^2 B}{\partial t\,\partial z} = \mu_0\epsilon_0 \frac{\partial^2 E}{\partial t^2}.$$

Between these two equations the equal magnetic-field terms may be eliminated, leaving

$$\frac{\partial^2 E}{\partial z^2} - \mu_0\epsilon_0 \frac{\partial^2 E}{\partial t^2} = 0. \tag{17.87}$$

A similar procedure to eliminate E between Equations 17.85 and 17.86 leads to

Wave equations for E and B

$$\frac{\partial^2 B}{\partial z^2} - \mu_0\epsilon_0 \frac{\partial^2 B}{\partial t^2} = 0. \tag{17.88}$$

We see that E and B must satisfy the *same* equation. This equation is called the *wave equation*.

The wave equation has many solutions. One that is quite general (although not the most general) is

$$E = f(z - ct), \tag{17.89}$$

A propagating wave solution

where f is *any* twice differentiable function* and where c is given by Equation 17.77. Let us define $u = z - ct$. Then

$$\frac{\partial^2 E}{\partial z^2} = \frac{d^2 f}{du^2},$$

$$\frac{\partial^2 E}{\partial t^2} = c^2 \frac{d^2 f}{du^2}.$$

Putting these two expressions into the wave equation shows that $f(u)$ is indeed a solution, provided

$$c^2 = \frac{1}{\mu_0\epsilon_0}.$$

---

* One must also verify that this solution satisfies Gauss's law in empty space, $\oint \mathbf{E}\cdot d\mathbf{S} = 0$, and that it can be linked to **B** through Equations 17.85, 17.86, and 17.88. It does meet these requirements.

This solution, Equation 17.89, is a *propagating* solution (Figure 17.20). A fixed value of the argument u, say $u = u_1$, propagates along the z axis. For $E = f(u_1) = constant$, z and t are related by

$$z = ct + u_1. \tag{17.90}$$

The disturbance moves in the z direction with speed c. It is an easy matter to show that the corresponding solution for B propagates in the same way.

Wave properties derived from laws of induction

From the considerations so far, we have reached several very significant conclusions. (1) The laws of interacting fields (or laws of induction) lead to wave equations for **E** and **B** that have propagating solutions. (2) The speed of propagation is a fixed constant c determined by μ_0 and ϵ_0. (3) The waves are transverse; for $\mathbf{E} = E\mathbf{i}$ and $\mathbf{B} = B\mathbf{j}$, the waves travel parallel to the z axis.

A propagating wave of special interest is a sinusoidal wave,

A propagating sine wave

$$E = E_0 \sin \left[\frac{2\pi}{\lambda} (z - ct) \right]. \tag{17.91}$$

This is a wave of wavelength λ and frequency $v = c/\lambda$ propagating with speed c in the z direction. Since it has the form of Equation 17.89, it is a solution of Equation 17.87. To find the corresponding solution for B, we may use Equations 17.85 and 17.86. These give

$$\frac{\partial B}{\partial t} = - \frac{2\pi}{\lambda} E_0 \cos \left[\frac{2\pi}{\lambda} (z - ct) \right],$$

$$\frac{\partial B}{\partial z} = \frac{1}{c^2} \frac{2\pi c}{\lambda} E_0 \cos \left[\frac{2\pi}{\lambda} (z - ct) \right].$$

(In the second equation, $\mu_0 \epsilon_0$ has been replaced by $1/c^2$.) It is easy to see that an expression for B that has these derivatives is

B is in phase with E

$$B = B_0 \sin \left[\frac{2\pi}{\lambda} (z - ct) \right], \tag{17.92}$$

with

$$B_0 = \frac{E_0}{c}. \tag{17.93}$$

Thus B and E vibrate in phase as they propagate together along the z axis. This particular solution is the one depicted in Figure 16.12.

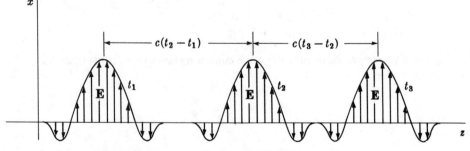

FIGURE 17.20   "Snapshots" of $\mathbf{E} = f(z - ct)\mathbf{i}$ at several times. The pulse propagates at the speed $c = 1/\sqrt{\mu_0 \epsilon_0}$.

Finally, we may inquire about the energy density in the propagating wave. Since the average value of $\sin^2 \theta$ is $\frac{1}{2}$, the mean-square values of E and B are

$$\overline{E^2} = \tfrac{1}{2}E_0{}^2,$$

$$\overline{B^2} = \tfrac{1}{2}B_0{}^2 = \frac{\tfrac{1}{2}E_0{}^2}{c^2} = \tfrac{1}{2}\mu_0\epsilon_0 E_0{}^2.$$

The average energy density of the electric field is

$$u_E = \tfrac{1}{2}\epsilon_0\overline{E^2} = \tfrac{1}{4}\epsilon_0 E_0{}^2. \tag{17.94}$$

The average energy density of the magnetic field is

Energy is equally divided

$$u_B = \frac{1}{2\mu_0}\,\overline{B^2} = \tfrac{1}{4}\epsilon_0 E_0{}^2. \tag{17.95}$$

These results confirm Equation 17.76. The energy is equally divided between the electric and magnetic fields. It is a peculiarity of SI units that for this state of balance, E_0 and B_0 are *not* equal. However, we may say that in a physical sense the relationship $B_0 = E_0/c$ (Equation 17.93) corresponds to "equal intensity" for the electric and magnetic fields.

17.10   The electromagnetic spectrum

Although Maxwell's theory provided a speed restriction—that all electromagnetic waves must travel in empty space at the same speed c—it provided no restriction on frequency or wavelength. In fact, far from restricting frequency, it opened up the possibility of a limitless range of frequencies and wavelengths. At the time of Maxwell's work, the known band of frequencies extended from infrared to ultraviolet, including visible light and extending somewhat beyond the visible both to higher and lower frequencies. The vast panorama of electromagnetic radiation, of which visible light forms only a narrow slice (Figure 17.21), remained to be discovered.

The wave equation places no limit on λ or v

When a narrow beam of white light passes through a prism, the fact that different wavelengths are refracted differently causes the beam to diverge so that the beam emerging from the prism produces a spread-out image showing the distinct colors from red to violet (Figure 17.22). To this band of colors Newton gave the name *spectrum* (the Latin word for appearance or visible manifestation). By now the term "spectrum" has evolved to mean any orderly arrangement according to wavelength or frequency,* be it visual, photographic, graphical, or tabular.

The meaning of a spectrum

The fact that the speed predicted for electromagnetic radiation was equal to the known speed of light was by itself strong evidence in favor of Maxwell's suggestion that light is electromagnetic radiation. To this piece of evidence were added the facts that the new theory explained the transverse character of light

---

* Since photon energy is proportional to frequency, modern physicists refer also to energy spectra. Led further by the mass-energy equivalence, we speak of the mass spectrum of elementary particles.

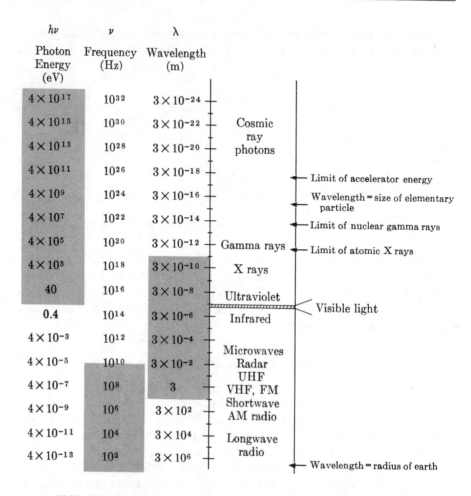

$h\nu$ Photon Energy (eV)	ν Frequency (Hz)	λ Wavelength (m)		
4×10^{17}	10^{32}	3×10^{-24}		
4×10^{15}	10^{30}	3×10^{-22}	Cosmic ray photons	
4×10^{13}	10^{28}	3×10^{-20}		
4×10^{11}	10^{26}	3×10^{-18}		Limit of accelerator energy
4×10^9	10^{24}	3×10^{-16}		Wavelength = size of elementary particle
4×10^7	10^{22}	3×10^{-14}		Limit of nuclear gamma rays
4×10^5	10^{20}	3×10^{-12}	Gamma rays	Limit of atomic X rays
4×10^3	10^{18}	3×10^{-10}	X rays	
40	10^{16}	3×10^{-8}	Ultraviolet	Visible light
0.4	10^{14}	3×10^{-6}	Infrared	
4×10^{-3}	10^{12}	3×10^{-4}	Microwaves	
4×10^{-5}	10^{10}	3×10^{-2}	Radar UHF	
4×10^{-7}	10^8	3	VHF, FM	
4×10^{-9}	10^6	3×10^2	Shortwave AM radio	
4×10^{-11}	10^4	3×10^4	Longwave radio	
4×10^{-13}	10^2	3×10^6		Wavelength = radius of earth

FIGURE 17.21   The electromagnetic spectrum. As indicated by the shading, waves are usually characterized by frequency at the low-frequency end of the spectrum, by photon energy at the high-frequency end, and by wavelength in an intermediate region.

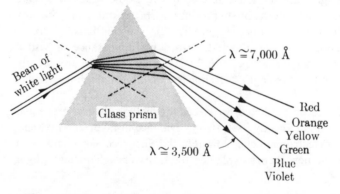

FIGURE 17.22   The spectrum of visible light. Since a prism refracts different frequencies differently, it serves to separate a beam of white light into its component frequencies. This separation is called dispersion.

waves, that it predicted an equal speed for all colors (all wavelengths), and that it predicted that light should be slowed in material media. Nevertheless, a *direct* proof of the electromagnetic nature of light was lacking, for no one knew how to create light by electromagnetic means or how to detect electric and magnetic fields in a light beam. The first direct demonstration that waves of electric and magnetic fields can propagate through space came not through the study of light but through the generation of radio waves.

In 1887, Heinrich Hertz in Germany succeeded in creating and detecting electromagnetic waves.* His transmitter consisted of the oscillatory discharge of a capacitor across a spark gap. His detector (receiving antenna) consisted simply of a wire bent into a loop with its two ends not quite touching. A visible spark across the gap of the detector signaled the presence of an oscillatory current in the detecting loop, which in turn revealed the presence of an oscillatory electric field in the vicinity. The sensitivity of the detector was enhanced by designing it so that its natural oscillation frequency was equal to the frequency of the transmitting circuit. It is exactly this principle that is used in modern radios. Turning the dial of a radio changes the natural frequency of the detecting circuit and thereby changes the frequency of the electromagnetic radiation to which the radio is sensitive.

The earliest radio waves

Hertz was able to reflect his radio waves, to diffract them, to demonstrate that they were influenced by intervening matter, to show that they traveled at finite speed, to prove them to be transverse, and to measure their wavelength by means of interference effects. The frequencies utilized by Hertz were around 100 megahertz (10^8 Hz) in what is now called the VHF band (now used for television and aircraft communications, among other things). The wavelength of a 100 MHz wave is

$$\lambda = \frac{c}{v} = \frac{3 \times 10^8 \text{ m/sec}}{10^8 \text{ sec}^{-1}} = 3 \text{ m}.$$

Hertz's oscillator frequencies were a happy choice, because they provided macroscopic wavelengths of convenient size. This was not altogether a coincidence. A macroscopic antenna usually emits a macroscopic wavelength. A single atom, by contrast, is a submicroscopic "antenna" whose principal radiation is much shorter in wavelength than radio waves.

Beginning around 1800, knowledge of the radiant spectrum expanded gradually from the visible into the infrared and ultraviolet, and by 1900 the region accessible to optical experiments had grown from one octave to eight. After 1887, the longer wave radio spectrum was rapidly filled in. By the early years of this century wavelengths from less than 1 cm to many km had been successfully created and detected. Practical utilization of radio for communication began in 1900 at the lower frequencies, with the VHF and UHF

Extensions of the known spectrum

---

* David Hughes in England was probably the first person to create electromagnetic radiation by means of an oscillatory circuit and detect it at a distance. His work of 1879–1880 went unreported and unknown for many years. To Hertz belongs the priority of publication. The credit due Hertz, however, is not so much for the accident of first publication as for his achievement over an extended series of experiments in conclusively demonstrating the wave properties of the new radiation and discovering its points of similarity to light.

regions being exploited only in recent decades.* Radar operating with wavelengths from 1 to 10 cm was a development of the 1940s. A commonly encountered wavelength in modern student laboratories is 3 cm, quite convenient for studies of electromagnetic wave properties. Waves in this part of the spectrum are called (somewhat confusingly) microwaves because their wavelengths are very much less than the wavelengths of normal radio waves.

Like the transcontinental railroad, which was simultaneously pushed from east and west toward a meeting point, the electromagnetic spectrum was attacked from two directions—by electronic means at low frequencies and by optical means at higher frequencies—until a meeting point was reached in the 1930s around 0.01 to 0.1 cm, the frontier between microwaves and infrared waves. At the long wavelength end of the spectrum, commercial broadcasting in the United States extends down to 500 kHz (5×10^5 sec^{-1}), with aircraft and marine stations down to 100 kHz. Government use of the spectrum extends down to less than 1 kHz, where a single wavelength spans more than 300 kilometers.

At the other end of the spectrum, X rays were discovered by Wilhelm Roentgen in 1895 and nuclear gamma rays by Paul Villard in 1900. Still higher energy gamma rays showed up in the cosmic radiation in the 1920s. Man-made gamma rays at accelerators now extend to frequencies as great as 5×10^{24} Hz or wavelengths as short as 6×10^{-17} m, yet cosmic rays easily hold the frequency record at about 10^{32} Hz.

The discovery of X rays is a particularly interesting chapter of physics, for it was an accident and it triggered an even more famous accident, the discovery of radioactivity (Chapter 26). Roentgen found, by chance, that radiation emerging from the place where an energetic electron beam (then still called a cathode ray) struck the glass wall of a cathode-ray tube could produce fluorescence in certain salts. Because the radiation was new and its properties unknown, he called it X radiation. It was soon guessed that X radiation might be electro-

X rays proved to be electromagnetic waves

magnetic radiation.† The proof of its wave nature came in 1912, when Max von Laue successfully produced X-ray interference patterns and measured X-ray wavelengths. Von Laue's technique was simple and ingenious. He let the regular arrays of atoms in a crystal serve as centers of diffraction to produce measurable interference patterns. Microwaves can be significantly diffracted by strips of metal or wire, visible light waves by finely etched lines on a glass plate. X rays, with wavelengths one-thousandth of the wavelength of light or less, require a correspondingly finer mesh of lines or points to produce much diffraction. Fortunately, nature, in assembling crystals in row upon row of perfect order, provides exactly the array needed, with spacing between atoms of about one angstrom (10^{-10} m). Von Laue's method is still in use, but now X rays are the tools and crystals the objects of study instead of the other way around.

An electromagnetic wave can be characterized by its frequency, by its

---

* The long-distance communication record of 200 million miles established between earth and a Mariner space vehicle in 1966 utilized frequencies above 2,000 MHz in the UHF band.

† Support for this idea was provided by Charles Barkla's discovery in 1904 that X radiation could be polarized. Polarization is a feature of transverse waves.

wavelength, or by the energy of one of its photons. All three of these quantities are in common use (and all appear in Figure 17.21), each suited to a particular domain of the spectrum. At the low-frequency end of the spectrum, where the electric circuits used to create and detect radio waves are characterized by certain natural oscillation frequencies, the frequency of the wave is the convenient way to catalogue it. In the optical region, where diffraction and interference effects separate the spectrum into its components, wavelength is the usual measure. Gamma rays, detected individually as single photons, are most often specified by their energy. Photon energy is related to frequency by

Gamma rays are usually characterized by their energy

$$E = h\nu. \tag{17.96}$$

Planck's constant, h, in units commonly used in the nuclear domain, is

$$h = 4.136 \times 10^{-21} \text{ MeV sec.} \tag{17.97}$$

A visible photon has an energy around 2 eV. Typical nuclear gamma ray energies are 0.1 to 1 MeV.

Being infinite in extent, the electromagnetic spectrum can never be fully explored. However, with known wavelengths extending from one-billionth the size of an elementary particle to hundreds of kilometers, the exploration has been rather complete and no uncharted gaps remain. The ratio of the highest to the lowest frequency included in Figure 17.21 is 10^{30}. In musical language, this is about 100 octaves. By comparison, a piano covers about 7 octaves, the human ear about 10 octaves (of sound waves), an AM radio receiver two octaves, and an FM radio receiver less than one octave (of electromagnetic waves). Visible light accounts for only one of these 100 octaves of electromagnetic radiation.

200 years ago, 1 octave; today, 100 octaves

17.11   Emission and absorption

An electromagnetic wave can travel a billion light-years through empty space, or it can jump an angstrom from one atom to another in solid matter. Its wavelength can span the earth or it can fit comfortably inside an elementary particle. Whatever its history, whatever its intensity, whatever its wavelength, there is one sure constant feature of its origin and its termination: accelerated charge. An electromagnetic wave can be created only by the acceleration of charge; it can be absorbed only when it causes charge to be accelerated.* The mechanism of the radiation process is illustrated qualitatively in Figure 17.23. Note that the wave emitted in this example will be polarized (in which direction?).

Electromagnetic waves begin and end with accelerated charge

Energy change must accompany the acceleration of charge. An emitting charged particle loses energy; an absorbing charged particle gains energy. These energy changes in matter are of course precisely balanced by energy changes in the electromagnetic field. It is interesting to examine the entire electromagnetic spectrum in terms of the single idea of accelerated charge. For each part of the spectrum, what charged particle creates a particular wave? In what system does the charge move and over how great a distance? What causes the acceleration of the emitting particle? What charged particle is most likely to absorb the

---

* If magnetic poles exist, they too could create and absorb electromagnetic waves.

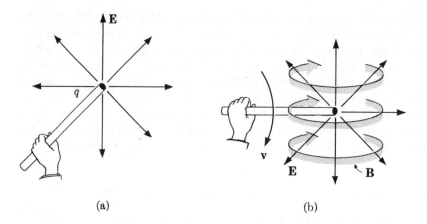

(a)   (b)

FIGURE 17.23   (a) Surrounding a stationary charge is an electric field but no magnetic field. The charge does not radiate. (b) The same charge in motion creates both an electric field and a magnetic field. If the stick is shaken back and forth at frequency v, a small fraction of the field energy escapes to propagate away as an electromagnetic wave of this frequency.

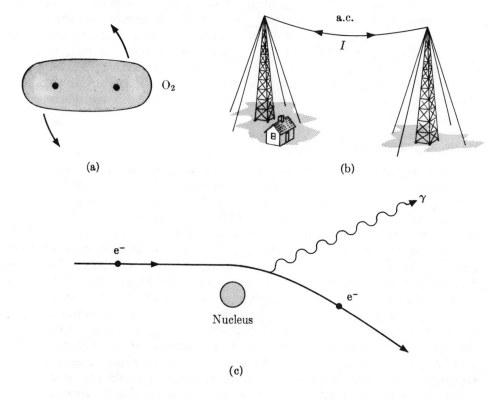

FIGURE 17.24   Sources of electromagnetic radiation. (a) Natural oscillation of charge, as in a rotating molecule. (b) Man-made oscillation of charge, as in a radio transmitter. (c) Acceleration of charge without oscillation, as in the deflection of a high-speed electron by a nucleus.

wave? To answer these questions in a survey of the entire spectrum, it is useful to discuss separately three kinds of accelerated motion: (1) oscillation of charged particles in nature; (2) man-made oscillation of charge; and (3) accelerated motion that is not oscillatory (Figure 17.24).

NATURAL OSCILLATION OF CHARGE

Long before Hertz—indeed, several billion years before—certain parts of the electromagnetic spectrum must already have been well filled with radiation. Every atom in nature has as the very basis of its structure accelerated charge in the form of circulating electrons. Therefore, every atom is potentially a radiator. There was a brief period of consternation in physics in the early part of this century, in the interval between the discovery that atoms contain electrons and the invention of the quantum theory of atoms. At that time the question was asked: Why don't all atoms radiate continuously? Niels Bohr gave the answer that they are prevented from doing so by the conservation of energy.

He postulated that every atom has a lowest energy state, or "ground state" (now a well-established fact). In its ground state an atom can lose no further energy and, therefore, cannot emit radiation despite the continual acceleration of its oscillating electrons. In a higher energy state, or "excited state," however, the electrons can give rise to electromagnetic radiation. According to classical theory, the frequency of the emitted radiation should be equal to the frequency of the oscillating electron. This is a familiar idea for sound waves. If a mechanical system (for instance, a piano string) vibrates at frequency v, it emits sound of frequency v. In the quantum domain, this equality is lost. The radiated frequency is determined only by the energy change of the atom, according to the Planck-Einstein equation, $\Delta E = hv$. Under certain circumstances, the oscillating electron can undergo a transition to a nearby energy state so that the energy ΔE is small. Then the emitted frequency v, being proportional to ΔE, is also small, possibly much less than the actual oscillation frequency of the electron. As a general rule, however, the radiated frequency from an atom or any other system is expected to be of the same order of magnitude as the oscillation frequency of the charged particles in the system. The classically expected connection between mechanical frequency and radiated frequency is roughly correct most of the time.

Radiation by atoms

In general, radiation frequency ≈ mechanical frequency

Consider an electron circling a proton at a distance of 1 Å ($r = 10^{-10}$ m). The electron experiences a Coulomb centripetal force given by

$$F = \frac{1}{4\pi\epsilon_0} \frac{e^2}{r^2}.$$

According to Newtonian mechanics, which will suffice for this approximate calculation, its acceleration is v^2/r. The mass of the electron times the acceleration is equal to the force:

$$\frac{mv^2}{r} = \frac{1}{4\pi\epsilon_0} \frac{e^2}{r^2}.$$

This equation can be solved for the speed v to give

$$v = \sqrt{\frac{e^2}{4\pi\epsilon_0 mr}}. \tag{17.98}$$

The oscillation frequency of the electron is equal to its speed divided by the circumference of its circular orbit, or

$$\nu_e = \frac{v}{2\pi r}.$$

Substituting for v from Equation 17.98 gives a final result for the electron frequency:

$$\nu_e = \frac{1}{2\pi} \sqrt{\frac{e^2}{4\pi\epsilon_0 mr^3}}. \tag{17.99}$$

Frequency of a circling electron

Evaluation of the right side of this equation in SI units gives

$$\nu_e = \frac{1}{2\pi} \sqrt{\frac{(9 \times 10^9 \text{ N m}^2/\text{C}^2)(1.60 \times 10^{-19} \text{ C})^2}{(9.1 \times 10^{-31} \text{ kg})(10^{-10} \text{ m})^3}}$$
$$= 2.5 \times 10^{15} \text{ Hz}.$$

An electromagnetic wave of this frequency lies in the ultraviolet, and indeed most atoms emit readily in the ultraviolet. The outermost, or valence, electrons of atoms, typically about 1 Å from the nucleus, are principally responsible for the emission of visible and ultraviolet light. Electrons closer to the nucleus, experiencing greater acceleration, are responsible for the higher frequency X rays. Molecules have a more complex range of possible emission frequencies, *Molecular radiation* because they have, besides electronic motion similar to atoms, bulk motion of rotation and vibration. Since the atoms composing a molecule are much more massive than electrons, they move at a more stately pace and emit correspondingly lower-frequency radiation than do electrons. Molecular rotation and vibration are important sources of infrared radiation.

Nuclear radiation
  Within a nucleus, a proton, although massive, experiences such a strong nuclear force that its oscillation frequency is actually much greater than the oscillation frequency of atomic electrons—in fact about one million times greater. Accordingly, nuclear gamma rays are about one million times more energetic than visible photons.

  To summarize the emission of radiation by naturally occurring oscillation of charge: Molecular vibration and rotation produce infrared radiation; oscillation of the outermost electrons in atoms and molecules produces primarily visible light and ultraviolet radiation; more tightly bound electrons near the nucleus of an atom produce X radiation; within the nucleus, the accelerated motion of protons and neutrons produce still higher frequency gamma rays. Some quantum transitions are also known in atoms and molecules whose energy changes are so small that the emitted radiation is in the radio and microwave region. However, these radiations are weak. Electrons "prefer" to emit radiation with a frequency not greatly different from their own frequency of oscillation.

Absorption parallels emission
  A good emitter of radiation is a good absorber of the same radiation. Molecules readily absorb infrared radiation; atoms absorb visible light and ultraviolet light; nuclei preferentially absorb gamma rays. X rays emitted by a

particular atom are readily absorbed by the same kind of atom. However, the very high frequency X rays emitted by heavy atoms are not easily absorbed by lighter atoms because in the lighter atom, not even the innermost electron has a sufficiently high frequency of oscillation to match the X-ray frequency. This fact underlies X-ray photography and explains why high-frequency, or "hard," X rays easily penetrate organic matter composed mostly of hydrogen, carbon, nitrogen, and oxygen (atomic numbers 1, 6, 7, and 8) but penetrate calcium-rich bone with difficulty (the atomic number of calcium is 20) and heavy metals scarcely at all.

Note that in the catalogue of natural emitters, the larger the system, the larger the wavelength (or the lower the frequency). Molecules are larger than atoms. Valence electrons occupy more space than inner electrons, which in turn occupy more space than nuclei. A longer wavelength (or lower frequency) can be achieved by either decreasing the speed of the oscillating charge or increasing the distance it traverses in each cycle of oscillation. An approximate formula relating the emitted wavelength to the speed of the emitting particle and to the size of its orbit is

$$\lambda \cong \frac{c}{v} d. \qquad (17.100)$$

Wavelength determined by size and speed of emitter

Here λ is the wavelength, c is the speed of light, v is the average speed of the oscillating particle, and d is the distance covered by the particle in each cycle. It is left as a problem to derive this equation. Notice that since the ratio c/v must be greater than 1, the emitted wavelength must be as large or larger than the emitting system.

MAN-MADE OSCILLATION OF CHARGE

Any wire conducting alternating current is a radiator of electromagnetic waves. At low frequency, such as 60 Hz, the radiated energy is small. At high frequency, such as 1 MHz, the radiated energy can be large, especially if the length of the radiating wire—the antenna—is comparable to the wavelength of the radiation. Information is superimposed on the radiated "carrier wave" either by varying its intensity (amplitude modulation, AM) or by varying its frequency slightly above and below the standard frequency (frequency modulation, FM). Television uses a combination of AM and FM.

Radio waves

A receiving antenna can be thought of as simply a collection of charged particles—the mobile conduction electrons in the metal antenna—ready and able to be accelerated by an arriving electromagnetic wave. Because the receiving antenna is coupled to a circuit with a characteristic natural frequency of oscillation, a large current will be generated in the antenna only by a wave whose frequency is equal to the characteristic frequency of the receiver circuit (Figure 17.25). The electric field in the incoming wave taps the electrons in the wire back and forth, perhaps two million times per second. If the receiver circuit oscillates naturally at this same rate, it is said to be in *resonance* with the incoming wave. This electrical resonance is closely analogous to the more familiar mechanical resonance. If a child on a swing is pushed repeatedly at a frequency different from the natural frequency of the swing, very little motion results.

Resonance is vital to radio reception

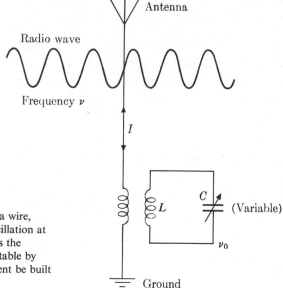

FIGURE 17.25   Part of the circuit in a radio receiver. In the antenna wire, connected to ground through an inductor, electrons are set into oscillation at the frequency v of the arriving radiation. Mutual induction couples the antenna to an oscillator circuit whose natural frequency v_0 is adjustable by means of a variable capacitor. Only when $v = v_0$ will a large current be built up in the oscillator circuit. This is the phenomenon of resonance.

However, if the pushes are in resonance with the natural frequency of the swing, each push adds a little more to the amplitude until the swing gains a large energy. Without the phenomenon of resonance, radio and TV receivers would be useless, for they would receive only a very weak jumble of the myriad of different frequencies impinging on their antennas.

Radio frequencies are "low"

In a typical AM broadcasting antenna, the current reverses direction 2 million times per second (1 million full cycles per second, or 1 MHz). This seems rapid, but viewed in proper perspective, it is slow. In 10^{-6} sec, radio waves can travel 300 m, about one-fifth of a mile. In much less than 10^{-6} sec, signals can travel from one part to any other part of a normal-sized electric circuit. Man-made oscillations of 1 MHz or even 100 MHz are not difficult to create with electrons in wires. At higher frequencies difficulties do arise, associated with the physical size of electric circuits. For infrared radiation, the "oscillator circuit" is a single molecule. As man pushed radio frequencies higher and higher toward the infrared, he had to devise ever smaller circuits, in which electric signals could get from one part of the circuit to another in less than the time of a single cycle of oscillation. In the microwave region, where wavelengths are measured in centimeters or millimeters, the oscillator is entirely contained by a single evacuated tube, a klystron or a magnetron. In these tubes, electrons oscillate over distances of a few millimeters in space, in contrast to their oscillation over many meters of wire in radio transmitters. Developed over the past few decades, these tubes have successfully bridged the gap between radio and infrared.

ACCELERATION WITHOUT OSCILLATION

At extremely high frequencies beyond the range of nuclear gamma rays, where neither man nor nature has constructed oscillators, single or nonrepeating accelerations are the only source of radiation. One form of such radiation is

called *bremsstrahlung* (one of many German words that have entered the   *Bremsstrahlung: radiation by*
international vocabulary of science: it means "deceleration radiation"). When   *deflection*
a high-energy charged particle is deflected, it can emit one or more photons
and so lose energy. Aside from the limitation imposed by the conservation of
energy, there is no restriction on the frequency of the photon. The particle
could give up almost all of its energy to a single high-frequency photon, or it
could lose but a tiny fraction of its energy to a low-frequency photon. However,
the modern quantum theory of electromagnetism successfully predicts the relative
probabilities for the emission of different frequencies.

Irregular and nonrepeating acceleration is also an important source of lower
frequency radiation. In the sun, electrons and protons move randomly, collide
frequently, and emit a broad spectrum of radiation. A metal heated to in-
candescence emits light in a similar way, from random accelerations of electrons
in the material. This type of radiation, called thermal radiation, contains a wide
range of frequencies but is particularly strong in photons whose energy is not
very different from the average energy of the randomly accelerated charged
particles. Mathematically, this statement reads

$$h\nu \cong \tfrac{3}{2}kT,$$

in which the left side is the energy of a "typical" photon and the right side is the
average kinetic energy of the particles. For ideal thermal radiation, called
"black-body radiation," resulting from perfectly established thermal equilibrium   *Black-body radiation*
between photons and material particles, the average photon energy is somewhat
less than twice the average particle energy:

$$h\nu_{\text{av}} = 2.70kT. \tag{17.101}$$

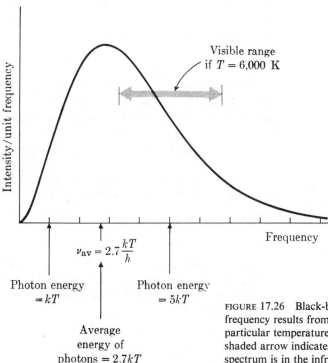

$$\nu_{\text{av}} = 2.7\frac{kT}{h}$$

Photon energy
$= kT$

Photon energy
$= 5kT$

Average
energy of
photons $= 2.7kT$

FIGURE 17.26   Black-body radiation. The distribution of intensity vs
frequency results from the random acceleration of atoms or molecules at a
particular temperature *T*. For the sun's surface temperature of 6,000 K, the
shaded arrow indicates the visible range of frequencies. The peak of the solar
spectrum is in the infrared region. Its tail extends into the ultraviolet.

The distribution of intensity in black-body radiation is shown in Figure 17.26. Solar radiation and radiation from the tungsten filament of a light bulb approximate this distribution. The yellow light from a sodium vapor lamp, by contrast, is predominantly of a single frequency (monochromatic). It results not from random accelerations of electrons but from a particular quantum transition of the valence electron in the sodium atom.

Every emission process has its corresponding absorption process. Since a single deflection of a charged particle can cause a photon to be emitted, photon absorption can give to a charged particle a single pulse of acceleration. Such an absorption process is called a free-free transition since the absorbing particle is in a free state both before and after the absorption.* This is a common process in the sun, where photons are constantly being absorbed as well as emitted.

One single important idea has been presented in this section: The emission and absorption of electromagnetic radiation is associated with the acceleration of charge. The acceleration can be the leisurely oscillation back and forth of a current in an antenna or the frenetic oscillation of an electron in an atom, the gentle deflection of a proton in a galactic magnetic field or the violent deflection of a pion in a nuclear collision. From one situation to another the frequency may be vastly different, the physical system unrelated, the physical manifestations of the radiation unrecognizably altered; but the underlying idea of an electromagnetic wave coupled to an accelerated charge remains the unchanged unifying thread tying all parts of nature together.

---

* A bound-bound transition is one in which an electron absorbs a photon and jumps from one bound state to another in an atom or molecule. In a bound-free transition, an atomic or molecular electron absorbs enough energy to be ejected from a bound state to a free state.

Summary of ideas and definitions

(Some of the most important equations and ideas are summarized in Section 17.5; they are not repeated here.)

The interrelationship and consistency of different laws of electromagnetism are revealed by considering the same phenomenon in different frames of reference and by using Newton's third law. For example:

Given: A charge moving through a static magnetic field experiences a force. *Change of frame*: A changing magnetic flux creates an electric field. *From Newton's third law*: A moving charge creates a magnetic field.

Static electric fields are conservative; changing electric fields are not.

Definition of the weber (Wb): A changing magnetic flux through a loop is 1 Wb/sec if it generates an emf of 1 V in the loop.

Definition of the tesla (T): 1 T = 1 Wb/m².

Principle of the electric generator: An emf is generated in a coil that rotates in a magnetic field. The motion determines the emf. External circuits determine the current.

In a betatron, a changing magnetic field serves both to accelerate electrons to higher speed and also to guide them in a circular track. The field at the orbital radius must be half the average field within the orbit.

"Displacement current" is defined as $\epsilon_0 \, d\Phi_E/dt$. When added to true current, it generalizes Ampère's law to include magnetoelectric induction.

Outside a circular parallel-plate capacitor being charged, the magnetic field is proportional to $1/r$ (Biot-Savart law, Equation 17.32); inside the capacitor, the field is proportional to r (Equation 17.35).

In processes of change, induced effects produce counter effects that oppose the change. This is Lenz's law, an implication of energy conservation.

An application of Lenz's law: The induced current in a generator must be in such a direction that the torque on the coil opposes its motion.

Inductance is defined by

$$L = -\frac{\mathscr{V}}{dI/dt},$$ (17.44)

the ratio of induced emf to rate of change of current in a circuit element. Its SI unit is the henry (H).

The inductance of a long solenoid is $L = \mu_0 N^2 A/l$ (Equation 17.49). A ferromagnetic core increases its inductance by a factor κ_m.

Because of inductance, current cannot change instantaneously. In an LR circuit, current obeys an exponential law of change, with a time constant $\tau = L/R$ (Equations 17.54 and 17.58).

An ideal LC circuit without resistance oscillates with frequency

$$\nu = \frac{1}{2\pi\sqrt{LC}}.$$ (17.65)

The potential and current in the circuit differ in phase by $\pi/2$.

The energy stored in an inductor is

$$U = \tfrac{1}{2}LI^2.$$ (17.71)

The phenomena of interference and diffraction gave crucial support to the wave theory of light.

Frequency and wavelength of electromagnetic radiation are related by

$$\lambda\nu = c.$$ (17.75)

The speed of light c is related to the electromagnetic constants ϵ_0 and μ_0 by

$$c = \frac{1}{\sqrt{\mu_0\epsilon_0}}.$$ (17.77)

In an electromagnetic wave, the electric and magnetic fields are related by $\overline{B^2} = \overline{E^2}/c^2 = \mu_0\epsilon_0\overline{E^2}$ so that the two fields share equally the energy in the wave.

In space free of matter, **E** and **B** satisfy the same partial differential equation, called the wave equation (Equations 17.87 and 17.88). This equation has solutions that propagate at speed c.

About 100 octaves of electromagnetic radiation have been explored. Visible light spans one octave.

Man-made oscillation of charge stimulates radiation from radio waves to infrared.

Natural oscillation of charge stimulates radiation from high-frequency radio waves (atoms and molecules) to gamma rays (atomic nuclei).

Acceleration of charge without oscillation accounts for bremsstrahlung and for thermal radiation, as from the sun or an incandescent bulb.

QUESTIONS

Section 17.1

Q17.1 A loop of wire is placed between the pole faces of a large electromagnet. (1) What should be the orientation of the loop in order to maximize the magnetic flux through it? (2) In what ways might the flux through the loop then be reduced to zero?

Q17.2 The lines of a uniform magnetic field are perpendicular to the plane of a loop of wire. As the loop is pulled to one side without change of orientation, does the magnetic flux through the loop change? Is an emf induced?

Q17.3 Is it necessary to have a loop of wire in order to define magnetic flux? Can the flux through a fixed path in space change? If so, how? If not, why not?

Q17.4 A charged particle moving across lines of magnetic field near a magnet experiences a force. Observer A, who is at rest with respect to the magnet, says the force is a magnetic force caused by the motion of the particle in the magnetic field. How does Observer B, who is traveling with the particle, describe the force?

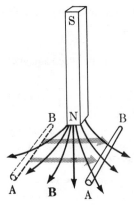

Section 17.2

Q17.5 As shown in the figure, a wire segment is moved near a magnet. Because of the motion, an emf is generated between points A and B. How should the conditions of this experiment be altered in order to (1) increase the magnitude of the emf without changing its sign? (2) change the sign of the emf?

Q17.6 It is changing magnetic *flux* (not field) that generates an emf. For the experiment described in the preceding question, how can it be said that magnetic flux is changing when both the magnet and the magnetic field are stationary?

Q17.7 A "gaussmeter" is a device that uses the emf induced in a rotating coil to measure the strength of a static magnetic field. (1) Would you attach an ac or a dc voltmeter to a gaussmeter? (2) What quantities would you need to know in order to translate the reading of the voltmeter into a value of the magnetic field?

Q17.8 The mechanical energy put into a generator at a power plant is transformed almost completely to electrical energy; that is, the generator operates at an efficiency near 100 percent. Explain why this does not violate the second law of thermodynamics.

Q17.9 The figure shows a hypothetical hand-powered device like a betatron used to accelerate positively charged particles. (1) Use the law of electromagnetic induction to explain why the particles are caused to rotate counterclockwise as seen from above. (2) Where does the energy given to the particles come from?

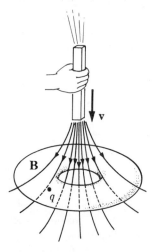

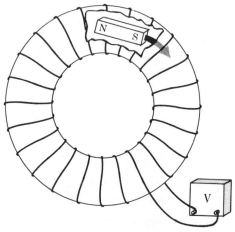

Q17.10 (1) A small magnet moves around inside a toroidal coil (see the figure). Explain why no net emf is induced in the coil. (2) If a piece of matter bearing a net pole strength moved in the torus, a net emf *would* be induced. Explain why. (This question illustrates the principle used in one experimental search for elementary magnetic poles.)

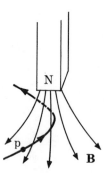

Q17.11 As shown in the figure, a proton passing near a magnet is deflected. (1) If the magnet is stationary, the kinetic energy of the proton remains constant. Why? (2) If the magnet is moving, the proton may gain or lose kinetic energy. Explain why.

Q17.12 Can the magnetomotive force $\oint \mathbf{B} \cdot d\mathbf{s}$ be determined experimentally by measuring the work required to move a magnetic dipole once around a closed loop? Why or why not?

Section 17.3

Q17.13 State one significant way in which displacement current and true current differ.

Q17.14 (1) Cite an example in which the first term on the right side of Equation 17.29 is zero and the second term is not zero. (2) Cite an example in which the first term is not zero and the second term is zero.

Q17.15 To keep the conducting rod in the diagram of Exercise 17.4 moving at constant speed requires the application of a force. Explain this fact in terms of (1) appropriate laws of field and force, (2) Lenz's law, and (3) the law of energy conservation.

Section 17.4

Q17.16 (1) A brass washer is placed on top of a small coil of wire (see the figure). When a switch is closed and current starts to flow in the coil, the washer springs upward into the air. Explain why. (2) The washer is retrieved and placed back on the coil. Then the switch is opened and the current in the coil rapidly dies out. Does the washer react? Why or why not?

Q17.17 In Figure 17.2, will the force on Mr. Goto's magnet draw him toward the coil, tend to slow down his approach to the coil, or do neither? Explain in terms of Lenz's law.

Q17.18 Describe the course of events if the force $\mathbf{F}_2$ in Figure 17.11 acted downward on the downward-moving magnet. Explain carefully how this violation of Lenz's law would violate the law of energy conservation.

Q17.19 In a simple relay a switch S is held closed by an electromagnet energized by a current I in a coil C (see the figure). Also wrapped around the iron core of the magnet is a single closed turn B of low-resistance wire. The purpose of this extra loop is to prevent the switch from opening during a momentary interruption of the current I. Explain how the loop B serves this function.

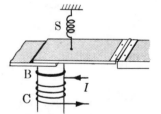

Q17.20 In a piece of material in which magnetic flux is changing, emf's are necessarily generated. The currents induced by these emf's and the resulting expenditure of energy depend on the nature of the material—its shape, size, and composition. (1) In most devices, the induced "eddy currents" are considered undesirable. Why? (2) The iron parts of machines that utilize changing magnetic fields are often made of thin laminations insulated from one another. Why? (See also Problem 17.10.)

Q17.21 With which of Maxwell's four equations (Equations 17.38–17.41) is each of the following facts most directly associated? Briefly state a reason for each answer. (1) The static electric field within a conductor is zero. (2) Lines of magnetic field circle around a steady current. (3) An alternating emf is induced in a coil that rotates in a uniform magnetic field.

Section 17.5

Q17.22 (1) Why is the magnetic flux through any specified area usually proportional to the current in the circuit that produces the flux? (2) This proportionality of flux and current need not be valid if matter—especially ferromagnetic matter—is present near the circuit. Why not?

Section 17.6

Q17.23 One cylindrical coil is twice the length of another. Both coils have the same cross-sectional area and the same number of turns, the shorter coil having twice as many turns per unit length. Which coil, if either, has the greater inductance?

Q17.24   You wish to design a circuit in which the current will build up extremely rapidly after a switch is closed. What are some features that your circuit should have?

Q17.25   To use as standards in your laboratory you would like to construct (a) an inductor with an inductance of 1 mH (10^{-3} H) and (b) a magnet that produces a magnetic field of 1 mT (10^{-3} T, or 10 G) in a certain region. Discuss the relative difficulty of achieving high precision for these standards.

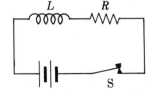

Q17.26   Discuss the behavior of the simple *LR* circuit shown in the figure when the switch S is opened, and resolve this apparent paradox: The law of electromagnetic induction requires that the current diminish gradually, yet the opening of the switch breaks the circuit and apparently puts an abrupt end to the flow of current.

Section 17.7   Q17.27   Why is it not possible to construct from wires and other metal parts a circuit whose natural frequency of oscillation is around 10^{14} Hz (a frequency of infrared radiation)?

Q17.28   Why is it not practical to construct a very-low-frequency *LC* circuit whose period of oscillation is many seconds?

Q17.29   Discuss the effect of resistance in a realistic *LC* circuit.

Q17.30   The tuning knob on a radio is connected to a capacitor. Turning the knob changes the capacitance. How does this enable you to change stations?

Section 17.8   Q17.31   Cite some evidence that sound is propagated as a wave, not as a stream of particles.

Q17.32   Often light must *diffract* before it can *interfere*. Why?

Q17.33   When light passes from one medium to another, its frequency, but not its wavelength, remains constant. Give a physical explanation for this fact.

Section 17.9   Q17.34   Discuss in qualitative terms the "meaning" of the differential laws of field expressed by Equations 17.85 and 17.86.

Q17.35   A certain FM signal is polarized (**E** and **B** are parallel to fixed lines as in Figure 16.12). How should a thin, straight rod used as an antenna be oriented in order to receive the strongest signal? Why?

Q17.36   In the United States, TV antennas usually consist of an array of horizontal rods. In Great Britain, TV antennas are usually constructed of vertical rods. Why the difference?

Q17.37   Many AM radios use a circular loop of wire as an antenna. (1) What fundamental law of electromagnetism accounts for the action of the loop antenna? (2) How should a loop antenna be oriented relative to the direction from the transmitter to the receiver? (SUGGESTION: If you have a radio with a loop antenna available, test your prediction.) *Optional:* Why might a loop be preferred to a straight rod for receiving AM signals?

Section 17.11   Q17.38   A charged particle moving with constant velocity creates both an electric and a magnetic field. Suggest a reason why it does not produce electromagnetic radiation. (HINT: Consider another frame of reference.)

Q17.39 From the moving charged rod in Figure 17.23(b) a weak electromagnetic wave propagates to the right. (1) Is this wave polarized? (2) Make a rough estimate of the frequency of this wave and explain the basis of your estimate.

Q17.40 If a charged particle oscillates through a distance d, the wavelength of the radiation it emits must be greater than d. Explain the reason for this rule.

Q17.41 Based on your own casual observation of various kinds of radiating antennas (broadcast stations, radar, taxicabs, police cars, ham radios, microwave relays, etc.), can you conclude that the wavelength of emitted radiation is at least as great as the dimension of the radiating antenna? Justify your answer for a few of these. Are there any apparent exceptions?

Q17.42 According to Figure 17.26, does the sun (whose surface temperature is about 6,000 K) emit more infrared energy than ultraviolet energy or more ultraviolet than infrared?

EXERCISES

Section 17.1

E17.1 At a certain place in the northern hemisphere, the earth's magnetic field has a magnitude of 4×10^{-5} T and is directed at an angle of 60 deg to the vertical. (1) What is the flux of the earth's magnetic field through a horizontal surface of area 1 m^2? (2) What are the maximum and minimum magnitudes of flux through a vertical surface of area 1 m^2?

E17.2 As shown in the figure, lines of magnetic field are directed perpendicular to a circular loop of wire of radius r. (1) If the magnitude of the field is given by

$$B = B_0 e^{-t/\tau},$$

where B_0 and τ are constants, what is the induced emf in the loop as a function of time? (In the figure, ds denotes the positive direction around the loop.) (2) Answer the same question if the loop is tilted through (a) 30 deg, (b) 60 deg, or (c) 90 deg.

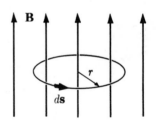

E17.3 The loop of wire shown in the preceding exercise has resistance R. (1) Show that for an arbitrary time-variation of the magnetic field, the power dissipated by the induced current in the wire is

$$P = \frac{A^2}{R} \left(\frac{dB}{dt}\right)^2,$$

where $A = \pi r^2$. (2) If B increases from 0 to B_0 at a linear rate in time T, show that the total energy released as heat in the wire is

$$E = \frac{A^2 B_0^2}{RT}.$$

E17.4 A conducting rod is pulled at constant speed v along parallel metal bars that are joined at one end (see the figure). A uniform magnetic field **B** is directed into the page. (1) Using the law of electromagnetic induction, show that the magnitude of the electric field **E** induced in the moving rod is $E = Bv$. (2) What is the direction of **E**?

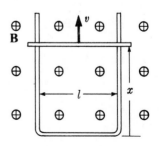

E17.5   Starting at large negative x, the loop of wire shown in the figure is moved with constant speed until it reaches large positive x. On the way, it passes a stationary bar magnet aligned as shown in the figure. Sketch an approximate graph of the current induced in the loop as a function of x. Take the positive current direction to be the direction indicated by the arrow on the loop; this is the initial direction of the induced current.

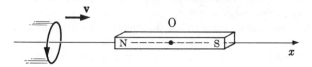

E17.6   A small metal casement, whose resistance is 0.01 Ω, surrounds a pane of glass of area 3×10^{-4} m^2 in a door located on the north side of a house. At that location, the horizontal component of the earth's magnetic field is 2×10^{-5} T. As the door is flung open, the magnetic flux through the pane changes from a maximum value to zero in 1 sec. What is the approximate magnitude of the induced current in the casement?

E17.7   A rectangular loop of wire of dimensions 0.2 m $\times$ 0.4 m is held in a fixed position in a uniform magnetic field. The accompanying graph shows the component of **B** perpendicular to the plane of the loop as a function of time. Sketch a reasonably accurate graph of the induced emf in the loop as a function of time.

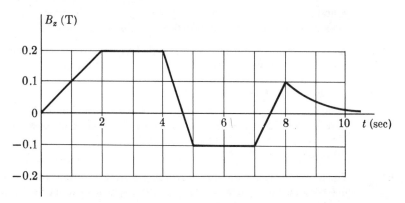

Section 17.2
E17.8   (1) At what angular speed would a 100-turn coil of area 1 cm^2 have to rotate in the earth's magnetic field of 5×10^{-5} T in order to generate a peak emf of 1 V? (2) At this rotation speed, what would be (a) the average value of the emf and (b) the rms value of the emf?

E17.9   The output of a generator of the form shown in Figure 17.7 is connected to a circuit of resistance R. Prove that the time-average of the power supplied by the generator is

$$\bar{P} = \frac{\omega^2 B^2 A^2}{2R}.$$

E17.10   You wish to design a generator whose emf alternates at 60 cycles per sec and has an rms value of 120 V. Specify reasonable values of magnetic field B, coil area A, and number of turns N that will produce the desired result.

E17.11　In a certain betatron the orbital radius of the electron beam is $r = 0.3$ m and the magnetic field at this radius is given by $B_r = 0.3 \sin 120\pi t$ (B_r is in teslas and t is in seconds). The acceleration of the electrons occurs during the time $t = 0$ to $t = 1/240$ sec (and in corresponding time periods in later cycles). (1) What is the induced electric field E experienced by the electrons at $t = 0$? Is this "large" or "small" (in comparison with typical static electric fields)? (2) For a particle moving near the speed of light, kinetic energy and momentum are related approximately by $K = pc$. With the help of this formula, find the final kinetic energy of the electrons in MeV when $B_r = 0.3$ T. (3) About how many trips around the betatron does an electron complete in 1/240 sec (use the fact that $v \cong c$)?

E17.12　(1) What is the SI unit of magnetomotive force? (2) How is magnetomotive force related to energy and pole strength?

Section 17.3

E17.13　The figure shows a "leaky" capacitor within which flows a current I_2 less than the current I_1 that is charging the capacitor. Show that

$$I_2 + \epsilon_0 \frac{d\Phi_E}{dt} = I_1,$$

where Φ_E is the electric flux in the capacitor. What is the significance of this result?

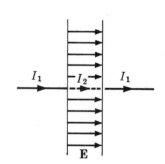

E17.14　Imagine the area A_2 in Figure 17.9(b) to be altered by contracting its edge C_1 until C_1 becomes a smaller circle between the capacitor plates. The bounding surface then extends out from between the plates and around one plate, where it is cut by one current-carrying wire. Using this surface and the law of magnetoelectric induction (Equation 17.29), derive Equation 17.35 for the magnetic field between the capacitor plates.

E17.15　The plates of a parallel-plate capacitor are circular disks of radius 0.05 m. The plates, initially at a potential difference of 10^3 V, are discharged through a resistor of resistance 10 Ω. (1) Just before the discharge begins, when the capacitor potential is constant, what is the magnetic field at the edge of the plates? (2) Just after the discharge begins, what is the magnetic field at the edge of the plates?

E17.16　Use Lenz's law to obtain the direction of induced current in the loop of Figure 17.3 as the magnet is moved downward.

Section 17.4

E17.17　Two identical insulated circular loops of wire are laid on a table, one on top of the other. A switch is closed that starts a current flowing clockwise in the upper loop. Use Lenz's law to determine the direction of the induced current in the lower loop.

E17.18　The north pole of the magnet depicted in Figure 16.7 experiences a downward force. If it moves downward in response to this force, it induces in the wire a current I' in addition to the current I already flowing. (1) In what direction is this induced current I'? Why? (2) Would you expect I' to be greater in magnitude than I, equal to I, or less than I? Why?

E17.19　The fact that parallel currents attract is not directly a manifestation of Lenz's law because no motion or energy exchange need be involved. However, the attraction can be inferred indirectly with the help of Lenz's law. Suppose that a steady current I_1 exists in one wire and that a current I_2 starts to flow in a

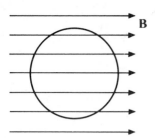

B

second wire that is parallel to the first one. If the second wire is free to move, it will move in such a direction that the current induced in it opposes the increase of I_2. Show that if I_2 is parallel to I_1, the requirement of Lenz's law is that the second wire is drawn toward the first one.

E17.20   The lines of magnetic field and the loop of wire in the figure are both in the plane of the page. When a current starts to flow clockwise in the loop, the loop starts to rotate. Use Lenz's law to find out in what direction it starts to rotate. Explain why Lenz's law can be applied.

Section 17.5   **E17.21**   From Equation 17.40 derive the following magnetic version of the Biot-Savart law: The electric field generated by an infinite straight magnetic current I_M (if such were to exist) would be directed in circles around the current and, at a distance r from the current, would have a magnitude given by

$$E = \frac{\mu_0 I_M}{2\pi r}.$$

E17.22   Pinpoint the terms in Maxwell's equations and the Lorentz force law that correspond to the six connecting links of the q-**E**-**B** triangle (Figure 16.42).

E17.23   (1) Show that Maxwell's equations (without poles) are invariant under the following transformation: $q \to q$, $I \to -I$, $\mathbf{E} \to \mathbf{E}$, $\mathbf{B} \to -\mathbf{B}$, $x, y, z \to x, y, z$, and $t \to -t$. This is a so-called time reversal transformation. (2) Is the Lorentz force law (Equation 17.42) changed by this transformation? (3) Why does it make sense physically that a reversal of time should be accompanied by a reversal of the sign of current?

E17.24   A certain region of space contains static nonzero electric and magnetic fields. (1) Give at least one example of relative orientations of **E** and **B** that permit a charged particle to move in a selected direction without acceleration. (2) Prove that there is no possible relative orientation of **E** and **B** that permits charged particles to move through the region in all directions without acceleration.

Section 17.6   **E17.25**   Verify the following units equations: (1) $1\ \text{H} = 1\ \text{J/A}^2$; (2) $1\ \text{H}/1\ \Omega = 1\ \text{sec}$; and (3) $1\ \text{H}/1\ \text{F} = (1\ \Omega)^2$.

E17.26   (1) Using the formula $u = B^2/2\mu_0$ for the energy density in a magnetic field, find the total energy stored in the field within a long thin solenoid and show that this energy can be expressed in terms of inductance and current by

$$E = \tfrac{1}{2}LI^2.$$

(2) If the energy stored in a 1-H inductor that carries a current of 10 A is transformed to mechanical energy and is used to lift a 1-kg weight, to what height can the weight be raised?

E17.27   Two toroidal inductors having inductances L_1 and L_2 are connected in series. What is the inductance of the combination? Give a reason for your answer. (Assume that the inductors are physically distinct so that they have no magnetic effect on each other.)

E17.28   The inductor described in the example of Section 17.6 is joined to a 100-Ω resistor. What is the time constant of the combination (a) without the iron core in place and (b) with the iron core in place?

E17.29 A wire that has both inductance and resistance can be represented by a series of N inductors, each of inductance L/N, and N resistors, each of resistance R/N (see the figure). (1) Show that when the switch S is closed, this circuit is described by Equation 17.57. (2) If $R = 100 \, \Omega$, $L = 0.1$ H, and $V_1 = 24$ V, how much time is needed for the current to increase to 0.12 A?

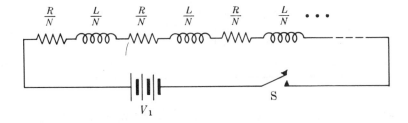

E17.30 (1) Verify that Equation 17.58, which gives the rising current in an LR circuit, is a solution to Equation 17.57. (2) Explain how Equation 17.57 is related to Kirchhoff's second rule.

E17.31 A toy train transformer is plugged into a 120-V line. (1) If the power supplied by the line is 140 W, of which 20 W is dissipated as heat in the transformer, what current flows in the 6-V secondary circuit? (2) Which has the greater number of turns, the primary winding or the secondary winding of the transformer? (3) Which winding is likely to have heavier wire? Why?

E17.32 (1) Verify the units consistency of Equation 17.66 ($T = 2\pi\sqrt{LC}$). (2) Verify that the unit of $\sqrt{L/C}$ is the same as the unit of resistance (see Equation 17.68).

Section 17.7

E17.33 An inductor with $L = 10^{-2}$ H and a capacitor with $C = 10^{-6}$ F are connected together. (1) What is the natural frequency of oscillation of this circuit? (2) If the oscillating potential across the capacitor were connected to a loudspeaker, would the resulting tone be audible?

E17.34 An LC circuit oscillates at a frequency of 1 MHz. The inductance in the circuit is 1 mH. (1) What is the capacitance in the circuit (expressed in pF)? (2) If the peak potential across the capacitor is $V_0 = 100$ V, what is the peak current I_0 in the circuit?

E17.35 (1) Show that $I = a \sin \omega t + b \cos \omega t$ is an expression for current in an LC circuit that satisfies Equation 17.62. (2) Show that if this expression for current is used the peak current is $I_{max} = \sqrt{a^2 + b^2}$.

E17.36 Prove that in an LC circuit the charge q on the capacitor and the potential V across the capacitor are governed by the same differential equation that governs the current I (Equation 17.62): that is, $d^2q/dt^2 = -q/LC$ and $d^2V/dt^2 = -V/LC$.

E17.37 Equation 17.63 gives $I(t)$, the current in an idealized LC circuit. (1) Obtain the charge on the capacitor by integration: $q(t) = \int I(t) \, dt$. How is the constant of integration determined? (2) Using the simple connection between the charge and potential of a capacitor, find $V(t)$ and show that the expression you obtain is consistent with Equations 17.67 and 17.68.

E17.38   (1) On the same graph sketch curves of stored energy vs time for (a) the capacitor and (b) the inductor in an *LC* circuit.   (2) Give the rms values of each of these energies.

Section 17.8   E17.39   A certain radio station broadcasts at a frequency of 800 kHz.   What is the wavelength of its radiation?

E17.40   A radio transmitting antenna is linked to an oscillator circuit containing an inductance of 0.1 mH and a capacitance of 25 pF.   Find the frequency and the wavelength of the emitted radiation.

Section 17.9   E17.41   Show that $E = f(z + ct)$ is a solution to the wave equation (Equation 17.87).   Is this a propagating solution?   If so, what is the direction of propagation?

E17.42   Show that the electric field in a propagating wave, $\mathbf{E} = f(z - ct)\mathbf{i}$ (Equations 17.80 and 17.89), satisfies Gauss's law in empty space, $\oint \mathbf{E} \cdot d\mathbf{S} = 0$. (SUGGESTION: Apply Gauss's law to a cubical surface whose edges are parallel to the x, y, and z axes.)

E17.43   The energy density in a certain radar beam is 10^{-6} J/m^3.   What are the *peak* values of electric and magnetic field in the beam?   How do these compare with typical magnitudes of static fields?

E17.44   *Wavelength* is the distance in which a wave completes one full cycle of oscillation at a fixed instant of time.   *Frequency* is the number of cycles of oscillation per unit time at a fixed point in space.   Using these definitions, verify that in Equation 17.91, λ is the wavelength and c/λ is the frequency.

E17.45   A transverse wave running down a rope is described by the equation

$$y = 0.3 \sin (3x - 20t),$$

where x is horizontal distance (in m), y is vertical distance (in m), and t is time (in sec).   For this wave, find (a) the peak displacement, (b) the wavelength, (c) the frequency, (d) the speed, and (e) the direction of propagation.

Section 17.10   E17.46   How many photons of microwave radiation ($\lambda = 3$ cm) are needed to equal the energy of one photon of visible light ($E \cong 2$ eV)?

E17.47   An audible sound wave in air has a wavelength of 10 cm.   (1) What is its frequency?   (2) What is the frequency of an electromagnetic wave with the same wavelength?   In what part of the spectrum is this wave?

E17.48   Calculate approximately (1) the wavelength of 120 MHz radiation (in the VHF band) from an airport control tower, (2) the frequency of radiation in the 30-m shortwave radio band, and (3) the speed of a wave whose wavelength is 3 cm and whose frequency is 10 GHz.   What might this last wave be?

E17.49   The vertical scale in Figure 17.21 is logarithmic: Equal vertical distances correspond to equal *factors* of increase of frequency.   The well-tempered piano scale is also logarithmic: Each half-tone step increases frequency by the same factor, and twelve half-tone steps produce a factor-of-2 change in frequency.   (1) By what percentage is the frequency increased in each half-tone step?   (2) By what factor is the frequency increased in seven half-tone steps (a musical fifth)?

E17.50   The two protons in a hydrogen molecule are separated by 0.74×10^{-10} m. Show that if these protons rotate about their center of mass with an angular momentum equal to $\hbar$ or a few times $\hbar$, the rotational frequency of the molecule corresponds to a frequency of infrared radiation.

Section 17.11

E17.51   A proton in a nucleus oscillates in a domain of about 10^{-14} m at about 10 percent of the speed of light. What is its approximate frequency of oscillation? How does this compare with the frequencies of nuclear gamma rays?

E17.52   A charged particle oscillates through a distance d at an average speed v. Prove that the wavelength of the radiation it emits is given approximately by $\lambda \cong (c/v)d$ (Equation 17.100).

E17.53   (1) At approximately what temperature does a "black body" emit its maximum intensity per unit frequency in the middle of the visible spectrum? (2) Why is a body "red hot" at a substantially lower temperature than this?

PROBLEMS

P17.1   As shown in the figure, a hypothetical magnetic pole of pole strength P moves with constant speed v along the axis of a circular loop of wire of radius a. (1) Show that the total magnetic flux emanating from the pole is Φ_B (total) $= \mu_0 P$ (see Equation 16.6). (2) Show that the magnetic flux through the loop is $\Phi_B = \frac{1}{2}\mu_0 P(1 - \cos \theta)$, where θ is the angle defined in the figure. (3) Show that the magnitude of the emf induced in the loop at the moment the pole passes through the center of the loop is

Emf generated by a magnetic pole

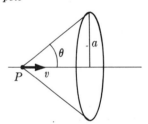

$$|\mathscr{V}| = \frac{\mu_0 P v}{2a}.$$

Optional: Consider a quantum pole of strength P_0 (see Exercise 16.6) passing through a coil of radius 10^{-2} m at 10 percent of the speed of light. About how many turns must the coil have in order that the total induced emf be 10^{-4} V?

P17.2   The two coaxial loops shown in the figure have radii of 20 cm and 1 cm respectively. If the rate of change of current in the outer loop is $dI_1/dt = 10^3$ A/sec, what is the reading of the voltmeter attached to the inner loop? (Ignore the question of its sign.)

Mutual induction

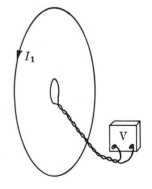

P17.3   Two insulated coils, one of N_1 turns and one of N_2 turns, are wound on the same long thin cylinder, whose length is l and whose cross-sectional area is A. The coils have negligible resistance and are linked by the same magnetic flux. (1) Show that the magnitudes of the emf's in the two coils are related by $\mathscr{V}_1/\mathscr{V}_2 = N_1/N_2$. (The transformer takes advantage of this relationship.) (2) A time-dependent current I_1 in the first coil induces an emf $\mathscr{V}_2$ in the second coil. Show that the mutual inductance (defined in the footnote on page 842) is given by

$$L_{21} = \frac{\mu_0 N_1 N_2 A}{l}.$$

(Note the implication of this formula that $L_{12} = L_{21}$.)

Two approaches to induction   **P17.4**   A primitive form of a generator is shown in the figure accompanying Exercise 17.4. Find the induced emf in the moving rod by two methods: (1) Apply the law of electromagnetic induction. (2) Consider the magnetic force acting on a charged particle in the rod as the rod moves through the magnetic field. In a frame of reference moving with the rod, this force must be interpreted as an electric force. From the electric force can be derived an electric field and an emf.

Force and energy related to induction   **P17.5**   One end of a rectangular loop of wire is in a region of approximately uniform magnetic field directed perpendicular to the plane of the loop. The other end of the loop is in an approximately field-free region. As shown in the figure, a force **F** is applied to keep the loop moving at constant speed v. Find the magnitude of **F** in the following two ways and verify that the answers agree. (1) If the loop has resistance R, the induced emf in the loop causes power to be dissipated in the loop. Equate this power to the rate of work by the external force. (2) The induced current experiences a force in the magnetic field (Section 16.7). This force must be equal and opposite to the force required to keep the loop moving.

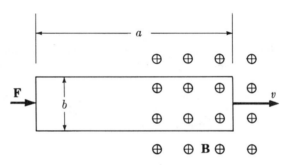

Electromagnetic friction   **P17.6**   A horizontal wire of mass m, length l, and resistance R is arranged as shown in the figure so that it can slide down the vertical rails of a U-shaped frame. The resistance of the frame is negligible in comparison with R. As the wire is pulled downward by gravity, it moves through a uniform magnetic field **B** directed perpendicular to the plane of the frame. (1) Show that if mechanical friction can be neglected, the terminal speed of the falling wire is

$$v_\mathrm{T} = \frac{mgR}{l^2 B^2}.$$

(2) For $m = 0.1$ kg, $R = 1\ \Omega$, $l = 0.1$ m, and $B = 10$ T (a very strong field), find (a) v_T and (b) the induced current I in the wire and frame. (3) What energy transformation is taking place in this process? Show that energy is conserved.

Magnetic field of a betatron   **P17.7**   The magnetic field of a betatron is shown schematically in Figure 17.8. (1) Using Ampère's law, prove that it is impossible to have a magnetic field in empty space that is fixed in direction but varies in magnitude in a direction perpendicular to the field [diagram (a)]. (2) Again using Ampère's law, show that if the field is unidirectional in a median plane [the dashed line in diagram (b)] and diminishes in magnitude as the radial distance r from a central point O increases, a radial component of field must exist that is directed inward above the median plane and outward below the median plane for **B** directed generally upward as in diagram (b). (3) What happens to a circling electron if it drifts out of the median plane?

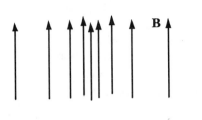

(a) Impossible   (b) Possible

P17.8 The magnetic field produced by a moving charge is given by Equation 16.36. Prove that the law of magnetoelectric induction (Equation 17.27) leads to the same result. Use the contour C and the shaded area shown in Figure 17.10. Why is it not necessary to use the more general Equation 17.29? (This derivation shows that the *magnetic* field produced by a moving charge can be associated with the fact that the *electric* field produced by the charge is varying in time.)

Magnetic field produced by a moving charge

P17.9 Using ideas of relative motion and the self-consistency of electromagnetic laws, prove that a magnetic pole moving through a static electric field must experience a force. Derive the directional properties of this force.

Force on a moving pole

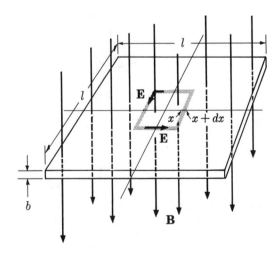

P17.10 The figure shows a slab of metal of dimensions $l \times l \times b$ through which pass lines of a uniform magnetic field **B** directed perpendicular to the square faces of the slab. Although uniform in space, the field varies in time; its magnitude is $B = B_0 \sin \omega t$. (1) Prove that the average power dissipated by induced currents (eddy currents) in the slab is

Power dissipated by eddy currents

$$\bar{P} = \tfrac{1}{64}\sigma\omega^2 B_0{}^2 b l^4,$$

where σ is the conductivity of the metal. (SUGGESTED METHOD: Find the induced emf $\mathscr{V}$, electric field **E**, and current dI in the square loop indicated by shading in the figure. From $\mathscr{V}$ and dI find the power dP dissipated in the shaded loop. Integrate over x from 0 to $\frac{1}{2}l$ to get the total power.) (2) What power is dissipated in a slab of iron ($\sigma = 10^7\,\Omega^{-1}\mathrm{m}^{-1}$) of dimensions 10 cm $\times$ 10 cm $\times$ 1 cm in a 60-cycle ($\omega = 120\pi$ radian/sec) field of peak magnitude $B_0 = 0.1$ T? (NOTE: No correction for permeability is required.) (3) If the slab were divided into n^2 smaller squares, each of side l/n with the same thickness b, by what factor would the power dissipation be reduced?

Inductance of a toroidal coil   P17.11   The figure shows a section of a toroidal coil of N turns. The average radius of the toroid is a and its rectangular cross section has sides b and c. (1) Show that the inductance of this coil is

$$ L = \frac{\mu_0 N^2 c}{2\pi} \ln \left(\frac{a + \frac{1}{2}b}{a - \frac{1}{2}b} \right). $$

(2) Using an approximation for the logarithm (see page A22), obtain an expression for L that is valid if $a \gg b$. Compare this approximate expression with the formula for the inductance of a cylindrical coil given by Equation 17.49. Comment on the comparison. (3) Suppose that the toroid is filled with ferromagnetic material of permeability κ_m so that the inductance is $L' = \kappa_m L$. Specify reasonable magnitudes of N, a, b, and c that will produce an inductance L' of about 30 mH.

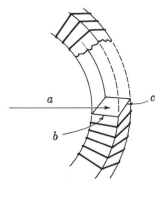

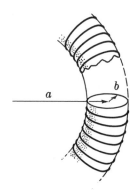

P17.12   A coil of N turns is wound on a torus whose average radius is a and whose circular cross section has radius b (see the figure). (1) Show that the inductance of this coil is

$$ L = \mu_0 N^2 (a - \sqrt{a^2 - b^2}). $$

(In evaluating the flux linking the coil, you will probably need to consult a table of integrals.) (2) Show that for $a \gg b$ this formula can be written

$$ L \cong \mu_0 \frac{N^2 \pi b^2}{2\pi a}, $$

which is consistent with Equation 17.49.

P17.13 Two parallel wires, whose centers are separated by a distance b, carry equal currents I in opposite directions. (Imagine the wires to be joined at some distant point so that they form a single circuit.) The radius of each wire is a. Show that if the contribution of magnetic flux within the wires is neglected, the inductance per unit length of the pair of wires is given by

$$\frac{dL}{dz} = \frac{\mu_0}{\pi} \ln \left(\frac{b-a}{a} \right).$$

(HINT: From the Biot-Savart law, the magnetic flux across the shaded area in the figure can be calculated. Why is the emf generated by a change of this flux concentrated along the wires, not across the space between the wires?)

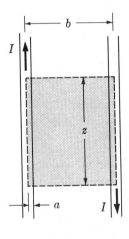
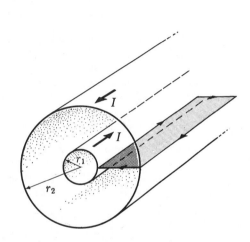

P17.14 A coaxial cable consists of thin coaxial cylinders of radii r_1 and r_2 (see the figure). The cylinders conduct equal current I in opposite directions. Obtain an expression for the inductance per unit length of the cable. (SUGGESTION: Apply the law of electromagnetic induction to the shaded area and rectangular contour in the figure.)

P17.15 A certain LC circuit contains a parallel-plate capacitor and a long thin solenoid with the following thermal properties: For temperature change ΔT, the fractional change of linear dimensions of the capacitor plates is $\Delta l / l = \alpha_1 \Delta T$ (the distance between the plates does not change) and the fractional change of *all* linear dimensions of the solenoid is $\Delta l / l = \alpha_2 \Delta T$. (The quantities α_1 and α_2 are coefficients of linear thermal expansion.) (1) Show that to first order in small quantities, the natural frequency of this LC circuit depends on temperature in the following way:

$$\frac{\Delta v}{v} = (-\alpha_1 - \tfrac{1}{2}\alpha_2) \Delta T.$$

(2) What changes would have to be made in the design of the capacitor and/or the inductor in this circuit in order to achieve a temperature-independent frequency?

RLC circuit

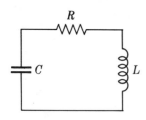

P17.16   A resistor, inductor, and capacitor are joined in a series circuit (see the figure). (1) Show that the current in this circuit is governed by the differential equation

$$L \frac{d^2 I}{dt^2} + R \frac{dI}{dt} + \frac{1}{C} I = 0.$$

(2) Show that a solution to this equation that is valid for "small" resistance ($R < 2\sqrt{L/C}$) is $I = I_0 \sin \omega t \, e^{-\alpha t}$. Express the constants ω and α in terms of R, L, and C. (3) Discuss qualitative features of this solution for (a) $R \ll 2\sqrt{L/C}$ and (b) R nearly equal to $2\sqrt{L/C}$.

Magnetoelectric induction in differential form

P17.17   Using the contour C_2 in Figure 17.19 and the special assumptions $\mathbf{E} = E\mathbf{i}$ and $\mathbf{B} = B\mathbf{j}$, derive Equation 17.86 from Equation 17.79.

Transverse propagating wave

P17.18   In a propagating wave, $\mathbf{E} = f(u)\mathbf{i}$, where $u = z - ct$, and $\mathbf{B} = g(z, t)\mathbf{j}$.   (1) Express g in terms of f and show that $\mathbf{B}$, like $\mathbf{E}$, propagates at speed c. (2) Verify that the rms energy densities $\frac{1}{2}\epsilon_0 \overline{E^2}$ and $(1/2\mu_0)\overline{B^2}$ are equal.

Wavelength related to size of antenna

P17.19   This problem requires examination and measurement of TV antennas. (1) The frequencies of VHF television channels are in the vicinity of 100 MHz. Are the lengths of the individual rods on a TV antenna approximately one-quarter wavelength, one-half wavelength, or one wavelength? (2) Find and measure a TV antenna with elements of two or three distinct sizes. What are the approximate frequencies of the lower frequency VHF channels (2–6), the higher frequency VHF channels (7–13), and the UHF channels?

Black-body intensity

P17.20   Figure 17.26 presents dI/dv (intensity per unit frequency) vs frequency v for a radiating black body. (1) Give a formula that relates $|dI/d\lambda|$ (intensity per unit wavelength) to dI/dv. (2) Which function has its peak at greater frequency, dI/dv or $|dI/d\lambda|$? (3) Intensity per unit frequency is given by

$$\frac{dI}{dv} = \frac{2\pi h}{c^2} \frac{v^3}{e^{hv/kT} - 1} \qquad \left(\frac{W}{m^2 \, Hz}\right).$$

Obtain the corresponding formula for $|dI/d\lambda|$ and sketch a graph of $|dI/d\lambda|$ vs λ.

18 Wave Phenomena

Of all the known kinds of waves, electromagnetic waves are the most universal, the fastest moving, and the most strikingly varied in their manifestations across the spectrum. Many of their properties, however, are common to waves in general and can be discussed in a wider context. In this chapter, we shall examine half a dozen properties of electromagnetic waves that are shared with some or all other forms of wave motion:

1. Polarization
2. Superposition
3. Reflection
4. Refraction
5. Diffraction
6. Interference

In addition, several sections are devoted to geometrical optics, which is the study of wave behavior with the approximation of straight-line propagation of the waves.*

18.1   Light and sound

The fundamental differentiation among waves is the nature of whatever it is that does the vibrating. By itself a wave is not a material thing but a name for a particular oscillatory state of motion of something else. This is an obvious *Light and sound contrasted* statement, but it is well to keep in mind how sound waves and light waves, with

---

* Many optical phenomena are discussed in the September, 1968, issue of *Scientific American*, which is devoted to light.

so many properties in common, do differ in the most fundamental way. One is the mechanical vibration of matter, the other the coupled vibration of electric and magnetic fields free of matter. Because matter is granular, divided into atoms and molecules, a sound wave or other mechanical vibration requires a domain of many atoms in order to exhibit an average wave behavior. Electromagnetic waves, on the other hand, can exist, so far as we know, in arbitrarily small volumes and with arbitrarily short wavelengths.

The speed of a wave is governed by the nature of the vibrating medium. The speed of light is a constant, associated with the coupling between electric and magnetic fields. The speed of sound is determined by the interaction between atoms or molecules. In a gas, the speed of sound depends on the temperature and the molecular weight, the quantities that affect molecular speed (see Equation 13.35). In air at normal temperature, sound waves travel at 340 m/sec, about one-millionth the speed of light. In a solid, the closely packed atoms conduct sound more rapidly. Some speeds of sound in common substances are shown in Table 18.1.

When a sound wave passes through matter, the material at each point is displaced from its equilibrium position. For a sinusoidal plane wave of frequency v and wavelength λ propagating in the x direction, the displacement may be written

$$A(x, t) = A_0 \sin \left(2\pi v t - \frac{2\pi x}{\lambda} + \alpha \right), \tag{18.1}$$

Amplitude and phase

where A_0 and α are constants. The constant A_0 is called the *amplitude* of the wave, and the combination $\alpha - 2\pi x/\lambda$ is called the *phase* of the wave. For notational convenience, $2\pi v$ may be replaced by the angular frequency ω, and a "wave number" k may be defined by

$$k = \frac{2\pi}{\lambda}. \tag{18.2}$$

Then Equation 18.1 takes the form*

A plane wave of sound

$$A(x, t) = A_0 \sin (\omega t - kx + \alpha). \tag{18.3}$$

The propagation of the wave is revealed by considering any fixed value of the argument of the sine function. For example, if the argument is set equal to zero, we find

$$x = \frac{\omega t + \alpha}{k}.$$

This is the equation of constant-speed motion in the x direction. The wave speed is

$$v = \frac{\omega}{k} = \lambdabar \omega = \lambda v, \tag{18.4}$$

the same as given by Equation 17.73. For a spherical wave emanating from the

---

* Another commonly used quantity is the "reduced wavelength" $\lambdabar$ (pronounced lambda-bar) defined by $\lambdabar = \lambda/2\pi = 1/k$. In terms of $\lambdabar$, Equation 18.3 is $A = A_0 \sin [\omega t - (x/\lambdabar) + \alpha]$. Sometimes the whole combination $\omega t - kx + \alpha$ is called the phase of the wave.

TABLE 18.1 THE SPEED OF SOUND IN COMMON SUBSTANCES

Material	Speed of Sound at Room Temperature (m/sec)	Ratio to Speed in Air
Air	343	1.0
Hydrogen	1,320	3.9
Chlorine	213	0.6
Water	1,490	4.4
Kerosene	1,340	3.9
Iron	6,000	17.5
Aluminum	6,400	18.7
Glass (Pyrex®)	5,600	16.3
Rubber	1,500–1,800	4.4–5.3

origin, we have, instead of Equation 18.3,

$$A(r, t) = A_0(r) \sin (\omega t - kr + \alpha). \qquad (18.5)$$ *A spherical wave*

The most important change is that the amplitude A_0 is a function of r. If the energy density in the wave is proportional to A^2, which is normally the case, the amplitude diminishes inversely with distance:

$$A_0 \sim \frac{1}{r}. \qquad (18.6)$$

The *intensity* of the wave may be defined to be the mean-square value of the displacement (a quantity proportional to energy density):

$$I = \overline{A^2}. \qquad (18.7)$$ *Intensity defined*

Since the average over time of $\sin^2 (\omega t - kr + \alpha)$ is $\frac{1}{2}$, the intensity is half the square of the amplitude:

$$I = \tfrac{1}{2}A_0{}^2. \qquad (18.8)$$

The description of a plane or spherical light wave is almost the same. The displacement A is replaced by the electric field $\mathbf{E}$. For a plane wave, the field is *Electromagnetic waves are similarly described*

$$\mathbf{E}(x, t) = \mathbf{E}_0 \sin (\omega t - kx + \alpha). \qquad (18.9)$$

The magnetic field need not be separately considered because it is uniquely related to $\mathbf{E}$ (see Equations 17.91–17.93). In any of the expressions above, A can be replaced by $\mathbf{E}$ and A_0 by $\mathbf{E}_0$. The intensity of an electromagnetic wave is

$$I = \overline{E^2} = \tfrac{1}{2}E_0{}^2. \qquad (18.10)$$

In this chapter, we shall concentrate on electromagnetic waves. However, all of the results except the few concerned with polarization apply equally well to sound waves of small amplitude. Simply substitute A for $\mathbf{E}$ and A_0 for $\mathbf{E}_0$.

18.2 Polarization

A wave is said to be *polarized* in its direction of vibration. For a longitudinal wave, the direction of polarization is uniquely determined by the direction of

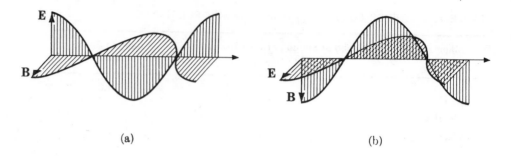

(a)   (b)

FIGURE 18.1   (a) Vertically polarized light wave. (b) Horizontally polarized
light wave.

propagation. They are the same. For a transverse wave, on the other hand, any
of the infinity of directions perpendicular to the direction of propagation is a
possible direction of polarization. The concept of polarization is therefore more
interesting and more important for transverse waves. A water wave, for example,
is vertically polarized. A pulse sent down a stretched rope by snapping the rope
to one side is horizontally polarized. In a light wave, the direction of polarization is *defined* to be the direction in which the *electric* field is vibrating. (This is
an arbitrary matter. The magnetic field could equally well have been chosen to
define the direction of polarization.)   Vertically and horizontally polarized

*Electric field defines
polarization of light wave*

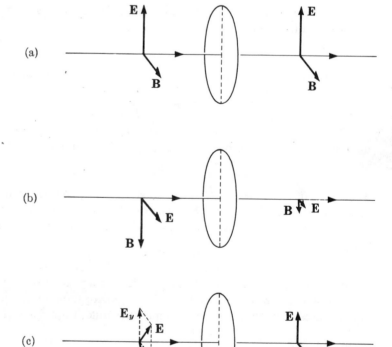

FIGURE 18.2   Action of a polarizing sheet.
(a) Light polarized in one direction is
transmitted with little absorption. (b) Light
polarized perpendicular to the favored
direction is almost completely absorbed.
(c) Light polarized at an intermediate angle is
partially absorbed and emerges with the
favored direction of polarization. (Dotted
line indicates the polarizer "axis." The
actual direction of molecular alignment
is horizontal.)

light waves are illustrated in Figure 18.1.

Light coming from the sun or from an electric bulb is unpolarized. Its myriad of photons stream out with randomly oriented polarizations; every possible direction of vibration of the electric field is equally likely. Any device that selects from this array a particular direction of polarization is called a polarizer. A doubly refracting crystal is a polarizer because it refracts different polarizations differently and permits two polarized beams to be separated (Figure 17.18). The material used in Polaroid® sunglasses is an efficient polarizer that works by a different principle, selective absorption. This material is nearly transparent to light whose electric field vibrates perpendicular to a direction of molecular alignment in the material, and it is nearly opaque to light whose electric field vibrates parallel to this direction (Figure 18.2). The "axis" of the polarizer is defined as a line perpendicular to the actual direction of molecular alignment.

The use of polarizing material in sunglasses is related to another mechanism of polarization, ordinary reflection. Light reflected from glass and water is partially polarized, and at a certain critical angle for each substance it is completely polarized. The reflected beam (we now know) is strongest in light that is polarized parallel to the surface of the reflector; the refracted beam is strongest in light that is oppositely polarized (Figure 18.3). The axis of the polarizing sunglasses, therefore, is oriented in order to absorb horizontally polarized light and thereby eliminate some of the glare of reflected light. A sunbather lying on her side (Figure 18.4) forgoes this advantage, for her rotated sunglasses preferentially transmit the reflected light rather than preferentially absorbing it.

Light is partially polarized by reflection

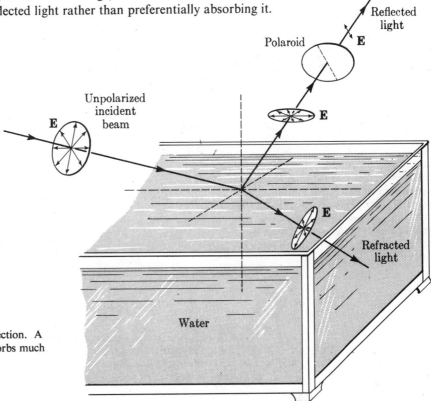

FIGURE 18.3   Polarization by reflection. A polarizer, oriented as shown, absorbs much of the reflected light.

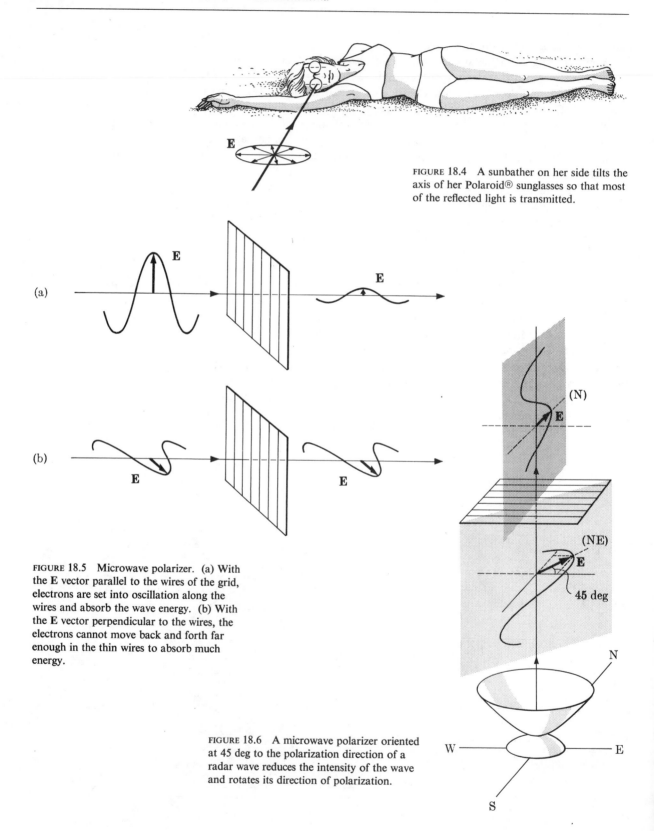

FIGURE 18.4   A sunbather on her side tilts the axis of her Polaroid® sunglasses so that most of the reflected light is transmitted.

(a)

(b)

FIGURE 18.5   Microwave polarizer. (a) With the **E** vector parallel to the wires of the grid, electrons are set into oscillation along the wires and absorb the wave energy. (b) With the **E** vector perpendicular to the wires, the electrons cannot move back and forth far enough in the thin wires to absorb much energy.

FIGURE 18.6   A microwave polarizer oriented at 45 deg to the polarization direction of a radar wave reduces the intensity of the wave and rotates its direction of polarization.

A microwave polarizer, acting on macroscopic wavelengths, is easy to understand (if approached warily). It consists of a grid of parallel wires (Figure 18.5), the length of each wire being greater than the wavelength of the radiation and the spacing of the wires being less than the wavelength. If unpolarized microwaves fall on this grid with its wires running vertically, which direction of polarization will pass through? Here is where caution is required. One might think uncritically of a skinny prisoner slipping between two bars of his cell and answer, "Vertically polarized waves pass through." This is wrong. The vibrating electric field in the vertically polarized wave sets the electrons in the wires into up-and-down oscillation. Energy is transferred from the field to the electrons, so the wave is absorbed. For the horizontally polarized wave, on the other hand, the vertical wire is a very poor absorber because its electrons are prevented from swinging back and forth horizontally through more than the small diameter of the wire. Therefore, it is the horizontally polarized wave that sneaks through the vertical grid almost undiminished, whereas the vertically polarized wave is absorbed.

A wire grid polarizes microwaves

This microwave polarizer illustrates how marked can be the effect of changing the wavelength of electromagnetic radiation. For microwaves, the grid is wholly transparent to one polarization, largely opaque to another; for light, it has no sensitivity whatever to polarization. For microwaves, it acts as a single unit; for light, it is a series of alternate transparent and opaque stripes acting separately. Similar illustrations could be drawn from many parts of nature. Always the important quantity is the scale of the object relative to the wavelength of the radiation.

A vitally important aspect of polarization is its vector character. This means that a wave polarized in any direction can be regarded as the sum of two or more waves polarized in other directions—that is, it can be resolved into components. Also, two or more differently polarized waves propagating in the same direction precisely in phase act in concert as a single wave with a single polarization. The idea of component polarization was shown in Figure 18.2. A second example is illustrated in Figure 18.6. An electromagnetic wave propagates straight upward from a radar antenna, polarized in the northeast-southwest direction. This wave can also be treated as two equally intense waves, one polarized north-south and one polarized east-west. If a wire grid polarizer is superposed with its wires running east-west, what gets through? The common-sense answer (and the correct one) is a north-south polarized wave half as intense as the original wave. Although this answer is both sensible and correct, actually some subtlety lies behind it. By the cosine law for vector components, if the peak electric field to the northeast is E, the peak fields to north and east are

The vector nature of polarization

$$E_{north} = E \cos (45 \text{ deg}) = 0.707E, \qquad (18.11)$$

$$E_{east} = E \cos (45 \text{ deg}) = 0.707E. \qquad (18.12)$$

The field strength slipping through the polarizer is not half of the original field strength but more than 70 percent of it. However, since the *intensity* of the wave is proportional to the square of the electric field strength (Equation 18.10), the energy in the transmitted wave is indeed half the original energy.

18.3   Superposition

The superposition of electric and magnetic fields has been discussed before (Sections 15.5 and 16.2). It means that an electric field (or a magnetic field) at a point arising from several sources is the vector sum of the separate fields that would be present if each source were acting alone. Applied to electromagnetic waves, the law of superposition has two implications: (1) To find the total intensity of two or more waves at a point, one must first add the field vectors of the separate waves to get a total field vector. It is incorrect to add the intensities (or energies) of the separate waves. (2) Waves from different sources can interpenetrate or coexist in space without mutual interaction. A simple example of such interpenetration is the intersection of two searchlight beams.

Implications of superposition for electromagnetic waves

The idea of superposition can be extended to other kinds of waves. For surface waves or sound waves in material media, superposition means that displacements of the vibrating matter contributed by two or more sources are additive. For sound waves, water waves, or waves in a stretched wire, the law of superposition is usually valid to good approximation but is never precisely valid. Figure 18.7 shows superposed water waves interpenetrating with no noticeable mutual effect. The condition required for superposition is that the wave disturbance be relatively weak—gentle waves on water, for example, but not breaking waves at the beach; or mild sound waves but not shock waves. If two shock waves cross one another, the resulting displacement at their point of intersection is not the sum of the two separate displacements, and they do not continue on their way uninfluenced by the encounter.

Approximate validity of superposition for other waves

As mentioned in Section 15.5, the law of superposition is not precisely valid for electromagnetic waves either. If two photons meet in space there is a chance—an exceedingly small chance—that they will interact and be deflected by the encounter. This violates the principle of superposition because the resulting radiation flow is not the same as if each photon had passed separately by. This process, known as the scattering of light by light, has been measured in the laboratory, but it is too improbable to have any perceptible effect on radio communications or on any of the other practical examples of superposed electromagnetic waves. It is interesting, however, that if two extremely intense beams of light (more intense than any known) intersected, they could interact strongly, as shock waves do, and seriously violate the principle of superposition.

γ_2 γ_1

Usually

γ_1 γ_2

Interaction

Occasionally

FIGURE 18.7   Superposed water waves. (Photograph courtesy of Film Studio, Education Development Center, Inc.)

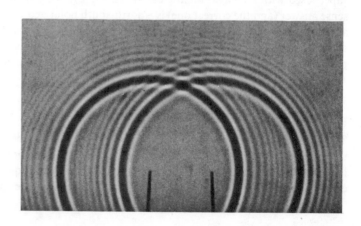

Another way to say this is that photons, if crowded together densely enough, would begin to act like bits of matter.

COHERENCE AND INCOHERENCE

Several important aspects of superposition can be illustrated by considering the overlap of two waves radiated by point sources S_1 and S_2 (Figure 18.8). To be specific, we suppose the waves to be electromagnetic. At a point P, the electric field is

$$\mathbf{E_P} = \mathbf{E} + \mathbf{E'}, \tag{18.13}$$

Fields from two sources superposed

where $\mathbf{E}$ and $\mathbf{E'}$ are the fields that would exist at this point if either source were acting alone. The intensity at P is the time-average of E_P^2.* Since $E_P^2 = \mathbf{E_P} \cdot \mathbf{E_P} = (\mathbf{E} + \mathbf{E'}) \cdot (\mathbf{E} + \mathbf{E'})$, the intensity of the superposed waves is

$$I_P = \overline{E^2} + \overline{E'^2} + 2\overline{\mathbf{E} \cdot \mathbf{E'}}$$

$$= I + I' + 2\overline{\mathbf{E} \cdot \mathbf{E'}}, \tag{18.14}$$

Intensity of superposed waves

where I and I' are the intensities that would be contributed by each source acting alone.

Now let us focus attention on the so-called "interference term" in Equation 18.14, the term $2\overline{\mathbf{E} \cdot \mathbf{E'}}$ whose presence in the equation means that I_P is not necessarily equal to $I + I'$. To discuss this term, we must distinguish between coherent and incoherent sources. If the interference term is zero, not only at a particular point P but at all points, the two sources are said to be *incoherent*. There are various reasons why the average scalar product, $\overline{\mathbf{E} \cdot \mathbf{E'}}$, might be equal to zero at all points. (1) The sources might be emitting waves of various

Incoherent sources:
$\overline{\mathbf{E} \cdot \mathbf{E'}} = 0$ *at all points*

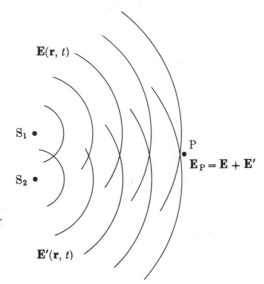

$\mathbf{E(r}, t)$

$S_1 \bullet$

$S_2 \bullet$

P

$\mathbf{E_P} = \mathbf{E} + \mathbf{E'}$

$\mathbf{E'(r}, t)$

FIGURE 18.8 Superposed fields from two point sources. The equality $\mathbf{E_P} = \mathbf{E} + \mathbf{E'}$ is valid whether the sources are coherent or not.

---

* Since the energy density of the electric field is $u = \frac{1}{2}\epsilon_0 E^2$ and since, in an electromagnetic wave, the magnetic field stores an equal energy, the mean energy density at point P is $\overline{u_P} = \epsilon_0 I_P$.

randomly oriented polarizations. At any instant, the scalar product $\mathbf{E} \cdot \mathbf{E}'$ is as likely to be positive as negative. Its average value is zero. (2) The sources might be emitting radiation of different frequencies. If $\mathbf{E}$ and $\mathbf{E}'$ are parallel at one instant (waves in phase), they will be antiparallel at a later instant (waves out of phase). No definite phase relationship can prevail for waves of different frequency. Again, $\mathbf{E} \cdot \mathbf{E}'$ is as likely to be positive as negative and has a zero average value. (3) Each source might be emitting a succession of waves of random relative phase. (Atoms, for instance, could be emitting distinct and uncorrelated photons.) Even if the waves have the same frequency and the same polarization, such a random variation of phase causes $\overline{\mathbf{E} \cdot \mathbf{E}'}$ to be zero. Most of our common sources of light of other radiation are incoherent sources. Several examples of incoherent sources are shown in Figure 18.9(a).

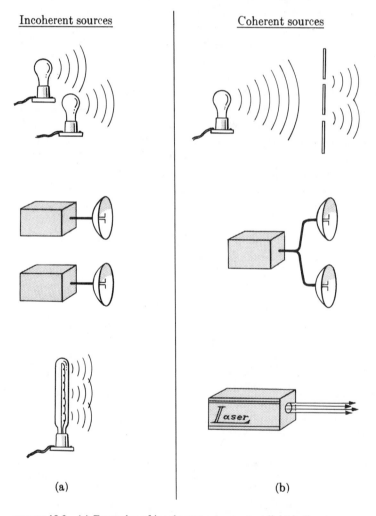

Incoherent sources   Coherent sources

(a)   (b)

FIGURE 18.9   (a) Examples of incoherent sources: two light bulbs; two microwave antennas driven by different oscillators; different parts of the same filament of a light bulb. (b) Examples of coherent sources: two slits illuminated by a single source; two antennas driven by the same oscillator; two parts of the same laser beam.

In order that two sources be *coherent*, very special conditions must prevail. The two waves must have the same frequency, a fixed relative polarization, and a fixed relative phase. This can be achieved, for example, by having two microwave antennas driven by the same oscillator [Figure 18.9(b)]. Different parts of the same laser beam are also coherent,* unlike radiation from different parts of a tungsten filament. Another interesting example of coherent sources is a pair of slits illuminated by a single source of light. Classically, the radiation from an ordinary light bulb can be thought of as many individual wave trains, all of different frequency, polarization, and phase. Each one is incoherent with an average over many others. However, when any one wave train strikes the pair of slits, it establishes oscillating electromagnetic fields at the two slits that are coherent and that act as coherent sources. A single wave train, we might say, is coherent with itself. To make the situation easier to think about, we could imagine that the wave trains arrive at the pair of slits one at a time. Then the slits would always continue to act as coherent sources even though there is no particular relationship between one wave train and another.

Coherent sources: same frequency, fixed relative polarization, fixed relative phase

Slits in a screen act as coherent sources

The quantum description of this phenomenon is quite similar in principle but harder to visualize. Think of photons (instead of wave trains) leaving the light bulb one at a time. Although a photon is a "particle," it also has wave properties, and the behavior of the light on the far side of the slits shows that a single photon must actually illuminate both slits at once. Even if the light is made so dim that indeed only one photon at a time reaches the slits, the two slits continue to act as coherent sources.

To see the effect of coherence more clearly, we may postulate sinusoidal variation for the waves from both sources. Suppose that the electric fields **E** and **E′** at point P contributed by the two sources (refer to Figure 18.8) are

$$\mathbf{E} = \mathbf{E}_1 \sin(\omega t + \varphi_1), \tag{18.15}$$

$$\mathbf{E}' = \mathbf{E}_2 \sin(\omega t + \varphi_2). \tag{18.16}$$

The angular frequency ω ($= 2\pi\nu$) must be the same for the two waves if they are to be coherent. The vectors $\mathbf{E}_1$ and $\mathbf{E}_2$ may depend on the location of the point P but they are independent of time.† Coherence requires that the phase difference,

$$\varphi = \varphi_1 - \varphi_2, \tag{18.17}$$

be constant. Now consider the various terms in Equation 18.14. For the first two terms, we have

$$I = \overline{E^2} = \tfrac{1}{2}E_1{}^2, \tag{18.18}$$

$$I' = \overline{E'^2} = \tfrac{1}{2}E_2{}^2. \tag{18.19}$$

These are the single-source intensities. To find the interference term, we need the scalar product of **E** and **E′**, which is

$$\mathbf{E} \cdot \mathbf{E}' = \mathbf{E}_1 \cdot \mathbf{E}_2 \sin(\omega t + \varphi_1) \sin(\omega t + \varphi_2).$$

---

* The explanation of the coherence of a laser beam is found in Section 24.12.

† For coherence, a somewhat weaker condition is sufficient: that $\overline{\mathbf{E}_1 \cdot \mathbf{E}_2}$ be independent of time.

With the help of a trigonometric formula from Appendix 6, this may be written

$$\mathbf{E} \cdot \mathbf{E}' = \tfrac{1}{2}E_1 \cdot E_2[\cos \varphi - \cos (2\omega t + \varphi_1 + \varphi_2)],$$

where φ is defined by Equation 18.17. Since the time-average of

$$\cos (2\omega t + \varphi_1 + \varphi_2)$$

is zero, we get, for the interference term,

Interference term for sinusoidal waves

$$2\overline{\mathbf{E} \cdot \mathbf{E}'} = \mathbf{E}_1 \cdot \mathbf{E}_2 \cos \varphi. \tag{18.20}$$

Substitution from Equations 18.18–18.20 into Equation 18.14 gives, for the total intensity of the coherent superposed waves at P,

Intensity depends on relative polarization and relative phase

$$I_P = \tfrac{1}{2}(E_1{}^2 + E_2{}^2 + 2\mathbf{E}_1 \cdot \mathbf{E}_2 \cos \varphi). \tag{18.21}$$

Even for coherent waves, it is *possible* for the interference terms to vanish. However, if $\cos \varphi = 0$ at one point, it would not be expected to be zero at another point. The phase difference depends on the point being considered (see, for instance, the x-dependence of phase in Equation 18.9).

We may specialize somewhat further and suppose the two waves to have the same polarization direction. Then the amplitude vectors $\mathbf{E}_1$ and $\mathbf{E}_2$ may be chosen to be parallel, so that $\mathbf{E}_1 \cdot \mathbf{E}_2 = E_1 E_2$. The combined intensity is then

Polarizations equal

$$I_P = \tfrac{1}{2}(E_1{}^2 + E_2{}^2 + 2E_1 E_2 \cos \varphi). \tag{18.22}$$

This result could be applied, for instance, to the water waves in Figure 18.7, or to sound waves, if E_1 and E_2 were replaced by displacement amplitudes A_1 and A_2. The maximum value of the right side of Equation 18.22 occurs for $\cos \varphi = 1$ (waves in phase); the minimum value occurs for $\cos \varphi = -1$ (waves out of phase). These maximum and minimum values are

Polarizations equal and $\cos \varphi = \pm 1$

$$I_P(\text{max}) = \tfrac{1}{2}(E_1 + E_2)^2 = (\sqrt{I} + \sqrt{I'})^2, \tag{18.23}$$

$$I_P(\text{min}) = \tfrac{1}{2}(E_1 - E_2)^2 = (\sqrt{I} - \sqrt{I'})^2. \tag{18.24}$$

For the special case that $I = I'$, as might be true if P is nearly equidistant from S_1 and S_2, the minimum intensity is zero and the maximum intensity is $4I$.

This discussion is continued in Section 18.10, where the dependence of the phase difference φ on the location of the point P is brought in.

HUYGENS'S PRINCIPLE

In the seventeenth century, long before the full import of superposition was appreciated for electromagnetic waves, Christiaan Huygens made use of the idea of superposition in describing the propagation of a single wave. He asserted that each point on an advancing wave front can be regarded as the source of a new wavelet and that the subsequent position of the wave front is determined by the superposition of all of the tiny wavelets. (By a wave front is meant a line or curve of constant phase, such as the crest of a water wave.) This idea, now known as Huygens's principle, can also be stated in this way: Points along a line of constant phase act as coherent sources for the further propagation of the wave.

Statement of Huygens's principle

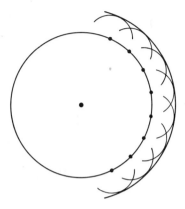

Spherical wave   Plane wave

FIGURE 18.10   Application of Huygens's principle to broad advancing wave front. The dots indicate sources of new wavelets along a surface of constant phase.

Figure 18.10 shows how the principle can be simply applied to the propagation of a spherical wave and a plane wave. From one wave front another wave front can be constructed as the envelope of the wavelets that have all propagated the same distance.

Huygens's principle is only *approximate* and cannot be applied uncritically in all cases. For one thing, to make the principle conform with more accurate but more difficult methods of handling wave superposition, the backward propagating wavelet must be ignored except at reflecting surfaces. Nevertheless, the principle is useful and is accurate for dealing with various kinds of wave phenomena, such as: (1) The *direction* of propagation of a broad wave front that encounters reflecting or refracting media; (2) the *intensity* of interference and diffraction patterns over a limited range of angles; and (3) the *locations* of maxima and minima resulting from interference. The first use of the principle, taken up in Sections 18.4 and 18.6, is concerned with reflection and refraction. The second use of the principle will be taken up in Section 18.10, the third in Section 18.11.

It is not exact

But it gives accurate results for many wave phenomena

18.4   Reflection

A tennis ball thrown against a wall is "reflected." If it is not spinning, it obeys approximately the law of reflection: The angle of incidence is equal to the angle of reflection. A broad wave front of light striking a perfectly flat mirror obeys this law exactly, but the mechanism of its reflection is much more complicated than the mechanics of the tennis ball's reflection. Light waves, or photons, do not simply bounce from the reflecting surface. They are absorbed and reemitted. They are diminished in intensity, they suffer a phase change of π radians, and they are partially polarized. These details need not concern us here, however. We wish only to understand the law of reflection in terms of Huygens's principle of superposed wavelets. The diagram in Figure 18.11 is useful for this purpose. We consider a particular wave front, initially at AA′, later at BB′, and an equal time later at C. As each point on this wave front reaches the reflecting surface, it gives rise to a new wavelet propagating back outward from the reflecting surface.

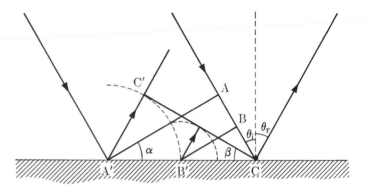

FIGURE 18.11   Reflection of a wave. The
equal angles of incidence and reflection are
designated by θ_i and θ_r.

In the time it has taken the incoming wave front to move from A to C, the
wavelet beginning at A′ has expanded to a radius A′C′ equal to the distance AC.
The wavelet beginning at B′, starting later, has propagated back only half as far.
The dashed curves outline these two wavelets at the instant the incoming wave
front reaches the point C. At this instant, the wavelet emanating from C has
not yet moved; it is indicated by a heavy dot at C. The reflected wave front is
then the line CC′, touching the two circles and the dot at C. The essential physical
fact underlying the proof that the angle of reflection, θ_r, is equal to the angle of
incidence, θ_i, is the fact that the speed of the reflected wave is the same as the
speed of the incident wave. This means that the distances AC and A′C′ are
equal. Accordingly the two right triangles, A′C′C and CAA′, are congruent, and
the angles α and β are equal. Since $\alpha = \theta_i$ and $\beta = \theta_r$, it follows that

*Huygens's principle accounts
for the law of reflection*

$$\theta_i = \theta_r . \tag{18.25}$$

After this demonstration and others like it were given by Huygens, there
was no theoretical bar to the acceptance of light waves. He showed that waves
could account as well as particles for the properties of light known at that time.
Crucial tests of the wave theory came more than a century later.

18.5   Mirrors

When the breadth of a beam of light is much larger than the wavelength of
the light and when the dimensions of obstacles and apertures in the way of the
beam are also large compared with the wavelength, certain wave aspects of the
light—notably diffraction—are relatively unimportant. Then, to good approximation, light rays, which are lines drawn perpendicular to surfaces of constant
phase, follow particle-like trajectories. They move in straight lines except when
reflected or refracted. The study and description of light in terms of such straight

*The approximation of
geometrical optics*

line propagation is called *geometrical optics* or *ray optics*. The idea can be simply
illustrated with a plane mirror.

Light coming from any point P on an object is considered to spread in rays
from that point (Figure 18.12). If the object is placed before a mirror, a ray
striking the mirror at angle θ is reflected at angle θ. To a viewer looking at the
reflected light, it seems to come from behind the mirror. For a plane mirror,
as shown in Figure 18.12, all of the reflected rays from point P seem to emanate

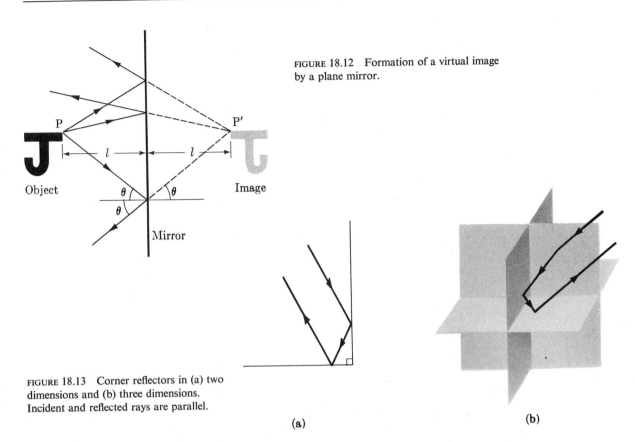

FIGURE 18.12   Formation of a virtual image
by a plane mirror.

FIGURE 18.13   Corner reflectors in (a) two
dimensions and (b) three dimensions.
Incident and reflected rays are parallel.

(a)   (b)

from point P′; the source P and its image P′ lie along a line perpendicular to the mirror and are equidistant from its surface. The entire object then has a reversed image behind the mirror, as shown in the figure.* As everyone knows from practical experience, the image is the same size as the object.

*Action of a plane mirror:
The virtual image is
unmagnified*

An interesting use of plane mirrors is in the so-called corner reflector. Three mutually perpendicular plane mirrors reflect light back in the direction from which it came, regardless of the angle of the light relative to the mirrors. The principle is illustrated in two dimensions in Figure 18.13(a). Figure 18.13(b) shows a design that returns light from any direction whatever. Such a reflector in orbit about the earth returns radar waves much more intensely to their source than would a sphere or an irregularly shaped object and, therefore, makes it easier to determine the exact location of the orbiting reflector. In 1969, the first astronauts to land on the moon left behind a set of small corner reflectors in a rectangular array, designed to reflect the light from lasers back to earth.† The pulsed laser beams serve the same purpose as radar, to determine the precise distance to the moon and learn how it varies in time.

Corner reflectors

---

* A challenging, and surprisingly subtle, question is this: Why is your image in a mirror inverted left-to-right but not top-to-bottom?

† See James E. Faller and E. Joseph Wampler, "The Lunar Laser Reflector," *Scientific American,* March, 1970.

CONCAVE MIRRORS

If a concave mirror has the shape of a paraboloid, it brings a parallel beam of light to a focus [Figure 18.14(a)]. Conversely, it transforms light from a source at the focal point F into a parallel beam. Such parabolic mirrors are used in reflecting telescopes and in searchlights. A concave mirror that is a small section of a sphere [Figure 18.14(b)] behaves in approximately the same way. Consider an incident ray SP parallel to the axis of the mirror. It makes an angle θ with the radial line CP drawn from the center of curvature of the mirror. The reflected ray PF makes the same angle θ with the radial line. The triangle CFP is therefore an isosceles triangle, and one of its sides s is related to its base R by

$$s = \tfrac{1}{2}R \sec \theta.$$

The distance f from the mirror to the point F, the so-called focal distance, is equal to $R - s$:

$$f = R(1 - \tfrac{1}{2} \sec \theta). \tag{18.26}$$

For small angles (small compared with 1 radian), sec θ is nearly equal to 1.* Then

Focal distance of spherical mirror

$$f = \tfrac{1}{2}R, \tag{18.27}$$

a distance independent of θ. All incident rays parallel to the axis pass approximately through the same point F after reflection. This property, as we may now demonstrate, leads to a simple formula for the magnifying or demagnifying power of the mirror.

If a point source S is located on the axis of the mirror, a ray from S making angle α with the axis is reflected from point P to cross the axis again at I (Figure 18.15). The distance from mirror to source S is d_1; the distance from mirror to image I is d_2; and the angles of incidence and reflection at P are both β. The path of a ray parallel to the axis, with angle of incidence $\alpha + \beta$, is shown by

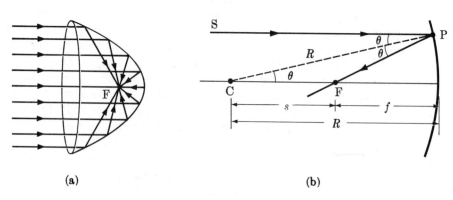

(a)   (b)

FIGURE 18.14   (a) A parabolic mirror brings a parallel beam of light to a focus.   (b) A concave mirror that is a small section of a sphere brings parallel rays approximately to a focus.

* Sec (1 deg) = 1.00015; sec (5 deg) = 1.0038; sec (10 deg) = 1.015; sec (15 deg) = 1.035.

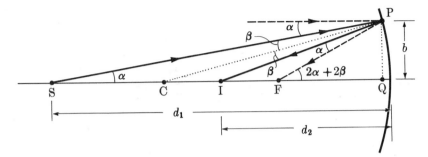

FIGURE 18.15   A source S at distance d_1 from a concave spherical mirror forms a real image I at distance d_2 from the mirror. A simple relationship among d_1, d_2, and f (Equation 18.31) is valid if the angles α and β are much less than 1 radian.

a dashed line in the figure. If the distance from the point P to the axis of the mirror is called b, we have the following approximate relations for small angle:

$$\tan \alpha \cong \alpha \cong \frac{b}{d_1}, \tag{18.28}$$

$$\tan (\alpha + 2\beta) \cong \alpha + 2\beta \cong \frac{b}{d_2}, \tag{18.29}$$

$$\tan (2\alpha + 2\beta) \cong 2\alpha + 2\beta \cong \frac{b}{f}. \tag{18.30}$$

These are properties of the right triangles SQP, IQP, and FQP. From the sum of Equations 18.28 and 18.29, we can form the same combination that appears in Equation 18.30, $2\alpha + 2\beta$. This manipulation gives $(b/d_1) + (b/d_2) = b/f$, or, after cancellation of the factors b,

$$\frac{1}{d_1} + \frac{1}{d_2} = \frac{1}{f}. \tag{18.31}$$

Object and image distances related to f

We write this as an equality, but it must be borne in mind that it is an approximation valid only for small angles. The fact that the final expression is independent of b means that the point P is arbitrary. All reflected rays from S pass through I; this confluence of rays at I is called a *real image*. It is to be contrasted with a *virtual image*, like the one shown in Figure 18.12.

Figure 18.16 shows a geometrical construction to find the image of an extended object. The source AB is a tube of length l, oriented perpendicular to the axis of the mirror, at a distance d_1 from the mirror. According to the discussion above, the end of the tube on the axis (A) produces an image A′, also on the axis, at distance d_2 from the mirror, with d_1 and d_2 related by Equation 18.31. It is left as a problem to show that the image B′ of the point B is also at distance d_2 so that the entire image A′B′ is perpendicular to the axis. Assuming the correctness of this result, we note that ABQ and A′B′Q are similar right triangles. Therefore,

$$\frac{l'}{l} = \frac{d_2}{d_1}. \tag{18.32}$$

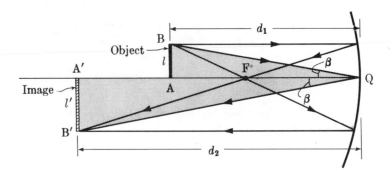

FIGURE 18.16   Formation of a real image by a concave spherical mirror. Because the two shaded triangles are similar, the magnification, l'/l, is equal to d_2/d_1.

The ratio of image size to source size is equal to the ratio of image distance to source distance. This ratio is the magnification M:

$$M = \frac{d_2}{d_1}.$$

(18.33)

More usefully, M may be expressed in terms of d_1 and f. From Equation 18.31, we may write

$$1 + \frac{d_1}{d_2} = \frac{d_1}{f}.$$

Solve this equation for d_2/d_1 and substitute in Equation 18.33 to obtain

The magnification of a concave mirror

$$M = \frac{1}{(d_1/f) - 1}.$$

(18.34)

For $d_1 = 2f$, there is no magnification ($M = 1$). For d_1 greater than $2f$, there is demagnification ($M < 1$). For d_1 less than $2f$ but greater than f (the case illustrated in Figure 18.16), there is magnification ($M > 1$). For d_1 less than f, Equation 18.34 gives a negative value for M. The interpretation of this interesting case is left to the problems.

CONVEX MIRRORS

Quantitative discussion of the convex mirror follows very closely the discussion of the concave mirror. For small angles, a convex spherical mirror has a focal point F, as shown in Figure 18.17(a), from which reflected parallel rays seem to diverge. The focal distance and radius of curvature are again related by Equation 18.27. The image of an object placed before a convex mirror is always virtual and demagnified [Figure 18.17(b)]. The object distance d_1 and image distance d_2 are related by

$$\frac{1}{d_2} - \frac{1}{d_1} = \frac{1}{f},$$

(18.35)

Equations of a convex mirror   and the demagnification M is given by

$$M = \frac{d_2}{d_1} = \frac{1}{(d_1/f) + 1}. \tag{18.36}$$

These equations are superficially similar to, but not identical to, Equations 18.31 and 18.34. To show their underlying unity, we may alter them in an illuminating way. Suppose we define the focal distance f to be negative for a convex mirror and define the distance d_2 and magnification M to be negative for a virtual image. These changes reverse the signs of two terms in Equation 18.35, giving

$$-\frac{1}{d_2} - \frac{1}{d_1} = -\frac{1}{f}, \tag{18.37}$$

which is equivalent to Equation 18.31. In Equation 18.36, the sign of the ratio d_1/f and the sign of M are reversed, giving

$$-M = \frac{1}{-(d_1/f) + 1}, \tag{18.38}$$

With suitable sign conventions, equations of concave and convex mirrors are the same

which is equivalent to Equation 18.34.

Among common applications of spherical mirrors are the concave shaving mirror, which is used for magnification, and the convex driving mirror, which is used to gain a more panoramic—though demagnified—view to the rear.

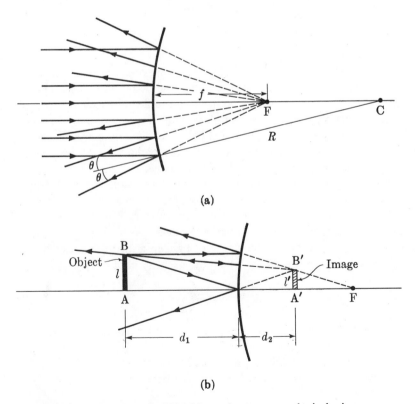

(a)

(b)

FIGURE 18.17 Formation of a virtual image by a convex spherical mirror. The demagnification, l'/l, is equal to d_2/d_1.

■ EXAMPLE: A concave spherical mirror used in a small telescope has a diameter of 15 cm and a radius of curvature of 1 m. By how much is the image of a star spread out along the axis of the mirror? Consider rays parallel to the axis striking the mirror. Those very close to the axis are deflected to cross the axis at a distance $f_0 = \frac{1}{2}R$ from the mirror. Those striking the edge of the mirror [see Figure 18.14(b) and Equation 18.26] are caused to cross the axis at a distance $f = R(1 - \frac{1}{2}\sec\theta)$ from the mirror. The spread of the image along the axis is, therefore,

$$\Delta f = f_0 - f = \frac{1}{2}R(\sec\theta - 1). \qquad (18.39)$$

For small θ, an approximation for $\sec\theta$ is useful:

$$\sec\theta = \frac{1}{\cos\theta} \cong \frac{1}{1 - \frac{1}{2}\theta^2} \cong 1 + \frac{1}{2}\theta^2.$$

Putting this into Equation 18.39 gives

$$\Delta f = \frac{1}{4}R\theta^2.$$

In this example, $R = 1$ m and $\theta \cong 7.5$ cm/100 cm $= 0.075$ radian, so

$$\Delta f \cong \frac{1}{4} \times 1 \text{ m} \times (0.075)^2$$

$$= 1.4 \times 10^{-3} \text{ m} = 1.4 \text{ mm}.$$

Use of a parabolic mirror would eliminate this small spread.   ■

18.6   Refraction

Refraction, the deflection of a wave passing from one medium to another, is caused by the difference in the speed of the wave in the two media. Why light is slowed in passing from air to glass is by no means a simple matter. The speed of light, c, is no less a universal constant in glass than in air or in empty space. However, in making its way through glass, light is continually being absorbed and reemitted. Thinking in terms of photons, we can picture a jerky process in which the light is alternately moving at the constant speed c and not moving at all. This start-and-stop progression through the glass results in an average speed less than the constant c. Light moves most rapidly in a vacuum. In any material medium, its average speed is less. In air at ordinary density the average speed is about 0.03 percent less than c. In glass the average speed may be 30 percent less than c. The ratio of c to the speed of light in a medium is called the *index of refraction* of the medium, for which the usual symbol is n:

The index of refraction defined

$$n = \frac{c}{v}. \qquad (18.40)$$

The index of refraction is evidently dimensionless, and it is greater than 1 in matter.

Huygens accounted for refraction much as he accounted for reflection, by considering wavelets emanating from the interface between two media.* His

---

* See Christiaan Huygens, *Treatise on Light* (Chicago, Ill.: University of Chicago Press, 1945).

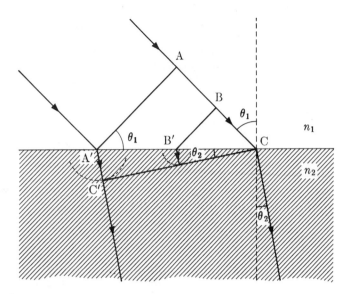

FIGURE 18.18   Refraction of a wave. The angle of incidence is θ_1, the angle of refraction is θ_2. The speed is less in the lower medium ($n_2 > n_1$).

geometrical construction is still a good way to gain an understanding of the wave aspect of refraction. Again consider a plane wave front approaching a flat interface between two media, whose indices of refraction are n_1 and n_2 (Figure 18.18). Let us suppose for convenience that the wave travels more slowly in the lower medium ($n_2 > n_1$). At the moment the wave front reaches the line AA′, a wavelet begins to spread out into the lower medium from A′ but at a speed less than the speed of the incident wave. While the incident wave front advances from A to C, the wavelet initiated at A′ has propagated a lesser distance A′C′. The ratio of these two distances is equal to the ratio of the speeds:

$$\frac{AC}{A'C'} = \frac{v_1}{v_2} = \frac{n_2}{n_1}. \tag{18.41}$$

The new wave front in the lower medium extending from C to C′ has been deflected. (It is left to the reader to show that the midpoint wavelet beginning at B′ had advanced just far enough to touch the line CC′). If θ_1 is the angle of incidence, it is also, as shown in Figure 18.18, the angle AA′C. The angle of refraction θ_2 is also the angle C′CA′. The sines of these angles are

$$\sin \theta_1 = \frac{AC}{CA'},$$

$$\sin \theta_2 = \frac{A'C'}{CA'}.$$

Taking the ratio of these two sines causes the distance CA′ to cancel from the two expressions and gives

$$\frac{\sin \theta_1}{\sin \theta_2} = \frac{AC}{A'C'}.$$

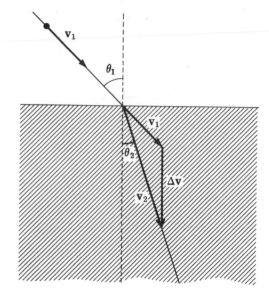

FIGURE 18.19 Refraction according to the particle theory of light. The particle moves faster in the lower medium.

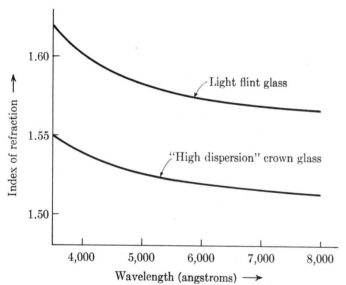

FIGURE 18.20 Index of refraction vs wavelength for two kinds of glass.

The ratio on the right is, according to Equation 18.41, the ratio of the indices of refraction, so

$$\frac{\sin \theta_1}{\sin \theta_2} = \frac{n_2}{n_1}. \tag{18.42}$$

This law of sines for refraction was discovered experimentally by Willebrord Snell early in the seventeenth century and is now referred to as Snell's law. Snell discovered that the ratio of the sines is a constant for any particular pair of media—such as air and glass—but he was probably unaware of the physical significance of the constant as a speed ratio.

To make Snell's law somewhat easier to remember, it is convenient to write it in the form

Snell's law of refraction

$$n_1 \sin \theta_1 = n_2 \sin \theta_2. \tag{18.43}$$

As the symmetry of this equation suggests, the law should remain valid if the direction of propagation is reversed. It is easy to prove, with the help of Figure 18.18, that a wave propagating upward, with θ_2 the angle of incidence and θ_1 the angle of refraction, still obeys Equation 18.43.

According to the particle view of light adopted by Descartes and explored by Newton, refraction is accounted for by an *increase* of speed of light in passing from air to a denser medium. Figure 18.19 illustrates this alternative conception of refraction. A particle of light entering glass from air is supposed to be attracted by the glass surface, thereby being given an inward impulse and deflected to a path more nearly perpendicular to the surface. Thus, even before the end of the seventeenth century, one crucial test of the wave vs the particle theory of light was clear. Does light travel more rapidly or more slowly in dense matter than in air? The answer to the question remained beyond the means of experimental physicists for more than 150 years. Finally, in 1850 Jean Leon Foucault succeeded in measuring the speed of light in water and found it to be less than in air.

Wave and particle theories make opposite predictions of relative speed

The index of refraction of air at normal density is 1.00029. The index of refraction of water is 1.33. Indices of refraction of different kinds of glass are in the range 1.4 to 1.8. Besides the variation from one substance to another, the average speed of light in matter varies slightly with the wavelength of the light. Figure 18.20 is a graph of index of refraction vs wavelength for two kinds of glass. The greater the index of refraction, the greater the refraction. Therefore, upon entering glass at an angle, blue light (shorter wavelength) is deflected more than red light (longer wavelength). This dependence of refraction on wavelength, called *dispersion*, explains why a prism spreads a beam of white light into a rainbow of colors* (see Figure 17.22).

$\lambda\,(\text{Å})$	$n(H_2O)$ at 20 °C
3,968	1.3438
4,340	1.3407
4,861	1.3375
5,893	1.3333
6,563	1.3315

Dispersion: n depends on λ

TOTAL INTERNAL REFLECTION

Any equation is likely to yield interesting insights if examined in one or more limiting situations. This is true of Equation 18.43 expressing Snell's law. You might consider the implications of Snell's law if n_2 is nearly equal to n_1 or if n_2 is much greater than n_1. Here we wish to consider another limit, the limit of maximum angle of refraction. This consideration leads to a wholly new idea, total internal reflection. To be specific, consider light passing from air to glass whose index of refraction is $n = 1.5$. For zero angle of incidence, it enters the glass undeflected, perpendicular to the surface. As the angle of incidence increases, so does the angle of refraction, but the latter increases less rapidly. When the angle of incidence has reached its maximum, so that the light beam grazes the surface, $\theta_1 = 90$ deg and $\sin\theta = 1$. If we make the good approximation, $n_1 = 1$; and set $n_2 = n$, Equation 18.43 reads

$$\sin\theta_2{}^{max} = \frac{1}{n}. \qquad (18.44)$$

---

* The colors of a rainbow in the sky are similarly accounted for by the dependence on wavelength of the index of refraction of water droplets.

If $n = 1.5$, then $\sin \theta_2^{\max} = 0.667$, and $\theta_2^{\max} = 41.8$ deg.   This particular situation is illustrated in Figure 18.21. All light entering the glass, from whatever direction, is confined to an allowed range of angles within the glass. The other angles, comprising the "forbidden" region, receive no light.

In order to extract more from this analysis, we must now consider the reverse process; light passing from glass to air. According to Snell's law, the angle of refraction of the light beam in the air is given by

$$\sin \theta_1 = n \sin \theta_2 . \tag{18.45}$$

At the critical angle $\theta_2^{\max}$, $n \sin \theta_2^{\max} = 1$, and $\theta_1 = \pi/2$. The refracted light just escapes into the air, grazing the glass surface. If we insist on going further, to larger values of θ_2—which is certainly possible—mathematical difficulties seem to result. Equation 18.45 states that $\sin \theta_1$ is greater than 1. In effect the equation is telling us that there is *no* angle θ_1 of a refracted beam beyond the surface, and this is indeed the case. All the light is reflected at the surface and

Total internal reflection when $\theta_2 > \theta_2^{\max}$

remains within the glass. This phenomenon is called *total internal reflection*. It can occur whenever light is incident on a surface where the speed of light outside the surface is greater than within the surface.

Total internal reflection can be harnessed for several useful purposes. One is to change the direction of light more efficiently than a mirror can do it. A mirror absorbs some light and is spoiled by dirt. An internally reflecting surface is almost perfectly efficient, and its action is less marred by dirt outside

Applications: prisms, light pipes, and fiber optics

the surface. Prisms reflecting light through 90 deg and 180 deg are shown in Figure 18.22. In binoculars, pairs of prisms, arranged as in Figure 18.22(b), are used in order to lengthen the light path between the lenses without incon-

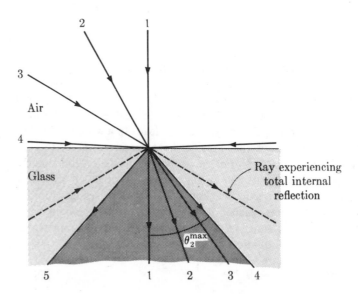

FIGURE 18.21   Refraction at air-glass interface with $n_2/n_1 = 1.5$. Light entering the glass from the air is confined in angle within the darkly shaded cone. Angles greater than $\theta_2^{\max}$ are "forbidden." A ray of light moving at a "forbidden angle" in the glass (dashed line) cannot escape the glass. It experiences total internal reflection.

veniently lengthening the barrels of the binoculars. Another interesting use of total internal reflection is in light pipes (Figure 18.23). Experimental physicists use Lucite® light pipes to conduct light from a scintillating crystal to a light-sensitive photomultiplier tube, and some dentists use them to conduct light to a

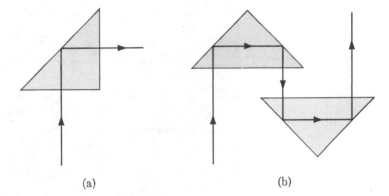

FIGURE 18.22 Practical utilization of total internal reflection in prisms. (a) Deflection of light through 90 deg. (b) Quadruple reflection to lengthen light path in binoculars.

(a)   (b)

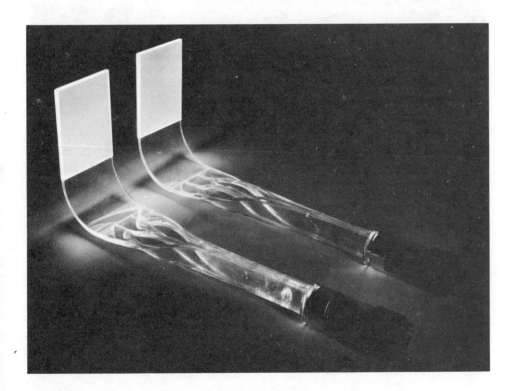

FIGURE 18.23 Light pipes. Light originating in a scintillator plate (painted white) makes its way via total internal reflections through the curved and twisted Lucite® to a light-sensitive photomultiplier tube. (Photograph courtesy of Lawrence Radiation Laboratory, University of California, Berkeley.)

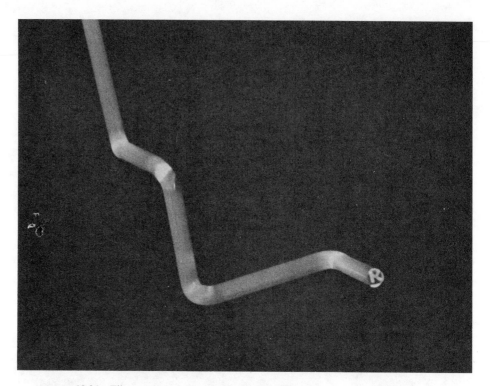

FIGURE 18.24   Fiber optics. A bundle of many fine fibers transmits an image because each fiber acts like a tiny light pipe. [Photograph from N. S. Kapany, *Fiber Optics: Principles and Applications* (New York: Academic Press, 1967), p. 312. Courtesy of N. S. Kapany.]

localized region in their patients' mouths. A light pipe is literally what its name implies. It "pipes" light from one point to another by a series of *total internal reflections*. A bundle of many fine fibers, each acting as a separate light pipe, can be used to transmit images along paths of almost any shape (Figure 18.24).

★18.7 Prisms

Because they disperse light into its component wavelengths, prisms are useful in spectroscopes. First, we consider the effect of a prism on light of a single wavelength.

Suppose that a ray of light is incident at point B on a prism whose apex angle is α (Figure 18.25). At B its angles of incidence and refraction are θ_1 and θ_2. It leaves the prism at point D with angles of incidence and refraction φ_2 and φ_1. These angles follow Snell's law:

Snell's law at two interfaces

$$\sin \theta_1 = n \sin \theta_2, \tag{18.46}$$

$$\sin \varphi_1 = n \sin \varphi_2. \tag{18.47}$$

The total angle of deflection of the light ray, which we call δ, is the sum of its deflections at the two interfaces, $\theta_1 - \theta_2$ and $\varphi_1 - \varphi_2$:

$$\delta = \theta_1 - \theta_2 + \varphi_1 - \varphi_2. \tag{18.48}$$

Inspection of Figure 18.25 reveals that $\theta_2 + \varphi_2$ must be equal to the fixed apex angle α. Since ABC and ADC are both right angles and since the sum of four angles inside a quadrilateral is 2π, the angle at C must be $\pi - \alpha$, as indicated in the figure. Consider then the triangle BCD, whose interior angles, θ_2, φ_2, and $\pi - \alpha$ must sum to π. This condition implies

$$\theta_2 + \varphi_2 = \alpha. \tag{18.49}$$

Equation 18.48 can therefore be rewritten

$$\delta = \theta_1 + \varphi_1 - \alpha. \tag{18.50}$$ *Total angle of deflection*

In spectroscopic applications, it is usual practice to rotate the prism relative to the incoming light beam to find the angle of minimum deflection, δ_{min}. As one might expect from symmetry considerations, minimum deflection occurs when $\theta_1 = \varphi_1$ and $\theta_2 = \varphi_2$. A proof of this condition goes as follows: In Equation 18.50, regard θ_1 as the independent variable and δ as the dependent variable. The angle φ_1 is a function of φ_2 (Equation 18.47), which is a function of θ_2 (Equation 18.49), which in turn is a function of θ_1 (Equation 18.46). The differentiation of Equation 18.50 then gives

$$\frac{d\delta}{d\theta_1} = 1 + \frac{d\varphi_1}{d\varphi_2} \cdot \frac{d\varphi_2}{d\theta_2} \cdot \frac{d\theta_2}{d\theta_1} \tag{18.51}$$

(recall that α is constant). From Equation 18.49, $d\varphi_2/d\theta_2 = -1$. Equation 18.51 can therefore be written

$$\frac{d\delta}{d\theta_1} = 1 - \frac{d\varphi_1/d\varphi_2}{d\theta_1/d\theta_2}. \tag{18.52}$$

The functions $\theta_1(\theta_2)$ and $\varphi_1(\varphi_2)$ are known; they are $\theta_1 = \arcsin (n \sin \theta_2)$ and $\varphi_1 = \arcsin (n \sin \varphi_2)$. For our purposes, however, it is unnecessary to carry out the differentiation explicitly. It is enough to note that the two functions are identical. The derivative $d\varphi_1/d\varphi_2$ is some function $f(\varphi_2)$. The derivative $d\delta/d\theta_1$ can, therefore, be written

$$\frac{d\delta}{d\theta_1} = 1 - \frac{f(\varphi_2)}{f(\theta_2)}.$$

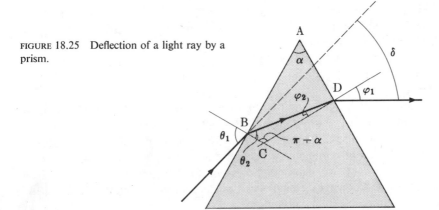

FIGURE 18.25   Deflection of a light ray by a prism.

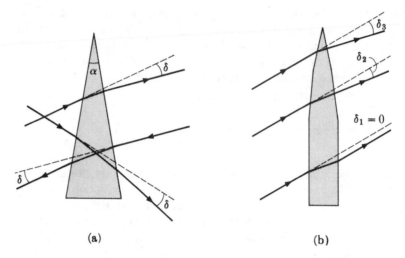

FIGURE 18.26   (a) If the apex angle α of a prism is small, all rays are deflected through approximately the same angle δ, which is given by Equation 18.54. (b) A lens may be approximated as a series of prisms.

To find δ_{min}, we set this derivative equal to zero. This implies $f(\varphi_2) = f(\theta_2)$, which in turn implies

Condition for minimum deflection

$$\varphi_2 = \theta_2, \tag{18.53}$$

the symmetric condition that we anticipated.

For a very narrow prism [Figure 18.26(a)], the deflection angle δ is, to a good approximation, independent of the angle of incidence. For small angles, $\sin \theta \cong \theta$, so that Equations 18.46 and 18.47 read

$$\theta_1 \cong n\theta_2, \qquad \varphi_1 \cong n\varphi_2.$$

Substituting these approximations for θ_1 and φ_1 in Equation 18.48 gives

$$\delta \cong \theta_2(n - 1) + \varphi_2(n - 1) = (\theta_2 + \varphi_2)(n - 1).$$

Since $\theta_2 + \varphi_2 = \alpha$, this can be written more simply as

Approximate deflection for narrow prism

$$\delta \cong \alpha(n - 1). \tag{18.54}$$

As indicated in Figure 18.26(b), this equation is quite useful in analyzing light propagation through thin lenses. A lens may be approximated as a series of prisms of different apex angles α. Because of the simple behavior dictated by Equation 18.54, the deflection angle of a light ray passing through a thin lens depends only on the ray's point of incidence on the lens and not on its angle of incidence.

A common laboratory tool is the prism spectroscope (Figure 18.27), used to sort and to measure wavelengths. Basically, it is a device for the accurate measurement of angles. Through the relative angle of the collimating tube and the telescope tube, the angle of deflection δ is determined for any given wavelength. Certain known wavelengths provide calibration points for a given prism. Then unknown wavelengths can be determined by interpolation.

18.8   Lenses

A lens is any device that uses refraction to concentrate beams of light at a point or in a small area. Known to the Greeks as burning glasses, lenses were used in antiquity to concentrate the sun's rays to start fires or melt wax, or perhaps, as boys use them now, to play pranks. Both Kepler and Newton made important contributions to the theory of lenses, and Kepler's contemporary, Galileo, was the first to use a telescope with two lenses for astronomical observation. Modern lens designers have available many different kinds of glass and they rely on computers to help them trace the paths of light through complex lenses.

The simplest lens—the kind used by Galileo—has one flat face and one face that is a small segment of a sphere. Figure 18.28 shows a beam of light deflected by such a lens from a path initially parallel to the lens axis to a path that intersects the axis a distance f from the lens. The radius of curvature of the spherical surface of the lens is R. The angle of incidence of the beam on this surface from within is θ_2, and the angle of refraction is θ_1. As is clear from the diagram in Figure 18.28, the *deflection* angle between the initial and final directions is the difference between θ_1 and θ_2. It is

$$\delta = \theta_1 - \theta_2. \tag{18.55}$$

Finally, the distance between the lens axis and the point where the light beam is deflected is b. The deflection is dictated by Snell's law applied to the second surface, $\sin \theta_1 = n \sin \theta_2$.

FIGURE 18.27   A prism spectroscope. The collimating tube is on the left, the telescope tube on the right. Their relative angle is measured with the help of the circular scale on the base. (Gaertner spectroscope; photograph by Steve Poucher.)

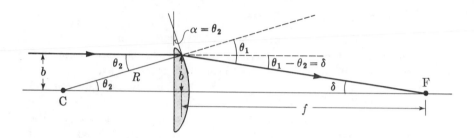

FIGURE 18.28   Simple converging lens. A ray of light initially parallel to the lens axis is undeflected at the flat left surface of the lens; it is refracted at the right surface, which is a spherical surface of radius R. The part of the lens through which the ray passes is equivalent to a prism of apex angle $\alpha = \theta_2$.

A "perfect" lens is one in which every incoming beam parallel to the axis is deflected in such a way that it passes through the single point F, the focal point, regardless of the original distance b from the axis and regardless of the wavelength of the light. There is no such thing as a truly perfect lens, but nearly perfect lenses can be constructed from several pieces of glass joined together. These are called compound lenses. If they focus light of different wavelengths at nearly the same point, they are called achromatic. The simple lens illustrated in Figure 18.28 is not achromatic, but it does a good job of focusing light of a particular wavelength if it is thin enough. In the thin lens approximation, all relevant angles are small enough that an angle, its sine, and its tangent may be equated. Snell's law takes the form

$$\theta_1 \cong n\theta_2 , \tag{18.56}$$

and for θ_2 and δ we write

$$\theta_2 \cong \sin \theta_2 = \frac{b}{R} , \tag{18.57}$$

$$\delta \cong \tan \delta = \frac{b}{f} . \tag{18.58}$$

Equation 18.55 can then be written

$$\delta \cong n\theta_2 - \theta_2 = (n - 1)\theta_2 . \tag{18.59}$$

Using Equations 18.57 and 18.58 for θ_2 and δ gives

$$\frac{b}{f} = (n - 1) \frac{b}{R} ,$$

from which follows a simple relation between f and R:

Focal distance of thin lens with spherical face

$$f = \frac{R}{n - 1} . \tag{18.60}$$

The disappearance of b from the final result shows that all rays parallel to the axis are brought to the same point F, as illustrated in Figure 18.29—provided

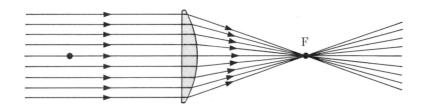

FIGURE 18.29   The focusing
action of a thin lens.

that the thin-lens approximations, as exemplified by Equations 18.57 and 18.58, are satisfied. Since the index of refraction depends on wavelength, the focal distance f is also wavelength-dependent.

The portion of the lens through which the ray in Figure 18.28 passes may be regarded as a segment of a prism of apex angle α. As the figure makes clear, α is the same as θ_2, or

$$\alpha \cong \frac{b}{R}. \tag{18.61}$$

According to the thin prism approximation, Equation 18.54, the deflection angle is $\delta \cong \alpha(n - 1) = (n - 1)b/R$, which is equivalent to Equation 18.59 and leads to the same formula for f as just derived. The real importance of Equation 18.54 comes in considering the deflection of incident rays not parallel to the axis (Figure 18.30). Since δ depends only on b and not on the angle of incidence, Equation 18.58 remains valid. In Figure 18.30, a light ray emanates from a point a distance d_1 to the left of a thin lens, strikes the lens a distance b from the axis, where it is deflected through the angle δ, and crosses the axis again a distance d_2 to the right of the lens. The initial and final angles of the ray with the axis are called β and γ. The deflection angle is the sum of these two angles:

$$\delta = \beta + \gamma. \tag{18.62}$$

The small angles β and γ are approximated by

$$\beta \cong \frac{b}{d_1},$$

$$\gamma \cong \frac{b}{d_2};$$

and δ is approximated by Equation 18.58. These three approximations substituted into Equation 18.62 give

$$\frac{b}{f} = \frac{b}{d_1} + \frac{b}{d_2}.$$

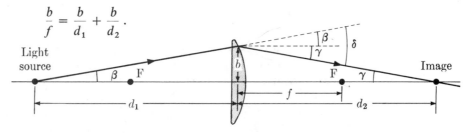

FIGURE 18.30   Action of a thin, converging lens on a ray not parallel to the axis.

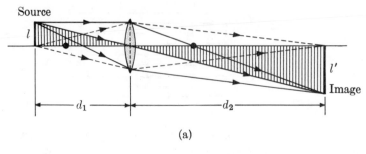

(a)

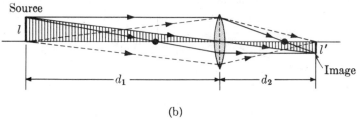

(b)

FIGURE 18.31   (a) Magnification and (b) demagnification of a
neon tube light source by a thin lens. Since the shaded
triangles in each diagram are similar triangles, the
magnification factor, l'/l, is equal to d_2/d_1.

Again the distance b cancels, and we are left with

Object and image distances
related for thin lens

$$\frac{1}{f} = \frac{1}{d_1} + \frac{1}{d_2}, \tag{18.63}$$

a relation among f, d_1, and d_2 identical to that for a concave mirror
(Equation 18.31).

For an extended source, a thin lens may produce a magnified or demagnified
image, much as a concave mirror may do. Figure 18.31 shows the geometrical
construction appropriate for the calculation of magnification for a real image.
The magnification is

Magnification

$$M = \frac{d_2}{d_1}.$$

With the help of Equation 18.63 this becomes

$$M = \frac{1}{(d_1/f) - 1}, \tag{18.64}$$

again identical to the result for a concave mirror (Equation 18.34).

If d_1 is less than f, Equation 18.63 leads to a negative value for d_2, and
Equation 18.64 gives a negative value for M. As with the concave mirror, these

For real image, $M > 0$;
for virtual image, $M < 0$

negative values can be made meaningful. The magnitude of the negative d_2 is
the distance from the lens to a virtual image, and the magnitude of M (always
greater than 1) is the magnification of the virtual image. An example appears in
Figure 18.32.

The study of the behavior of diverging lenses is left to the problems. Like
convex mirrors, they form only virtual demagnified images (Figure 18.33).

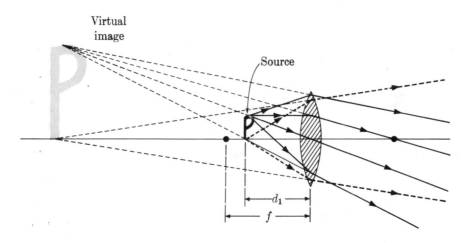

FIGURE 18.32   Formation of a virtual image by a thin lens. When the distance
d_1 is less than the focal distance f, the rays seem to come from an enlarged
image on the same side of the lens as the object. A hand magnifier forms a
virtual image of this kind. Note that the image is not inverted.

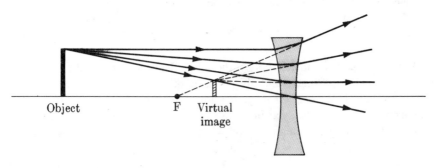

FIGURE 18.33   The formation of a virtual demagnified image by a diverging lens.

THE MICROSCOPE

Cameras, film projectors, microscopes, telescopes, spectacles: All are optical
devices designed to control or use light for some purpose. Here we single out for
attention the microscope; although technically sophisticated in practice, it is
simple in principle. It consists of two converging lenses (or lens systems) at
opposite ends of a tube (Figure 18.34). The objective lens, near the sample to
be viewed, is of short focal length. Its focal points are lettered F. The ocular lens,
or eyepiece, is of longer focal length. One of its focal points is lettered F'. The
functioning of the microscope can be understood as a two-stage process. The
object O, located just beyond the focal length of the objective, forms a real image
I within the tube. This is a considerably magnified image, and it can be thought
of as a new "object" viewed by the eyepiece. The eyepiece then functions as
an ordinary hand magnifier (see Figure 18.32). Since the image I lies closer to
the eyepiece than the focal distance of the eyepiece, the final image I' is virtual
and further magnified. The net magnification is the product of the two magnifi-
cations. It is limited only by the quality of the lenses and by diffraction effects
which invalidate the approximations of geometrical optics.

$$M_\text{T} = M_1 M_2$$

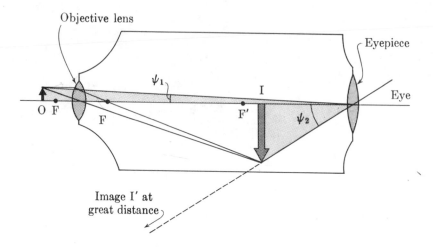

FIGURE 18.34   Principle of the microscope. An objective lens forms a real
image I of the object O. An eyepiece forms a more distant virtual image I′.
The "power" of the microscope is defined by the angular magnification,
ψ_2/ψ_1. (In this diagram, the dimensions of object and image are highly
exaggerated relative to the dimensions of the lenses.)

*Angular magnification is
relevant for microscopes
and telescopes*

For microscopes and telescopes, the magnification as defined so far—the
ratio of dimensions of image and object—is actually not very important. What
is really relevant is the *angular* magnification, the ratio of the angles subtended
by image and object at the eye. In Figure 18.34, these angles are denoted by ψ_2
and ψ_1, and the angular magnification M' is

$$M' = \frac{\psi_2}{\psi_1}. \tag{18.65}$$

In astronomical observation, the *size* of the image is much less than the size of
the object (a galaxy, let us say, might have an image 1 mm in diameter), yet the
angular magnification may be quite large.

EYES AND EYEGLASSES

*The camera: Image distance
is variable*

The eye and the camera have much in common. Both use a converging lens to
focus an inverted real image on a surface behind the lens. Both can adjust to
differing object distance d_1. The camera (Figure 18.35) does so by changing the
distance d_2 from lens to film. About how big a change is required? Let us
suppose that the lens has a focal distance of 6 cm. To photograph objects at
great distance ($d_1 \to \infty$), the lens must be 6 cm from the film ($d_2 = f$). Suppose
further that the camera is designed to photograph objects as close as 2 ft away.
This is about 60 cm. Set $d_1 = 60$ cm and $f = 6$ cm. From Equation 18.63,

$$\frac{1}{d_2} = \frac{1}{6 \text{ cm}} - \frac{1}{60 \text{ cm}}.$$

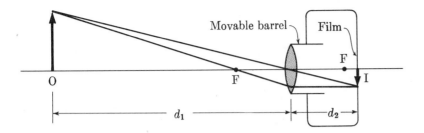

FIGURE 18.35 Principle of the camera. When the lens is moved back until its focal point is at the film surface, objects at infinity are in focus. As the lens is moved farther from the film, nearer objects are brought into focus.

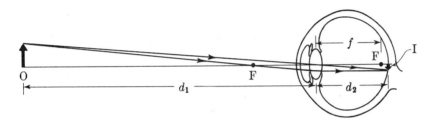

FIGURE 18.36 The eye. For a normal relaxed eye, focused on infinity, the focal point lies on the retina. As the lens is contracted to bring nearer objects into focus, the focal point moves to a position in front of the retina, as shown here.

The solution is $d_2 = 6.67$ cm. The total range of travel required for the lens is 0.67 cm.

In the eye (Figure 18.36), the distance d_2 from lens to retina is not adjustable. The eye gains its flexibility not from variable d_2 but from variable f. Muscles can alter the curvature of the lens surface and so alter its focal distance. In a normal relaxed eye, $f = d_2$; then distant objects are focused on the retina. To focus on close objects, the eye muscles squeeze the lens to smaller diameter, greater curvature, and lesser focal distance. This is the situation illustrated in Figure 18.36. As with the camera, a numerical calculation is instructive. For $d_1 = \infty$, let $d_2 = f = 3$ cm. What value of f is required in order to focus on an object 15 cm (about 6 inches) away? In Equation 18.63 set $d_1 = 15$ cm and $d_2 = 3$ cm to get

The eye: Focal distance is variable

$$\frac{1}{f} = \frac{1}{15 \text{ cm}} + \frac{1}{3 \text{ cm}}.$$

The solution is $f = 2.5$ cm. The eye lens must change its focal distance by 0.5 cm.

An eye is called farsighted if its lens has a focal distance greater than its lens-to-retina distance or, more commonly, if the eye muscles cannot contract

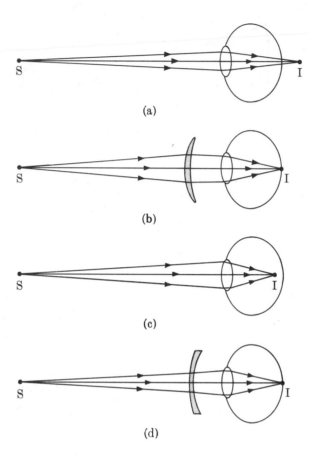

FIGURE 18.37   (a) A farsighted eye: The image is behind the retina. (b) Farsightedness is corrected with a converging lens. (c) A nearsighted eye: The image is in front of the retina. (d) Nearsightedness is corrected with a diverging lens. In each diagram, S designates the source and I the image. For clarity, the size of the lens of the eye is exaggerated somewhat.

Corrective lenses

the lens sufficiently to bring near objects into focus. In either case, an extra converging lens is called for. The opposite eye problem, nearsightedness, means that the lens of the eye has too great a curvature and too short a focal distance. Nearsightedness is corrected with diverging lenses. The effect of eyeglasses on eyes suffering from these minor faults is shown in Figure 18.37.

Geometrical optics: important application but not basic science

At every point in the study of science it is important to distinguish as well as one can the fundamental from the nonfundamental, the exact from the approximate, the pure from the applied. This is often rendered difficult by the fact that what has direct impact on man may be of little significance for our basic comprehension of nature. Geometrical optics is a case in point. Because of cameras, projectors, telescopes, microscopes, and the human eye, it is a branch of physics that touches everyone. Yet it is an elaborate area of application based on two simple physical ideas—that waves can be reflected and refracted. The equations appearing in the last few sections, despite their practical importance, must not be confused either in exactness or in fundamental significance with equations such as those expressing Coulomb's law of electric force or Newton's laws of mechanics.

18.9   The phenomenon of diffraction

Diffraction can be defined as any deviation of wave motion away from straight-line propagation. It is especially manifested when waves pass through apertures or around obstacles. Because of diffraction, shadows are not sharp. Rather there is a gradual transition of intensity from the illuminated to the shadowed region. The breadth of this transition region depends on the wavelength (increasing as the wavelength increases) and may also depend on the size of the obstacle or aperture. As shown in Figure 18.38, the shadow transition zone contains fringes of alternately greater and lesser intensity. An important physical example, diffraction by a single slit, will be treated quantitatively in Section 18.12.

The diffraction of light, discovered around 1660 by Francesco Grimaldi, was known to both Newton and Huygens. Somewhat surprisingly, this discovery had little impact on the controversy over the nature of light. Not until after Young's discovery of interference fringes in 1803 was diffraction studied with enough care to provide definitive evidence in favor of the wave nature of light. Up to that time it was assumed that the deflection of light particles in passing near matter could also account for the smudging of shadows.

According to Huygens's principle, every point on an advancing wave

FIGURE 18.38 Diffraction produced by the sharp edge of a screen. A well-defined but not abrupt change from darkness to light at the shadow boundary is followed by a series of fringes of gradually decreasing intensity extending into the illuminated region. [Photograph from M. Cagnet, M. Françon, and J. C. Thrierr, *Atlas of Optical Phenomena* (Berlin: Springer-Verlag, 1962). Courtesy of Professor Françon.]

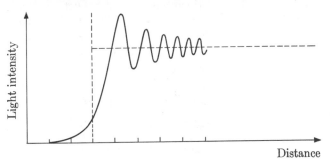

FIGURE 18.39   The reality of the Huygens wavelet. When all but a narrow segment of an advancing wave front is stopped by a screen, a circular or spherical wave spreads in all directions from this part of the wave front. (Photograph courtesy of Film Studio, Education Development Center, Inc.)

front acts as a source of a new wavelet that fans out from that point. This is really a principle of diffraction, in fact a principle of maximum diffraction. In seeking a wave explanation of diffraction, we are faced not so much with the problem of explaining why diffraction *does* occur as with the problem of explaining why it does *not* occur always—and obviously—for all propagating waves. Why does sunlight not bend around the earth and keep the far side bright in the middle of the night? Why does a searchlight beam seem to travel in a perfectly straight line into the sky? Just such questions were asked by Newton. He had doubts about the wave theory because he questioned its ability to explain the simple fact of straight-line propagation of light.

How can straight-line propagation be reconciled with Huygens's principle?

The resolution of the apparent conflict between Huygens's principle and straight-line propagation is to be found in the idea of superposition. When a wave front is sufficiently broad, the superposed Huygens wavelets turn out to produce near-zero intensity in all directions except the direction straight ahead, perpendicular to the wave front. The approximation of geometrical optics is valid. When the breadth of a wave front is sharply restricted, on the other hand, it becomes evident that the extreme diffraction predicted by Huygens's principle is fact and not fiction. If a screen with a small hole or slit in it blocks all but a narrow portion of a wave front, the Huygens wavelet will appear on the far side of the screen spreading in all directions, unperturbed by superposition with other wavelets. Figure 18.39 shows an example of such a diverging wave coming from a narrow part of a straight wave front on water. The effects of widening the aperture are shown in Figure 18.40. The requirement for extreme diffraction—the "pure" Huygens spreading wavelet—is that the width of the hole or slit be less than one wavelength. (Notice that this is a *relative* requirement. A 1-mm slit is narrow for radar waves but wide for light.) When the width of the wave front becomes comparable to a single wavelength, inter-

For broad wave fronts, superposition wipes out most diffraction effects

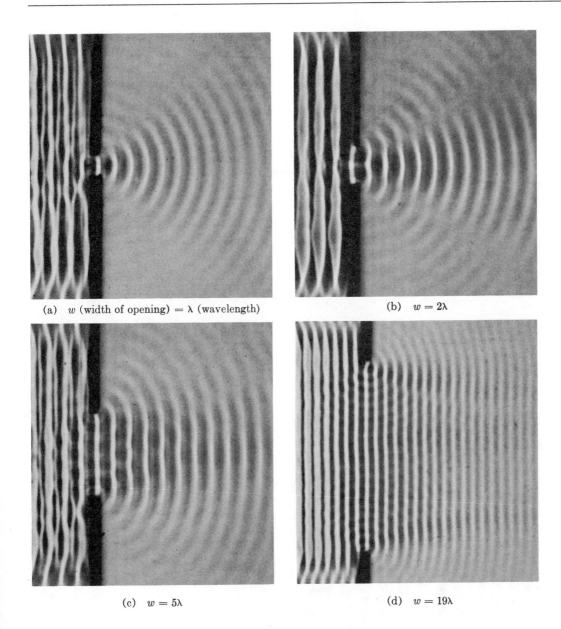

(a) w (width of opening) $= \lambda$ (wavelength)   (b) $w = 2\lambda$

(c) $w = 5\lambda$ (d) $w = 19\lambda$

FIGURE 18.40   The effect of slit width on diffraction of water waves. As the
slit gets wider, wavelets from different parts of the opening interfere to produce
a wave more nearly like the incident plane wave. (Photographs courtesy of
Film Studio, Education Development Center, Inc.)

ference effects between different parts of the wave front set in and begin to
narrow the angle of diffraction. Nearly straight-line propagation is restored
when the width of the aperture becomes much greater than the wavelength,
although residual diffraction effects at the shadow boundary always remain.

18.10   Interference

In this section we shall pursue an important idea that was introduced in Section 18.3. If waves from two or more *coherent* sources are superposed, they may interfere. This means that the total intensity is not equal to the sum of the intensities that would be produced by the sources if taken one at a time. See Equation 18.14, for example, which contains an "interference term." We speak of both *constructive interference*, when the total intensity is greater than the sum of the individual intensities, and *destructive interference*, when the total intensity is less than the sum of the individual intensities (see Equations 18.23 and 18.24). An *interference pattern* is a pattern of observed maxima and minima of intensity arising from wave superposition. It is conventional to refer to the pattern produced by a small number of sources

Constructive and destructive interference

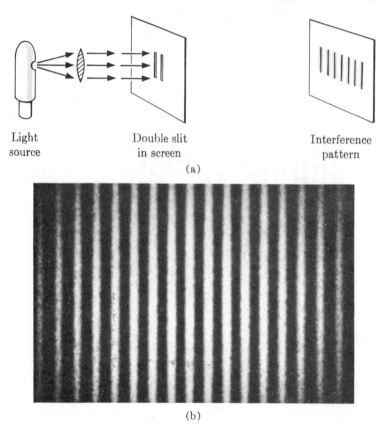

Light source

Double slit in screen

Interference pattern

(a)

(b)

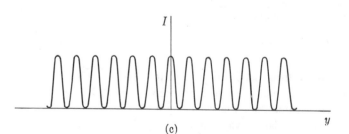

(c)

FIGURE 18.41   (a) A possible arrangement to produce a two-slit interference pattern. (b) Photograph of interference fringes produced by two slits. (c) Theoretical intensity in the small-angle approximation (Equation 18.74). (Photograph courtesy of Brian J. Thompson, The Institute of Optics, University of Rochester.)

approximated as point sources as an "interference pattern" and to speak of the pattern produced by a large number of sources or a continuous distribution of sources (such as the Huygens wavelets along a wave front) as a "diffraction pattern." Actually, there is no fundamental difference between the two: Both arise from the interference of superposed coherent waves. As a matter of convenience, however, we shall specialize to idealized point sources in this section and the next, and we shall deal with a continuous distribution of sources in Section 18.12.

Interference and diffraction patterns are basically the same

DOUBLE SLIT

Young's classic two-slit experiment remains the simplest and most direct demonstration of wave interference. He illuminated one side of a sheet containing a pair of narrow parallel slits and examined the pattern of intensity projected onto a screen on the other side (Figure 18.41). The alternating dark and light fringes that appeared gave the first wholly convincing evidence for the wave nature of light. Such interference was already known for sound waves and water waves. Since then, interference has been demonstrated for waves in most other parts of the electromagnetic spectrum as well as for electron waves and neutron waves. Figure 18.42 compares interference patterns produced by X rays with those produced by electrons.

In an idealized version, the two-slit experiment can be analyzed quantitatively in a simple way. The idealization consists in supposing that the width

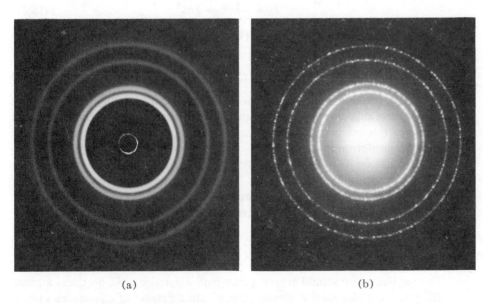

(a)   (b)

FIGURE 18.42 (a) X rays passing through powdered aluminium crystals were diffracted and produced the interference pattern on the left. (b) A very similar interference pattern produced by electrons passing through the same material clearly demonstrates the wave nature of material particles. (Photographs courtesy of Film Studio, Education Development Center, Inc.)

Exact analogy: narrow slits and point sources

of each slit is much less than a single wavelength. (For microwaves, this condition is easy to satisfy in practice; for light, it is more difficult.) According to Huygens's principle, the slits may then be regarded as coherent point sources. The double slit is mathematically identical to the double source treated in Section 18.3. In particular, if the slits are illuminated by a plane sinusoidal wave, they are equivalent to sources of equal intensity and the same polarization, vibrating in phase. (The two upper diagrams in Figure 18.9(b), for instance, represent equivalent physical systems.)

We wish to consider the intensity pattern on a screen placed parallel to the sheet containing the slits and perpendicular to the original direction of the incident light (Figure 18.43). The slit separation is a, and the distance from the midpoint of the slits to the observing screen is L. At a point P on the screen, the intensity is given by Equation 18.22, which we repeat here:

Intensity from coherent sources of the same polarization

$$I_P = \tfrac{1}{2}(E_1{}^2 + E_2{}^2 + 2E_1E_2 \cos \varphi). \tag{18.66}$$

The quantities E_1 and E_2 are the amplitudes of the separate waves (see Equations 18.15 and 18.16), and φ is the phase difference between the two waves at point P (Equation 18.17). To complete the nomenclature, we call O the point on the screen opposite the midpoint of the slits; y the distance from O to P; and x_1 and x_2 the distances from the slits S_1 and S_2 to P. In a typical experiment, L is much greater than a so that the distances x_1 and x_2 are nearly equal. This means that the amplitudes E_1 and E_2 are also nearly equal since the waves have propagated approximately the same distance from equal sources.* We may call the intensity that would be produced by either slit alone I_0:

$$I_0 = \tfrac{1}{2}E_1{}^2 = \tfrac{1}{2}E_2{}^2 \tag{18.67}$$

(see Equations 18.18 and 18.19). With this approximation, Equation 18.66 takes the simpler form,

Intensity if waves are also of equal amplitude

$$I_P = 2I_0(1 + \cos \varphi). \tag{18.68}$$

Finally, we make the approximation $y \ll L$. This will simplify the calculation of the phase difference φ and will enable us to treat I_0 as a constant since all points of interest in the interference pattern will then be approximately the same distance from the slits.

Because the two waves start with equal phase at S_1 and S_2, their phase difference at P is determined by the difference in propagation distances, $x_2 - x_1$. According to Equation 18.9, the phase of one wave is $-kx_1 + \alpha$ and the phase of the other wave is $-kx_2 + \alpha$. The phase difference, $\varphi = \varphi_1 - \varphi_2$, is

Exact phase difference of two waves

$$\varphi = k(x_2 - x_1) = \frac{x_2 - x_1}{\lambda}. \tag{18.69}$$

This implies, as we should expect, that a path difference of $\tfrac{1}{2}\lambda$ produces a phase difference of π (destructive interference), a path difference of λ produces a phase difference of 2π (constructive interference), and so on. To relate $x_2 - x_1$ to y, consider the two right triangles S_1AP and S_2BP shaded in Figure 18.43. For

---

* To good approximation, $E_1/E_2 = x_2/x_1$.

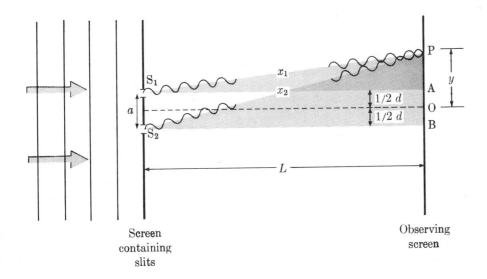

Screen
containing
slits

Observing
screen

FIGURE 18.43   Diagram for analyzing two-slit interference patterns. A bright fringe is centered at point O. In this illustration, a dark fringe is located at point P because x_2 is greater than x_1 by half a wavelength.

the first of these, the Pythagorean theorem states:

$$x_1{}^2 = L^2 + (y - \tfrac{1}{2}a)^2.$$

For the second, the Pythagorean theorem states:

$$x_2{}^2 = L^2 + (y + \tfrac{1}{2}a)^2.$$

Subtraction gives

$$x_2{}^2 - x_1{}^2 = (y + \tfrac{1}{2}a)^2 - (y - \tfrac{1}{2}a)^2,$$

an equation that can be simplified to

$$(x_2 - x_1)(x_2 + x_1) = 2ya. \tag{18.70}$$

Because of the postulated condition $y \ll L$, the distances x_1 and x_2 differ little from L, and their sum can be approximated by $2L$. From Equation 18.70 we therefore obtain the approximate expression for the path difference,

$$x_2 - x_1 = \frac{ya}{L}. \tag{18.71}$$

Then, according to Equation 18.69, the phase difference is

$$\varphi = \frac{kya}{L} = \frac{ya}{L\lambda}. \tag{18.72}$$

Approximate phase difference

Putting the first expression for φ into Equation 18.68, we obtain finally a formula for the intensity in the interference pattern as a function of y:

$$I_P = 2I_0 \left[1 + \cos\left(\frac{kay}{L}\right) \right]. \tag{18.73}$$

With the help of a trigonometric identity $(1 + \cos x = 2 \cos^2 \tfrac{1}{2}x)$, this formula may also be written

$$I_\mathrm{P} = 4I_0 \cos^2 \left(\frac{kay}{2L}\right). \tag{18.74}$$

This theoretical intensity is plotted in Figure 18.41(c).

From either Equation 18.73 or 18.74, we may conclude that the points of maximum constructive interference, where $I_\mathrm{P} = 4I_0$, occur where kay/L is an integral multiple of 2π. This means $y = 2\pi n L/ka = 2\pi n \lambdabar L/a$. Going from reduced wavelength back to wavelength, we may write

$$y(\text{bright fringes}) = n\frac{\lambda L}{a}, \tag{18.75}$$

where n is a positive or negative integer or zero. The points of maximum destructive interference, where $I_\mathrm{P} = 0$, occur where $ay/L\lambdabar$ is equal to $\pm\pi$, $\pm 3\pi$, etc. This condition locates the dark fringes:

$$y(\text{dark fringes}) = \left(n - \frac{1}{2}\right)\frac{\lambda L}{a}. \tag{18.76}$$

In summary: The interference pattern produced by a pair of very narrow slits consists of equally spaced fringes of equal intensity, provided two conditions are met: $L \gg a$ and $L \gg y$.

■ EXAMPLE: Green light, with a wavelength of 5,000 Å $(\lambda = 5 \times 10^{-7}$ m), falls on a pair of slits separated by 1 mm $(a = 10^{-3}$ m). What will be the interference pattern on a screen 2 m distant $(L = 2$ m)? At the center of the pattern will be a bright fringe. According to Equation 18.75, the first bright fringe on either side of the center will be located at a distance $\lambda L/a$ from the center:

$$y(\text{first bright fringe}) = \lambda\frac{L}{a} = \frac{5 \times 10^{-7}\text{ m} \times 2\text{ m}}{10^{-3}\text{ m}}$$

$$= 10^{-3}\text{ m} = 1\text{ mm}. \tag{18.77}$$

The next bright fringe will be 2 mm from the center, the next 3 mm, and so on, with equal spacing. Between each pair of bright fringes is a dark fringe, the one closest to the center being located by the equation

$$y(\text{first dark fringe}) = \frac{1}{2}\lambda\frac{L}{a} = 0.5\text{ mm}.$$

Here is an interesting number. In this example there is darkness exactly opposite each slit (half a millimeter above and below the center), where straight-line propagation would predict light. There could be no clearer proof of interference. Where either slit alone would produce light, the two acting together produce darkness. The conditions $L \gg a$ and $L \gg y$ are well satisfied in this example. A pattern of 20 bright fringes occupies only 2 cm, which is 1 percent of the distance L.

Fringe separations of 1 mm can readily be seen by the unaided eye or may be photographed. One interesting way to think about the two-slit interference pattern is as a wavelength magnifier. In Equation 18.77 the wavelength λ is multiplied by a "magnification factor" L/a, which, in this example, is equal to 2,000. The fringe separation is 2,000 times larger than the wavelength; thereby the microscopic wavelength is, so to speak, rendered visible. Either by increasing the distance L or by decreasing the slit separation a we can increase the magnification factor and further spread out the interference pattern. ■

Interference does more than demonstrate the existence of waves. It provides a valuable tool for measuring wavelength. Young followed up his earliest experiments on interference with measurements of the wavelengths of light, and interference effects still provide the basis of all accurate wavelength measurements. In the simple two-slit interference pattern, the fringe separation is directly proportional to wavelength. Equation 18.75 implies that the separation of adjacent bright fringes is $\Delta y = \lambda L/a$. Turning this around, we can express the wavelength in terms of the fringe spacing:

Measurement of wavelength

$$\lambda = \frac{a}{L}\Delta y. \qquad (18.78)$$

Now the observed spacing Δy is "demagnified" by the ratio of known distances, a/L, to give the unknown wavelength.

For a given arrangement of slits and screen, the distances a and L remain fixed, and different wavelengths reveal themselves through differently spaced interference patterns. If two or more wavelengths illuminate the slits simultaneously, their separate interference patterns will overlap on the screen. The two slits and screen constitute a crude version of a spectroscope—a device that makes it possible to determine the components of the spectrum present in some unknown radiation. The key to the action of any spectroscope is dispersion, the fragmenting of radiation into its separate constituent wavelengths. As discussed in Section 18.7, dispersion can be achieved by the variable index of refraction of a glass prism. It can also be achieved by the phenomenon of interference. White light passing through a pair of slits produces a different fringe spacing for each wavelength and therefore a pattern of many rainbows. (The central fringe remains white. Why?)

18.11   The diffraction grating

As the heart of a spectroscope, a double slit has a serious disadvantage: The fringes it produces are broad (Figure 18.41). As a result, it is impossible to locate the centers of fringes precisely enough to make very accurate wavelength measurements, and it is impossible to discriminate the patterns produced by two wavelengths that differ very little from one another. In addition to suffering from these shortcomings on account of fringe breadth, the double slit allows but a small fraction of the incident light to reach the observer. These problems are all beautifully cured by the diffraction grating, which in its simplest form is a picket fence of alternating opaque and transparent strips, an array of many parallel slits. The first gratings for interference studies and accurate wavelength measurements were constructed by Joseph von Fraunhofer around 1820. These consisted of fine wires strung on a frame like the warp of a rug before weaving

Early gratings

begins. His best wire gratings had as many as 19 wires per millimeter. Fraunhofer went on to construct finer gratings by scratching parallel lines on glass and in this way achieved up to 300 lines/mm. This method of making gratings grew in technical perfection during the remainder of the nineteenth century, until in the 1880s Henry A. Rowland succeeded in making near-perfect glass gratings with as many as 1,000 lines/mm. (The spacing between lines in such a grating—10^{-6} m, or 10,000 Å—is about equal to $1\frac{1}{2}$ wavelengths of red light.) Some of Rowland's gratings, and replicas of them, are still in use.

A real grating: any periodic structure

An idealized grating: equally spaced slits

A glass grating need not have any opaque strips or any specified shape for its grooves. All that is necessary is that its successive grooves be equally spaced and nearly identical—that the grating, viewed end on, show a regularly repeating structure [Figure 18.44(a)]. The analysis of the grating, however, is much simplified—without losing the essence of its action—if it is idealized as a set of very narrow slits separated by wider opaque stripes [Figure 18.44(b)]. Then each slit may be regarded as the source of an elementary Huygens wavelet. In a typical grating spectroscope, the light diffracted through an angle θ is gathered by a lens and brought to a focus (Figure 18.45). Therefore, the interference between wavelets from different slits may be dealt with by considering the path difference between successive parallel tracks. A subtle but important point requires mention here. If the wavelets reaching points A, B, C, D, and E in Figure 18.45 are in phase, they will still be in phase at the focal point F. Despite the shorter distance from C to F than from A to F, the *time* from C to F is the same as the time from A to F because the wave going from C to F traverses more glass and is delayed just long enough to permit it to be overtaken by the wave going from A to F at the instant at which both reach the focal point. This equality of time for all the tracks corresponds also to an equality of *number* of wavelengths. Waves vibrating in phase at A, B, C, D, and E also vibrate in phase when they converge at F. Now we ask: For what angle of diffraction θ will the wavelets arriving at A, B, C, D, and E indeed be in phase in order to produce a bright image at F? This condition of reinforcement requires that the path difference Δx between successive tracks be an integral number of wavelengths:

$$\Delta x = n\lambda. \qquad (18.79)$$

Since Δx is the side of a right triangle whose hypotenuse is the slit separation a, the path difference is

$$\Delta x = a \sin \theta. \qquad (18.80)$$

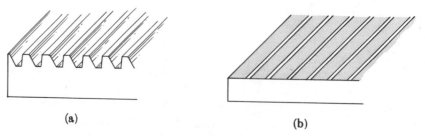

(a)   (b)

FIGURE 18.44 Diffraction grating. (a) Highly magnified view of grating consisting of equally spaced array of identical grooves in glass. (b) Idealized version of grating suitable for analysis: a thin screen with narrow parallel slits separated by wider opaque stripes.

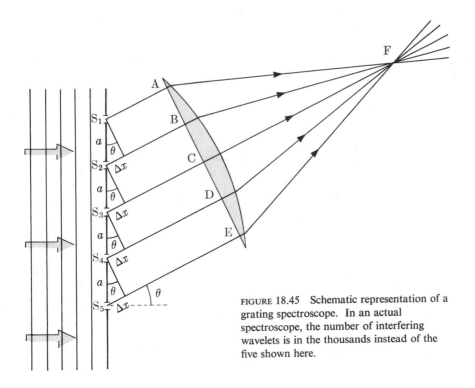

FIGURE 18.45   Schematic representation of a grating spectroscope. In an actual spectroscope, the number of interfering wavelets is in the thousands instead of the five shown here.

Therefore, wavelength and diffraction angle for maximum constructive interference are related by

$$n\lambda = a \sin \theta. \qquad (18.81)$$

The condition for maximum intensity

This is the fundamental equation of the grating spectroscope. Since a and θ can be measured accurately, the wavelength can be determined accurately. The integer n specifies the "order" of the diffraction peak: $n = 1$ is first-order diffraction, $n = 2$ is second-order diffraction, etc.

The advantage of many slits (tens of thousands in practice) rather than only two becomes evident if we consider what happens when the angle θ is slightly changed away from the angle given by Equation 18.81, which locates the center of a bright fringe. For a slight change of θ, the path difference Δx between two successive tracks, such as $S_1 A$ and $S_2 B$, changes slightly so that the wavelets reaching A and B are no longer perfectly in phase. If these were the only two slits acting, the intensity at F would diminish only slightly because the two wavelets would still be far from a condition of destructive interference. With a very large number of slits acting, however, the intensity at F drops sharply. Although the wavelet from S_2 differs in phase only slightly from the wavelet from S_1, the wavelet from S_3 differs slightly more in phase, that from S_4 slightly more, and so on. Eventually, there will be a slit whose wavelet is exactly out of phase with the wavelet from S_1. Summing the contributions of thousands of slits, there will be almost complete destructive interference and darkness at F despite the fact that the angle θ has shifted only slightly from a fringe center. As a result, the broad fringes characteristic of the two-slit interference pattern collapse in the grating spectroscope into narrow lines separated by expanses

Qualitative explanation of narrow maxima

of darkness. Figure 18.46 shows the beginning of this effect as the number of slits is increased from 2 to 6. Because of the appearance of the narrowed interference fringes in a grating spectroscope, light of a particular wavelength is often referred to as a spectral line.

"Spectral line" defined

★WIDTH OF A SPECTRAL LINE

A good estimate of the angular width of a spectral line may be achieved by means of the following reasoning. Let φ be the phase difference between the paths from adjacent slits. It is given by (see Equations 18.69 and 18.80)

Phase difference related to path difference and angle

$$\varphi = k \, \Delta x = \frac{\Delta x}{\lambdabar} = \frac{a \sin \theta}{\lambdabar}. \tag{18.82}$$

Small changes in the phase difference φ and the angle θ are related by

$$\Delta \varphi = \frac{d\varphi}{d\theta} \, \Delta \theta = \frac{a \cos \theta}{\lambdabar} \, \Delta \theta. \tag{18.83}$$

At the central maximum of a spectral line, θ satisfies Equation 18.81, and $\varphi = 2\pi n$. Since a phase difference of $2\pi n$ (with n an integer) is exactly equivalent to a phase difference of zero, we can say that all of the superposed waves are exactly in phase at this angle θ. Now vary θ by a small increment $\Delta \theta$. This introduces a phase difference $\Delta \varphi$ between successive waves. If the grating has a total of N lines, the phase difference between the first and last is $(N - 1) \, \Delta \varphi$. The relative phases of the N superposed waves are

$$0, \Delta \varphi, 2 \, \Delta \varphi, 3 \, \Delta \varphi, \ldots, (N - 1) \, \Delta \varphi.$$

What is required to get complete destructive interference? If $(N - 1) \, \Delta \varphi$ were, let us say, $\pi/2$ radians, the destructive interference would be partial but not complete. The phases would all lie between 0 and $\pi/2$. The smallest value of $(N - 1) \, \Delta \varphi$ that can produce complete destructive interference is approximately 2π. Then the phases are distributed uniformly from 0 to 2π. For any particular wave, there is another wave exactly out of phase with it (phase difference of π). These two interfere destructively and cancel. The situation is shown schematically in Figure 18.47, where phases are plotted around the circumference of a circle. The exact condition for complete cancellation of the waves is $N \, \Delta \varphi = 2\pi$, or

Quantitative explanation of narrow maxima

$$\Delta \varphi = \frac{2\pi}{N}. \tag{18.84}$$

What this condition means physically is that a wave from one side of the grating is cancelling a wave from the middle of the grating, a wave from one quarter of the way across the grating is cancelling a wave from three quarters of the way across, and so on. Equations 18.83 and 18.84 combine to yield

$$\Delta \theta = \frac{\lambda}{aN \cos \theta}. \tag{18.85}$$

This is the angular "width" of the line, actually the angular distance from the point of peak intensity at the center of the line to the first minimum of intensity

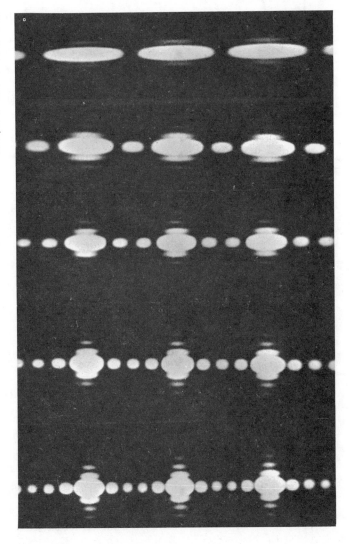

FIGURE 18.46   Interference patterns produced by gratings with (from top to bottom) 2, 3, 4, 5, and 6 slits. These photographs were made using a point source rather than the usual line source. With further increase in the number of slits, the principal maxima become narrower and the subsidiary maxima become dimmer. (Photograph courtesy of Brian J. Thompson The Institute of Optics, University of Rochester.)

FIGURE 18.47   Phases of the waves from the slits of a diffraction grating, displayed for convenience around the circumference of a circle. (a) At an angle of observation corresponding to the center of a spectral line, all waves are in phase. All can be said to have zero phase ($\varphi = 0$). (Phases of successive waves actually differ by a multiple of 2π.)   (b) At a nearby angle of observation, phases of successive waves differ by $\Delta\varphi$; the phases of the first and last wave differ by $(N - 1)\Delta\varphi$. In this illustration, there are 36 slits, and $\Delta\varphi = 4$ deg. Because of partial interference, the observed intensity is somewhat less than at the center of the spectral line. (c) The first minimum of intensity next to the spectral line is achieved when the phases are spread uniformly from 0 to 2π. Then, as indicated by the dashed line, for every wave with phase φ_A there is another wave with phase $\varphi_B = \varphi_A + \pi$. Each such pair cancels by complete destructive interference. In this illustration, with 36 slits, successive waves need differ in phase by only 10 deg to achieve complete destructive interference.

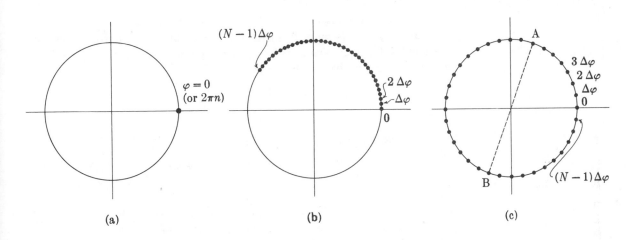

(a)   (b)   (c)

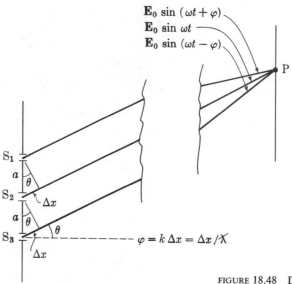

$\mathbf{E}_0 \sin (\omega t + \varphi)$
$\mathbf{E}_0 \sin \omega t$
$\mathbf{E}_0 \sin (\omega t - \varphi)$

$\varphi = k\,\Delta x = \Delta x / \lambdabar$

FIGURE 18.48   Diagram for the analysis of the three-slit interference pattern.

to one side of the line. Since the length l of the grating—the distance from its first to its last line—is equal to $a(N-1)$, Equation 18.85 may be written

"Width" of spectral line (central peak to first minimum)

$$\Delta\theta = \frac{\lambda}{(l+a)\cos\theta} \cong \frac{\lambda}{l\cos\theta}. \qquad (18.86)$$

For a normal grating, l is much greater than a, and the approximate expression after the second equality is valid. For light, the ratio λ/l can be made as small as about 10^{-5} so that $\Delta\theta$ can be an exceedingly small angle.

★TREATMENT OF THREE SLITS

For three slits (Figure 18.48), we may write the electric field contributed by the wave from the center slit at an observation point P as

$$\mathbf{E}_2 = \mathbf{E}_0 \sin \omega t.$$

The zero of time is chosen so that the phase of this wave at this point is zero. Waves arriving at this point from the other two slits have approximately the same amplitude; their phases differ from the phase of the central wave by φ and $-\varphi$, where φ is given by Equation 18.82. The fields of these two waves are

$$\mathbf{E}_1 = \mathbf{E}_0 \sin (\omega t + \varphi),$$

$$\mathbf{E}_3 = \mathbf{E}_0 \sin (\omega t - \varphi).$$

The total field, $\mathbf{E}_P = \mathbf{E}_1 + \mathbf{E}_2 + \mathbf{E}_3$, is

Field vector from three slits

$$\mathbf{E}_P = \mathbf{E}_0[\sin \omega t \cos \varphi + \cos \omega t \sin \varphi$$

$$+ \sin \omega t$$

$$+ \sin \omega t \cos \varphi - \cos \omega t \sin \varphi]. \qquad (18.87)$$

Here we have used the trigonometric formulas for sin $(A + B)$ and sin $(A - B)$. Two terms cancel, leaving

$$\mathbf{E_P} = \mathbf{E}_0 \sin \omega t (1 + 2 \cos \varphi). \tag{18.88}$$

The intensity is $I_P = \overline{E_P{}^2}$. As in previous examples, $\overline{\sin^2 \omega t} = \frac{1}{2}$, and the intensity is

$$I_P = I_0 (1 + 2 \cos \varphi)^2, \tag{18.89}$$

where $I_0 = \frac{1}{2}E_0{}^2$, the intensity that would be contributed by a single slit. To express this result explicitly as a function of the angle of observation θ, we use Equation 18.82 to express φ and obtain

$$I_P = I_0 [1 + 2 \cos (ka \sin \theta)]^2. \tag{18.90}$$

Intensity in three-slit interference pattern

The intensity as a function of $ka \sin \theta$ is plotted in Figure 18.49. The intensities at the principal maxima are $9I_0$ and at the subsidiary maxima I_0. Compare this graph with the second pattern from the top in Figure 18.46. (In that photograph, the principal maxima are overexposed in order to make the subsidiary maxima clear.)

For small θ, sin $\theta \cong \theta \cong y/L$ (y and L are defined in Figure 18.43). With this approximation, the intensity is

$$I_P = I_0 \left[1 + 2 \cos \left(\frac{kay}{L} \right) \right]^2 \quad (\theta \ll 1). \tag{18.91}$$

Intensity in small-angle approximation

This is to be compared with Equations 18.73 and 18.74, which give the intensity pattern produced by two slits in the small-angle approximation.

★TREATMENT OF *N* SLITS

The generalization from three slits to many is not difficult. For convenience, let N be an odd number, and write

$$N = 2m + 1. \tag{18.92}$$

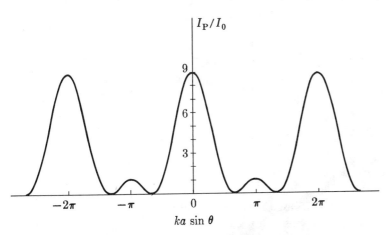

FIGURE 18.49   Intensity of three-slit interference pattern as a function of $ka \sin \theta$ (Equation 18.90).

Then m is the number of slits above or below the central slit. Again choose the zero of time so that the wave from the central slit has zero phase at the observation point. Waves from other slits have phases $\pm\varphi$, $\pm 2\varphi$, $\pm 3\varphi, \ldots, \pm m\varphi$. Paralleling the treatment of three slits, we write, for the total field at P,

Field vector from N slits

$$\mathbf{E_P} = \mathbf{E}_0[\sin \omega t + \sin (\omega t + \varphi) + \cdots + \sin (\omega t + m\varphi)$$
$$+ \sin (\omega t - \varphi) + \cdots + \sin (\omega t - m\varphi)].$$

When this expression is expanded in the manner of Equation 18.87, all terms containing cos ωt cancel in pairs, leaving

$$\mathbf{E_P} = \mathbf{E}_0 \sin \omega t[1 + 2 \cos \varphi + 2 \cos 2\varphi + \cdots + 2 \cos m\varphi]. \quad (18.93)$$

With the help of a trigonometric formula from Appendix 6, the sum in the brackets condenses to

$$1 + \frac{2 \cos \left[\tfrac{1}{2}(m + 1)\varphi\right] \sin \left(\tfrac{1}{2}m\varphi\right)}{\sin \left(\tfrac{1}{2}\varphi\right)}.$$

The time average of $E_P{}^2$ is taken, as from Equation 18.88 to Equation 18.89, to give, for the intensity at P,

Intensity in N-slit pattern

$$I_P = I_0 \left[1 + \frac{2 \cos \left[\tfrac{1}{2}(m + 1)\varphi\right] \sin \left(\tfrac{1}{2}m\varphi\right)}{\sin \left(\tfrac{1}{2}\varphi\right)}\right]^2. \quad (18.94)$$

Again, because φ is a function of θ (Equation 18.82), this may be regarded as a formula for I_P as a function of the angle of observation θ.

The intensity I_P has sharp principal maxima separated by alternating minima and subsidiary maxima (see the bottom pattern in Figure 18.46, for example). We state without proof the fact that the principal maxima occur at angles for which the term sin $(\tfrac{1}{2}\varphi)$ appearing in the denominator in Equation 18.94 is zero. This term vanishes when $\varphi = 2\pi n$, which implies

Maximum constructive interference for $\tfrac{1}{2}\varphi = n\pi$

$$n\lambda = a \sin \theta,$$

the same as Equation 18.81. As $\tfrac{1}{2}\varphi$ approaches a multiple of π, the cosine factor in Equation 18.94 approaches ± 1, and the ratio sin $(\tfrac{1}{2}m\varphi)/\sin (\tfrac{1}{2}\varphi)$ approaches $\pm m$. Therefore, at the principal maxima,

$$I_P = (2m + 1)^2 I_0 = N^2 I_0. \quad (18.95)$$

It is left as a problem to find the location of the first minimum next to a principal maximum.

★18.12   Diffraction by a single slit

Fresnel and Fraunhofer diffraction distinguished

Diffraction observed at a finite distance from a diffracting screen (as in Figure 18.43) is called *Fresnel diffraction*. Usually, in Fresnel diffraction, the light source is also at a finite distance so that the diffracting screen is illuminated with spherical waves and not plane waves. When the light source and the observing screen are moved to very great distance or, with the help of lenses, effectively moved to infinite distance (as in Figure 18.45), the resulting diffraction is called *Fraunhofer diffraction*. We treat the single slit (Figure 18.50) in the approximation of Fraunhofer diffraction.

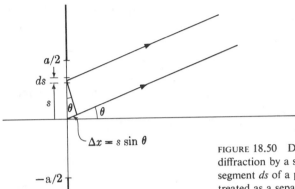

FIGURE 18.50   Diagram for the analysis of diffraction by a single slit. Each infinitesimal segment ds of a plane wave front at the slit is treated as a separate source.

Let the total width of the slit be a, which no longer need be less than the wavelength λ. Each part of the slit is to be treated as a separate infinitesimal source. We choose an origin at the center of the slit and call s the position coordinate within the slit (see the figure) so that the edges of the slit are at $s = a/2$ and $s = -a/2$. At the distant observation point, the field contributed by a segment ds of the slit is

The single slit: a continuous array of sources

$$dE = \frac{E_0}{a} \sin (\omega t + \varphi)\, ds. \qquad (18.96)$$

The choice of amplitude, $E_0\, ds/a$, means that the total field at $\theta = 0$, where all wavelets add constructively, is E_0. In this expression, φ is the phase difference between the wavelet from the center of the slit and the wavelet being considered from the position s. As shown in the figure, the path difference is $s \sin \theta$. The phase difference is therefore

$$\varphi = ks \sin \theta = \frac{s \sin \theta}{\lambda}. \qquad (18.97)$$

It is convenient to define

$$\Phi = \frac{a \sin \theta}{2\lambda}; \qquad (18.98)$$

this is the phase difference between wavelets coming from the center and the edge of the slit. Any other phase difference can then be written

$$\varphi = \frac{2\Phi}{a} s,$$

and the field dE, written as a function of s, is

$$dE = \frac{E_0}{a} \sin \left[\omega t + \frac{2\Phi}{a} s \right] ds. \qquad (18.99)$$

Summing the contributions of the infinitesimal sources means integrating over s from $-a/2$ to $+a/2$:

$$E = \frac{E_0}{a} \int_{-a/2}^{a/2} \sin \left(\omega t + \frac{2\Phi}{a} s \right) ds.$$

The total field is an integral

The integral is simply a cosine (recall that only s is variable; the time t is being held constant). The result of the integration is

$$\mathbf{E} = -\frac{\mathbf{E}_0}{a}\frac{a}{2\Phi}\cos\left(\omega t + \frac{2\Phi}{a}s\right)\Bigg|_{-a/2}^{a/2}.$$

When the cosine is evaluated at the two limits, this expression for E becomes

$$\mathbf{E} = \frac{\mathbf{E}_0}{2\Phi}\left[\cos(\omega t - \Phi) - \cos(\omega t + \Phi)\right].$$

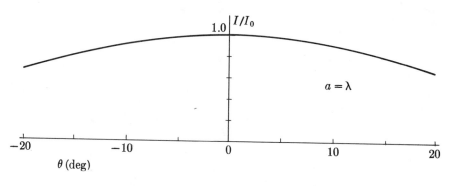

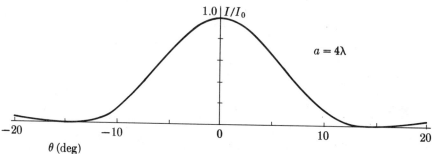

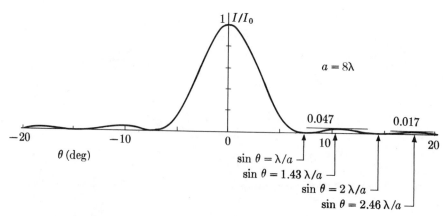

FIGURE 18.51   Intensity in single-slit diffraction pattern vs angle of observation for three different slit widths.

Application of trigonometric formulas causes the quantity in brackets to reduce to $2 \sin \omega t \sin \Phi$, so

$$\mathbf{E} = \mathbf{E_0} \sin \omega t \, \frac{\sin \Phi}{\Phi} . \tag{18.100}$$

As in previous examples, we square $\mathbf{E}$ and average over time to obtain the intensity. Defining $I = \overline{E^2}$ and $I_0{}^2 = \frac{1}{2}E_0{}^2$, we obtain

$$I = I_0 \left(\frac{\sin \Phi}{\Phi} \right)^2 , \tag{18.101}$$

a simple expression for the intensity in the single-slit diffraction pattern. Substitution from Equation 18.98 gives I explicitly as a function of the angle of observation θ:

$$I = I_0 \left[\frac{\sin (a \sin \theta / 2\lambda)}{(a \sin \theta / 2\lambda)} \right]^2 . \tag{18.102}$$

The intensity in the single-slit diffraction pattern

Figure 18.51 shows graphs of I vs θ for several values of the ratio a/λ.

Since $(\sin x)/x \to 1$ as $x \to 0$, Equation 18.102 gives $I = I_0$ at the central peak of the diffraction pattern. The first minimum on one side of the central peak occurs where $\Phi = a \sin \theta / 2\lambda = \pi$, or

$$\sin \theta \text{ (first minimum)} = \frac{\lambda}{a} . \tag{18.103}$$

Angle of the first minimum for a single slit

As this formula and Figure 18.51 both make clear, a narrow slit gives rise to a broad central peak, and a wide slit gives rise to a narrow central peak. The subsidiary maxima are much less intense than the central maximum. For the first subsidiary maximum, which occurs at

$$\sin \theta \text{ (secondary maximum)} = 1.43 \, \frac{\lambda}{a} , \tag{18.104}$$

the intensity is $I = 0.047 I_0$.

For apertures or obstacles of any shape, the general method of attack is the same as that used here for the single slit. The area transmitting light is divided into infinitesimal sources, and the fields from the sources are summed (integrated) to give the total field at the observation point. Many diffraction patterns are esthetically pleasing as well as scientifically interesting. Several, including the pattern from the single slit, are shown in Figure 18.52.

THE RESOLVING POWER OF OPTICAL INSTRUMENTS

A diffraction pattern of special practical importance is that of a circular aperture. The pattern shown in Figure 18.52(c) is an example of *Fresnel* diffraction. The *Fraunhofer* pattern from a circular hole differs in that it has a central peak of intensity surrounded by subsidiary maxima of considerably less intensity. Qualitatively, it is similar to the pattern of a single slit (except, of course, that its fringes are circles, not parallel lines). The angle of the first minimum next to the central maximum is given by

$$\sin \theta \text{ (first minimum)} = 1.22 \, \frac{\lambda}{a} , \tag{18.105}$$

Angle of the first minimum for a circular aperture

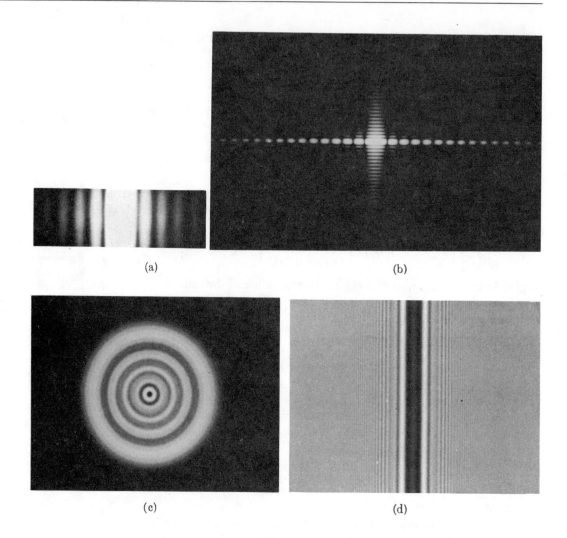

FIGURE 18.52   Patterns of interference resulting from diffraction produced by
single apertures and a single obstacle. (a) Single slit. (b) Rectangular hole.
(c) Circular hole. (d) Wire obstacle. [Photographs (a) and (d) courtesy of
Brian J. Thompson, The Institute of Optics, University of Rochester.
Photographs (b) and (c) from M. Cagnet, M. Françon, and J. C. Thrierr,
Atlas of Optical Phenomena (Berlin: Springer-Verlag, 1962). Courtesy of
Professor Françon.]

where a is the diameter of the hole. Compare this formula with Equation 18.103.

   An important consequence of diffraction—especially diffraction by a
circular opening—is that it limits the "resolving power" of optical instruments,
the ability to discriminate between closely-spaced sources of light. To study the
resolving power of a telescope, it is sufficient to consider the action of a converging lens in bringing light from a distant source to a focus. Figure 18.53
shows a plane beam of light from a remote source S_1 impinging on a lens of
diameter a and focal distance f. According to geometrical optics, the light is

brought to an image point at distance f from the lens. In fact, however, no matter how perfect the lens, the light will not converge to a point. The lens acts also as a circular aperture; it *diffracts* as well as *deflects* the light. The diffraction phenomenon is indicated schematically in Figure 18.53 by the rays that slightly diverge to the right of the lens. The image in the focal plane is spread into the characteristic diffraction pattern of a circular aperture. The angle between the central peak and the first minimum of intensity is, from Equation 18.105 (with $\lambda/a \ll 1$),

A lens diffracts like a circular aperture

$$\Delta\theta = 1.22 \frac{\lambda}{a}. \tag{18.106}$$

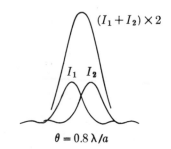

Also shown in Figure 18.53 is the image of a second source S_2 whose angular separation from S_1 is θ. (To avoid confusion in the diagram, only the ray passing through the center of the lens is shown for S_2.) If θ is greater than $\Delta\theta$, the images are said to be resolved. If θ is exactly equal to $\Delta\theta$, the minimum of one diffraction pattern lies under the maximum of the other. This represents the approximate dividing line between being able to resolve the sources and not being able to do so. This choice for the smallest resolvable angle is called "Rayleigh's criterion." We may write

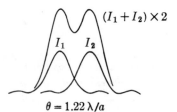

$$\theta_R = 1.22 \frac{\lambda}{a}. \tag{18.107}$$

This particular angle is what is called the theoretical resolving power of the telescope. It is a fundamental limit set by the wave nature of light. The angle θ_R can be decreased only by using light of shorter wavelength, such as ultraviolet, or by using a telescope of larger aperture.

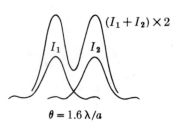

Similar reasoning applies to a microscope. The main difference is that the distance between the lens and object being viewed is only slightly greater than the focal distance f rather than being "infinite." For a microscope, the term "resolving power" is used to indicate the minimum resolvable *distance* (rather than angle) between the two points being viewed. With the help of Figure 18.54,

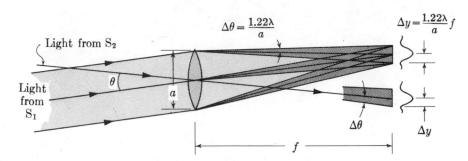

FIGURE 18.53   Resolving power of a telescope. In this illustration, the angle θ between two point sources is greater than the angular width $\Delta\theta$ of each diffracted image. The images are resolved. If θ were less than $\Delta\theta$, the images would overlap and not be resolved. The minimum angle θ for which the images of two sources can be resolved is defined to be the resolving power. It is approximately equal to $\Delta\theta$.

The microscope: object near,
image far

we may derive an expression for the resolving power. This diagram looks complicated, but the ideas, taken one at a time, are simple. Two source points, S_1 and S_2, separated by distance Δs, are at approximately the focal distance f from the objective lens. Their images, centered at P and Q, are so far from the lens that they may be approximated as being infinitely distant.

Consider first the image of S_1. It is centered at P, on the axis of the lens. Because of the finite diameter a of the lens, the image is spread out into a diffraction pattern. The first minimum of this pattern occurs at Q, whose angular separation from P is $\Delta\theta = 1.22\lambda/a$ (Equation 18.106). This corresponds to the path length S_1AQ being longer than the path length S_1BQ by the distance

$$\Delta x = 1.22\lambda. \tag{18.108}$$

Note that $S_1A = S_1B = x_0$ so that Δx is the distance by which AQ exceeds BQ. The right triangle ABC then has the property $\Delta\theta \cong \sin\Delta\theta = 1.22\lambda/a$.

Suppose now that S_2 is a barely resolvable source whose image is centered at Q (the Rayleigh criterion). This means that the paths S_2AQ and S_2BQ through the edges of the lens must be of equal length (for zero phase difference), just as the paths S_1AP and S_1BP are of equal length. Since $CQ = BQ$, this condition can be stated as

Condition for constructive
reinforcement of outermost
paths

$$x_1 + \Delta x = x_2, \tag{18.109}$$

where x_1 and x_2 are defined in the figure. Next consider two right triangles, one with sides f and $\frac{1}{2}a - \Delta s$ and hypotenuse x_1, the other with sides f and $\frac{1}{2}a + \Delta s$ and hypotenuse x_2. An analysis exactly like that for the double slit (see Figure 18.43 and Equation 18.70) yields

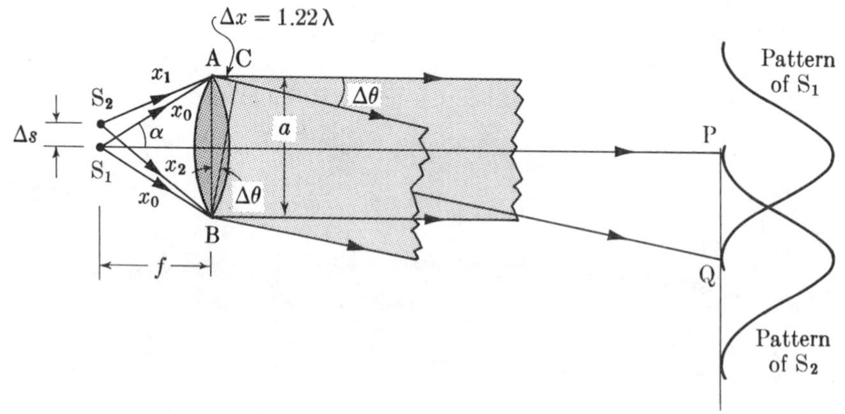

FIGURE 18.54 Resolving power of a microscope. In this illustration, the sources are barely resolved because the maximum of one diffraction pattern falls at the first minimum of the other. The minimum distance Δs for which the images of two sources can be resolved is defined to be the resolving power. The key facts used in deriving an expression for Δs are that the path lengths S_2AQ and S_2BQ are equal, and the path lengths S_1AQ and S_1BQ differ by $\Delta x = 1.22\lambda$.

$$(x_2 - x_1)(x_2 + x_1) = 2a \, \Delta s. \tag{18.110}$$

According to Equation 18.109, we may replace $x_2 - x_1$ by Δx. Equation 18.110 then gives

$$\Delta s = \frac{(x_2 + x_1) \, \Delta x}{2a}. \tag{18.111}$$

If f were much larger than a, we could approximate $x_2 + x_1$ by $2f$. For a microscope, however, this may not be a good approximation. (Indeed, that is the whole reason for this somewhat elaborate analysis.) It *is* a good approximation, however, to treat the separation between S_1 and S_2 as a small quantity: $\Delta s \ll f$, and $\Delta s \ll a$. This approximation means that x_1 and x_2 do not differ much from x_0, so

$$x_1 + x_2 \cong 2x_0.$$

Accordingly, Equation 18.111 may be written

$$\Delta s = \frac{x_0 \, \Delta x}{a}.$$

For Δx we may substitute 1.22λ from Equation 18.108, and for a/x_0 we may substitute $2 \sin \alpha$, where the angle α, as defined in Figure 18.54, is the angle subtended by half the diameter of the lens at the source. These substitutions lead to a useful expression for the resolving power of the microscope:

$$\Delta s = \frac{1.22\lambda}{2 \sin \alpha}. \tag{18.112}$$

Resolving power of the microscope

Since $\sin \alpha < 1$, we can at once establish an important inequality:

$$\Delta s > 0.6\lambda. \tag{18.113}$$

Resolvable distances cannot be much less than λ

This says that even with the best designed microscope, and regardless of magnification, objects separated by less than about half a wavelength cannot be distinguished. This result should not be surprising. As a tool of analysis, a wave is necessarily limited in precision. Any effort to pinpoint a wave in a dimension substantially less than its own wavelength is thwarted by the large diffraction that then results.

One interesting technique for improving the resolving power of a microscope is used in the so-called oil-immersion microscope. A drop of oil fills the space between the objective lens and the object being viewed. Because of the index of refraction of the oil, the wavelength of light within the oil is less than it is in air. Accordingly, the resolving power Δs is somewhat decreased. A much bigger gain in resolving power is achieved by replacing light waves with electron waves, whose wavelength can easily be made much less than the wavelength of visible light.* The "lenses" that focus electron beams and produce magnified images consist of electric and magnetic fields.

Oil can replace air to shorten wavelength

The electron microscope: a bigger gain

---

* See Albert V. Crewe, "A High-Resolution Scanning Electron Microscope," *Scientific American*, April, 1971.

Summary of ideas and definitions

Electromagnetic waves, sound waves, and surface waves —despite some marked differences—share properties of superposition, reflection, refraction, diffraction, and interference.

The electric field in a plane electromagnetic wave may be written

$$\mathbf{E} = \mathbf{E}_0 \sin(\omega t - kx + \alpha). \qquad (18.9)$$

Its phase is $\alpha - kx$; its amplitude is $\mathbf{E}_0$; its intensity is $\overline{E^2} = \frac{1}{2}E_0^2$. ($\omega = 2\pi v$ and $k = 2\pi/\lambda = 1/\lambda$.)

A wave is polarized in its direction of vibration. For transverse waves, polarization has vector properties.

The intensities of incoherent sources are additive.

The displacements or fields of coherent sources are additive.

Coherence requires equal frequency, fixed relative polarization, and fixed relative phase.

The intensity of superposed coherent waves is

$$I_P = \frac{1}{2}(E_1^2 + E_2^2 + 2E_1 \cdot E_2 \cos \varphi). \quad (18.21)$$

Huygens's principle: Points along a line of constant phase act as coherent sources for the further propagation of the wave.

The law of wave reflection is $\theta_i = \theta_r$ (Equation 18.25).

A plane mirror gives an unmagnified virtual image.

Convex mirrors and diverging lenses give demagnified virtual images.

Concave mirrors and converging lenses can give magnified or demagnified real images and magnified virtual images.

For all thin lenses and mirrors,

$$\frac{1}{d_1} + \frac{1}{d_2} = \frac{1}{f} \quad \text{and} \quad M = \frac{1}{\dfrac{d_1}{f} - 1},$$

(18.31 and 18.63, 18.34 and 18.64)

with the following sign conventions:

d_1: always positive

d_2 and M: positive for real images, negative for virtual images

f: positive for concave mirrors and converging lenses, negative for convex mirrors and diverging lenses.

Snell's law of refraction is

$$n_1 \sin \theta_1 = n_2 \sin \theta_2. \qquad (18.43)$$

For $n_1 = 1$ and $n_2 = n$, total internal reflection occurs in medium 2 when $\sin \theta_2 > 1/n$.

For a thin prism of apex angle α ($\alpha \ll 1$), the deflection angle δ is the same for all rays:

$$\delta = \alpha(n - 1). \qquad (18.54)$$

The microscope has an objective lens that gives a magnified real image and an ocular lens that gives a further magnified virtual image.

In a camera, f is fixed and d_2 is variable; in the eye, d_2 is fixed and f is variable.

Converging lenses correct farsightedness; diverging lenses correct nearsightedness.

A small finite number of coherent sources produce what is called an interference pattern; a large number of sources or a continuous distribution of sources produce what is called a diffraction pattern. There is no important difference between the two.

In a small-angle approximation, the intensity pattern of a double slit is

$$I_P = 4I_0 \cos^2 \left(\frac{kay}{2L}\right). \qquad (18.74)$$

The fringes are equally spaced and equally intense.

A diffraction grating produces narrow lines of constructive interference at angles given by

$$n\lambda = a \sin \theta. \qquad (18.81)$$

The angular width of a spectral line produced by a grating is given by Equation 18.86.

The 3-slit pattern of intensity is given by Equation 18.90; the N-slit pattern is given by Equation 18.94.

The Fraunhofer diffraction pattern of a single slit is given by

$$I = I_0 \left(\frac{\sin \Phi}{\Phi}\right)^2, \qquad (18.101)$$

where $\Phi = \frac{1}{2}ka \sin \theta = a \sin \theta / 2\lambda$. It has a strong central peak and weak subsidiary peaks.

For a slit of width a, the angular separation of the central maximum and the first minimum is given by $\sin \theta = \lambda/a$; for a circular aperture of diameter a, it is given by $\sin \theta = 1.22\lambda/a$.

The resolving power of a telescope (minimum angle of discrimination) is, approximately,

$$\theta_R = 1.22 \frac{\lambda}{a}.$$ (18.107)

The resolving power of a microscope (minimum distance of discrimination) is, approximately,

$$\Delta s = \frac{1.22\lambda}{2 \sin \alpha}.$$ (18.112)

It cannot be much less than λ.

QUESTIONS

Q18.1 (1) About what range of frequencies is audible to the human ear? How many octaves is this? (2) About how many octaves are covered by an average singing voice?

Section 18.1

Q18.2 A sound wave in air strikes a metal surface. It is partially reflected and partially transmitted into the metal. (1) Is the wavelength in the metal greater or less than the wavelength in air? (2) Is the wave in air longitudinal or transverse? (3) Is the wave in metal longitudinal or transverse?

Q18.3 Which of the following are standing waves and which are propagating waves: (1) radio waves emanating from a transmitting antenna, (2) the vibration of a piano string, (3) the pattern of rising and falling air on the downwind side of a mountain range, and (4) the water wave generated by dropping a stone into a still pond?

Q18.4 Some scientists speculate that space and time might have a quantum structure, or granular structure (analogous to but finer-grained than the atomic granularity of matter). What effect might such a spacetime granularity have on the electromagnetic spectrum?

Q18.5 The electric field in an electromagnetic wave radiating outward in all directions from the origin is described by

$$\mathbf{E} = \mathbf{E}_0(r) \sin (\omega t - kx + \alpha).$$

Explain why $\mathbf{E}_0(r)$ must be proportional to $1/r$. In what significant way does this radial dependence differ from that of a *static* electric field?

Q18.6 A surface wave on water is a combination of longitudinal and transverse vibrations. (1) How does a bubble on the surface move as a wave passes by? (2) Why is it permissible to describe this wave as being vertically polarized? (3) Name one other wave that is neither purely longitudinal nor purely transverse.

Section 18.2

Q18.7 When you place a fireplace screen between yourself and a fire, you notice a significant decrease in the radiant energy striking your face. If you go outside on a sunny day and place the same screen between yourself and the sun, you do not notice an appreciable decrease in the solar intensity. What is the essential difference in the two kinds of radiation that accounts for the different effect of the screen?

Q18.8 Would you expect a window screen to polarize sunlight? Would you expect it to polarize FM radio signals (whose wavelength is about 3 m)? Give reasons for your answers.

Q18.9 (1) Explain why a microwave polarizer (Figure 18.5) does not polarize light. (2) Describe a hypothetical physical system that acts on microwaves in the same way that the microwave polarizer acts on light.

Q18.10 Sunlight scattered from molecules in the atmosphere is polarized. Using a polarizer outdoors, find (a) the approximate angle of scattering at which maximum polarization occurs and (b) the relationship between the polarization direction of the scattered light and the plane defined by the incident and scattered directions of the light.

Q18.11 Is the human eye sensitive to the polarization of light (that is, does the eye respond differently to different polarizations)? Obtain an answer experimentally by carrying out one or more simple tests. (NOTE: Because bees can "see" polarization, they can use scattered sunlight for navigational guidance—see the preceding question.)

Section 18.3 **Q18.12** If the point P in Figure 18.8 is equidistant from identical coherent sources S_1 and S_2, the intensity at P may be 4 times greater than the intensity that would be produced by either source acting alone. Why is this fact not inconsistent with the law of energy conservation?

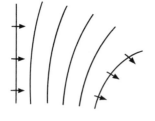

Q18.13 Suppose that polarizers are placed in front of the slits in the upper diagram of Figure 18.9(b) and that the axes of these polarizers are perpendicular to each other (the polarizers do not overlap). (1) Will the waves emanating from the two slits still be coherent? (2) Can the waves emanating from the slits interfere?

Q18.14 The figure shows successive wave fronts (lines of constant phase) for a wave propagating in a material medium. What conclusions can you draw about the properties of the medium? (Reason with the help of Huygen's principle.)

Q18.15 Why is the direction of wave propagation perpendicular to a wave front (a line of constant phase)? Explain in terms of Huygen's principle.

Section 18.5 **Q18.16** Why does a plane mirror show your image inverted left-to-right but not inverted top-to-bottom?

Q18.17 Describe your image in a two-dimensional corner reflector (see the figure).

Q18.18 A fluorescent light source is located on a focal line within a reflecting elliptical cylinder. (1) Where is the image located? (2) If the source is moved slightly away from the focal line, how does the image move? Illustrate your answer with suitable diagrams.

Q18.19 Most truck drivers use both plane mirrors *and* convex mirrors for looking to the rear. What is the advantage of the plane mirror relative to the convex mirror? What is the advantage of the convex mirror relative to the plane mirror?

Q18.20 As you back away from a concave shaving mirror, your image becomes larger, then blurs into indistinguishability, then reappears inverted. If you measure the distance from your face to the mirror at the point of maximum blurring, what property of the mirror have you measured?

Q18.21 (1) Can a virtual image be photographed by exposing a film at the location of the virtual image? (2) Can a real image be photographed by exposing a film at the location of the real image? Give reasons for both answers.

Q18.22 (1) Can sound waves be refracted? (2) Can surface waves on water be refracted? Give reasons for your answers.

Section 18.6

Q18.23 Suggest a way in which index of refraction might be defined for sound propagation.

Q18.24 Why does a swimming pool filled with water appear to be shallower than it actually is?

Q18.25 A 6-ft fisherman stands at the edge of a pond. To a fish studying the fisherman from beneath the surface of the pond, does the height of the fisherman appear to be greater than, equal to, or less than 6 ft?

Q18.26 If you believed in the particle theory of light, how would you explain total internal reflection?

Q18.27 The mechanism of rainbow formation is discussed and illustrated in Problem 18.21. (1) Explain in simple terms why a rainbow is colored. (2) The secondary rainbow is formed by light that is reflected twice within water droplets (see the accompanying figure). Why is the order of colors in the secondary rainbow opposite to the order of colors in the primary rainbow?

Section 18.7

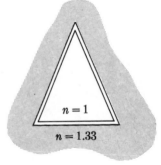

Q18.28 A hollow transparent rod has a triangular cross section. When it is inserted into a container of water, it forms an "air prism" in the water (see the figure). Discuss the effect of this air prism on light. Does it separate white light into a spectrum of colors?

Q18.29 (1) If the eye is placed close to a hand magnifier such as the one pictured in Figure 18.32, there is no angular magnification (the object and the image subtend the same angle at the eye). Explain why this is so. (2) Despite the absence of angular magnification, a hand magnifier held close to the eye can be effective in revealing details of small objects. Why?

Section 18.8

Q18.30 At what distance from a converging lens should an object be placed in order that the object and its image be the same size? How does the image differ from the object?

Q18.31 An aerial photographer has two lenses available for his camera. Lens 1 has a focal length of 0.4 m; lens 2 has a focal length of 0.8 m. (1) Which lens should he use in order to get the larger image of a given object on the ground? (2) Which lens should he use in order to photograph the larger area of ground on a given area of film?

Q18.32 A concave mirror and a converging glass lens have the same focal distance in air. Do they have the same focal distance when they are submerged in water? If not, which has the greater focal distance?

Q18.33   In any optical device, light rays are reversible: that is, if light were caused to propagate in the opposite direction, the rays would retrace the same path. Explain why this reversibility is a general phenomenon that does not depend on any details of construction within optical devices.

Q18.34   (1) Can a converging lens form a demagnified virtual image? (2) Can a diverging lens form a demagnified virtual image? (3) Can a diverging lens form a real image? (In each case, assume that the image is an image of a real object, not the image of an image.)

Q18.35   The text describes instances in which the image distance or the magnification of a lens is conveniently treated as a negative quantity. Under certain circumstances, the object distance may also be treated as negative. This occurs when the image of one lens serves as the "object" of another lens. Show in a sketch how an image that would be formed by one lens if that lens were present alone can become a "virtual object" for a second lens that is added near the first one.

Q18.36   The "f number" of a lens is its focal length divided by its effective diameter. In given light conditions, why must a photographer double his exposure time when he increases the f number of his camera lens by a factor $\sqrt{2}$?

Q18.37   All of the lenses and mirrors diagrammed in this chapter have spherical surfaces. Suppose that the surfaces are cylindrical instead. (1) Would the figures in the text correctly represent the paths of light rays (a) for cylindrical mirrors? (b) for cylindrical lenses? (2) Describe the action of a converging cylindrical lens on a parallel beam of light.

Q18.38   Borrow the reading glasses of a far-sighted friend and measure approximately the focal distance of the lenses. With the help of a diagram, describe how you carried out the measurement. (If suitable eyeglasses are not available, use any converging lens or hand magnifier.)

Q18.39   A person wears bifocal eyeglasses in which both the upper and lower parts are converging lenses. Which part has the shorter focal length? Why?

Q18.40   A watchmaker uses diverging eyeglasses for driving, no glasses for reading, and converging glasses in his work. Is he slightly near-sighted or slightly far-sighted?

Section 18.9   Q18.41   Reception of FM and TV signals is good only for "line-of-sight" transmission (this means that neither terrain nor man-made structures block the straight-line path from the transmitting antenna to the receiving antenna). The reception of AM signals is not so restricted. Explain the difference in terms of diffraction. (NOTE: Diffraction accounts for the difference for relatively short-distance transmission. For long-distance transmission, reflection from the ionosphere must also be considered.)

Q18.42   Radio reception is poor on a bridge made of steel girders. Is this because the girders cast shadows of the radio waves? Is it because the waves diffract and interfere destructively? Is it for some other reason?

Q18.43   At the center of the dark shadow of a circular disk an experimenter finds a bright spot. Explain his finding in terms of diffraction and interference.

Section 18.10   Q18.44   Discuss the appearance of the interference pattern produced by a pair of slits if the slits are illuminated by (a) light of a single wavelength, (b) light of two wavelengths—4,400 Å and 6,600 Å—and (c) light from an incandescent bulb.

Q18.45 If the output of a monaural recording is fed to both speakers of a stereo system, the speakers act as coherent sources of sound waves. (1) Explain why interference effects can degrade the fidelity of the sound: that is, cause the relative perceived intensities of different frequencies to differ from the relative intensities that were recorded. (2) Where should you sit in order that interference effects not degrade the fidelity?

Q18.46 A wave front is, by definition, a line (or surface) of constant phase. Use this fact together with Huygens's principle to explain why, if a plane wave is brought to a focus by any combination of mirrors and lenses, the different parts of the wave that overlap at the focal point will interfere constructively.

Section 18.11

Q18.47 (1) Which experiences greater deflection in a prism spectroscope, red light or violet light? (For guidance, see Figure 18.20.) (2) Which of these colors experiences greater deflection in a grating spectroscope?

Q18.48 An opaque card is inserted into a grating spectroscope in such a way that it covers half the lines of the grating. Does each of the following quantities increase, decrease, or remain unchanged: (a) the angle at which a certain spectral line is observed, (b) the width of the spectral line, (c) the peak intensity in the spectral line, and (d) the total integrated intensity in the spectral line?

Q18.49 One way to produce a narrowly directed beam of microwaves is to place a radiating antenna at the focal point of a parabolic reflector. Another way is to use an array of parallel, equally spaced antennas. (1) Explain why the latter arrangement works. (2) Suggest a way in which the direction of the beam radiated by the array could be changed without rotating the array.

Q18.50 At a given angle of observation in a spectroscope, spectral lines of two or more different wavelengths might appear as a result of diffraction in different orders. Suggest one or more ways in which the lines of different order near a given angle might be distinguished.

Q18.51 What was the orientation of the rectangular aperture that produced the diffraction pattern shown in Figure 18.52(b)? What is the approximate ratio of the lengths of the sides of this aperture?

Section 18.12

Q18.52 Experiment shows that if the width of a single slit is doubled, the peak intensity in its diffraction pattern quadruples, although the energy passing through the slit per unit time only doubles. How can these different factors of increase be reconciled?

Q18.53 Give two reasons why the 200-in. Hale telescope (see Figure 1.2) is a more powerful research instrument than a 100-in. telescope.

EXERCISES

E18.1 What is the wavelength in standard dry air of sound whose frequency is (a) 50 Hz and (b) 5,000 Hz?

Section 18.1

E18.2 An organ pipe 2 m long emits sound whose wavelength in air is 8 m. If this note is sounded for 1 sec, how many full vibrations of the wave are generated?

E18.3   When a hammer strikes one end of an iron coil (point A in the figure), two sound pulses are generated. One pulse propagates straight through the air; the other propagates along the helical coil. Both pulses reach point B at the same time. Show that the ratio of the diameter to the pitch of the helix is given approximately by $d/l \cong 5.5$.

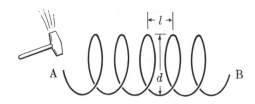

E18.4   In order that a sound wave be physically defined, its wavelength must encompass at least several atoms or molecules. An approximate criterion for the definition of the wave is $\lambda\!\!\!^- > l$, where $\lambda\!\!\!^-$ is the reduced wavelength ($\lambda\!\!\!^- = \lambda/2\pi$) and l is the mean spacing between molecules. According to this criterion, what are the minimum wavelength and maximum frequency of a sound wave in air? (Use standard conditions, for which there are 6×10^{23} molecules in 0.0224 m^3.)

E18.5   (1) Show that each of the following equations describes a wave propagating with speed $v = \omega/k$:

$$A = A_0 \sin(\omega t - kx + \alpha),$$

$$A = A_0 \cos(\omega t - kx + \alpha),$$

$$A = A_0 \sin(\omega t + kx + \alpha).$$

(2) How do the first and second waves differ physically? (3) How do the first and third waves differ physically?

E18.6   A plane electromagnetic wave propagating in a vacuum has a frequency $\nu = 1$ GHz and a peak electric field $E_0 = 10^{-3}$ V/m. Find (1) the angular frequency ω, (2) the wavelength λ, (3) the wave number k, and (4) the peak magnetic field B_0 in this wave.

E18.7   In a certain part of space the magnetic field is given by

$$\mathbf{B} = B_0 \sin(3 \times 10^7 t - 0.1z)\,\mathbf{i}.$$

Give (1) the wavelength, (2) the frequency, and (3) the direction of propagation of the electromagnetic wave associated with this field.

Section 18.2   E18.8   Show that the following electric field represents a plane polarized wave:

$$\mathbf{E} = E_1 \sin(\omega t - kx)\,\mathbf{j} + E_2 \cos(\omega t - kx - \tfrac{1}{2}\pi)\,\mathbf{k},$$

where E_1 and E_2 are positive constants. What is the intensity of the wave? What is its direction of polarization (answer with the help of a diagram)?

E18.9   An electromagnetic wave propagating in the z direction is characterized by the following electric field:

$$\mathbf{E} = (E_0\mathbf{i} + 2E_0\mathbf{j}) \sin(\omega t - kz).$$

(1) Express the intensity of the wave in terms of E_0. (2) What is the direction of polarization of the wave? (3) What fraction of the energy in this wave is

transmitted through an ideal polarizer whose axis (as defined in Figure 18.2) is (a) parallel to the x axis and (b) parallel to the y axis?

E18.10   An electromagnetic wave of unit intensity is polarized in the x direction and propagates in the z direction. As shown in the figure, the wave encounters two polarizers, the first with its axis inclined at 45 deg to the x axis, the second with its axis parallel to the y axis. (1) What is the intensity beyond the second polarizer (region R in the figure)? (2) Polarizer 2 is removed. Then what is the intensity in region R? (3) Polarizer 2 is put back in place and polarizer 1 is removed. Then what is the intensity in region R?

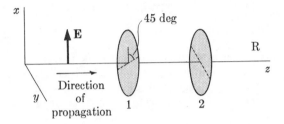

E18.11   Express Equation 18.22 in terms of the individual source intensities I and I' Section 18.3
instead of the field magnitudes E_1 and E_2.

E18.12   The sources S_1 and S_2 in Figure 18.8 emit waves that are coherent but are not of identical polarization. The electric fields $\mathbf{E}$ and $\mathbf{E}'$ that are superposed at an observation point P are given by Equations 18.15 and 18.16. (1) Give an expression for the intensity at P as a function of the angle θ between the two polarization directions, the phase difference φ between the two waves, and the intensities I and I' that would be contributed by the sources acting one at a time. (2) For a fixed relative polarization angle θ, give expressions for the maximum and minimum intensities that could occur at P. Then specialize these answers to the case $I = I'$.

E18.13   One microwave transmitter, with a power output of 10 W, is kept on continuously. A second nearby microwave transmitter, with a power output of 1 W, can be switched on and off. Show that when the second transmitter is switched on, the intensity at a distant observation point may increase by as much as 73 percent or may decrease by as much as 53 percent (i.e., to 47 percent of its original value). What conditions are required to make possible these maximum changes of intensity?

E18.14   The figure depicts a wave front of a wave propagating outward from a line source in a homogeneous medium. Apply Huygens's principle in order to show that the wave fronts at a great distance from the source approach circles (or, in three dimensions, spheres).

E18.15   In Figure 18.11, which depicts the mechanism of wave reflection, $\alpha = \theta_i$ Section 18.4
and $\beta = \theta_r$. Give the geometrical reason for these equalities.

E18.16   (1) If a reflected wave had less speed than the incident wave, would the angle of reflection be greater or less than the angle of incidence? To answer this question, consider a modified version of Figure 18.11. (2) When a ball bounces obliquely from a wall with some loss of energy, is its angle of reflection greater or less than its angle of incidence? Answer with the help of experiment if necessary.

E18.17   A woman 1.6 m tall stands 1.2 m from a wall on which is hung a plane mirror. What is the minimum vertical dimension of the mirror that enables the woman to see her entire image from head to toe?

E18.18   Prove that a light ray reflected from a two-dimensional 90-deg corner reflector such as the one shown in Figure 18.13(a) is antiparallel to the incident ray.

E18.19   By mistake, the angle between two plane mirrors intended to serve as a corner reflector is $\frac{1}{2}\pi + \alpha$, where α is a small positive quantity. (1) Prove that for most incident directions, a light ray striking these mirrors experiences a net deflection given by $\delta = \pi - 2\alpha$. (2) With the help of a diagram, show that for certain incident directions the net deflection need not be given by this formula.

E18.20   The surface of a certain concave mirror is a small section of a sphere of radius 0.50 m. (1) What is the focal distance of the mirror? (2) At what distance from the mirror should an object be placed in order that its image be the same distance from the mirror as the object? (3) At this distance, is the image larger than the object, smaller than the object, or equal in size to the object?

E18.21   For a concave spherical mirror, sketch a graph of magnification M vs object distance d_1 (see Equation 18.34). Include values of d_1 from 0 to about $4f$. Discuss the meaning of the graph for $0 < d_1 < f$.

E18.22   In the figure the point C is the center of curvature of a concave spherical mirror and the point F is the focal point of the mirror. (1) If your head is in the position shown, a real and inverted image of your head is formed to the left of point C (see Figure 18.16). Show that what you *see*, however, is *not* inverted: you must look upward to see your forehead and downward to see your chin. (2) Next you back away from the mirror so that your head is to the left of point C. Show that what you see in the mirror now *is* inverted: you must look downward to see your forehead and upward to see your chin. (Provide answers with the help of carefully drawn diagrams; calculations are not required.)

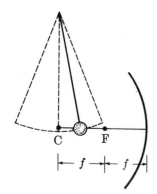

E18.23   In a certain "executive toy" a colored ball swings back and forth in front of a concave spherical mirror (see the figure). Suppose that the motion of the ball is described approximately by $x = f \sin \omega t$, where f is the focal distance of the mirror, x is distance measured along the axis of the mirror, and the origin ($x = 0$) is at the center of curvature C. (1) Show that the distance from the mirror to the image of the swinging ball is given by

$$d_2 = f\,\frac{2 - \sin \omega t}{1 - \sin \omega t}.$$

(2) Obtain a formula for v_2, the speed of the image as a function of time. What is the maximum speed of the image according to this formula? (3) At what point(s) does the swinging ball appear to collide with its image?

E18.24   A chair has a height of 1 m. When the chair is placed 3 m from a convex spherical mirror, a virtual image is formed whose height is 0.5 m. (1) What is the focal distance f of the mirror? (2) What is the radius of curvature R of the surface of the mirror? (3) What is the distance from the chair to its image?

E18.25 Prove that the Huygens wavelet emanating from point B in Figure 18.18 just touches the refracted wavefront line CC'.   Section 18.6

E18.26 Use Huygens's principle and a geometrical construction analogous to that in Figure 18.18 to show that Equation 18.43 remains valid when the wave propagates from medium 2, where its angle of incidence is θ_2, into medium 1, where its angle of refraction is θ_1.

E18.27 A beam of light falls on the surface of a sheet of glass having an index of refraction of 1.40. (1) If the angle of incidence of the light is 30 deg, what is its angle of refraction within the glass? (2) What is the average speed of light inside the glass?

E18.28 A ray of light is incident on the interface between two sheets of glass with different indices of refraction, as shown in the figure. (1) Is the light deflected toward or away from the line perpendicular to the surface? (2) By how many degrees is it deviated from its straight-line course?

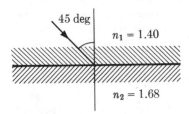

E18.29 A parallel beam of white light strikes a plate of "high-dispersion" crown glass at an angle of incidence of 45 deg. What is the approximate angular spread *inside* the glass between violet light of wavelength 4,000 Å and red light of wavelength 7,000 Å? (Make a rough calculation, based on the data presented graphically in Figure 18.20.)

E18.30 A tank 3 m in diameter and 1 m deep with a small opening in the center of its top is completely filled with water (see the figure). Looking in from the top, what fraction of the bottom surface could you see directly (without any multiple reflections)?

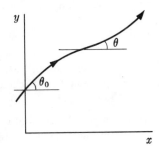

E18.31 In a medium in which the index of refraction depends on x, Snell's law takes the form $n(x) \sin \theta = n_0 \sin \theta_0$, where θ is the angle between a light ray and the x axis (see the figure). (1) Explain why this formula is correct. (It may be helpful to consider refraction by a large number of thin layers.) (2) State qualitatively how $n(x)$ depends on x if a light ray follows the path shown in the figure.

E18.32   (1) What is the average speed of light in a glass prism that is just barely able to produce total internal reflection of the kind shown in the figure? (Take the index of refraction of air to be exactly 1.00.) (2) Would the prism still exhibit total internal reflection if submerged in water?

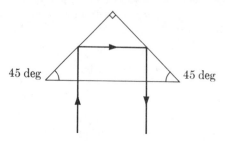

45 deg   45 deg

E18.33   A pencil of light approaches the surface of a piece of glass from within the glass. The space outside the surface is evacuated. For each of several indices of refraction from 1.0 to 1.8, calculate the maximum angle of incidence of the light beam in the glass, $\theta_2{}^{max}$, for which the light can escape through the surface. Present the results of these calculations in graphical form.

Section 18.7

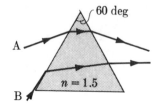

60 deg

A

B

$n = 1.5$

E18.34   A glass prism has an index of refraction $n = 1.5$ and an apex angle $\alpha = 60$ deg. (1) Find δ_{min}, the angle of minimum deflection for a light ray passing through the prism (ray A in the figure). (2) Find the deflection angle δ for ray B, whose angle of incidence at one face of the prism is nearly 90 deg.

E18.35   A glass prism has an index of refraction $n = 1.5$ and an apex angle $\alpha = 20$ deg. (1) Find δ_{min}, the angle of minimum deflection for a light ray passing through the prism. (2) Find the angle of deflection δ for a light ray incident normal to one face of the prism ($\theta_1 = 0$). Compare both answers with the approximate formula given by Equation 18.54.

E18.36   A prism whose index of refraction is n_2 is imbedded in a medium whose index of refraction is n_1. (1) Show that if the apex angle α of the prism is small and if the angle of incidence θ_1 is small, the deflection angle of a light ray passing through the prism is given approximately by

$$\delta \cong \left| \frac{n_2}{n_1} - 1 \right| \alpha.$$

(2) Evaluate this expression numerically for (a) the prism described in the preceding exercise and (b) an "air prism" in water (see Question 18.28) with an apex angle of 20 deg.

Section 18.8

E18.37   A parallel beam of white light is incident on a thin lens like the ones shown in Figure 18.28 and 18.29; one face of the lens is flat and the other face has a radius of curvature of 0.50 m. For red light, the index of refraction of the lens is $n = 1.60$; for violet light, its index of refraction is $n = 1.64$. (1) What is the approximate focal length f of this lens? (2) Since this lens is not achromatic, different colors are focused at different points. What is the separation between the focused red light and the focused violet light?

E18.38   A marble of diameter 1 cm is placed 30 cm from a converging lens of focal length 20 cm. (1) Where is the image of the marble? Is the image real or virtual? (2) What is the diameter of the image?

E18.39 Answer the questions in the preceding exercise if the marble is placed 15 cm from the lens.

E18.40 Imagine the lens in Figure 18.28 to be replaced by a thin double convex lens (one with two convex surfaces). By considering the action of this lens on a ray of light that is initially parallel to the lens axis, derive the following formula for the inverse focal length of the lens:

$$\frac{1}{f} = (n - 1)\left(\frac{1}{R_1} + \frac{1}{R_2}\right),$$

where R_1 and R_2 are the radii of curvature of the two faces of the lens. (Note that Equation 18.60 is a special case of this result.)

E18.41 Make a geometrical construction analogous to those in Figure 18.31 that shows the formation of a virtual image when the object distance d_1 is less than the focal length f of a converging lens. Show that the magnification of the virtual image in this case is given by

$$|M| = \frac{1}{1 - (d_1/f)}.$$

(As a matter of convenience, a negative value of M may be associated with a virtual image. Then Equation 18.64 can be used for both real and virtual images.)

E18.42 (1) Use geometrical properties of the rays shown in Figure 18.33—especially of the highest and lowest of the four rays shown—in order to derive the following relationship for a diverging lens:

$$\frac{1}{f} = \frac{1}{d_2} - \frac{1}{d_1},$$

where d_1 is the distance from the lens to the object, d_2 is the distance from the lens to the image, and f is the focal distance (all three of these distances being positive). (2) What sign conventions are appropriate in order to make Equation 18.63 apply to a diverging lens?

E18.43 This exercise uses the result of the preceding exercise. (1) The distance of an object from a diverging lens in $d_1 = 60$ cm. The focal length of the lens is $f = 30$ cm. What is the image distance d_2? (2) What is the demagnification factor M?

E18.44 A certain camera is supplied with three interchangeable lenses, whose focal lengths are 35 mm, 50 mm, and 140 mm. (1) A girl of height 1.5 m stands 15 m from the camera. What is the height of her image on the film produced by each of the three lenses? (2) How many photographs must be taken using the 140 mm lens in order to cover the same *area* of a distant scene that is covered in one photograph using the 35 mm lens?

E18.45 The focal length of the lens on a 16 mm projector is 5 cm. The picture size on the film is 7.6 mm × 10.5 mm. What is the size of the image projected on a screen 4 m from the lens?

E18.46 On a movie film, each picture is approximately 18.75 mm × 25 mm. In a certain theater, the 6 m × 8 m screen is located 30 m from the projector. (1) What is the focal length of the lens in the projector? (2) What is the distance of the film from the nearer focal point of the lens?

E18.47   Show that if a thin lens of focal length f_1 and a thin lens of focal length f_2 are placed close together, the focal length of the combination is given by

$$f = \frac{1}{(1/f_1) + (1/f_2)}.$$

Section 18.10   E18.48   Orange light of wavelength 6,000 Å is incident on a screen containing a pair of narrow slits separated by 2 mm. (1) Calculate and sketch the interference pattern produced on a screen 4 m beyond the slits. Would this pattern be visible to the unaided eye? (2) In a companion sketch beside the first one, indicate the pattern that would be observed if light traveled in straight lines without diffraction.

E18.49   In a laboratory a girl shines a laser at a pair of slits of known separation a and measures the spacing of interference fringes on a screen 2.5 m beyond the slits. She then repeats the measurement for two other pairs of slits. Her results are shown in the accompanying table. (1) What is the wavelength of the laser light? (2) What is the approximate uncertainty in this determination of wavelength if the uncertainties in the slit separation and the slit-to-screen distance are negligible?

Slit separation a (mm)	Fringe spacing Δy (mm)
1.00	1.60 ± 0.02
0.50	3.15 ± 0.02
0.20	7.90 ± 0.02

E18.50   You have been given a microwave transmitter labeled "Guaranteed to emit radiation of wavelength 3 cm." Design an interference experiment to test the claim, specifying the numerical magnitudes of all significant dimensions, and calculating the expected distance to be measured between two points of constructive interference.

Section 18.11   E18.51   A helium-neon laser provides light of known wavelength, $\lambda = 6,328$ Å, which is used to calibrate a grating spectroscope. The angle of first-order diffraction is found to be 22 deg. (1) What is the grating spacing a? (2) At what angle will the second-order diffraction line be observed?

E18.52   A certain grating is 3 cm wide and has 6,000 lines/cm. It is illuminated by green light whose wavelength is $\lambda = 5,000$ Å. (1) At what angle θ is the first-order spectral line observed? (2) What is the angular width $\Delta\theta$ of this line? Give also the *relative* width, $\Delta\theta/\theta$. (3) How many orders of diffraction can be observed?

E18.53   Red light from three different sources is mixed and illuminates a spectroscope whose grating has 250 lines/mm.

Source	Wavelength
Hydrogen	6,563 Å
Neon	6,402 Å
Argon	6,965 Å

Find the angle of first-order diffraction for each of these three spectral lines. Would you expect these three lines to be clearly distinct and easily identifiable?

E18.54   Let the visible range of wavelengths be defined as 4,000 to 7,000 Å. (1) Show that the first- and second-order visible spectra do not overlap in a grating spectroscope but that the second- and third-order spectra do overlap. (2) Approximately what range of wavelengths in the second-order visible spectrum is overlapped by the third-order visible spectrum?

E18.55   A grating having N lines ($N \gg 1$) and a grating spacing a is illuminated by light of wavelength λ. (1) Show that the approximate angle of the first minimum of intensity next to the zero-order (undeflected) maximum is $\theta_{\min} \cong \lambda/Na$. (2) Show that this angle of minimum intensity becomes an angle of maximum intensity if the grating is converted to a double slit by blocking all but the *first* and *last* of its lines.

E18.56   The derivative $d\theta/d\lambda$ may be called the "dispersive power" of a grating spectroscope. (1) Show that in the nth-order spectrum it is given by

$$ \frac{d\theta}{d\lambda} = \frac{n}{a \cos \theta} = \frac{n/a}{\sqrt{1 - (n\lambda/a)^2}} . $$

(2) What dispersive power is required in order that the yellow D lines of sodium ($\lambda_1 = 5,890$ Å and $\lambda_2 = 5,896$ Å) be separated by 3×10^{-4} radian? (3) What grating spacing a is needed to achieve this separation of the D lines in first order?

E18.57   Two spectral lines in a grating spectroscope are barely resolved if the peak of one line falls at the first minimum of the other line. This means that the *width* of one line, as defined by Equation 18.85, is equal to the angular *spacing* between the lines. Show that the wavelength difference of two barely resolved lines in first order is $\Delta\lambda = \lambda/N$, where N is the total number of lines in the grating.

E18.58   The distance between a maximum and the adjacent minimum in a two-slit interference pattern can be deduced from Equations 18.75 and 18.76. The angular width of a spectral line (maximum to minimum) is given by Equation 18.85. Show that for $N = 2$ and for $\theta \ll 1$ radian, these results agree.

E18.59   On the same graph, sketch curves of intensity vs angle in the patterns produced by (a) a single slit of width a and (b) a pair of narrow slits separated by the distance a. Normalize the central peak of both curves to unity, and include the angular range $-\lambda/a \leq \theta \leq \lambda/a$.

Section 18.12

E18.60   Slits are sometimes used to diffract sound waves in order to spread the sound over a broad range of angles. If the sound from a loudspeaker passes through a slit of width 2.5 cm, for what frequency does the first minimum in the diffraction pattern occur at 45 deg? Is this an audible frequency? Are waves of lower frequency more widely or less widely diffracted?

E18.61   (1) Show that the maxima in the diffraction pattern of a single slit occur where $\tan \Phi = \Phi$ (Φ is defined by Equation 18.98). (2) Verify that the first subsidiary maximum occurs at $\sin \theta = 1.43\lambda/a$ (Equation 18.104) and that the intensity at this angle is $I = 0.047I_0$.

E18.62   An idealized diffraction grating consists of slits of width b whose centers are separated by a distance a. (1) Discuss qualitatively the effect of the finite slit width on the diffraction pattern produced by the grating. Does the slit width influence the positions of the spectral lines? Does it influence their relative intensity? (2) What orders of the spectrum are missing if (a) $a = 2b$ or (b) $a = 3b$?

E18.63   (1) What is the approximate angular separation of the closest pair of double stars that can be resolved visually using a telescope of 6-in. diameter? (2) Is the resolving power of a telescope better using red light or blue light?

E18.64   The length of a grain in a certain photographic emulsion is 0.5 μm. (1) How does this dimension compare with the wavelength of visible light? (2) Should it be possible to see a grain with a microscope? (3) Should it be possible to see details of the shape of the grain with a microscope?

PROBLEMS

Standing wave   P18.1   (1) Discuss in detail the properties of the wave described by the following equation:

$$A(x, t) = A_0 \sin kx \sin \omega t.$$

Locate the nodes (points of minimum vibration) and antinodes (points of maximum vibration) of this wave. Why is it called a standing wave? (2) Show that this standing wave is equivalent to the superposition of two propagating waves. Give the properties of these propagating waves.

Energy flux in an electromagnetic wave   P18.2   The intensity of an electromagnetic wave may be defined by $I = \overline{E^2} = \frac{1}{2}E_0^2$ (Equation 18.10). This is a convenient quantity for assessing the *relative* strength of different waves. To characterize the absolute strength of a wave a more useful quantity is the *energy flux* W: this is the energy transmitted per unit time across a unit area normal to the direction of propagation. The SI unit of energy flux is W/m^2. For a plane electromagnetic wave characterized by Equation 18.9, express W in terms of I and in terms of E_0. (SUGGESTION: First find the energy *density*, then the energy *flux*. Keep in mind that half the energy is in the magnetic field.)

Group velocity   P18.3   Two waves that have equal amplitude and that differ slightly in wavelength and frequency are superposed. The net displacement is given by

$$A = A_0[\sin(\omega_1 t - k_1 x) + \sin(\omega_2 t - k_2 x)];$$

the fractional differences between ω_1 and ω_2 and between k_1 and k_2 are small. (1) Show that the displacement can be written

$$A = 2A_0 \cos(\omega' t - k' x) \sin(\omega_0 t - k_0 x).$$

Relate ω', k', ω_0, and k_0 to ω_1, k_1, ω_2, and k_2. (2) Explain why the net displacement has the form shown in the figure: because of amplitude modulation it consists of a series of wave "packets," or "groups." (3) Show that the *group velocity* v_g—the speed at which the modulated groups propagate—is given by $v_g = d\omega/dk = -\lambda^2 dv/d\lambda$. (4) Show that for electromagnetic waves in a vacuum, $v_g = c$.

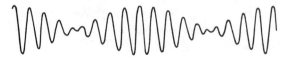

Circular polarization   P18.4   An electromagnetic wave is said to be circularly polarized if its electric field at a fixed point has a constant magnitude and rotates at a fixed rate. (1) Show that the following electric field satisfies the conditions of circular polarization:

$$\mathbf{E} = E_0 \sin(\omega t - kz)\,\mathbf{i} + E_0 \cos(\omega t - kz)\,\mathbf{j}.$$

In what direction does $\mathbf{E}$ rotate from the point of view of someone looking along the z axis (the direction of propagation)? At what angular speed does $\mathbf{E}$ rotate? (2) What is the intensity of this wave? (3) Show that a polarizer transmits half the intensity of this wave, regardless of the orientation of the polarizer axis. (4) Write an expression for the electric field in a wave of opposite circular polarization—a wave whose electric field rotates in a direction opposite to that of the $\mathbf{E}$ field given above.

P18.5 Upon reflection from a plane surface, light suffers a phase change. In a treatment based on Huygens's principle (see Figure 18.11), this phase change can be treated as a time delay. Prove that the law of reflection, $\theta_i = \theta_r$, is valid if a wave experiences an arbitrary but fixed time delay Δt at the reflecting surface.

Reflection from a plane surface

P18.6 Prove that a light ray reflected from a three-dimensional corner reflector such as the one shown in Figure 18.13(b) is antiparallel to the incident ray.

Corner reflector

P18.7 A vertical cross section through the mirror shown in the figure is a parabola described by the equation $y = ax^2$. Prove that all incoming rays parallel to the y axis are reflected in such a way that they pass through the focal point F whose distance from the bottom of the mirror is $f = 1/4a$.

Parabolic mirror

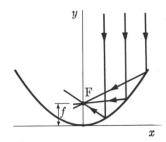

P18.8 Prove that if an object AB is oriented perpendicular to the axis of a concave spherical mirror (as in Figure 18.16), its image A'B' is also oriented perpendicular to the axis. (Assume that the distances d_1 and d_2 in Figure 18.16 are much greater than the dimensions l and l'.)

Concave spherical mirror

P18.9 Figure 18.16 shows the formation of an image by a concave spherical mirror when the object lies outside the focal point ($d_1 > f$). (1) Make an analogous sketch showing image formation by a concave spherical mirror when the object lies inside the focal point ($d_1 < f$). Is the image real or virtual? Is it magnified or demagnified? (2) Show that Equation 18.31 is still valid in this case provided the image distance d_2 is assigned a negative value. (3) Show that Equation 18.34 is still valid in this case provided the magnification M is assigned a negative value. (Assume that all light rays make small angles with the axis of the mirror.)

P18.10 Some properties of a convex spherical mirror are shown in Figure 18.17. (1) Prove that the radius of curvature R and the focal distance f of such a mirror are related approximately by $R = 2f$. (2) Derive Equations 18.35 and 18.36. (Assume that all light rays make small angles with the axis of the mirror.)

Convex spherical mirror

Huygen's principle applied
to the action of a thin prism

P18.11   As shown in the figure, a plane wave strikes a prism of apex angle α and is deflected through the angle δ. Use Huygens's principle to prove that for small α, the deflection angle is given approximately by $\delta \cong \alpha(n - 1)$ (Equation 18.54), where n is the index of refraction of the prism. For simplicity, let the direction of propagation of the incoming wave be perpendicular to the left surface of the prism. (METHOD: Consider wavelets emanating from points A and C on the incident wave front. Points B and D are points reached by these wavelets in equal time. Because the angles α and δ are small, the lines AB and CD may both be approximated as being parallel to the direction of propagation of the incoming wave.)

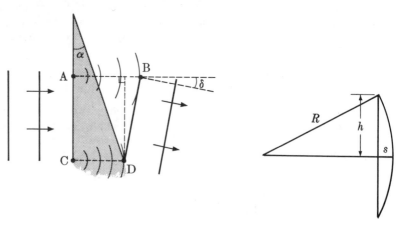

Approximating the sagitta
of an arc

P18.12   A chord of length $2h$ joins the ends of an arc of radius R. (1) Obtain an expression for the *sagitta* s (defined in the figure) as a function of h and R. (2) Show that

$$s = \frac{h^2}{2R}$$

is a good approximation if $h \ll R$. This approximation is used in the next two problems.

Huygen's principle and image
formation

P18.13   The dashed line in the accompanying diagrams is a spherical wave front associated with a wave expanding from a source point S. The dotted line in the diagrams is a spherical wave front associated with the reflected wave that is converging toward an image point I. The reflecting surface, which is indicated by a heavy solid line, is a section of a sphere of radius R centered at point C. Diagram (b) shows the situation at an instant of time when the edges of the

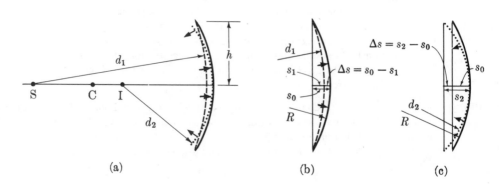

(a)   (b)   (c) expanding wave have just reached the mirror and the center of the expanding wave is a distance Δs from the center of the mirror. Diagram (c) shows the situation at a later instant when the center of the expanding wave has reached the center of the mirror and the outer edges of the reflected wave have moved back a distance Δs. (1) With the help of the approximate formula given in the preceding problem, and assuming the radial distances d_1, d_2, and R to be much greater than the lateral distance h, derive Equation 18.31, which relates the distances d_1 and d_2 to the focal distance f (use the fact that $f = \frac{1}{2}R$). (2) Explain carefully what role Huygens's principle plays in this derivation.

P18.14 Use the method of the preceding problem to locate the reflected wave front and to derive Equation 18.31 when the source point S is located inside the focal point of a concave spherical mirror ($d_1 < f$). A required sign convention in this case is $d_2 < 0$ (see the discussion following Equation 18.36).

P18.15 A plane wave is incident from the left on the flat face of a thin lens. In the figure, the line ACA′ is a plane wave front and the curve BDB′ is a spherical wave front centered at the focal point F. Apply Huygens's principle to the transmission of the wave through the lens in order to derive Formula 18.60 for the focal length of the lens (the approximation for the sagitta of an arc given in Problem 18.12 may be helpful).

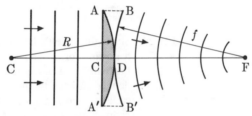

P18.16 Generalize the treatment of the preceding problem by considering a wave that expands from a source point on the axis of the lens, passes through the lens, and converges to an image point on the axis (see Figure 18.30). By applying Huygens's principle to the passage of a wavefront through the lens (assuming that directions of propagation make small angles with the axis), derive the thin-lens formula

$$\frac{1}{d_1} + \frac{1}{d_2} = \frac{1}{f}.$$

P18.17 Snell's law in a medium in which the index of refraction depends on x is given in Exercise 18.31: $n(x) \sin \theta = n_0 \sin \theta_0$. (1) Prove that this equation can also be expressed in the following way:

Snell's law in a continuously variable medium

$$\frac{dy}{dx} = \frac{C}{\sqrt{n^2(x) - C^2}},$$

where $C = n_0 \sin \theta_0$. (It may be helpful to refer to the figure accompanying Exercise 18.31.) (2) The index of refraction of a certain medium is given by $n(x) = n_0\sqrt{1 + ax}$. Show that the path of a light ray that enters this medium at $x = y = 0$ with an initial angle θ_0 to the x axis is described by the equation

$$y = \frac{2 \sin \theta_0}{a} \left(\sqrt{\cos^2 \theta_0 + ax} - \cos \theta_0\right).$$

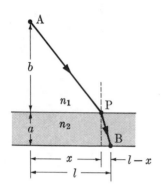

Fermat's principle

P18.18 Geometrical optics can be formulated in terms of a principle stated by Pierre de Fermat: Between two fixed points a light ray follows a path for which the time is an extremum (usually a minimum). Obviously straight-line propagation in a uniform medium satisfies this principle. Prove that Fermat's principle applied to refraction at a plane boundary leads to Snell's law. (SUGGESTED METHOD: Let A and B in the figure be fixed points, and let P, the point of refraction, be considered a variable point. Adjust the position of P to minimize the time of propagation from A to B.)

P18.19 The figure shows a light ray propagating from point A to point B via a single reflection at a plane surface. Apply Fermat's principle (stated in the preceding problem) to this phenomenon and prove that it leads to the law of reflection: $\theta_i = \theta_r$.

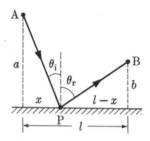

Reflection and refraction in terms of the ray vector

P18.20 Show that Snell's law and the law of reflection can be stated jointly in the following form: At a surface, the tangential component of the ray vector is unchanged. The *ray vector*, which is associated with a light ray, is a vector defined to have the direction of light propagation and to have a magnitude equal to the index of refraction of the medium in which the light ray is propagating.

Rainbow angle

P18.21 The primary rainbow in the sky is formed by sunlight that is influenced by water droplets in the manner shown in the figure. A light ray is refracted as it enters a droplet, is reflected once inside the droplet, and is refracted as it leaves the droplet. (1) Show that the total angle of deflection δ experienced by the ray is given by $\delta = \pi + 2\theta_1 - 4\theta_2$ (the angles θ_1 and θ_2 are defined in the figure). (2) In this expression for δ, regard θ_1 as the independent variable and θ_2 as a known function of θ_1 (the link between θ_1 and θ_2 is provided by Snell's law, which in this case takes the form $\sin \theta_1 = n \sin \theta_2$). The extremal deflection angle δ_r is defined by $d\delta/d\theta_1 = 0$. Show that $\delta = \delta_r$ when

$$\sin \theta_1 = \sqrt{\frac{4 - n^2}{3}}.$$

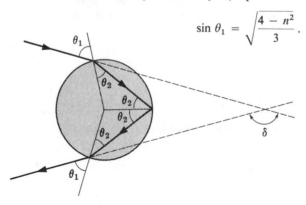

(3) The extremal deflection angle δ_r is the *rainbow angle*. Evaluate the rainbow angle numerically for $n = 1.33$ and show it to be approximately 138 deg. (4) Which has the greater rainbow angle, red light or violet light? Translate this answer to what is seen in the sky: is it the outer part of the bow or the inner part of the bow that is red? *Optional:* Explain why the visible rainbow is seen at the extremal angle δ_r and not at other deflection angles δ.

P18.22   A glass prism has an apex angle of 60 deg. In a certain part of the visible spectrum its index of refraction is $n = 1.5$ and its dispersive power (its ability to separate light of different wavelengths) is specified by $dn/d\lambda = 10^5 \text{ m}^{-1}$, where λ is wavelength. In a spectroscope set up to work near minimum deflection angles for this prism, what angular spread is produced between radiations differing in wavelength by 30 Å?

Dispersion by a prism

P18.23   The figure shows a converging lens forming a real image I of an object O. The distance of the object from one focal point is x_1; the distance of the image from the other focal point is x_2. (1) Show algebraically that the formula

$$x_1 x_2 = f^2$$

is equivalent to the thin-lens formula given by Equation 18.63. This more compact form of the lens formula was used by Newton. (2) Show that the magnification is given by $M = f/x_1 = x_2/f$. (3) Determine how x_1 and x_2 must be defined in order that the formula $x_1 x_2 = f^2$ remain valid for the formation of a virtual image by a converging lens.

Newton's lens formula

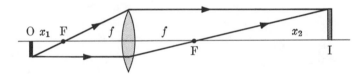

P18.24   (1) Using methods similar to those presented in Section 18.8, develop the theory of the thin diverging lens. In particular, do the following: (a) By considering the ray shown in the accompanying figure, obtain a relationship between the focal length f and the radius of curvature R of the curved face of the lens. (b) For a point source on the lens axis, obtain a relationship among the object distance d_1, the image distance d_2, and the focal length f. (c) Express the magnification M in terms of d_1 and f. Show that M is always less than 1. (2) Show that with suitable sign conventions, the three preceding results agree exactly with the corresponding results for a converging lens (Equations 18.60, 18.63, and 18.64). What are the appropriate choices of sign for d_1, d_2, and f?

Diverging lens

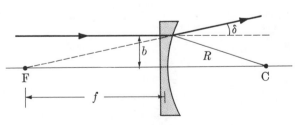

*Angular magnification of a
microscope*

P18.25   The figure shows an object O just outside a focal point F of the objective lens of a microscope (see also Figure 18.34). The real image I is located near the focal point F' of the eyepiece lens. Various distances are defined in the figure. Show that if d_1 and d_1' are both much less than d_2 and if d_1' is nearly equal to f', the angular magnification (defined by Equation 18.65) is given approximately by

$$M' \cong \frac{d_2^2}{ff'}.$$

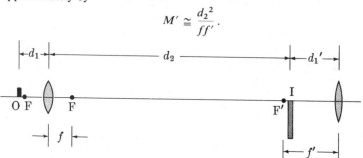

Telescopes

P18.26   A certain telescope contains two converging lenses, an objective lens of focal length f and an eyepiece of focal length f' (see the figure). Inside the barrel of the telescope the focal points F and F' are nearly coincident. (1) What is the location of the real image formed by the objective lens (assume that the object being viewed is quite remote)? (2) Show that the angular magnification is given approximately by $M' \cong f/f'$. (3) Is the image seen by the viewer erect or inverted?

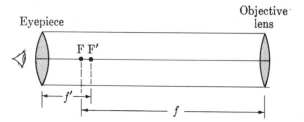

P18.27   An opera glass, which follows the design of a Galilean telescope, consists of a converging objective lens of focal length f and a diverging eyepiece of focal length f' (see the figure). Outside the eyepiece, the focal points F and F' are nearly coincident. (1) Where would the real image of a distant object be located if the eyepiece were not in place? (This image becomes the "virtual object" viewed through the eyepiece.) (2) Show that the angular magnification is given approximately by $M' \cong f/f'$. (3) Is the image seen by the viewer erect or inverted?

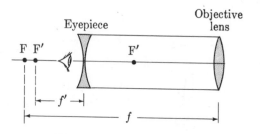

P18.28 (1) Show that the intensity in the two-slit interference pattern is given by

Two-slit interference pattern

$$I_P = 2I_0[1 + \cos(ka \sin \theta)] \qquad \text{if} \qquad a \ll L,$$

where k is the wave number and I_0 is the intensity that would be produced by a single slit; other notation is defined in the figure. (2) Explain why the condition $a \ll L$ is required for the validity of this result and why the condition $y \ll L$ is *not* required. (3) Show that if the condition $y \ll L$ is also satisfied, Equation 18.73 is a good approximation to this result.

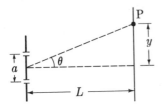

P18.29 The figure shows a thin lens whose index of refraction is n. It has one flat face and one face whose radius of curvature is R; its focal length is $f = R/(n - 1)$. (1) Show that the times required for light to propagate from A to F and from C to F are the same. (Assume $b \ll R$.) (2) Explain why this equal-time condition means that waves in phase at A and C will also be in phase when they converge at F.

Equal-time property for focused rays

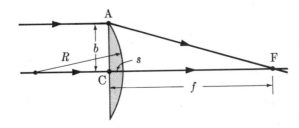

P18.30 (1) Show that Equation 18.94, which gives the intensity in the N-slit interference pattern (for odd N), can be written more compactly as follows:

Diffraction by N slits

$$I_P = I_0 \left(\frac{\sin \frac{1}{2}N\varphi}{\sin \frac{1}{2}\varphi} \right)^2,$$

where $\varphi = ka \sin \theta$. (2) Given that the principal maxima occur where the phase difference between successive slits in $\varphi = 2\pi n$ (n is an integer), show that (a) the intensity at a principal maximum is $I_P^{\text{max}} = N^2 I_0$ and (b) the first minimum next to a principal maximum occurs at $\varphi = 2\pi n + \Delta\varphi$, with $\Delta\varphi = 2\pi/N$. (Note that these two results agree with Equations 18.95 and 18.84.) *Optional.* Prove that the principal maxima occur where $\varphi = 2\pi n$.

P18.31 The derivation of the intensity in the N-slit interference pattern given in Section 18.11 is valid for odd N. (1) Carry out a similar derivation for even N and show that the result can be written $I_P = I_0(\sin \frac{1}{2}N\varphi/\sin \frac{1}{2}\varphi)^2$, where $\varphi = ka \sin \theta$. This is identical to the result for odd N stated in the preceding problem. (2) For $N = 2$ and for small angles, show that this result agrees with Equation 18.73 or 18.74.

Appendices

APPENDIX 1.   Units in the international system (SI)

(This appendix is adapted from E. A. Mechtly, "The International System of Units," NASA Report SP-7012, 1969, available for 30 cents from the Superintendent of Documents, U.S. Government Printing Office, Washington, D.C. 20402.)

Basic units

Length
: The METER (m) is the length equal to 1,650,763.73 wavelengths in vacuum of the radiation corresponding to the transition between the levels $2p_{10}$ and $5d_5$ of the krypton 86 atom.

Mass
: The KILOGRAM (kg) is the mass of the international prototype of the kilogram (a particular cylinder of platinum-iridium alloy preserved in a vault in Sèvres, France).

Time
: The SECOND (sec*) is the duration of 9,192,631,770 periods of the radiation corresponding to the transition between the two hyperfine levels of the ground state of the cesium 133 atom.

Current
: The AMPERE (A) is that constant current which, if maintained in two straight parallel conductors of infinite length, of negligible circular cross section, and placed 1 m apart in vacuum, would produce between those conductors a force per unit length equal to 2×10^{-7} N/m.

Temperature
: The KELVIN (K) is the fraction 1/273.16 of the thermodynamic temperature of the triple point of water.

Luminous intensity
: The CANDELA (cd) is the luminous intensity, in the perpendicular direction, of a surface of $1/600,000$ m^2 of a blackbody at the temperature of freezing platinum under a pressure of 101,325 N/m^2.

Some other important units

Force
: The NEWTON (N) is that force which gives to a mass of 1 kg an acceleration of 1 m/sec^2.

Energy
: The JOULE (J) is the work done when the point of application of 1 N is displaced a distance of 1 m in the direction of the force.

Power
: The WATT (W) is the power which gives rise to the production of energy at the rate of 1 J/sec.

Charge
: The COULOMB (C) is the charge transported in 1 sec by a current of 1 A.

Potential
: The VOLT (V) is the difference of potential between two points of a conducting wire carrying a constant current of 1 A when the power dissipated between these points is equal to 1 W.

Resistance
: The OHM (Ω) is the resistance between two points of a conductor

---

* The symbol s is also commonly used for the second.

A3

when a constant difference of potential of 1 V, applied between these two points, produces in this conductor a current of 1 A, this conductor not being the source of any electromotive force.

Capacitance

The FARAD (F) is the capacitance of a capacitor between the plates of which there appears a difference of potential of 1 V when it is charged by 1 C.

Inductance

The HENRY (H) is the inductance of a closed circuit in which an electromotive force of 1 V is produced when the current in the circuit varies uniformly at a rate of 1 A/sec.

Magnetic flux

The WEBER (Wb) is the magnetic flux which, linking a circuit of one turn, produces in it an electromotive force of 1 V as it is reduced to zero at a uniform rate in 1 sec.

APPENDIX 2.   Physical quantities: symbols and SI units

Quantity	Common Symbol	Unit	Unit Expressed in Terms of Basic SI Units
Acceleration	**a**	m/sec^2	m/sec^2
Angle	θ, φ	radian	
Angular acceleration	α	radian /sec^2	sec^{-2}
Angular frequency	ω	radian/sec	sec^{-1}
Angular momentum	**L, J**	kg m^2/sec	kg m^2/sec
Spin	**S**		
Angular velocity	ω	radian/sec	sec^{-1}
Angular speed	ω		
Area	**S**, A	m^2	m^2
Atomic number	Z		
Capacitance	C	farad (F) (= C/V)	A^2 sec^4/kg m^2
Charge	q, e	coulomb (C)	A sec
Charge density			
Volume	ρ	C/m^3	A sec/m^3
Surface	σ	C/m^2	A sec/m^2
Line	τ	C/m	A sec/m
Conductivity	σ	1/Ω m	A^2 sec^3/kg m^3
Current	I	AMPERE	A
Current density	**J**	A/m^2	A/m^2
Density	ρ	kg/m^3	kg/m^3
Dielectric constant	κ_e		
Displacement	**s**	METER	m
Distance	d		
Length	l, L		
Electric dipole moment	**p**	C m	A sec m
Electric field	**E**	V/m	kg m/A sec^3
Electric flux	Φ_E	V m	kg m^3/A sec^3
Electromotive force	$\mathscr{V}$	volt (V)	kg m^2/A sec^3

A5

Quantity	Common Symbol	Unit	Unit Expressed in Terms of Basic SI Units
Energy	E	joule (J)	kg m^2/sec^2
Internal energy	U		
Kinetic energy	K		
Potential energy	U		
Entropy	S	J/K (often kcal/K)	kg m^2/sec^2 K
Force	$\mathbf{F}$	newton (N)	kg m/sec^2
Frequency	ν	hertz (Hz)	sec^{-1}
Heat	Q	joule (J) (often cal or kcal)	kg m^2/sec^2 J/A^2
Inductance	L	henry (H)	kg m^2/A^2 sec^2
Magnetic dipole moment	μ	N m/T	A m^2
Magnetic field	$\mathbf{B}$	tesla (T) (= Wb/m^2)	kg/A sec^2
Magnetic flux	Φ_B	weber (Wb)	kg m^2/A sec^2
Mass	m, M	KILOGRAM	kg
Mass number	A		
Molar specific heat	C'	J/kmole K (often kcal/kmole K)	kg m^2/sec^2 kmole K
Molecular weight	$M.W.$	kg/kmole (= gm/mole) (= amu/molecule)	kg/kmole
Moment of inertia	I	kg m^2	kg m^2
Momentum	$\mathbf{p}$	kg m/sec	kg m/sec
Period	T	sec	sec
Permeability	κ_m		
Permeability constant	μ_0	N/A^2 (= H/m)	kg m/A^2 sec^2
Permittivity of space	ϵ_0	C^2/N m^2 (= F/m)	A^2 sec^4/kg m^3
Pole strength	P	N/T	A m
Potential Voltage	V	volt (V) (= J/C)	kg m^2/A sec^3
Power	P	watt (W) (= J/sec)	kg m^2/sec^3 J/s
Pressure	P, p	N/m^2	kg/m sec^2
Resistance	R	ohm (Ω) (= V/A)	kg m^2/A^2 sec^3

Quantity	Common Symbol	Unit	Unit Expressed in Terms of Basic SI Units
Specific heat (see also molar specific heat)	C	J/kg K (often kcal/kg K)	m^2/sec^2 K
Temperature	T	KELVIN	K
Time	t	SECOND	sec
Torque	**T**	N m	kg m^2/sec^2
Velocity	**v**	m/sec	m/sec
Speed	v		
Volume	V	m^3	m^3
Wave function	ψ	Usually $m^{-3/2}$ ($m^{-1/2}$ in one dimension)	$m^{-3/2}$
Wave number	$k, 1/\lambda$	m^{-1}	m^{-1}
Wavelength	λ	m	m
Work	W	joule (J) (= N m)	kg m^2/sec^2

ALPHABETICAL LIST OF STANDARD ABBREVIATIONS OF UNITS

Abbreviation	Unit	Abbreviation	Unit
A	ampere	Hz	hertz
Å	angstrom	in	inch
A.U.	astronomical unit	J	joule
amu	atomic mass unit	K	kelvin
atm	atmosphere	kcal	kilocalorie
C	coulomb	kg	kilogram
°C	degree Celsius	kmole	kilomole
cal	calorie	lb	pound
cm	centimeter	m	meter
deg	degree (angle)	min	minute
esu	electrostatic unit	N	newton
eV	electron volt	°R	degree Rankine
F	faraday	rpm	revolutions per minute
°F	degree Fahrenheit	sec	second
fm	fermi, femtometer	T	tesla
ft	foot	V	volt
G	gauss	W	watt
gm	gram	Wb	weber
H	henry	μm	micrometer, micron
hr	hour	Ω	ohm

APPENDIX 3. Numerical data

For physical data, see, in addition to this appendix, appropriate tables in the text.

A. Physical constants

[This table is adapted from B. N. Taylor, W. H. Parker, and D. N. Langenberg, *The Fundamental Constants and Quantum Electrodynamics* (New York: Academic Press, 1969). A good popular article on the fundamental constants, by the same authors, is to be found in the October, 1970, issue of *Scientific American*. The numbers recorded here have been truncated so that the uncertainty in each is at most ± 1 in the last digit.]

Quantity	Symbol	Value
Gravitational constant	G	6.67×10^{-11} N m^2/kg^2 (or m^3/kg sec^2)
Avogadro's number	N_0	6.0222×10^{23} particles/mole (or amu/gm)
Boltzmann's constant (microscopic gas constant)	k	1.3806×10^{-23} J/K 8.617×10^{-5} eV/K
	$\dfrac{1}{k}$	$11{,}605$ K/eV
Macroscopic gas constant	$R\,(=N_0 k)$	8.314 J/mole K 1.9872 kcal/kmole K
Quantum unit of charge	e	1.60219×10^{-19} C 4.8033×10^{-10} esu
Faraday constant (1 mole of electricity)	$F\,(=N_0 e)$	9.6487×10^4 C/mole 2.8926×10^{14} esu/mole

Quantity	Symbol	Value
Permittivity of space	$\epsilon_0 \left(= \dfrac{1}{\mu_0 c^2} \right)$	8.85419×10^{-12} C^2/N m^2
	$4\pi\epsilon_0 \left(= \dfrac{4\pi}{\mu_0 c^2} \right)$	1.112650×10^{-10} C^2/N m^2
	$\dfrac{1}{4\pi\epsilon_0} \left(= \dfrac{\mu_0 c^2}{4\pi} \right)$	8.98755×10^9 N m^2/C^2
Permeability constant	μ_0	$4\pi \times 10^{-7}$ N/A^2 *exact, by definition* or 1.256637×10^{-6} N/A^2
	$\dfrac{\mu_0}{4\pi}$	*exactly* 10^{-7} N/A^2
Speed of light	c	2.997925×10^8 m/sec
Planck's constant	h	6.6262×10^{-34} J sec 4.1357×10^{-15} eV sec 4.1357×10^{-21} MeV sec
	$\hbar \left(= \dfrac{h}{2\pi} \right)$	1.05459×10^{-34} J sec 6.5822×10^{-16} eV sec 6.5822×10^{-22} MeV sec
Charge-to-mass ratio or electron	$\dfrac{e}{m_e}$	1.75880×10^{11} C/kg 5.2728×10^{17} esu/gm
Mass of electron	m_e	9.1096×10^{-31} kg 5.4859×10^{-4} amu
Mass of proton	m_p	1.67261×10^{-27} kg 1.0072766 amu $1836.11 m_e$
Mass of neutron	m_n	1.67492×10^{-27} kg 1.0086652 amu $1838.64 m_e$
Intrinsic energy of electron	$m_e c^2$	0.51100 MeV
Intrinsic energy of proton	$m_p c^2$	938.26 MeV
Intrinsic energy of neutron	$m_n c^2$	939.55 MeV
Rydberg constant for infinitely massive nucleus	$\mathscr{R}_\infty \left[= \left(\dfrac{1}{4\pi\epsilon_0} \right)^2 \dfrac{m_e e^4}{4\pi\hbar^3 c} \right]$	1.0973731×10^7 m^{-1}
Rydberg constant for hydrogen 1	$\mathscr{R}_H$	1.0967758×10^7 m^{-1}
Fine structure constant	$\alpha \left(= \dfrac{1}{4\pi\epsilon_0} \dfrac{e^2}{\hbar c} \right)$	7.29735×10^{-3} or 1/137.036

Quantity	Symbol	Value
Bohr radius	$a_0 \left(= \dfrac{4\pi\epsilon_0 \hbar^2}{m_e e^2} \right)$	5.29177×10^{-11} m 0.529177 Å
Compton wavelength of the electron	$\lambda_\mathrm{C} \left(= \dfrac{h}{m_e c} \right)$	2.42631×10^{-12} m
Reduced Compton wavelength of the electron	$\lambdabar_\mathrm{C} \left(= \dfrac{\hbar}{m_e c} \right)$	3.86159×10^{-13} m 386.159 fm
Bohr magneton	$\mu_\mathrm{B} \left(= \dfrac{e\hbar}{2m_e} \right)$	9.2741×10^{-24} J/T

Useful Combinations of Constants

	$\dfrac{e^2}{4\pi\epsilon_0}$	2.3071×10^{-28} J m 14.400 eV Å 1.4400 MeV fm
	$\hbar c$	3.1616×10^{-26} J m 1.97329×10^3 eV Å 197.329 MeV fm
	$\dfrac{\hbar^2}{2m_e}$	6.1044×10^{-39} J m^2 3.8100 eV Å^2 3.8100×10^4 MeV fm^2
	$\dfrac{\hbar^2}{2m_p}$	3.3246×10^{-42} J m^2 2.0751×10^{-3} eV Å^2 20.751 MeV fm^2
	c^2	8.98755×10^{16} J/kg 9.3148×10^8 eV/amu 931.48 MeV/amu

B. Terrestrial data*   (Footnote on page A12)

Quantity	Value
Acceleration of gravity at sea level (g)	9.80665 m/sec^2, standard reference value 9.7804 m/sec^2 at equator 9.8322 m/sec^2 at poles
Mass of earth (M_E)	5.98×10^{24} kg
Mass of earth times gravitational constant ($M_\mathrm{E}G$)	3.9860×10^{14} N m^2/kg (or m^3/sec^2)
Radius of earth (R_E)	6.37×10^6 m 6370 km $\quad$ approximate average value 3960 miles 6378.2 km at equator 6356.8 km at poles
Equatorial circumference of earth	4.008×10^7 m 24,902 miles

Quantity	Value
	The Atmosphere
Standard air pressure at sea level (760 mm of Hg)	1.013×10^5 N/m^2
Standard dry air density at sea level and 0 °C	1.293 kg/m^3
Typical moist air density at sea level and 20 °C	1.20 kg/m^3
Speed of sound in standard air at 0 °C	331 m/sec 740 mile/hr
Typical speed of sound in moist air at 20 °C	344 m/sec 770 mile/hr
Approximate composition . of atmosphere, by number of molecules	N$_2$, 78 percent O$_2$, 21 percent Ar, 1 percent
Mean molecular weight of dry air	28.97
Specific heats of standard air	$C_p = 0.2403$ kcal/kg K $C_v = 0.1715$ kcal/kg K $C'_p = 3.503R$ $C'_v = 2.500R$
Ratio of specific heats of standard air (γ)	1.401

C. Densities of common materials at standard conditions of temperature and pressure

Substance	Density (gm/cm^3)	(kg/m^3)
Hydrogen (H$_2$)	8.99×10^{-5}	0.0899
Helium (He)	1.785×10^{-4}	0.1785
Nitrogen (N$_2$)	1.250×10^{-3}	1.250
Oxygen (O$_2$)	1.429×10^{-3}	1.429
Air	1.293×10^{-3}	1.293
Gasoline	$\sim 0.7 \sim 700$	660–690
Alcohol (ethanol)	0.806	806
Water	1.000	1.000×10^3
Mercury	13.60	1.360×10^4
Aluminum	2.70	2.70×10^3
Iron	7.86	7.86×10^3
Copper	8.96	8.96×10^3
Lead	11.4	1.14×10^4

D. Astronomical data*

Quantity	Value
Distance from center of earth to center of moon	3.844×10^8 m 2.389×10^5 miles
Period of moon	27.32 days 2.360×10^6 sec
Mass of moon	7.35×10^{22} kg $0.0123 M_E$
Radius of moon	1.738×10^6 m $0.2728 R_E$
Acceleration of gravity at the surface of the moon	1.62 m/sec^2 $0.165g$
Distance from center of earth to center of sun (1 A.U.)	$\left.\begin{array}{l} 1.496 \times 10^{11} \text{ m} \\ 9.30 \times 10^7 \text{ miles} \end{array}\right\}$ average 1.471×10^{11} m at perihelion 1.521×10^{11} m at aphelion
Mass of sun (M_S)	1.99×10^{30} kg $3.329 \times 10^5 M_E$
Mass of sun times gravitational constant ($M_S G$)	1.3272×10^{20} N m^2/kg (or m^3/sec^2)
Radius of sun (R_S)	6.960×10^8 m $109.2 R_E$
Period of earth	365.26 days 3.156×10^7 sec
Average orbital speed of earth	2.98×10^4 m/sec
Average orbital acceleration of earth	5.93×10^{-3} m/sec^2 $6.05 \times 10^{-4}g$

* Reference: C. W. Allen, *Astrophysical Quantities*, second edition (London: The Athlone Press, University of London, 1963). Other useful references for physical data are the *Handbook of Chemistry and Physics* (Cleveland, Ohio: The Chemical Rubber Co.), frequently revised; and the *American Institute of Physics Handbook*, third edition (New York: McGraw-Hill Book Co., 1972).

APPENDIX 4. Conversion factors

For convenience in units arithmetic, this appendix lists conversion factors directly (such as 2.54 cm/in.) rather than equations (such as 1 in. = 2.54 cm). Any quantity can be multiplied or divided by appropriate conversion factors since each conversion factor is equivalent to unity.

Conversion factors preceded by a dot (●) are exact and serve to define one unit in terms of another. For example, the factor 0.3048 m/ft defines the foot as exactly 0.3048 m.

1. Length
- ● 10^2 cm/m
- ● 10^3 m/km

- ● 2.54 cm/in.
- ● 12 in./ft
- ● 5,280 ft/mile

- ● 0.3048 m/ft
- ● 1.609344×10^3 m/mile
- ● 1.609344 km/mile

  1.49598 $\times$ 10^{11} m/A.U.
  9.461 $\times$ 10^{15} m/light-year
  3.084 $\times$ 10^{16} m/parsec

- ● 10^{-6} m/μm (or m/micron)
- ● 10^{-10} m/Å
- ● 10^{-15} m/fm

2. Volume
- ● 10^{-3} m^3/liter
- ● 10^3 cm^3/liter
  0.94635 liter/quart
  3.7854 $\times$ 10^{-3} m^3/gallon

3. Time
  (The day is a mean solar day; the year is a sidereal year.)
- ● 3,600 sec/hr
- ● 8.64 $\times$ 10^4 sec/day
  365.26 day/year
  3.1558 $\times$ 10^7 sec/year

4. Speed
- ● 0.3048 (m/sec)/(ft/sec)
  1.609 $\times$ 10^3 (m/sec)/(mile/sec)
  0.4470 (m/sec)/(mile/hr)
  1.609 (km/hr)/(mile/hr)

5. Acceleration
- ● 0.3048 (m/sec^2)/(ft/sec^2)

6. Angle
- ● 60 second of arc($''$)/minute of arc($'$)
- ● 60 minute of arc($'$)/deg
- ● 180/π ($\cong$ 57.30) deg/radian
- ● 2π ($\cong$ 6.283) radian/revolution

7. Mass
- ● 10^3 gm/kg

  453.59 gm/lb
  0.45359 kg/lb
  2.2046 lb/kg

  1.66053 $\times$ 10^{-27} kg/amu
  6.0222 $\times$ 10^{26} amu/kg
  6.0222 $\times$ 10^{23} amu/gm

8. Density
- ● 10^3 (kg/m^3)/(gm/cm^3)
  16.018 (kg/m^3)/(lb/ft^3)
  1.6018 $\times$ 10^{-2} (gm/cm^3)/(lb/ft^3)

9. Force
- ● 10^5 dyne/N
- ● 10^{-5} N/dyne
  4.4482 N/lbf
  (1 lbf = weight of 1 pound at standard gravity [g = 9.80665 m/sec^2])

10. Pressure

- 0.1 $(N/m^2)/(dyne/cm^2)$
- 10^5 $(N/m^2)/bar$

- 1.01325×10^5 $(N/m^2)/atm$
- 1.01325×10^6 $(dyne/cm^2)/atm$
- 1.01325 bar/atm

    133.32 $(N/m^2)/mm$ of Hg (0 °C)

    3.386×10^3 $(N/m^2)/in.$ of Hg (0 °C)

    6.895×10^3 $(N/m^2)/(lbf/in.^2,$ or psi)

11. Energy

   (For mass-to-energy conversion, see the values of c^2 at the end of Appendix 3A.)

- 10^7 erg/J
- 10^{-7} J/erg

- 4.184 J/cal
- 4,184 J/kcal
- 10^3 cal/kcal

    (The kilocalorie [kcal] is also known as the food calorie, the large calorie, or the Calorie.)

    1.60219×10^{-19} J/eV

    1.60219×10^{-13} J/MeV

- 10^6 eV/MeV

- 3.60×10^6 J/kW hr

    4.20×10^{12} J/kiloton

    4.20×10^{15} J/megaton

    0.04336 (eV/molecule)/(kcal/mole)

    23.06 (kcal/mole)/(eV/molecule)

12. Power

- 746 W/horsepower

13. Temperature

- 1.00 F°/R°
- 1.00 C°/K
- 1.80 F°/C°
- 1.80 R°/K
- $T(K) = T(°C) + 273.15$
- $T(°C) = [T(°F) - 32]/1.80$
- $T(K) = T(°R)/1.80$

14. Electrical quantities

   (Note that 2.9979 is well approximated by 3.00.)

   Charge: 2.9979×10^9 esu/C

   Current: 2.9979×10^9 (esu/sec)/A

   Potential: 299.79 V/statvolt

   Electric field: 2.9979×10^4 (V/m)/(statvolt/cm)

- Magnetic field: 10^4 G/T
- Magnetic flux: 10^8 G cm²/Wb
- Pole strength: 10 cgs unit/michell

    (cgs unit = $\sqrt{erg\ cm}$;

    michell = A m)

APPENDIX 5. Equations of electromagnetism for SI (mks) and Gaussian (cgs) units

Magnetic poles are excluded from the equations that follow. Equation numbers match those of the text.

A. Equations that are the same for both sets of units

Description of Equation's Content	Equation	
Relation of current and charge	$I = \dfrac{dq}{dt}$	(15.5)
Relation of electric field and electric force	$\mathbf{F_E} = q'\mathbf{E}$	(15.18)
Definition of electric flux	$\Phi_E = \displaystyle\int \mathbf{E} \cdot d\mathbf{S}$	(15.30)
Definition of magnetic flux	$\Phi_B = \displaystyle\int \mathbf{B} \cdot d\mathbf{S}$	(16.19)
Solenoidal character of magnetic field	$\displaystyle\oint \mathbf{B} \cdot d\mathbf{S} = 0$	(16.23)
Definition of potential	$V = \dfrac{U}{q}$	(15.55)
Relations of potential and static electric field	$V_2 - V_1 = -\displaystyle\int_{\mathbf{r_1}}^{\mathbf{r_2}} \mathbf{E} \cdot d\mathbf{s}$	(15.48)
	$\mathbf{E} = -\boldsymbol{\nabla} V$	(15.67)
Ohm's law	$\mathbf{J} = \sigma\mathbf{E}$	(15.84)
	$V = IR$	(15.88)
Power associated with current and potential difference	$P = IV$	(15.57)
Power in linear circuit	$P = I^2 R$	(15.107)
	$P = \dfrac{V^2}{R}$	(15.108)
Definition of electric dipole moment	$\mathbf{p} = q\mathbf{l}$	(15.71)
Energy of electric dipole	$U = -\mathbf{p} \cdot \mathbf{E}$	(15.73)
Energy of magnetic dipole	$U = -\boldsymbol{\mu} \cdot \mathbf{B}$	(16.16)
Definition of capacitance	$C = \dfrac{q}{V}$	(15.109)
Energy stored in capacitor	$U = \tfrac{1}{2}CV^2$	(15.119)
Definition of inductance	$L = -\dfrac{\mathscr{V}}{\left(\dfrac{dI}{dt}\right)}$	(17.44)
Energy stored in inductor	$U = \tfrac{1}{2}LI^2$	(17.71)

B. Equations that are different for the two sets of units

Description of Equation's Content	Equation for SI Units	Equation for Gaussian Units
Coulomb's law	$\mathbf{F}_{12} = \dfrac{1}{4\pi\epsilon_0}\dfrac{q_1 q_2 \mathbf{i}_{12}}{r^2}$ (15.15)	$\mathbf{F}_{12} = \dfrac{q_1 q_2 \mathbf{i}_{12}}{r^2}$
Electric field of point charge	$\mathbf{E} = \dfrac{1}{4\pi\epsilon_0}\dfrac{q\mathbf{i}_r}{r^2}$ (15.20)	$\mathbf{E} = \dfrac{q\mathbf{i}_r}{r^2}$
Potential of point charge	$V = \dfrac{1}{4\pi\epsilon_0}\dfrac{q}{r}$ (15.60)	$V = \dfrac{q}{r}$
Gauss's law	$\oint \mathbf{E}\cdot d\mathbf{S} = \dfrac{q}{\epsilon_0}$ (15.36)	$\oint \mathbf{E}\cdot d\mathbf{S} = 4\pi q$
Electric field near a conductor	$E = \dfrac{\sigma}{\epsilon_0}$ (15.44)	$E = 4\pi\sigma$
Capacitance of a parallel plate capacitor	$C = \dfrac{\epsilon_0 A}{d}$ (15.112)	$C = \dfrac{A}{4\pi d}$
Energy density of electromagnetic field	$u = \tfrac{1}{2}\epsilon_0 E^2 + \dfrac{1}{2\mu_0}B^2$ (16.25)	$u = \dfrac{1}{8\pi}(E^2 + B^2)$
Magnetic force on a moving charge	$\mathbf{F}_M = q'\mathbf{v}\times\mathbf{B}$ (16.27)	$\mathbf{F}_M = \dfrac{q'}{c}\mathbf{v}\times\mathbf{B}$
Magnetic force on a current element	$d\mathbf{F} = I'\,d\mathbf{s}\times\mathbf{B}$ (16.43)	$d\mathbf{F} = \dfrac{I'}{c}\,d\mathbf{s}\times\mathbf{B}$
Magnetic field created by a moving charge	$\mathbf{B} = \dfrac{\mu_0}{4\pi}\dfrac{q\mathbf{v}\times\mathbf{i}_r}{r^2}$ (16.36)	$\mathbf{B} = \dfrac{q}{c}\dfrac{\mathbf{v}\times\mathbf{i}_r}{r^2}$
Magnetic field created by a current element	$d\mathbf{B} = \dfrac{\mu_0}{4\pi}\dfrac{I\,d\mathbf{s}\times\mathbf{i}_r}{r^2}$ (16.56)	$d\mathbf{B} = \dfrac{I}{c}\dfrac{d\mathbf{s}\times\mathbf{i}_r}{r^2}$
Radius of curvature of charge orbiting in magnetic field	$r = \dfrac{p_\perp}{q'B}$ (16.30)	$r = \dfrac{p_\perp c}{q'B}$
Magnetic moment of circling particle	$\boldsymbol{\mu} = \dfrac{q}{2m}\mathbf{L}$ (16.54)	$\boldsymbol{\mu} = \dfrac{q}{2mc}\mathbf{L}$
Magnetic moment of current loop	$\boldsymbol{\mu} = I\mathbf{A}$ (16.49)	$\boldsymbol{\mu} = \dfrac{I\mathbf{A}}{c}$
Force per unit length on parallel currents	$\dfrac{dF}{ds} = \dfrac{\mu_0}{2\pi}\dfrac{I_1 I_2}{d}$ (16.74)	$\dfrac{dF}{ds} = \dfrac{2I_1 I_2}{c^2 d}$
Magnetic field of long straight wire	$B = \dfrac{\mu_0 I}{2\pi x}$ (16.61)	$B = \dfrac{2I}{cx}$
Magnetic field within a long solenoid	$B = \mu_0 nI$ (16.69)	$B = \dfrac{4\pi nI}{c}$
Law of electromagnetic induction	$\oint \mathbf{E}\cdot d\mathbf{s} = -\dfrac{d\Phi_B}{dt}$ (17.1)	$\oint \mathbf{E}\cdot d\mathbf{s} = -\dfrac{1}{c}\dfrac{d\Phi_B}{dt}$

Description of Equation's Content	Equation for SI Units	Equation for Gaussian Units
Ampère's law and law of magnetoelectric induction	$$\oint \mathbf{B} \cdot d\mathbf{s} = \mu_0 I + \mu_0 \epsilon_0 \frac{d\Phi_E}{dt} \quad (17.29)$$	$$\oint \mathbf{B} \cdot d\mathbf{s} = \frac{4\pi I}{c} + \frac{1}{c} \frac{d\Phi_E}{dt}$$
The speed of light	$$c = \frac{1}{\sqrt{\mu_0 \epsilon_0}} \quad (17.77)$$	No counterpart; c appears explicitly in the Gaussian equations

C. The differential form of Maxwell's equations

SI	Gaussian
$$\mathbf{\nabla} \cdot \mathbf{E} = \frac{\rho}{\epsilon_0}$$	$$\mathbf{\nabla} \cdot \mathbf{E} = 4\pi\rho$$
$$\mathbf{\nabla} \cdot \mathbf{B} = 0$$	$$\mathbf{\nabla} \cdot \mathbf{B} = 0$$
$$\mathbf{\nabla} \times \mathbf{E} = -\frac{\partial \mathbf{B}}{\partial t}$$	$$\mathbf{\nabla} \times \mathbf{E} = -\frac{1}{c} \frac{\partial \mathbf{B}}{\partial t}$$
$$\mathbf{\nabla} \times \mathbf{B} = \mu_0 \mathbf{J} + \mu_0 \epsilon_0 \frac{\partial \mathbf{E}}{\partial t}$$	$$\mathbf{\nabla} \times \mathbf{B} = \frac{4\pi \mathbf{J}}{c} + \frac{1}{c} \frac{\partial \mathbf{E}}{\partial t}$$

APPENDIX 6.   Mathematical formulas

Some of the formulas below go beyond the immediate needs of this text in order to provide a reference source for other courses or for optional additional work an instructor may wish to assign. For a much more extensive compendium of formulas, see Herbert Dwight's *Tables of Integrals and Other Mathematical Data*, 4th edition (New York: The Macmillan Company, 1961). This excellent reference volume, modest in size and price, is a good investment. It will prove useful throughout one's student and professional careers.

A. Mathematical signs

$=$ is equal to
$\neq$ is not equal to
$\cong$ is approximately equal to
$\equiv$ is identical to, is defined as
$>$ is greater than
$\geq$ is greater than or equal to
$\gg$ is much greater than
$<$ is less than
$\leq$ is less than or equal to
$\ll$ is much less than
$\sim$ is proportional to

B. Arithmetic: powers of 10

$$10^a 10^b = 10^{a+b}$$

$$10^a / 10^b = 10^{a-b}$$

$$(10^a)^b = 10^{ab}$$

C. Algebra

FRACTIONS

$$a\left(\frac{b}{c}\right) = \frac{ab}{c}$$

$$\frac{\left(\dfrac{b}{c}\right)}{d} = \frac{b}{cd}$$

$$\left(\frac{a}{b}\right)\left(\frac{c}{d}\right) = \frac{ac}{bd}$$

$$\frac{\left(\dfrac{a}{b}\right)}{\left(\dfrac{c}{d}\right)} = \frac{ad}{bc}$$

$$\frac{a}{b} + \frac{c}{d} = \frac{ad + bc}{bd}$$

A18

ROOTS OF A QUADRATIC EQUATION

If $ax^2 + bx + c = 0$ then $x = \dfrac{-b \pm \sqrt{b^2 - 4ac}}{2a}$.

If $x^2 + 2\beta x + \gamma = 0$ then $x = -\beta \pm \sqrt{\beta^2 - \gamma}$.

BINOMIAL EXPANSIONS

Factorial of an integer n: $n! = n(n - 1)(n - 2)\cdots 2\cdot 1$

Binomial coefficient for integers q and n: $\dbinom{q}{n} = \dfrac{q!}{n!\,(q - n)!}$

$(a \pm b)^2 = a^2 \pm 2ab + b^2$

$(a \pm b)^3 = a^3 \pm 3a^2b + 3ab^2 \pm b^3$

To evaluate $(a + b)^p$, write it as

  $a^p(1 + x)^p$,   where $x = b/a$, or as

  $b^p(1 + x)^p$,   where $x = a/b$.

$(1 \pm x)^p = 1 \pm px + \dfrac{p(p - 1)}{2!}\,x^2 \pm \dfrac{p(p - 1)(p - 2)}{3!}\,x^3 + \cdots.$

This is a finite series if p is a positive integer. For other values of p, it is an infinite series that converges for $|x| < 1$.

Special cases:

$p = -1$: $\dfrac{1}{1 \pm x} = 1 \mp x + x^2 \mp x^3 + x^4 \mp \cdots$

$p = -2$: $\dfrac{1}{(1 \pm x)^2} = 1 \mp 2x + 3x^2 \mp 4x^3 + 5x^4 \mp \cdots$

$p = \tfrac{1}{2}$: $\sqrt{1 \pm x} = 1 \pm \tfrac{1}{2}x - \tfrac{1}{8}x^2 \pm \tfrac{1}{16}x^3 - \cdots$

$p = -\tfrac{1}{2}$: $\dfrac{1}{\sqrt{1 \pm x}} = 1 \mp \tfrac{1}{2}x + \tfrac{3}{8}x^2 \mp \tfrac{5}{16}x^3 + \cdots$

COMPLEX NUMBERS

$(a + ib) + (c + id) = (a + c) + i(b + d)$

$(a + ib)(c + id) = (ac - bd) + i(bc + ad)$

$\dfrac{a + ib}{c + id} = \dfrac{(a + ib)(c - id)}{c^2 + d^2}$

$|a + ib|^2 = (a + ib)^*(a + ib) = (a - ib)(a + ib) = a^2 + b^2$

$a + ib = re^{i\theta}$,   where $r = \sqrt{a^2 + b^2}$, $\theta = \arctan(b/a)$

$e^{i\theta} = \cos\theta + i\sin\theta$

D. Trigonometry

DEFINITIONS OF TRIGONOMETRIC FUNCTIONS

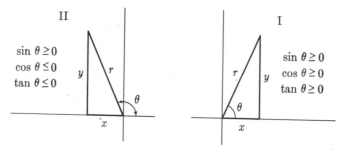

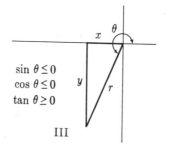
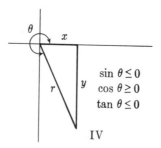

$$\sin \theta = \frac{y}{r}$$

$$\csc \theta = \frac{1}{\sin \theta} = \frac{r}{y}$$

$$\cos \theta = \frac{x}{r}$$

$$\sec \theta = \frac{1}{\cos \theta} = \frac{r}{x}$$

$$\tan \theta = \frac{\sin \theta}{\cos \theta} = \frac{y}{x}$$

$$\text{ctn } \theta = \frac{1}{\tan \theta} = \frac{x}{y}$$

Inverse functions: If $u = \sin \theta$, then $\theta = $ arc sin u, sometimes written $\theta = \sin^{-1} u$. The other inverse functions are similarly designated: arc cos u, arc tan u, etc.

SIMPLE PROPERTIES

$$\sin (-\theta) = -\sin \theta \qquad\qquad \cos (-\theta) = \cos \theta$$

$$\sin \left(\theta \pm \frac{\pi}{2}\right) = \pm \cos \theta \qquad\qquad \cos \left(\theta \pm \frac{\pi}{2}\right) = \mp \sin \theta$$

$$\sin (\theta \pm \pi) = -\sin \theta \qquad\qquad \cos (\theta \pm \pi) = -\cos \theta$$

$$\tan (-\theta) = -\tan \theta$$

$$\tan \left(\theta \pm \frac{\pi}{2}\right) = -\frac{1}{\tan \theta} = -\text{ctn } \theta$$

$$\tan (\theta \pm \pi) = \tan \theta$$

VALUES FOR SPECIAL ANGLES

			Angle		
Function	0 deg	30 deg	45 deg	60 deg	90 deg
$\sin \theta$	0	$\dfrac{1}{2}$	$\dfrac{1}{\sqrt{2}} = 0.7071$	$\dfrac{\sqrt{3}}{2} = 0.8660$	1
$\cos \theta$	1	$\dfrac{\sqrt{3}}{2} = 0.8660$	$\dfrac{1}{\sqrt{2}} = 0.7071$	$\dfrac{1}{2}$	0
$\tan \theta$	0	$\dfrac{1}{\sqrt{3}} = 0.5774$	1	$\sqrt{3} = 1.7321$	∞

For other values and for graphs, see Appendix 7.

TRIGONOMETRIC FORMULAS

$$\sin^2 \theta + \cos^2 \theta = 1 \qquad \sec^2 \theta - \tan^2 \theta = 1 \qquad \csc^2 \theta - \operatorname{ctn}^2 \theta = 1$$

$$\sin 2\theta = 2 \sin \theta \cos \theta \qquad\qquad \sin \tfrac{1}{2}\theta = \sqrt{\frac{1 - \cos \theta}{2}}$$

$$\cos 2\theta = \cos^2 \theta - \sin^2 \theta \qquad\qquad \cos \tfrac{1}{2}\theta = \sqrt{\frac{1 + \cos \theta}{2}}$$
$$\qquad\quad = 2 \cos^2 \theta - 1$$
$$\qquad\quad = 1 - 2 \sin^2 \theta$$

$$\tan 2\theta = \frac{2 \tan \theta}{1 - \tan^2 \theta} \qquad\qquad \tan \tfrac{1}{2}\theta = \sqrt{\frac{1 - \cos \theta}{1 + \cos \theta}}$$

$$\sin (A \pm B) = \sin A \cos B \pm \cos A \sin B$$

$$\cos (A \pm B) = \cos A \cos B \mp \sin A \sin B$$

$$\tan (A \pm B) = \frac{\tan A \pm \tan B}{1 \mp \tan A \tan B}$$

$$\sin A \pm \sin B = 2 \sin \left[\tfrac{1}{2}(A \pm B)\right] \cos \left[\tfrac{1}{2}(A \mp B)\right]$$

$$\cos A + \cos B = 2 \cos \left[\tfrac{1}{2}(A + B)\right] \cos \left[\tfrac{1}{2}(A - B)\right]$$

$$\cos A - \cos B = 2 \sin \left[\tfrac{1}{2}(A + B)\right] \sin \left[\tfrac{1}{2}(B - A)\right]$$

$$\tan A \pm \tan B = \frac{\sin (A \pm B)}{\cos A \cos B}$$

$$\sin A \sin B = \tfrac{1}{2}[\cos (A - B) - \cos (A + B)]$$

$$\cos A \cos B = \tfrac{1}{2}[\cos (A - B) + \cos (A + B)]$$

$$\sin A \cos B = \tfrac{1}{2}[\sin (A - B) + \sin (A + B)]$$

$$\sin \theta + \sin 2\theta + \sin 3\theta + \cdots + \sin n\theta = \frac{\sin \left[\tfrac{1}{2}(n + 1)\theta\right] \sin (\tfrac{1}{2}n\theta)}{\sin (\tfrac{1}{2}\theta)}$$

$$\cos \theta + \cos 2\theta + \cos 3\theta + \cdots + \cos n\theta = \frac{\cos \left[\tfrac{1}{2}(n + 1)\theta\right] \sin (\tfrac{1}{2}n\theta)}{\sin (\tfrac{1}{2}\theta)}$$

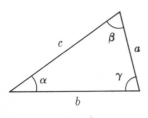

PROPERTIES OF A TRIANGLE

$\alpha + \beta + \gamma = \pi$

$a^2 = b^2 + c^2 - 2bc \cos \alpha$

$b^2 = c^2 + a^2 - 2ca \cos \beta$

$c^2 = a^2 + b^2 - 2ab \cos \gamma$

$$\frac{a}{\sin \alpha} = \frac{b}{\sin \beta} = \frac{c}{\sin \gamma}$$

For a right triangle $\left(\gamma = \frac{\pi}{2}\right)$, $a^2 + b^2 = c^2$

SERIES EXPANSIONS

$$\sin x = x - \frac{x^3}{3!} + \frac{x^5}{5!} - \frac{x^7}{7!} + \cdots$$

$$\cos x = 1 - \frac{x^2}{2!} + \frac{x^4}{4!} - \frac{x^6}{6!} + \cdots$$

These series converge for all x.

E. Exponential and logarithmic functions

For graphs and numerical values, see Appendices 8 and 9.

$e = 2.71828$ $e^0 = 1$

$e^x e^y = e^{x+y}$ $e^x/e^y = e^{x-y}$

$(e^x)^n = e^{nx}$ $a^x = e^{x \ln a}$

$e^{\ln x} = x$ $e^{-\ln x} = 1/x$

$e^{-t/\tau} = 0.5$ for $t = \tau \ln 2 = 0.6931\tau$

$e^{t/\tau} = 2$ for $t = \tau \ln 2 = 0.6931\tau$

$$e^{\pm x} = 1 \pm x + \frac{x^2}{2!} \pm \frac{x^3}{3!} + \frac{x^4}{4!} \pm \cdots.$$

Series converges for all x.

$\ln e = 1$ $\ln 1 = 0$

$\ln (xy) = \ln x + \ln y$ $\ln (x/y) = \ln x - \ln y$

$\ln (1/x) = -\ln x$ $\ln (x^n) = n \ln x$

$\ln (e^x) = x$ $\ln (a^x) = x \ln a$

$\ln a = 2.3026 \log_{10} a$ $\log_{10} a = 0.43429 \ln a$

$$\ln (1 \pm x) = \pm x - \frac{x^2}{2} \pm \frac{x^3}{3} - \frac{x^4}{4} \pm \cdots$$

$$\ln \left(\frac{1+x}{1-x}\right) = 2 \left(x + \frac{x^3}{3} + \frac{x^5}{5} + \frac{x^7}{7} + \cdots\right)$$

Series converge for $|x| < 1$.

F. Calculus

In what follows, f, g, and u are functions; a, b, and n are constants.

SOME RULES OF DIFFERENTIATION

$$\frac{d}{dx}(fg) = \frac{df}{dx}g + f\frac{dg}{dx}$$

$$\frac{d}{dx}\left(\frac{f}{g}\right) = \frac{\frac{df}{dx}g - f\frac{dg}{dx}}{g^2}$$

$$\frac{d}{dx}[f(u)] = \frac{df}{du} \cdot \frac{du}{dx}$$

LINEARITY PROPERTIES

$$\frac{d}{dx}(af + bg) = a\frac{df}{dx} + b\frac{dg}{dx}$$

$$\int (af + bg)\,dx = a\int f\,dx + b\int g\,dx$$

THE DEFINITE INTEGRAL

$$D = \int_a^b f(x)\,dx = I(x)\ \Big|_a^b = I(b) - I(a),$$

where I is the indefinite integral, $I(x) = \int f(x)\,dx$, or the antiderivative: $f(x) = dI(x)/dx$.

INTEGRATION BY PARTS

$$\int_a^b f(x)\frac{dg}{dx}\,dx = f(x)g(x)\ \Big|_a^b - \int_a^b \frac{df}{dx}g(x)\,dx$$

TAYLOR SERIES

If all derivatives of a function exist at a certain point, the function may be written as a power series about that point. Empirical functions may be similarly approximated.

$$f(x) = f(x_0) + (x - x_0)\left(\frac{df}{dx}\right)_{x_0} + \frac{(x - x_0)^2}{2!}\left(\frac{d^2f}{dx^2}\right)_{x_0}$$
$$+ \frac{(x - x_0)^3}{3!}\left(\frac{d^3f}{dx^3}\right)_{x_0} + \cdots.$$

All the derivatives are evaluated at $x = x_0$.

SOME DERIVATIVES   (See also Table 5.2.)

$$\frac{d}{dx}(x^n) = nx^{n-1}$$

$$\frac{d}{dx}(\sin ax) = a\cos ax$$

$$\frac{d}{dx}(\cos ax) = -a\sin ax$$

$$\frac{d}{dx}(\tan ax) = a\sec^2 ax = \frac{a}{\cos^2 ax}$$

$$\frac{d}{dx}\left(\arcsin\frac{x}{a}\right) = \frac{\pm 1}{\sqrt{a^2 - x^2}}$$

+ sign in 1st and 4th quadrants
− sign in 2nd and 3rd quadrants

$$\frac{d}{dx}\left(\arccos\frac{x}{a}\right) = \frac{\mp 1}{\sqrt{a^2 - x^2}}$$

− sign in 1st and 2nd quadrants
+ sign in 3rd and 4th quadrants

$$\frac{d}{dx}\left(\arctan\frac{x}{a}\right) = \frac{a}{a^2 + x^2}$$

$$\frac{d}{dx}(e^{ax}) = ae^{ax}$$

$$\frac{d}{dx}(\ln ax) = \frac{1}{x}$$

SOME INDEFINITE INTEGRALS (See also Table 5.7)

To each of the following integrals an arbitrary constant should be added.

$$\int x^n \, dx = \frac{x^{n+1}}{n+1}, \qquad n \neq -1$$

$$\int \frac{1}{x} \, dx = \ln|x|$$

$$\int (a + bx)^n \, dx = \frac{(a + bx)^{n+1}}{b(n+1)}, \qquad n \neq -1$$

$$\int \frac{dx}{a + bx} = \frac{1}{b}\ln|a + bx|$$

$$\int \frac{dx}{a^2 + x^2} = \frac{1}{a}\arctan\frac{x}{a}$$

$$\int \frac{dx}{a^2 - x^2} = \frac{1}{2a}\ln\left|\frac{a + x}{a - x}\right|$$

$$\int \sqrt{a + bx} \, dx = \frac{2}{3b}(a + bx)^{3/2}$$

$$\int \frac{dx}{\sqrt{a + bx}} = \frac{2}{b}\sqrt{a + bx}$$

$$\int \sqrt{x^2 + a^2} \, dx = \tfrac{1}{2}x\sqrt{x^2 + a^2} + \tfrac{1}{2}a^2 \ln(x + \sqrt{x^2 + a^2})$$

$$\int \frac{dx}{\sqrt{x^2 + a^2}} = \ln(x + \sqrt{x^2 + a^2})$$

$$\int \sqrt{x^2 - a^2} \, dx = \tfrac{1}{2}x\sqrt{x^2 - a^2} - \tfrac{1}{2}a^2 \ln|x + \sqrt{x^2 - a^2}|$$

$$\int \frac{dx}{\sqrt{x^2 - a^2}} = \ln|x + \sqrt{x^2 - a^2}|$$

$$\int \sqrt{a^2 - x^2}\, dx = \tfrac{1}{2}x\, \sqrt{a^2 - x^2} + \tfrac{1}{2}a^2 \arcsin \frac{x}{a}$$

$$\int \frac{dx}{\sqrt{a^2 - x^2}} = \arcsin \frac{x}{a}$$

$$\int \sin ax\, dx = -\frac{1}{a} \cos ax$$

$$\int \cos ax\, dx = \frac{1}{a} \sin ax$$

$$\int \tan ax\, dx = -\frac{1}{a} \ln |\cos ax|$$

$$\int \csc ax\, dx = \frac{1}{a} \ln |\tan \tfrac{1}{2}ax|$$

$$\int \sec ax\, dx = \frac{1}{2a} \ln \left(\frac{1 + \sin ax}{1 - \sin ax} \right)$$

$$\int \operatorname{ctn} ax\, dx = \frac{1}{a} \ln |\sin ax|$$

$$\int \arcsin \frac{x}{a}\, dx = x \arcsin \frac{x}{a} + \sqrt{a^2 - x^2}$$

$$\int \arccos \frac{x}{a}\, dx = x \arccos \frac{x}{a} - \sqrt{a^2 - x^2}$$

$$\int \arctan \frac{x}{a}\, dx = x \arctan \frac{x}{a} - \tfrac{1}{2}a \ln (a^2 + x^2)$$

$$\int e^{ax}\, dx = \frac{1}{a} e^{ax}$$

$$\int x e^{ax}\, dx = \frac{1}{a} \left(x - \frac{1}{a} \right) e^{ax}$$

$$\int \ln ax\, dx = x \ln ax - x$$

$$\int x \ln ax\, dx = \tfrac{1}{2}x^2 \ln ax - \tfrac{1}{4}x^2$$

G. Vectors

Unit vectors $\mathbf{i}$, $\mathbf{j}$, and $\mathbf{k}$ are parallel to the x, y, and z axes respectively.

Vector in terms of Cartesian components: $\mathbf{a} = a_x\mathbf{i} + a_y\mathbf{j} + a_z\mathbf{k}$

The position vector: $\mathbf{r} = x\mathbf{i} + y\mathbf{j} + z\mathbf{k}$

Magnitude of a vector: $|\mathbf{a}| = a = \sqrt{a_x{}^2 + a_y{}^2 + a_z{}^2}$

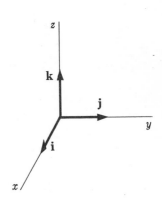

SCALAR PRODUCT

$\mathbf{a} \cdot \mathbf{b} = ab \cos \theta$; θ is the smaller angle between $\mathbf{a}$ and $\mathbf{b}$.

$\mathbf{a} \cdot \mathbf{b} = a_x b_x + a_y b_y + a_z b_z$

$\mathbf{a} \cdot \mathbf{b} = \mathbf{b} \cdot \mathbf{a}$

VECTOR PRODUCT

$\mathbf{a} \times \mathbf{b} = (a_y b_z - a_z b_y)\mathbf{i} + (a_z b_x - a_x b_z)\mathbf{j} + (a_x b_y - a_y b_x)\mathbf{k}$

$|\mathbf{a} \times \mathbf{b}| = ab \sin \theta;$ θ is the smaller angle between $\mathbf{a}$ and $\mathbf{b}$.

$\mathbf{a} \times \mathbf{b} = -\mathbf{b} \times \mathbf{a}$

PROPERTIES OF UNIT VECTORS

$\mathbf{i} \cdot \mathbf{i} = \mathbf{j} \cdot \mathbf{j} = \mathbf{k} \cdot \mathbf{k} = 1$

$\mathbf{i} \cdot \mathbf{j} = \mathbf{j} \cdot \mathbf{k} = \mathbf{k} \cdot \mathbf{i} = 0$

$\mathbf{i} \times \mathbf{j} = \mathbf{k},$ $\mathbf{j} \times \mathbf{k} = \mathbf{i},$ $\mathbf{k} \times \mathbf{i} = \mathbf{j}$

$\mathbf{j} \times \mathbf{i} = -\mathbf{k},$ $\mathbf{k} \times \mathbf{j} = -\mathbf{i},$ $\mathbf{i} \times \mathbf{k} = -\mathbf{j}$

H. Vector calculus

$\mathbf{F}$ and $\mathbf{G}$ are vector functions; f is a scalar function; a and b are numerical constants.

DERIVATIVES

$$\frac{d\mathbf{F}}{dt} = \frac{dF_x}{dt}\mathbf{i} + \frac{dF_y}{dt}\mathbf{j} + \frac{dF_z}{dt}\mathbf{k}$$

$$\frac{d}{dt}(f\mathbf{F}) = \frac{df}{dt}\mathbf{F} + f\frac{d\mathbf{F}}{dt}$$

$$\frac{d}{dt}(a\mathbf{F} + b\mathbf{G}) = a\frac{d\mathbf{F}}{dt} + b\frac{d\mathbf{G}}{dt}$$

$$\frac{d}{dt}(\mathbf{F} \cdot \mathbf{G}) = \frac{d\mathbf{F}}{dt} \cdot \mathbf{G} + \mathbf{F} \cdot \frac{d\mathbf{G}}{dt}$$

$$\frac{d}{dt}(\mathbf{F} \times \mathbf{G}) = \frac{d\mathbf{F}}{dt} \times \mathbf{G} + \mathbf{F} \times \frac{d\mathbf{G}}{dt}$$

INTEGRALS

$$\int \mathbf{F}(t)\, dt = \left[\int F_x(t)\, dt\right]\mathbf{i} + \left[\int F_y(t)\, dt\right]\mathbf{j} + \left[\int F_z(t)\, dt\right]\mathbf{k}$$

Line integral: $\int \mathbf{F} \cdot d\mathbf{s} = \int F_{\parallel}\, ds$, where $F_{\parallel}$ is the component of $\mathbf{F}$ parallel to the designated path of integration at each point.

Surface integral: $\int \mathbf{F} \cdot d\mathbf{S} = \int F_{\perp}\, dS$, where $F_{\perp}$ is the component of $\mathbf{F}$ perpendicular to the designated surface of integration (or parallel to the vector $d\mathbf{S}$) at each point.

VECTOR OPERATIONS NEEDED IN MORE ADVANCED WORK

The *gradient* of a scalar function is a vector function:

$$\nabla f = \frac{\partial f}{\partial x}\mathbf{i} + \frac{\partial f}{\partial y}\mathbf{j} + \frac{\partial f}{\partial z}\mathbf{k}$$

The *divergence* of a vector function is a scalar function:

$$\nabla \cdot \mathbf{F} = \frac{\partial F_x}{\partial x} + \frac{\partial F_y}{\partial y} + \frac{\partial F_z}{\partial z}$$

The *curl* of a vector function as an axial vector function:

$$\nabla \times \mathbf{F} = \left(\frac{\partial F_z}{\partial y} - \frac{\partial F_y}{\partial z}\right)\mathbf{i} + \left(\frac{\partial F_x}{\partial z} - \frac{\partial F_z}{\partial x}\right)\mathbf{j} + \left(\frac{\partial F_y}{\partial x} - \frac{\partial F_x}{\partial y}\right)\mathbf{k}$$

APPENDIX 7. Trigonometric functions

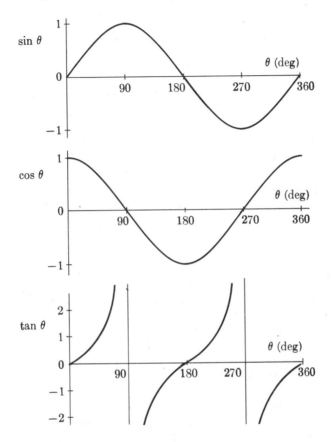

The table on the next page gives sin θ, cos θ, and tan θ in the first quadrant
(0 $\leq \theta \leq$ 90 deg).

For the second quadrant, measure backward from 180 deg, and use
$$\sin (\pi - \theta) = \sin \theta$$
$$\cos (\pi - \theta) = -\cos \theta$$
$$\tan (\pi - \theta) = -\tan \theta$$

For the third quadrant, measure forward from 180 deg, and use
$$\sin (\pi + \theta) = -\sin \theta$$
$$\cos (\pi + \theta) = -\cos \theta$$
$$\tan (\pi + \theta) = \tan \theta$$

For the fourth quadrant, measure backward from 0 deg (or 360 deg), and use
$$\sin (-\theta) = -\sin \theta$$
$$\cos (-\theta) = \cos \theta$$
$$\tan (-\theta) = -\tan \theta$$

Other trigonometric functions are defined by

$$\csc \theta = \frac{1}{\sin \theta} \qquad \sec \theta = \frac{1}{\cos \theta} \qquad \operatorname{ctn} \theta = \frac{1}{\tan \theta}$$

Angle θ		sin θ	cos θ	tan θ	Angle θ		sin θ	cos θ	tan θ
Degree	Radian				Degree	Radian			
0	0.0000	0.0000	1.0000	0.0000					
1	0.0175	0.0175	0.9998	0.0175	46	0.8029	0.7193	0.6947	1.0355
2	0.0349	0.0349	0.9994	0.0349	47	0.8203	0.7314	0.6820	1.0724
3	0.0524	0.0523	0.9986	0.0524	48	0.8378	0.7431	0.6691	1.1106
4	0.0698	0.0698	0.9976	0.0699	49	0.8552	0.7547	0.6561	1.1504
5	0.0873	0.0872	0.9962	0.0875	50	0.8727	0.7660	0.6428	1.1918
6	0.1047	0.1045	0.9945	0.1051	51	0.8901	0.7771	0.6293	1.2349
7	0.1222	0.1219	0.9925	0.1228	52	0.9076	0.7880	0.6157	1.2799
8	0.1396	0.1392	0.9903	0.1405	53	0.9250	0.7986	0.6018	1.3270
9	0.1571	0.1564	0.9877	0.1584	54	0.9425	0.8090	0.5878	1.3764
10	0.1745	0.1736	0.9848	0.1763	55	0.9599	0.8192	0.5736	1.4281
11	0.1920	0.1908	0.9816	0.1944	56	0.9774	0.8290	0.5592	1.4826
12	0.2094	0.2079	0.9781	0.2126	57	0.9948	0.8387	0.5446	1.5399
13	0.2269	0.2250	0.9744	0.2309	58	1.0123	0.8480	0.5299	1.6003
14	0.2443	0.2419	0.9703	0.2493	59	1.0297	0.8572	0.5150	1.6643
15	0.2618	0.2588	0.9659	0.2679	60	1.0472	0.8660	0.5000	1.7321
16	0.2793	0.2756	0.9613	0.2867	61	1.0647	0.8746	0.4848	1.8040
17	0.2967	0.2924	0.9563	0.3057	62	1.0821	0.8829	0.4695	1.8807
18	0.3142	0.3090	0.9511	0.3249	63	1.0996	0.8910	0.4540	1.9626
19	0.3316	0.3256	0.9455	0.3443	64	1.1170	0.8988	0.4384	2.0503
20	0.3491	0.3420	0.9397	0.3640	65	1.1345	0.9063	0.4226	2.1445
21	0.3665	0.3584	0.9336	0.3839	66	1.1519	0.9135	0.4067	2.2460
22	0.3840	0.3746	0.9272	0.4040	67	1.1694	0.9205	0.3907	2.3559
23	0.4014	0.3907	0.9205	0.4245	68	1.1868	0.9272	0.3746	2.4751
24	0.4189	0.4067	0.9135	0.4452	69	1.2043	0.9336	0.3584	2.6051
25	0.4363	0.4226	0.9063	0.4663	70	1.2217	0.9397	0.3420	2.7475
26	0.4538	0.4384	0.8988	0.4877	71	1.2392	0.9455	0.3256	2.9042
27	0.4712	0.4540	0.8910	0.5095	72	1.2566	0.9511	0.3090	3.0777
28	0.4887	0.4695	0.8829	0.5317	73	1.2741	0.9563	0.2924	3.2709
29	0.5061	0.4848	0.8746	0.5543	74	1.2915	0.9613	0.2756	3.4874
30	0.5236	0.5000	0.8660	0.5774	75	1.3090	0.9659	0.2588	3.7321
31	0.5411	0.5150	0.8572	0.6009	76	1.3265	0.9703	0.2419	4.0108
32	0.5585	0.5299	0.8480	0.6249	77	1.3439	0.9744	0.2250	4.3315
33	0.5760	0.5446	0.8387	0.6494	78	1.3614	0.9781	0.2079	4.7046
34	0.5934	0.5592	0.8290	0.6745	79	1.3788	0.9816	0.1908	5.1446
35	0.6109	0.5736	0.8192	0.7002	80	1.3963	0.9848	0.1736	5.6713
36	0.6283	0.5878	0.8090	0.7265	81	1.4137	0.9877	0.1564	6.314
37	0.6458	0.6018	0.7986	0.7536	82	1.4312	0.9903	0.1392	7.115
38	0.6632	0.6157	0.7880	0.7813	83	1.4486	0.9925	0.1219	8.144
39	0.6807	0.6293	0.7771	0.8098	84	1.4661	0.9945	0.1045	9.514
40	0.6981	0.6428	0.7660	0.8391	85	1.4835	0.9962	0.0872	11.430
41	0.7156	0.6561	0.7547	0.8693	86	1.5010	0.9976	0.0698	14.301
42	0.7330	0.6691	0.7431	0.9004	87	1.5184	0.9986	0.0523	19.081
43	0.7505	0.6820	0.7314	0.9325	88	1.5359	0.9994	0.0349	28.636
44	0.7679	0.6947	0.7193	0.9657	89	1.5533	0.9998	0.0175	57.290
45	0.7854	0.7071	0.7071	1.0000	90	1.5708	1.0000	0.0000	∞

APPENDIX 8. The exponential function

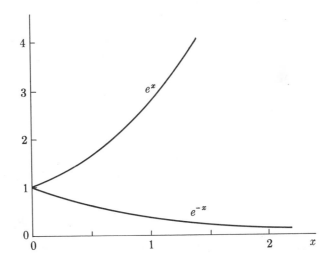

x	e^x	e^{-x}	x	e^x	e^{-x}
0	1.0000	1.0000	2.6	13.464	0.07427
0.1	1.1052	0.9048	2.8	16.445	0.06081
0.2	1.2214	0.8187	3.0	20.086	0.04979
0.3	1.3499	0.7408	3.2	24.533	0.04076
0.4	1.4918	0.6703	3.4	29.964	0.03337
0.5	1.6487	0.6065	3.6	36.598	0.02732
0.6	1.8221	0.5488	3.8	44.701	0.02237
0.7	2.0138	0.4966	4.0	54.598	0.01832
0.8	2.2255	0.4493	4.2	66.686	0.01500
0.9	2.4596	0.4066	4.4	81.451	0.01228
1.0	2.7183	0.3679	4.6	99.484	0.01005
1.1	3.0042	0.3329	4.8	121.51	0.00823
1.2	3.3201	0.3012	5.0	148.41	0.00674
1.3	3.6693	0.2725	5.5	244.69	0.00409
1.4	4.0552	0.2466	6.0	403.43	0.00248
1.5	4.4817	0.2231	6.5	665.14	0.00150
1.6	4.9530	0.2019	7.0	1096.6	0.00091
1.7	5.4739	0.1827	7.5	1808.0	0.00055
1.8	6.0496	0.1653	8.0	2981.0	0.00034
1.9	6.6859	0.1496	8.5	4914.8	0.00020
2.0	7.3891	0.1353	9.0	8103.1	0.00012
2.2	9.025	0.11080	9.5	13,360.	0.00007
2.4	11.023	0.09072	10.0	22,026.	0.00005

APPENDIX 9. The logarithmic function

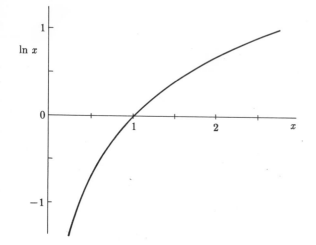

x	$\ln x$	x	$\ln x$
10^{-9}	-20.723	1.05	0.0488
10^{-6}	-13.816	1.10	0.0953
10^{-5}	-11.513	1.15	0.1398
10^{-4}	-9.210	1.20	0.1823
10^{-3}	-6.908	1.25	0.2231
0.01	-4.6052	1.30	0.2624
0.02	-3.9120	1.35	0.3001
0.03	-3.5066	1.40	0.3365
0.04	-3.2189	1.45	0.3716
0.05	-2.9957	1.50	0.4055
0.06	-2.8134	1.55	0.4383
0.07	-2.6593	1.60	0.4700
0.08	-2.5257	1.65	0.5008
0.09	-2.4079	1.70	0.5306
0.10	-2.30259	1.75	0.5596
0.12	-2.1203	1.80	0.5878
0.14	-1.9661	1.85	0.6152
0.16	-1.8326	1.90	0.6419
0.18	-1.7148	1.95	0.6678
0.20	-1.6094	2.00	0.69315
0.22	-1.5141	2.1	0.7419
0.24	-1.4271	2.2	0.7885
0.26	-1.3471	2.3	0.8329
0.28	-1.2730	2.4	0.8755
0.30	-1.2040	2.5	0.9163
0.35	-1.0498	2.6	0.9555
0.40	-0.9163	2.7	0.9933
0.45	-0.7985	2.8	1.0296
0.50	-0.6931	2.9	1.0647
		3.0	1.0986
0.55	-0.5978	3.1	1.1314
0.60	-0.5108	3.2	1.1632
0.65	-0.4308	3.3	1.1939
0.70	-0.3567	3.4	1.2238
0.75	-0.2877	3.5	1.2528
0.80	-0.2231	3.6	1.2809
0.85	-0.1625	3.7	1.3083
0.90	-0.1054	3.8	1.3350
0.95	-0.0513	3.9	1.3610
1.00	0.0000	4.0	1.3863

x	ln x	x	ln x
4.2	1.4351	16	2.773
4.4	1.4816	17	2.833
4.6	1.5261	18	2.890
4.8	1.5686	19	2.944
5.0	1.6094	20	2.996
5.2	1.6487	22	3.091
5.4	1.6864	24	3.178
5.6	1.7228	26	3.258
5.8	1.7579	28	3.332
6.0	1.7918	30	3.401
6.2	1.8245	32	3.466
6.4	1.8563	34	3.526
6.6	1.8871	36	3.584
6.8	1.9169	38	3.638
7.0	1.9459	40	3.689
7.2	1.9741	42	3.738
7.4	2.0015	44	3.784
7.6	2.0281	46	3.829
7.8	2.0541	48	3.871
8.0	2.0794	50	3.912
8.2	2.1041	55	4.007
8.4	2.1282	60	4.094
8.6	2.1518	65	4.174
8.8	2.1748	70	4.248
9.0	2.1972	75	4.317
9.2	2.2192	80	4.382
9.4	2.2407	85	4.443
9.6	2.2618	90	4.500
9.8	2.2824	95	4.554
10.0	2.30259	100	4.605
10.5	2.3514	200	5.298
11.0	2.3979	300	5.704
11.5	2.4423	400	5.991
12.0	2.4849	500	6.215
12.5	2.5257	600	6.397
13.0	2.5649	10^3	6.908
13.5	2.6027	10^4	9.210
14.0	2.6391	10^5	11.513
14.5	2.6741	10^6	13.816
15.0	2.7081	10^9	20.723

$$\frac{6}{9} = \frac{x}{2}$$

$$1\frac{2}{9} = x$$

Index

INDEX

Italic letters following page numbers are used with the following meanings: *f*, figure; *n*, footnote; and *t*, table. Parentheses following a page number enclose the number of a question, exercise, or problem; such an end-of-chapter item is referenced only if it contains factual information that does not occur elsewhere in the book.

SOME DATES OF INTEREST IN THE HISTORY OF PHYSICS

c. 330 B.C.	**Aristotle** describes motion in terms of innate tendencies
c. 250 B.C.	**Archimedes** initiates the mechanical theory of solids and fluids
c. 140 B.C.	**Hipparchus** discovers the precession of the equinoxes
c. 150 A.D.	**Ptolemy** refines the earth-centered system of the world
1543	**Copernicus** publishes his sun-centered system of the world
1576–1596	**Brahe** achieves precision data on planetary positions in the sky
1600	**Gilbert** suggests that the earth is a magnet
1609	**Galileo** first uses the telescope as an astronomical tool
1609/1619	**Kepler** publishes three laws of planetary motion
1634	**Galileo** develops the kinematics of accelerated motion
1662	**Boyle** relates pressure and volume for gases of constant temperature
1676	**Römer** demonstrates that light has finite velocity
1678	**Huygens** develops the wave theory of light
1687	**Newton** gives the theory of mechanics in his *Principia*
1702	**Amontons** invents the gas thermometer and predicts an absolute zero of temperature
1738	**Bernoulli** works out the kinetic theory of gases
1747	**Franklin** suggests the conservation of electrical fire (charge)
1750	**Michell** measures the law of force between poles of magnets
1780	**Galvani** discovers "animal electricity"
1785	**Coulomb** precisely determines the law of electric force
1787	**Charles** relates the volume of a gas to its absolute temperature
c. 1795	**Cavendish** measures the gravitational constant
1798	**Rumford** argues that heat is a form of motion
1800	**Volta** invents the battery
1802	**Young** uses wave theory to account for interference
1811	**Avogadro** suggests that at equal temperature and pressure, all gases have equal numbers of molecules per unit volume
1815–1820	**Fresnel, Arago,** and **Young** provide evidence for the wave theory of light
1820	**Oersted** discovers the magnetic effect of electric current
1820	**Ampère** establishes the law of force between current-carrying wires
1821	**Fraunhofer** invents the diffraction grating
1824	**Carnot** states that heat cannot be wholly transformed to work
1831	**Faraday** and **Henry** discover electromagnetic induction
1842–1843	**Mayer** and **Joule** suggest the convertibility and conservation of energy
1846	**Adams** and **Leverrier** predict the new planet Neptune
1865	**Maxwell** gives the electromagnetic theory of light